American Casino Guide

2001 Edition

Written and Edited By
Steve Bourie

Contributing Writers

Anthony Curtis
Larry Edell
John Grochowski
Bill Haywood
Bill Here
Skip Hughes
John Kelly
H. Scot Krause
Charles Lund
Dan Paymar
Frank Scoblete
Jean Scott
Tom Ski
Arnold Snyder
Henry Tamburin

This book is dedicated to my wife and children.
Thank you for your love, support and help.

American Casino Guide - 2001 edition

Published By:
Casino Vacations
P.O. Box 703
Dania, Florida 33004
(954) 989-2766
Fax (954) 966-7048

e-mail: casinos@aol.com
web site: www.americancasinoguide.com

ISBN: 1-883768-10-1
ISSN: 1086-9018

Table of Contents

About Your Guide

This guide has been written to help you plan your visit to casino gambling areas and also to help you save money once you are there. The first edition of this guide began 11 years ago as an eight-page newsletter and it has continued to grow each year as casino gambling has spread throughout the country. We have listed information on all of the states that offer any type of traditional casino table games or slot machines (including video lottery terminals). We have also included stories to help you understand how casinos operate; how video poker and slot machines work; how to make the best plays in blackjack, craps, roulette and baccarat; and how to take advantage of casino promotional programs. Additionally, we have included a casino coupon section that should save you many times the cost of this book.

Besides listing general information about each casino, this guide also notes those casinos that offer free fun books as well as those that have casino marketing departments. Knowing this information can be very helpful. As an example: almost every large casino has a "comp" program whereby you can get free rooms, food, shows, gifts or cash based upon your level of play at their table games or slot machines. Just call the casino marketing department for details on their current programs. Another program many casinos offer is a free fun book. These are coupon books that contain free and discounted offers on various items such as: bets, food, drinks, shows, rooms, souvenirs and more. Your guide lists all of the casinos that offer fun books, plus details on how to get them.

A good suggestion to save you money when visiting a casino is to join their slot club. It doesn't cost anything and you would be surprised at how quickly those points can add up to earn you gifts, cash, food or other complimentaries. Also, as a slot club member you will usually receive periodic mailings from the casino with money-saving offers that are generally not available to the public.

When using your guide please remember that all of the listed room rates reflect the lowest and highest prices charged during the year. During holidays and peak periods, however, higher rates may apply. Also, since the gambling games offered at casinos vary from state to state, a listing of available games is found at the start of each state heading. We hope you enjoy your guide and we wish you good luck on your casino vacation!

Your Best Casino Bets - Part I

by Henry Tamburin

The majority of casino players leave too much to chance when playing in a casino. To put it bluntly, they do not have a clue as to how to play. They are literally throwing their money away with little chance of winning. Luck most certainly has a lot to do with your success in a casino but what really separates the winners from the losers is the skill of the players. Granted, there is no guarantee that you will win, but on the other hand, there is no guarantee that you must lose. My objective in this article is to educate you on the casino games so that at the very least, you'll be able to enjoy yourself in the casino with a minimum risk to your bankroll.

Let's begin our understanding of casino gambling by learning how casinos win as much as they do. They don't charge admission, and they certainly don't depend on the luck of their dealers to generate the income they need to pay their overhead. In fact, they guarantee themselves a steady income by having a built in advantage, or house edge, on every bet. Think of it as a very efficient hidden tax that generates them a guaranteed daily profit.

Here's an example of how this works. Suppose we take a coin and play heads or tails. Every time you lose a flip of the coin you pay me $1. Every time you win a flip, I pay you 90¢. Would you play? I hope you said no. Here's why. In this simple game I would have an advantage over you and I created that advantage by not paying you at the true odds of one-to-one (or $1).

Casinos do this very same thing to create their advantage. They simply pay off winning bets at less than the true odds. For example, the true odds of winning a bet on number 7 on roulette are 37-to-1 (the latter means you have 37 chances to lose vs. one chance to win). If you get lucky and the roulette ball lands in the number seven slot, you'd expect the casino to pay you 37 chips as winnings for the one chip you bet on number 7 (37- to-1 payoff). If they did that, the casino's advantage would be zero. However, as I mentioned above, the casinos create their advantage by paying off winning bets at less than true odds. In the case of our bet on number 7, the winning payoff is 35 chips (instead of 37 chips). The two chips the casino quietly kept is what pays their bills. Mathematically, the casino advantage is 5.26% on this bet which simply means day in and day out, the casino expects to win (or keep) 5.26 % of all money wagered in roulette.

The casino games with the lowest casino advantage (less than 1.25%) and your best bets are blackjack, craps, baccarat, and video poker. Now don't sell the ranch and run over to your nearest casino just yet. These games, plus table poker, are your best bets but you must learn how to play these games properly to enhance your chances of winning. Here are some tips to get you started:

BLACKJACK - This is your best casino game, but you must learn how to play your hands (when to hit, stand, double-down, split, etc.). This is known as the basic strategy. Learn it and you can reduce the casino's advantage to virtually zero. And if you learn how to keep track of the cards as they are played (i.e. card counting) you can actually turn the tables on the casino and have the edge over them! Do not try to play blackjack if you haven't learned the correct basic strategy. If you do, your chances of winning are slim.

CRAPS - The game of craps intimidates most casino players because of the complicated playing layout and the multitude of bets. In fact craps is an easy game to play. And it also has some of the best bets in the casino (and also some of the worst). Your best bet is the pass line with odds and come with odds. Next best is a place bet on six or eight. Stay away from all other bets on the layout because the casino's advantage is too high.

ROULETTE - Every bet on the American roulette layout (with 0 and 00 on the wheel) has a high casino advantage. That goes for bets straight up on numbers that pay 35 to 1, as well as even money wagers on red or black. Atlantic City players get a break. If you bet on an even money payoff bet and 0 or 00 hits, you lose only half your wager. This cuts the casino's advantage in half. Also, some casinos offer a European layout with only one zero. This is a better bet than wheels with 0 and 00.

BACCARAT - Many casinos offer a low stakes version called mini-baccarat. Not a bad game to play. If you bet on the bank hand, the casino's edge is only 1.17%. And when you play baccarat, there are no playing decisions to make which makes the game very easy to play.

BIG SIX WHEEL - Stay away from spending a lot of time (and money) at this game. The casino's advantage is astronomical (11% to 26%). Its drawing card for the novice player is the low minimum bet ($1). Save your money for the better games.

CARIBBEAN STUD POKER - This popular cruise ship game has found its way to land and dockside casinos. Unlike regular table poker where players compete against each other, in this game the players play against the house. But the rules favor the casino and their advantage is about 5%. The part of this game that appeals to players is the progressive jackpot side bet. You should not make this side bet, however, unless the jackpot exceeds $280,000 for the $1 ante and the $1 jackpot bet.

PAI GOW POKER - Strange name for a casino game. The game is a cross between Pai Gow, a Chinese game of dominoes, and the American game of seven-card poker. Players are dealt seven cards and they must arrange (or set) their cards into a five-card poker hand and a two-card poker hand. Skill is involved in setting the two hands which can help reduce the casino's advantage.

SLOT MACHINES - Casinos earn more money from slot machines than all the table games combined. The casino's advantage varies from one machine to another. Typically the higher denomination machines ($1 and up) pay back more than the nickel, quarter and fifty cent machines. Slots are not your best bet in the casino, but here are a few tips: Always play the maximum number of coins the machine will accept or you won't be eligible for a bonus payoff for the jackpot. Don't waste hours looking for a machine that's "ready to hit." Join the slot clubs. They are free and you'll be rewarded with discounts and other freebies. Machines that have lower jackpots pay smaller amounts more frequently which means you normally get more playing time for your money. Some casinos now certify their machines to return 98% or more and these machines are your best bets.

VIDEO POKER - Your best bet if you enjoy playing slot machines. Skill is involved as well as learning to spot the better payoff machines. Check the full house, flush payoff schedule. On machines that pay on jacks or better the better paying machines pay nine coins for a full house and six coins for the flush for each coin played. These machines are known as 9/6 machines. They are readily available; seek them out.

KENO - This casino game has a very high casino advantage (usually 20% and up). Stay away if you are serious about winning.

RED DOG - This is the casino version of the old acey-deucey. The stakes are low, but the casino edge is a wee-bit steep (3.5%). If you play, only make the raise wager when the spread between the two cards is seven or more.

SIC BO - This is an oriental game in which players bet on the outcome of the roll of three dice. There are lots of bets on the layout, some that pay odds of 150 to 1. However, most have a very high casino advantage. Your best bet is a bet on the big or small wager.

LET IT RIDE - This relatively new casino table game is based on the all-American game of poker. Like Caribbean Stud Poker, players compete against the house rather than against each other. What makes this game so unique is that the players can remove up to two of their initial mandatory three bets if they don't think they can win. The objective is to end up with a five-card poker hand of at least 10's or higher. The higher the rank, the greater the payoff; up to 1,000 to 1 for the royal flush. The casino edge is about 3% and about 70% of the hands will be losing hands. Let It Ride gaming tournaments offer top prizes of up to $3 million. If you are lucky enough to catch a high payoff hand, be smart, push your chair back, and take the money and run!

Henry Tamburin has more than 27 years experience as a casino player, author, columnist and instructor. He has written more than 500 articles on casino gambling for numerous national gaming publications. He is also the author of numerous books and instructional videos. You can visit his web site at http://www.smartgaming.com.
Ordering information for his books and videos can be found on page 178 .

Your Best Casino Bets - Part II

by Steve Bourie

In the previous story Henry gave you his choices for your best casino bets based on which ones offer you the best mathematical odds. Now, Henry is a great mathematician who is truly an expert at crunching numbers to figure out what the theoretical odds are, but what about real life? By this I mean - at the end of the week, or the month, or the year, how much does a casino really make from blackjack, or craps, or roulette? Sure, you can do the math to calculate the casino advantage on a bank hand in mini-baccarat as 1.17%, but at the end of the day what percent of those bets on mini-baccarat actually wind up in the hands of the casino? Is it precisely 1.17%? or is it less? or is it more? And, if you knew how much the casino truly averaged on all of the games it offered, which one would turn out to be your best bet based on that information?

To find the answer to this question I began my search by looking at the annual gaming revenue report issued by Nevada's State Gaming Control Board. It lists the win percentages, based on the drop (an explanation of this term later), for all of the games offered by the casinos and you might be surprised at which game had the lowest win percentage. Go ahead and take a guess...nice try, but you're wrong! The answer is bingo, where casinos only won 2% of the money they handled! The first column below lists the actual win percentages (based on the drop) for Nevada's various games for the fiscal year from July 1, 1999 through June 30, 2000:

GAME	WIN %	ADJUSTED WIN %
Keno	27.25	27.25
Race Book	16.33	16.33
Wheel of Fortune	44.24	8.84
Caribbean Stud Poker	27.40	5.45
Roulette	23.75	4.75
Let It Ride	21.68	4.33
Pai Gow Poker	21.49	4.29
Pai Gow	21.05	4.21
Baccarat	18.66	3.73
Craps	13.92	2.78
Twenty-One	12.65	2.53
Mini-Baccarat	12.28	2.45
Sports Pool	4.59	4.59
Bingo	2.07	2.07

Usually bingo would rank as one of the games with the worst odds, but not in Nevada where it's sometimes used as a "loss leader." Just like your local Kmart runs especially low prices on a couple of items to bring you into the store where they believe you'll buy some other items, Nevada casinos use bingo to bring people into their casinos, believing that while they're there they'll play other games and also develop a loyalty to that casino. Actually, in many years the casinos offering bingo actually lose money on the game rather than make money. So, if you're a bingo player Nevada casinos are the best places you'll ever find to play your game.

Before we go on to the other games though you'll need a brief explanation of how the win percentages are calculated and we'll start off with a basic lesson in how casinos do their accounting.

Casinos measure their take in table games by the *drop* and the *win*. The *drop* is the count of all of the receipts (cash and credit markers) that go into the drop box located at the table. Later, an accounting is made to see how much more (or less) they have than they started with. This amount is known as the *win*.

What the first column in the table shows you is how much the casinos won as a percentage of the drop. For example, on the roulette table for every $100 that went into the drop box the casino won $24.23 or 24.23%. What it doesn't tell you, however, is how much the casinos won as a percentage of all the bets that were made. In other words, the drop tells you how many chips were bought at that table, but it doesn't tell you how many bets were made with those chips. For example, if you buy $100 worth of chips at a blackjack table and play $10 a hand you don't bet for exactly 10 hands and then leave the table, do you? Of course not. You win some hands and you lose some hands and if you counted all of the times you made a $10 bet before you left the table you would see that your original $100 in chips generated many times that amount in bets. In other words, there is a multiplier effect for the money that goes into the drop box. We know that for every dollar that goes into the drop box there is a corresponding number of bets made. To find out exactly what that number is I asked Henry for some help. He replied that there is no exact answer, but during a 1982 study of the roulette tables in Atlantic City it was discovered that the total amount bet was approximately five times the amount of the buy-in. This means that for every $100 worth of chips bought at the table it resulted in $500 worth of bets being made.

The multiplier effect for the money that goes into the drop box is also dependent on the skill of the player. A blackjack player that loses his money quickly because he doesn't know good playing strategy will have a much lower multiplier than a player who uses a correct playing strategy. For purposes of this story, however, we'll assume that they balance each other out and we'll also assume that all games have the same multiplier of five. We can now return to our win percentage tables and divide by five the percentages for those games that have a multiplier effect. These new adjusted numbers lets us know approximately how much the casinos actually won as a percentage of the amount bet on each of those games. Keep in mind, however, that besides bingo there are three other game categories that do not need to be adjusted: keno, race book and sports pool. They need no adjustment because there is no multiplier factor involved. On these particular games the casinos know the exact total of the bets they take in and the exact total of the bets they pay out.

After calculating our adjusted win numbers we can now go back and take another look at which games are your best casino bets. The worst game, by far, is keno with its 27.25% edge. Next comes the race book with 16.33%. Then we have the relatively high casino advantage game of wheel of fortune (big six wheel) at 8.84%. This is followed by Caribbean stud poker at 5.45%; roulette at 4.75%; let it ride at 4.33% pai gow poker at 4.29%; and pai gow at 4.21%.

Sports betting is in the same 4% range with a win rate of 4.59%. That number, however, deserves a closer look. There are actually six different types of bets that make up that 4.59% figure: football - 4.98%; basketball - 3.79%; baseball - 1.85%; sports parlay cards - 34.88%; pari-mutuel sports - 18.44; and other sports - 4.72%. As you can see, all sports bets carry a relatively low house edge, except for sports parlay cards which you may want to avoid.

Finally, we come to the four best casino bets that all have roughly the same house edge of less than four percent: baccarat at 3.73%; craps at 2.78%; twenty-one (blackjack) at 2.53%; and minibaccarat at 2.45%.

So there you have it. After discounting bingo, mini-baccarat is your best casino bet! Henry said it was the a good game to play and he was right. But didn't he also say that blackjack was your *best* casino bet? Was he wrong about that? Not really, because he prefaced it by saying "you must learn how to play your hands."

You should remember that of all the table games offered in a casino (other than poker), blackjack is the only one that is a game of skill. This means that the better you are at playing your cards, the better you will be able to beat the house average. The 2.63% figure shown is just an average and if you learn your basic strategies you should be able to cut it down a lot more which would then make it your best casino bet. Good luck!

Casino Comps

by Steve Bourie

In the world of casino gambling a "comp" is short for complimentary and it refers to anything that the casino will give you for free in return for your play in their casino.

Naturally, the more you bet, the more the casino will be willing to give you back. For the truly "high roller" (those willing to bet thousands, tens of thousands or even hundreds of thousands on the turn of a card) there is no expense spared to cater to their every whim, including: private jet transportation, chauffeur-driven limousines, gourmet chef-prepared foods, the finest wines and champagnes, plus pampered butler and maid service in a $10 million penthouse suite. But what about the lower-limit bettor?

Well, it turns out that pretty much any gambler can qualify for comps no matter what their level of play and if you know you're going to be gambling anyway, you might as well ask to get rated to see what you can get on a comp basis.

When you sit down to play be sure to tell the dealer that you want to be rated and they'll call over the appropriate floorperson who will take down your name and put it on a card along with information on how long you play and how much you bet. The floorperson won't stand there and constantly watch you, instead they'll just glance over every once in awhile to see how much you're betting and note it on the card. If you change tables be sure to tell the floorperson so that they can continue to track your play at the new table.

Usually a casino will want you to play for at least three hours and virtually all casinos use the same formula to calculate your comp value. They simply take the size of your average bet and multiply it by: the casino's advantage on the game you're playing; the decisions per hour in your game; and the length of your play in hours. The end result is what the casino expects to win from you during your play and most casinos will return about 40% of that amount to you in the form of comps.

So, let's say you're a roulette player that averages $20 a spin and you play for four hours. What's that worth in comps? Well, just multiply your average bet ($20), by the casino's advantage in roulette (5.3%) to get $1.06, which is the average amount the casino expects to make on you on each spin of the wheel. You then multiply that by the number of decisions (or spins) per hour (40) to get $42.40, which is the average amount the casino expects to make on you after one hour. Then, multiply that by the total hours of play (4) to get $169.60, which is the average amount the casino expects to make on you during your

4 hours of play. Since the average casino will return about 40% of that amount in comps you should qualify for $67.84 in casino comps.

One thing to keep in mind about comps is that you don't have to lose in order to qualify. The casino only asks that you put in the time to play. So, in our example if, after 4 hours of gambling, our roulette player ended up winning $100, they would still be eligible for the same amount of $67.84 in comps.

The last thing to mention about comps is that some casino games require skill (blackjack and pai gow poker), or offer various bets that have different casino advantages (craps) so those factors are sometimes adjusted in the equation when determining the casino advantage in those games. Just take a look at the chart below to see how the average casino will adjust for skill in blackjack and pai gow poker as well as for the types of bets that are made in craps.

Game	Game Advantage	Decisions Per Hour
Blackjack	.0025 (Card Counter) .01 (Good Basic Strategy) .015 (Soft Player)	70
Roulette	.053	40
Craps	.005 (Pass Line/Full Odds) .01 (Knowledgeable) .04 (Soft)	144
Baccarat	.012	70
Mini-Baccarat	.012	110
Pai Gow Poker	.01 (Knowledgeable) .02 (Average)	25

Taking Advantage of Slot Clubs

by H. Scot Krause

Slot Clubs originated in Atlantic City over 20 years ago as a way to begin recognizing and rewarding the casino's good players. Today, slot clubs are the casino's most powerful marketing tool and the player's best benefit the casino has to offer. It's the best of both worlds for both the player and the casino.

To begin, perhaps the word "club" is a little misleading, since there are no dues to pay, meetings to attend or any of the usual aspects associated with joining a club. You do get a slot club membership card (also called a player's card) which is your key to unlocking the benefits and rewards of the casino you're playing in.

Typically, your slot club membership card is a plastic card, with your identifying number on it, that you will use while playing at any of the casino's slot or video poker machines or while playing table games. It resembles a credit card, but only in its appearance, and is in no way an actual credit card. I mention that because there are some people who actually, mistakenly believe they will be inserting a credit card into their slot machine and play on credit, and therefore they refuse to get their player's card and are basically denied any and all benefits they are entitled to!

So let's start at the beginning and walk through the slot card program, when and why to do it and discuss some benefits, rewards and perks.

When you enter any casino for the first time, ask someone immediately where you can find the slot club or players club booth before you put any money at play. At the booth, or club, you should find a rather friendly group of employees who will get you started, signed up and get your card for you pronto.

You'll probably need to fill out a short application form or at least give your identification card to the clerk. It's simply a way to register the card in your name. You usually don't need to give your social security number if you don't want to, but always give your birthday and anniversary dates when asked. They help identify you with the casino in the event others have your same name and many times the birthday benefits are nothing short of fantastic.

Always ask the slot club personnel about how to use the card and any other current promotions or benefits in addition to using your card. There will usually be a brochure or literature available that you can take explaining all the club benefits. There may also be a sign-up bonus such as a free gift or free points when you register. Be sure to ask. Sometimes an easily obtainable coupon may be required, and the clerks can tell you where or how to get one. Finally, I like to request two cards when I join, and you might like to do the same. You'll find that you may lose one, or want to play two machines at one time. That's it! You're on your way.

When you're out on the casino floor, you'll notice a slot on the machines that your card fits into. When you decide which machine you want to play, put your card in the slot and leave it in the entire time you play that machine. (Note: Take a moment to look for the card reader slot and not the bill acceptor. If you accidentally put your card in the bill acceptor you'll probaly strip the magnetic reader off your card and it won't work).

Most machines will have some type of reader that will display your name, points earned or at least let you know your card has been accepted. It's not a swipe card, and you must leave it in the machine while you play. It's simply counting the coins, or credits, that go through the machine while you're playing and giving you credit in the form of points for the amount of money that cycles through the machine. (Some casinos consider time on the machine as well as money being cycled, but that is a little more rare than in years past). Now, while your playing, you'll be earning valuable points that become redeemable for anything from cashback to restaurant complimentaries (refered to as "comps") show tickets, gifts, reduced room rates or free rooms, to almost any amenity you may want or require.

Be sure to keep your card in the machine until you have completed your play and cashed all coins out of the machine. Some clubs base their points on a coin-out system, rather than coin-in. Of course, these rewards are based on total play and your rewards may vary according to point formulas created exclusively for the casino at which you're playing. I do caution you not to continue to play beyond your comfortable gambling range and budget just to earn a point level or comp. Let the comps fall in place as you play or when you return again in the future. Which brings me to another interesting thought. I've heard players refuse to get a card because they believe they won't return to the casino again. First of all, you never know what your future plans may hold. Second, you may earn enough points while you're on this trip to at least earn a small comp or some cash back before you leave.You'll at least get on the casino's mailing list for future specials and events. You may win a jackpot that will allow you to return sooner that you originally thought was possible. And finally, with as many consolidations and buy-outs as there are in the casino business today, the casino you're playing at today may be owned by someone else tomorrow, who may in turn, be closer to your home, and you'll be able to use your points with them. There's just no good excuse not to get a player's card at any casino you visit.

Here are a couple other tips when you plan to visit a casino and need to get a slot club card. Sometimes you can apply or sign-up in advance by mail registration or visiting the casino's website on the Internet. They will often mail you the card in advance or have it already prepared for you when you get to the casino. Call and ask ahead of time for this service and you'll save time and won't have to stand in long lines when you hit the casino floor. Sometimes, when you receive your card by mail or Internet sign-up, you'll get additional offers, coupons, gifts and funbook offers along with it.

Many casinos now employee slot club ambassadors, cash hosts, or enrollment representatives who will sign you up on the casino floor, making it even easier for you to enroll in the slot club. They often have additional incentives or perks they can give you when you sign up with them. You might also check to see if a card you have from another casino might work where you're playing now. Many casino corporations are beginning to combine their clubs to offer you benefits at any of their respective properties. We're sure to see more of this as consolidations and mergers continue to take place.

Now, let's take a little closer look at the benefits and reasons why you want to belong to these slot clubs. Obviously, the casinos want your business and will go to great lengths to have you return. In addition to the points you're earning while playing, which will entitle you to various comps as mentioned previously, your most valuable asset from joining the slot club will be your mailing list advantage. Offers to slot club members are mailed often and repeatedly for room specials, many times even free room offers, meal discounts (two for ones), and often other free offers. We've been mailed match play offers, double and triple point coupons, show and movie theater tickets, spa specials, gifts and gift certificates, drawing tickets, and a myriad of other offers.

The casino offers are based on levels of play, and better offers including lavish parties, Superbowl and New Year's Eve invitations, free participation to invited guest slot tournaments, limousine services, and even free round-trip airfare, are offerd to the casino's best players. Don't rule yourself out just because you don't think you'll reach those levels of play to be awarded those opportunities. Everyone is rewarded in some way for even the most nominal play. Just wait until your birthday rolls around and I can almost guarantee you'll get some fabulous offers from the casinos to spend your celebration with them!

Finally, we'll now take a look at some of the myths regarding slot clubs and player's cards and dispose of them accordingly. Here are some of the arguments I've heard against slot club cards, or excuses as to why players don't use them...

"I never win when I play with my card." The truth is your results would be the same regardless if you had a card in or not. There is no relation between the card counting coins through the machine and what comes up on the screen when you push the button. The card just records how much money is wagered. It has no memory of whether you have won or lost and it doesn't care.

"I don't want to be tracked," or "I don't want the casino to know how much I'm playing," or "I don't want the IRS to have my records." In fact, you do want the casino to track you so you can be rewarded for your play. They have no way of knowing you, or how they can help and reward you unless they know who you are, what you're playing and how much you're spending. The IRS does not have access to your gambling activities, but you, in fact, do. The slot club can provide you with a year end win-loss record of your play that may help you offset wins with losses for tax purposes.

"I don't need a card, I'm a local," or "I'm a tourist." Basically, you're one or the other, but either way you still should have a card. The casino's computers usually separate locals from tourists and tailor their offers accordingly. If you're going to play anyway, get a card!

"I always lose those cards." You can always have another card made. Get extras made. Why play without it? It's like losing your wallet. The card has so much value for you, yet you leave it in the machine. You don't forget your airline frequent flier card at the airport, or your grocery savings card when you go shopping, do you?

"I don't need a card, I'm leaving in an hour." It doesn't matter how long you will be staying or how soon you will be leaving. Remember that all-important mailing list, and that you just might return some time in the future or play at a sister property somewhere else. (Don't worry. Most casinos do not sell their mailing list names. They want you for themselves and are very selfish!)

All-in-all, I've never heard of one good reason not to join a slot club. In fact, I hope I've given you enough good reasons to always join every slot club at every casino you ever visit. Good luck and happy slot clubbing!

H. Scot Krause is employed in the casino business and has worked in entertainment and marketing. He has visited casinos from the Bahamas and Atlantic City, to Mississippi, and currently resides in Las Vegas, Nevada, with his wife, Donna. He writes promotional articles about Las Vegas and currently has a weekly column called "Vegas Values" which can be viewed at: www.americancasinoguide.com

Riviera Players Club

After you properly insert your slot card into the card reader, your name will appear and the number of your accumulated points. The device will then display a fresh count. After counting down to *zero,* the card reader will offer congratulations and display your new slot total, thus giving you a running count of your slot points.

On your birthday, you will be greeted with "Happy Birthday," but the computer system is discreet enough not to mention your age. Inactive accounts are terminated after 12 months.

Slot Point Accrual

Denomination	Input/Point Slots	Video Poker
5¢, 25¢, $1	$10/1	$20/1

Slot Benefits

Cash: $1/20 points
Minimum: 20 points
Increments: 20 points

Denomination	Rebate/Input Slots	Rebate/Input Video Poker	Input/Rebate Slots	Input/Rebate Video Poker
5¢, 25¢, $1	.50%	.25%	200	400

Scrip (Casino Cash): Riviera Bucks, available at the rate of 5 Riviera Bucks/40points can be used only at the gift shop. There are a few items available at the slot booth where the minimum redemption is ten points for a petty knickknack.

Food: Points for Buffets

Breakfast	Lunch	Dinner
60	100	120

Las Vegas Slot Clubs

by Steve Bourie

The opposite page shows information about the slot club at the Riviera Hotel and Casino in Las Vegas. It's taken from a new book titled *Las Vegas Slot Clubs 2000/2001* by Charles Lund, who is also the author of *Robbing the One-Armed Banits.*

In his *Las Vegas Slot Clubs* book Lund gives details on all Las Vegas and surrounding-area slot clubs. For each club Lund explains how points are accumulated and what benefits are offered. For the Riviera club you can see that you will earn one slot club point for every $10 put through a slot machine, or for every $20 put through a video poker machine. Some clubs have different point levels depending on the denomination of the machine but the Riviera doesn't do that, instead it treats nickel, quarter and dollar machines equally.

Next, you can see that the Riviera does give cash back to its slot club members. Generally, all Strip-area slot clubs do give cash back but many "locals" casinos do not. For every 20 points that Riviera members accumulate they receive $1 back in cash. Additionally, members only have to earn a minimum of 20 points in order to get their first cash redemption (some clubs require $5, or higher) and the cash is only given out in 20-point ($1) increments.

The next information refers to the cash rebate. It shows what percentage rebate members are receving and how much cash must be put through a machine in order to earn $1 cash back. Percentage-wise the slot rebate is .50% which means that members earn 50 cents for every $100 put through a slot machine. The video poker rebate is only .25% which means members are getting back just 25 cents for every $100 put through a video poker machine. Additionally, you can see that members receive $1 for every $200 put through a slot machine, or $1 for every $400 put through a video poker machine. Most slot clubs do cut the cashback benefit in half for video poker players (video poker offers better returns for players than slots, remember?), however, there are a few clubs that do give equal benefits to members for both slot and video poker play.

Finally, you can see that the points you accumulate at the Riviera can also be redeemed for "Riviera Bucks" at a rate of 40 points equals $5. This is two-and-a-half times the regular cash redemption rate and the Riviera Bucks can be used instead of cash at the buffet or the gift shop.

For more information on ordering the Charles Lund book be sure to see the ad on the next page.

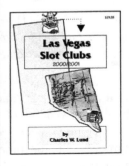

Slot Machines

by Steve Bourie

Virtually anyone who visits a casino, even for the first time, is familiar with a slot machine and how it operates: just put in your money, pull the handle and wait a few seconds to see if you win. It isn't intimidating like table games where you really need some knowledge of the rules before you play and it's this basic simplicity that accounts for much of the success of slot machines in the modern American casino.

As a matter of fact, the biggest money-maker for casinos is the slot machine with approximately 60 to 65 percent of the average casino's profits being generated by slot machine play. As an example, in Nevada's fiscal year ending June 30, 2000 the total win by all of the state's casinos was a little more than $9.4 billion. Of that amount, slightly more than $6 billion, or about 64 percent, was from slot machine winnings.

With this in mind, you must ask yourself, "can I really win money by playing slot machines?" The answer is a resounding yes...and no. First the "no" part: in simplest terms a slot machine makes money for the casino by paying out less money than it takes in. In some states, such as Nevada and New Jersey, the minimum amount to be returned is regulated. In Nevada the minimum is 75 percent and in New Jersey it's 83 percent. However, if you look at the slot payback percentages for those particular states in this book you will see that the actual average payback percentages are much higher. In New Jersey it's about 91 percent and in Nevada it's about 95 percent. Even though the actual paybacks are higher than the law requires, you can still see that on average for every $1 you play in an Atlantic City slot machine you will lose 9¢ and in a Las Vegas slot machine you will lose 5¢. Therefore, it doesn't take a rocket scientist to see that if you stand in front of a slot machine and continue to pump in your money, eventually, you will lose it all. On average, it will take you longer to lose it in Las Vegas rather than Atlantic City, but the result is still the same: you will go broke.

Gee, sounds kind of depressing, doesn't it? Well, cheer up because now we go on to the "yes" part. But, before we talk about that, let's first try to understand how slot machines work. All modern slot machines contain a random number generator (RNG) which is used to control the payback percentage for each machine. When a casino orders a slot machine it tells the manufacturer what percentage it wants that machine to pay back and that amount is programmed into the RNG. A casino can always change the payback percentage, but in order to do that it must go back to the manufacturer to get a new RNG programmed with the new amount. For this reason, most casinos rarely change their payback percentages unless there is a major revision in their marketing philosophy. And what exactly is a random number generator? Well, it's a little computer chip that is constantly working (as its name implies) to generate number combinations on a random basis. It does this extremely fast and is capable of producing hundreds of combinations each second. When you put in a coin, or push the bet button, the RNG stops and the combination it stops at is used to determine where the reels will stop in the pay window. Unlike video poker machines, you have no way of knowing what a slot machine is programmed to pay back just by looking at it. The only way to tell is by knowing what is programmed into the RNG.

Okay, now let's get back to the "yes" part. Yes, you can win money on slot machines by using a little knowledge, practicing some money management and, mostly, having lots of luck. First, the knowledge part. You need to know what kind of player you are and how much risk you are willing to take. Do you want to go for the giant progressive jackpot that could make you a millionaire in an instant or would you be content walking away just a few dollars ahead?

An example of a slot machine with a wide-area progressive jackpot is Nevada's Megabucks where the jackpot starts at $5 million. These $1 machines are located at more than 125 Nevada casinos at various locations around the state and are linked together by a computer. It's fine if that's the kind of machine you want to play, but keep in mind that the odds are fairly astronomical of you hitting that big jackpot. Also, the overall payback percentage is lower on these machines than the average $1 machine. During Nevada's fiscal year ending June 30, 2000 Megabucks averaged around 89% payback while the typical $1 machine in Nevada averaged a little more than 95%. So, be aware that if you play the machines with the wide-area progressive jackpots you'll win fewer small payouts and it will be very difficult to leave as a winner. Unless, of course, you hit that big one! If you really like to play the wide-area progressive machines your best bet is probably to set aside a small percentage of your bankroll (maybe 10 to 15 percent) for chasing that big jackpot and saving the rest for the regular machines.

One other thing you should know about playing these wide-area progressives is that on most of them, including Megabucks, you will receive your jackpot in equal payments over a period of years (usually 25). You can avoid this, however, by playing at one of the casinos that link slot machines at their own properties and will pay you in one lump sum. The Circus Bucks slots at Circus Circus casinos in Nevada offer this as well as the Million Dollar Babies at Caesars Palace. There is also a wide-area progressive slot system called Cool Millions which will pay the first one million dollars immediately.

Knowledge also comes into play when deciding how many coins to bet. You should always look at the payback schedule posted on the machine to see if a bonus is payed for playing the maximum number of coins that the machine will accept. For example, if it's a two-coin machine and the jackpot payout is 500 coins when you bet one coin, but it pays you 1,200 coins when you bet two coins, then that machine is paying you a 200 coin bonus for playing the maximum number of coins and you should always bet the maximum two coins to take advantage of that bonus. However, if it's a two-coin machine that will pay you 500 coins for a one-coin bet and 1,000 coins for a two-coin bet, then there is no advantage to making the maximum bet on that machine and you should only bet the minimum amount.

Knowledge of which casinos offer the best payback percentages is also helpful. When available, we print that information in this book to help you decide where to go for the best return on your slot machine dollar. You may want to go to the Las Vegas Strip to see the free pirate show at Treasure Island, but take a look at the slot machine payback percentages for the Strip area casinos in the Las Vegas section and you'll see that you can get better returns for your slot machine dollar by playing at the off-Strip area casinos.

The final bit of knowledge you need concerns slot clubs. Every major casino has a slot club and you should make it a point to join the slot club before you insert your first coin. It doesn't cost anything to join and as a member you will be able to earn complimentaries from the casinos in the form of cash, food, shows, drinks, rooms or other "freebies." When you join the club you'll be issued a card (similar to a credit card) that you insert in the machine before you start to play and it will track how much you bet, as well as how long you play. Naturally, the more money you gamble, the more "freebies" you'll earn. Just make sure you don't get carried away and bet more than you're comfortable with just to earn some extra "comps." Ideally, you want to get "comps" for gambling that you were going to do anyway and not be pressured into betting more than you had planned.

Now let's talk about money management. The first thing you have to remember when playing slot machines is that there is no skill involved. Unlike blackjack or video poker, there are no decisions you can make that will affect whether you win or lose. It is strictly luck, or the lack of it, that will determine whether or not you win. However, when you are lucky enough to get ahead (even if it's just a little) that's where the money management factor comes in. As stated earlier, the longer you stand in front of a machine and put in your money, the more likely you are to go broke. Therefore, there is only one way you can walk away a winner and that's to make sure that when you do win, you don't put it all back in. You really need to set a "win goal" for yourself and to stop when you reach it. A realistic example would be a "win goal" of roughly 25 percent of your bankroll. If you started with $400, then you should stop if you win about $100. The "win goal" you decide on is up to you, but keep in mind that the higher your goal, the harder it will be to reach it, so be practical. And what if you should happen to reach your goal? Take a break! Go have a meal, see a show, visit the lounge for a drink or even just take a walk around the casino. You may have the urge to keep playing, but if you can just take a break from the machines, even it's just for a short time, you'll have the satisfaction of leaving as a winner. If, later on, you get really bored and find that you just *have* to go back to the machines you can avoid a total loss by not risking more than half of your winnings and by playing on smaller denomination machines. If you made your winnings on $1 machines, move down to quarters. If you won on quarters, move down to nickels. The idea now is basically to kill some time and have a little fun knowing that no matter what happens you'll still leave as a winner.

And now, let's move on to luck. As stated previously, the ultimate decider in whether or not you win is how lucky you are when you play. But, is there anything you can do to help you choose a "lucky" or "winning" machine? Not really, because there is no such thing as a "winning" machine. Remember, in the long run, no machine will pay out more than it takes in. There are, however, some things you could try to help you find the more generous machines and avoid the stingy ones. Keep in mind that all of the slot machine payback percentages shown in this book are averages. Some machines are programmed to pay back more than average and some machines are programmed to pay less. Also, like everything else in life, machines have good cycles where they pay out more than average and bad cycles where they pay out less than average. Ultimately, what you want to find is a high-paying machine in a good cycle. Of course if I knew how to find that machine I wouldn't be writing this story, instead I'd be standing in front of it with a $100 bill in my hand and looking for the change attendant. So, I guess you'll have to settle for my two recommendations as to how you *might* be able to find the better paying machines.

First, is the "accounting" method. With this method you always start with a pre-determined number of coins and after playing them in the machine you take an accounting of your results. If you have more than you started with you stay at that machine and start another cycle. Just keep doing this until the machine returns less than you started with. As an example, let's say you start with 20 coins. After playing those 20 coins you count how many you got back. If it's more than 20 you start over again with another 20 coins and then do another accounting. If, after any accounting, you get back less than the 20 you started with, stop playing and move on to a different machine. This is an especially good method because you have to slow down your play to take periodic accountings and you will always have an accurate idea of how well you are doing.

The other method is even simpler and requires no math. It's called the "baseball" method and is based on the principle of three strikes and you're out. Just play a machine until it loses three times in a row, then move on to a different machine. Both of these methods will prevent you from losing a lot of money in a machine that is either set for a low payback or is going through a bad cycle; yet both will still allow you to take advantage of a high payback machine or one that is going through a good cycle. Give one of them a try on your next trip. Good luck!

Slot Tournaments

by Steve Bourie

Slot tournaments are special contests arranged by casinos where participants who get the highest scores on slot machines within an allotted amount of time, or credits, are awarded cash or prizes. Some slot tournaments are offered free of charge but most require an entry fee.

Virtually every casino today offers slot tournaments and they're used by each casino's marketing department as a promotional tool to generate more business for the casino. An interesting thing about slot tournaments is that they aren't necessarily designed as money-making events for the casino.

Some casinos will give back all of the entry fees in the form of prizes and some won't. Those casinos that give back all of the money are happy to have the tournament's contestants in their hotel rooms and playing in their casino. The thinking at these casinos is that the tournament is generating extra business and they don't have to make money off the tournament itself. These are the best kinds of tournaments to play in but they aren't always easy to find. In other instances the casinos look at tournaments strictly as a money-making venture and they'll keep part of the entry fees for themselves. In either case, tournaments can sometimes provide extra value to you and they are occasionally worth looking into.

Each month *Las Vegas Advisor* gives information on upcoming tournaments in that city and many gaming magazines do the same for all of the major casinos throughout the country. These publications don't list much more than the required entry fee so you'll have to call each casino for more information on the specifics. You can probably get that information over the phone but it's best to ask for a brochure to be mailed to you. This way, you'll have an official written record of the tournament rules and regulations.

When looking at the prize structure of the tournament be sure to add up the total cash value of all the prizes and compare it to the total amount of money the casino will be getting in entry fees. For instance, if the entry fee is $200 and they're limiting the tournament to 200 entrants then the casino is generating $40,000 in entry fees. Are they offering that much in cash prizes? If so, then it's a good tournament. If they're only offering $25,000 in cash, then the casino is keeping $15,000 and you may want to shop around for a different tournament that offers you more "equity." By equity we mean the value you'll be receiving in relation to the cost to enter. Positive equity means the casino is giving back more in cash and benefits than it's charging to enter the tournament. Negative equity means just the opposite: the casino is charging more than it's giving back in cash and benefits. You should always try to find a positive equity tournament.

Another thing you'll need to add into the equation when considering your equity are the extra "freebies," or discounts, that the casino will add to the package. Most casinos will host a welcoming party for the contestants, plus a free lunch or dinner and an awards banquet at the end when the winners are announced. Generally, all casinos will also offer a discounted room rate to tournament participants and some will even throw in a surprise gift for everyone. If you don't need a room then that benefit won't add anything to the value you'll be receiving but for some players a discounted room rate could mean the difference between a positive and negative equity situation. Each tournament is different and you should be sure to add up the total of all the benefits you'll receive when deciding which tournament you want to enter.

One more thing to keep in mind when looking at a tournament's structure is how the prizes are distributed. If too much is given to the top finishers that leaves less to be distributed among the other contestants. The chances are pretty good that you're not going to win one of the top prizes so it will help if the lower-tier prizes are worthwhile.

One last thing to remember about tournaments is that in many of them it pays to enter early. Most tournaments offer an "early-bird" discount if you enter by a certain date and the entry fee rises after that date. The discount can be as high as 25 percent and, once again, the reduced rate could make the difference between a positive and a negative equity situation.

Once you've found the tournament that offers you the most equity you'll need a strategy for winning. What's the best strategy? Get lucky! Slot tournaments are pure luck and there really isn't anything you can do to help you win. So, just keep pushing that spin button and hope for a good score!

Personally, I only like to play games of skill (like blackjack and video poker) so I usually don't play in slot tournaments. There was, however, one instance where I played in a tournament because of the value it offered. In October 1997 my friend Marvin and I were planning a trip to Las Vegas to attend the World Gaming Congress and Expo at the city's main convention center. This event is held each year and it's the world's largest trade show for the casino industry. The event took place during the middle of the week but we also wanted to stay over for the weekend. Unfortunately, the room rates are much higher on weekends and the hotels usually don't discount their rates very much on those days. After calling around to check rates we decided to look in the *Las Vegas Advisor* to find out about slot tournaments.

Boulder Station was having its *All Treats, No Trick*s slot tournament that same weekend. The entry fee was $199 but by entering before October 3, the fee was reduced to $149 and there was a total of $40,000 in prize money up for grabs. The rules required 268 entrants, or else the total prize money could be reduced, but based on that required number the casino would be receiving

$39,932 in prize money (assuming all early entrants) and awarding $40,000 in prize money which made this a slightly positive equity situation. Additionally, everyone received a t-shirt, a welcoming cocktail party, lunch at the *Pasta Palace,* an awards celebration and a reduced room rate of $25 for Friday and Saturday evening.

We had stayed at Boulder Station before and we both liked the property very much. We called the hotel's reservation department and they told us it would be $99 per night on Friday and Saturday. That was $198 for the two nights, plus 9% tax, for a total of $215.82 By entering the slot tournament our cost would be $149, plus $50 for the room for two nights, plus 9% tax (only on the room), for a total of $203.50 Hey, you want to talk about positive equity? This thing was great! Not only were they giving back all of the prize money, but in this case it was actually cheaper to enter the slot tournament than to get the room by itself!

The rules allowed us to enter as a team for the $149 fee and that also got us into the activities together. At the welcoming party we had an unlimited choice of alcoholic beverages or sodas, plus a large selection of finger sandwiches and other snacks. The *Pasta Palace* is a good restaurant and we had a great lunch there.

We weren't very lucky in the tournament and didn't finish high in the standings. Actually, we received the lowest cash prize which was $40. That brought our actual cost for the room and the tournament down to $163.50 which was still $52 cheaper than just getting the room by itself. Plus, we got the t-shirt, welcoming party and lunch as an added bonus.

As you can see, we saved some money by entering the slot tournament and we also had a lot of fun. You can do the same thing by checking out some of the tournaments that are available the next time you're planning a trip to a casino. Just use the toll-free numbers in this book to call the casino marketing departments, or pick up the latest issue of *Las Vegas Advisor,* or a general gaming magazine, for information on current tournaments.

The World's Greatest Slot Cheat?

by Steve Bourie

The first slot machines were invented in the late 1890's and it probably wasn't very long after those machines appeared that somebody had the brilliant idea of trying to cheat them. Yes, times may change but, unfortunately, greed is here to stay and there will always be people looking for a fast way to make a buck with a slot machine. Here's the true story of one of those people who probably had the most ingenious method ever used.

On January 14, 1995 Reid Errol McNeal should have been one of the luckiest men on earth. That Saturday afternoon he went to the keno desk at Bally's Park Place Casino Resort in Atlantic City and bought $100 worth of keno tickets: 10 tickets at $10 each with eight numbers picked on each card.

Defying odds of 230,000-to-1, McNeal hit for eight-of-eight on one of the tickets. The winning payoff of $100,000 was the highest amount ever won on a keno game in the history of Atlantic City and naturally caused quite a stir in the casino. According to published reports, however, McNeal hardly seemed like the typical winner of a once-in-a-lifetime jackpot. Not only was he unemotional about his big win, he also had no identification on him and he demanded to be paid in cash. Needless to say, officials were a little suspicious, or as one casino executive said, "this just didn't pass the smell test."

New Jersey law requires that any jackpot of $35,000 or more be verified by state gaming division officials and when they arrived they were accompanied by a couple of state troopers assigned to their department. The troopers went with McNeal to his hotel room at Bally's where they found a friend of McNeal's who identified himself as Ronald Harris. At this point the troopers were simply making an investigation into the oddness of the situation and left Harris in the room while they took McNeal back downstairs for some further questioning. It was then discovered that McNeal's friend was an employee of the Nevada Gaming Control Board which is responsible for regulating all of the gaming devices in that state.

The troopers returned to the room to speak to Harris but he was gone. They searched the room and, according to state police spokesman John Hagerty, found "computer equipment, computer chips, notes and books describing changes in Bally's machine and describing how to possibly scam or beat the machine."

Police theorized that as a computer technician in Nevada's Gaming Control Board Harris had access to a highly confidential "source code" which allowed him access to the programming in the keno machine's random number generator. Harris then used his computers to duplicate the calculations of the random number generator in Bally's keno machine and thus, was able to determine the outcome ahead of time. McNeal was arrested in Atlantic City and Ron Harris was arrested by Nevada authorities at the airport in Las Vegas. Both were charged by New Jersey police with computer fraud and attempted cheating. The *Las Vegas Review-Journal* reported that all charges against McNeal were dropped in return for his agreeing to testify against Harris and according to Keith Furlong, Public Information Officer for New Jersey's Division of Gaming Enforcement, "Harris pleaded guilty in July 1998 to attempted theft by deception."

Shortly after his arrest Harris was fired from his $48,000-a-year job with the Gaming Control Board where he had worked for 12 years. Officials there also began their own investigation into his past work for the Board and five months later he was indicted, along with his ex-wife and two friends, on charges of rigging slot machines in three northern Nevada casinos.

As part of his Gaming Control Board duties Harris was responsible for testing slot machines at casinos throughout the state. He and his co-workers would go into casinos and randomly test machines to make sure they only contained computer chips that were previously approved by the state agency. These computer chips are also known as EPROM's (erasable programmable read only memory) and control the payback percentages on slot machines. The key words here are *erasable* and *programmable* because authorities alleged that Harris erased the memory on the chips and substituted his own programming which forced the machines to pay out a jackpot whenever coins were inserted in a certain sequence. For example: if someone inserted 3 coins, followed by 2 coins, then another 2 coins, then 1 coin, then 3 coins, then 5 coins, the machine would automatically pay out the maximum jackpot.

Not wanting to win the jackpots himself, police charged that Harris used his accomplices to collect a $9,000 jackpot at Fitzgeralds in Reno, a $5,000 award at the Crystal Bay Club in North Lake Tahoe and another unspecified amount at the Comstock in Reno. According to a story in the *Las Vegas Review-Journal*, the attorney general's office later went on to charge him with rigging at least 24 jackpots throughout the state. In September 1997, Harris pleaded guilty to racketeering charges and was sentenced to seven years.

After these problems occurred authorities in both states took precautions to prevent them from happening again. New Jersey now requires that any electronic keno machines used in Atlantic City have a "source code" different from the same machines used in other states. Also, in Nevada the chairman of the state's Gaming Control Board, Bill Bible, ordered a review of its safeguard measures with an independent firm and now requires staff electronics employees to check each others work.

Obviously, Harris was brilliant with computers but evidently he wasn't too smart with people. Just imagine how much money he would still be making if his friend had only been carrying some ID with him in Atlantic City!

Professional Slot Players?

by Arnold Snyder

When I started playing blackjack back in the mid-70s, slot players were considered the dregs of the casino. Card counters have traditionally viewed themselves as the only smart players in the casino, the only players who were using strategies based on intelligence and logic, and whose efforts gave them an advantage over the house. In fact, the only slot machines that had any respect in the counters' eyes were those rare video blackjack machines that were exploitable via basic strategy and/or card counting. Most blackjack slots, however were not so exploitable.

In 1988, blackjack expert Stanford Wong radically altered this perspective with the publication of *Professional Video Poker* (Pi Yee Press). Suddenly, a new breed of player appeared on the scene - the video poker pro. More gambling experts and authors expanded on Wong's seminal work. Lee Frome, Dan Paymar and Bob Dancer became the new video poker gurus. Paymar even started publishing a newsletter - *Video Poker Times* - which became the voice of the Las Vegas VP community, where new variations of machines were analyzed as soon as they appeared in the slot jungle.

Then, a couple of years ago, a new type of slot machine was introduced - "Piggy Bankin." Similar to the progressive machines that had ever-growing $ jackpots, these machines banked credits from previous play. One attractive feature was that you could see the banked "coins" on the display so that you could estimate when the payoff would begin. With video poker, although you could see the progressive jackpot display, there was no way of knowing when you might actually be dealt a royal flush to collect it. It could be on the next hand, or 10,000 hands away. Unlike the VP progressives, the Piggy Bankin' payout would not go to some other player on a connected bank of machines either; the machines were independent.

Stanford Wong provided some of the initial analysis on his website, and soon the pros were buzzing. New banking machines appeared - Shopping Spree, Safe Cracker, Temperature's Risin' - the banking slots began taking over the slot departments. Then, Charles W. Lund, in a new book - *Robbing the One-Armed Bandits: Finding and Exploiting Advantageous Slot Machines* - analyzed some four dozen popular banking machines, and followed that with a supplement to his book, where another 16 machines are analyzed.

My eyes were opened to the realities of advantageous slot play that year when a pro player invited me to stay in one of his comped suites in a major Nevada casino. Solely as a result of his play on the casino's $1 and $5 slot machines, he not only had full RFB, but multiple suites of comped rooms that he was filling with his friends. He was comped just as fully as any high stakes blackjack player. This player was also to become one of the first slot pros I knew to be barred from the slot departments of numerous major casinos in Nevada.

What's that? Thrown out of a casino for beating slot machines? Can this really happen? Unfortunately, this is one more area where we may extend our analogy of advantageous slot play to blackjack. Some casinos are now barring the really good slot players.

The marketing concept behind the banking slots is not difficult to understand. As a player sees the credits building on the machine he is playing, getting ever closer to that "bonus round," he is tempted to continue playing longer than he would if no bonus round were impending. From the savvy player's perspective, and I don't necessarily mean the professional player but any player who has become familiar with how these devices work, it is now worthwhile to *shop* for the best machine in the slot department. Any player who sees two Piggy Bankin' machines available, one with the 25 coins in the bank, the other with 10 coins in the bank, would be foolish to choose the 10 coin machine, as that would require considerably more action before entering the lucrative bonus round.

To keep with the shopping metaphor, the banking machines that are engaged in (or fast approaching) their bonus rounds, can be considered a store's "loss leaders" - items available to the public that draw in customers, in hopes that the customers also purchase other items the store profits from.

A professional slot player, in essence, is like a supermarket shopper who only purchases the loss leaders. If you were to go into a grocery store and purchase nothing but the sale items, the loss leaders, the coupon specials, so that the store literally lost money on your visit, you would not expect to be barred from future shopping at that store. Lots of people do this. In fact, if any store attempted to throw you out because you were only purchasing sale items, you could sue them for false advertising, harassment, discrimination and other violations of local, state and federal consumer protection laws. There is, to be sure, an active subculture of grocery store couponomists who trade coupons with each other, subscribe to their own newsletters and have their own websites. They never worry about the cashiers refusing to ring them up, or the store manager reading them their rights. It's not illegal to take advantage of a deal, even if you did not fulfill the purpose of the deal (from the store's perspective), which was to generate other profitable transactions from your business.

In May 1995, attorney Anthony Cabot wrote an article for an industry trade journal describing why Nevada casinos are so reluctant to throw out video poker professionals, who descend like vultures on banks of machines as soon as their progressive jackpots give the players any significant advantage over the house. Cabot explained that there is a state gaming regulation that defines any progressive jackpot - which is to say any jackpot that accrues as a direct result of prior players' losses - as money which the casino no longer owns, but which is merely being held in "trust" for whatever member of the gaming public ultimately wins it.

Cabot did not go into great detail as to why this regulation exists, but I can think of several good reasons for it. Gaming regulations require that slot devices pay back a certain percentage to the players. Unless these amounts accrued in progressive jackpots are figured into the moneys paid out, a casino could "reset" their progressive jackpots any time they wanted. But since those accrued funds are figured into the machine's payout, if a casino "took them back," many machines would fail to meet these standards. And many casinos advertise payback percentages, such as 95%, 98%, etc. Unless these jackpot totals are figured into the paybacks, the casinos would also be guilty of false advertising. Cabot explained in his article that casinos may not pick and choose which members of the public will be allowed to stake their claim for that jackpot that is awaiting public distribution.

So, the video poker pros who are ejected from casinos today are the more aggressive teams of players who attempt to take over whole banks of machines by muscling out the casinos' regular customers. Such players are not ejected for being professional players, but - at least ostensibly - for being rude, and causing disturbances. To my knowledge, these types of team ejections have not been challenged in the courts. Provided the slot surveillance videos do show that the team employed aggressive and rude behavior to run off the casino's regular customers, the casino would probably prevail in the courts. Any business has the right to eject unruly patrons whose behavior is disturbing other customers. Neither the courts nor the general public condones such behavior.

Unlike the progressive jackpot slots, however, the banking slots do not display a dollar-and-cents total of accrued moneys for distribution to the public. The payouts from the banked credits, to be sure, do get tallied into the machine's payback percentage, but these credits are not tied to any specific dollars-and-cents "jackpot" that is displayed on the machine, or that is counted as money held in trust for the public. This factor alone probably means that casinos in Nevada, and most other states may eject professional players from their banking slots at their whim, just as they may from their blackjack tables.

This has already led to serious problems at one major Las Vegas Strip casino. This casino, which allowed security personnel to accept tips from patrons (which is unusual but not illegal), found out that their security guards were ejecting slot pros who didn't tip, but allowing those who greased their palms to monopolize the lucrative banking machines. The casino learned of this kickback scheme in a rather uncomfortable fashion - one of those ejected pros was Las Vegas writer Charles W. Lund, who also happened to be the gambling columnist for the *Valley Explorer*, a local tabloid. Lund wrote a scathing exposé of what was happening in this casino's slot department in which he named names, not only of the security personnel involved, but the slot team leaders who were pulling off this legal form of bribery.

One of the problems the slot pros have with the banking machines is that it is not always easy to disguise the fact that you are a professional player. A pro walks up and down the aisles looking for a banking machine that is vacant and close to its bonus round. If none are found, then the machines currently being used are looked at to see which are closest to being profitable. If one is found, then the pro must camp out nearby in hopes that the player on that machine will abandon it. Back in the pre-banking slot days, no one much cared if someone stood in the casino watching others play; "loitering" in the aisles is common, not only in the slot pits, but in all of the gaming areas other than the roped off V.I.P. high limit pits.

Nowadays, however, casinos know that pro players are lurking like vultures in their slot aisles, waiting to pounce on a valuable slot opportunity as soon as it appears. In January of this year, Charles Lund and his wife were permanently barred from the slot department of another major Las Vegas Strip casino. They were not part of a team. They did nothing to bother other patrons or muscle players off valuable machines. They had simply been profiting about $500 per day each for better than a month. They were informed bluntly, by casino security guards, that professional slot players were not allowed in the casino. They were also told that they were not allowed to play slots in any of the other four Las Vegas casinos owned by the same company! Following are two examples of advantageous slots taken directly from Lund's book:

Double Diamond Mine - Synopsis: Play at one credit per spin on machines which have nine diamonds in one shaft, or eight diamonds in each of two shafts, or seven or more diamonds in each of the three shafts. Terminate play when the machine does not meet any of the above conditions.

Double Diamond Mine is basically quite close to an ordinary slot machine. The slight difference is that each of the three reels contains some diamond symbols. These symbols do nothing as far as the pay table is concerned and alining three diamonds on the payline will not in any direct way earn you additional credits. Instead, a diamond, or diamonds, appearing on the payline will trigger the slot machine to drop a number of diamonds, equal to the number of credits wagered, into the corresponding mine shaft(s) on the display above the three reels. When any mine shaft is filled with a total of ten diamonds, the shaft is emptied of diamonds and you receive ten credits. Clearly, the items that are banked in Double Diamond Mine are the diamonds in the mine shafts.

The proper play of a Double Diamond Mine is to play one credit per spin on any machine which has nine diamonds in any one of its shafts. It is also profitable to play at the rate of one credit per spin any of these machines that have two shafts containing eight diamonds each. You can also profitably play any Double Diamond Mine that has three shafts, each containing at least seven diamonds, and again this is at the rate of one credit per spin. Play should be terminated when the slot machine does not satisfy the above conditions.

The above rule tends to be on the conservative side. What is interesting is that sometimes a machine which has several shafts with sizable numbers of diamonds will become a poor play before all of its shafts are emptied. Consider, for example, a machine that has three shafts of seven diamonds each. This machine is a good play. If perchance one of the shafts is emptied by fortuitous play before any diamonds are obtained in either of the other shafts, then with only two mine shafts of seven each, play on the machine should be stopped and the other mine shafts not emptied.

Generally, it will cost somewhat more than one credit to obtain a diamond. But, of course, the diamond will not necessarily be in the shaft that you want. Good luck with this machine, and here's hoping that someone gives you a good shaft.

Piggy Bankin'- *(Editor's note: this is not Big Bang Piggy Bankin, which requires a different strategy).* Synopsis: On $1, $2, and $5 machines with 18 or more credits in the piggy bank and on nickel and quarter machines with 21 or more credits in the piggy bank, play one credit per spin. Terminate play when a "Break the Bank" symbol appears on the payline.

Piggy Bankin' slot machines have tended to be plain headaches for many casinos. The machines generate substantial funds but create problems of supervision because numbers of undesirable individuals haunt the machines for their good profit potential for the knowledgeable individual. This is especially true for the dollar Piggy Bankin' machines.

The dollar denomination of Piggy Bankin' has extreme profit potential because the item which is banked is actually dollar credits. These credits are readily banked, but removing the banked credits is sometimes rather time-consuming and boring. The dollar denomination of these machines has such profit potential that the machines are extremely corrupting — not just to individuals who play them but also to those working in the casinos.

From the information that I have been able to glean from various sources, it appears that on Piggy Bankin' machines there are four settings used to determine the casino hold. Casinos generally use one of the three lower settings for the dollar and higher denomination machines, and usually use the highest setting for nickel and quarter Piggy Bankin' machines. With repeated play, you will discern the difference.

All Piggy Bankin' slot machines display a piggy bank on their visual. This piggy bank is seeded with an initial ten coins. Whenever you aline three blanks, the number of credits wagered is not lost but instead is transferred to the piggy bank. In this manner, additional coins are added to the piggy bank. As the bank grows, so the value of the machine grows. Clearly, what is being banked is the actual credits that are transferred into the piggy bank.

The bank is broken when the "Break the Bank" symbol, which is only on the right reel, lands on the payline. You then receive all the funds in the bank as credits on the credit meter. The machine then refills the bank with an initial ten credits.

The most advantageous procedure for profitably playing Piggy Bankin' machines is to wait until the piggy bank is sufficiently high and then play one credit per spin until the bank is broken. Then you should immediately terminate your play.

What is "sufficiently high" is different depending on the denomination of the machine that you are playing. For dollar and higher denomination machines, the piggy bank should contain at least 18 credits; nickel and quarter Piggy Bankin' machines should have a bank of at least 21. This is a reflection of the increased casino hold on nickel and quarter machines.

As an easy rule of thumb, a dollar machine with a bank of 25 is worth about eight credits (25 - 17 = 8) since on average the machine will generate an eight dollar profit. Similarly, a quarter machine with a bank of, for example, thirty is worth ten credits (30 - 20 = 10) or $2.50. A nickel machine with a bank of 24 is worth on average four credits (24 - 20 = 4) or twenty cents. These formulas are not precise but are reasonable for general usage.

Another figure related to the Piggy Bankin' slot machines is that on average it will take about eighty spins to break the bank. The interesting thing about this tidbit of information is that after every spin, the average remains the same. In other words, after each spin you are basically back to the same situation and it will still on average take about eighty spins to break the bank.

At Last - A Way To Beat The Slots!

Robbing The One Armed Bandits

New! Revised and Larger Edition!

Charles Lund does it again with the new and expanded version of his revolutionary bestselling book - *Robbing the One-Armed Bandits*. He reveals how the pros are beating the banking slots. It also describes how to get away with it without being recognized as a pro, and ejected.

The new edition covers covers the 49 machines from his first book, 15 machines from his supplement and 24 new machines like: An American Paris, Fireworks, Kool Kat, Pay Roll, Pushers and Wild Cherry Bonus Pie. Lund also discusses the value of casino slot clubs, how to search for machines of value, which banking machines to avoid and many more topics of interest for the SERIOUS SLOT PLAYER.

Some of the other banking slots analyzed by Lund include: Balloon Bars Balloon Race, Big Bang Piggy Bankin', Bonus 5 Line, Bonus Bank, Bonus Spin, Boom, Buccaneer Gold, Chuck Wagons, Double Diamond Mine, Empire, Flush Attack, Fort Knox, Isle of Pearls, Krazy Keno, Lady of Fortune, Money Factory, Piggy Bankin', Pirates Treasure, Playoff Deuces Wild, Playoff Jacks or better, Racing 7s, Red Ball, Red Hot 7s, Riddle of the Sphinx, Ring 'Em Up, Road Rally, Royal Hot 7s, Safe Buster, Safe Cracker, Shopping Spree, Slot Bingo, Spacequest, Super 7s, Super 8 Line, Super 8 Race, Temperature's Rising, Treasure Quest, Triple Crash Winfall, Triple Diamond Baseball Diamond, Triple diamond Mine, Wheel of Fortune, Wild Cherry Pie, X-Factor, Blackout Poker, Diamond Thief, Fishin' for Cash, Greased Lightning, Jewel in the Crown, Jungle King, Lost City Adventure, Merlin, Money Maze, Monopoly, Mystery Treasure, Neptune's Treasure, Super Double Diamond Mine, and Vacation USA. 150 pages. **$19.95**

Shipping Charges: $3 for first book and $1 for each additional book

Send Check or Money Order To:
Casino Vacations • P.O. Box 703
Dania, FL • 33004

Credit Card Orders Call Toll-Free:
(800) 741-1596

order online at:
www.americancasinoguide.com

The Slot Manager

by Steve Bourie

Today, the average U.S. casino makes about 65% of its profits off its slot machines. Actually, that number represents all different kinds of a casino's machines including video poker, video keno, video blackjack and all other varieties of electronic games. It didn't used to be that way. In fact, it used to be just the opposite! Table games were the big revenue producers for the casinos and it was usually the men who played those games while their wives were kept busy at the slot machines.

Back in the 40s and early 50s, the old mechanical slots were full of gears and springs and were actually powered by pulling the handle which started the reels spinning. One of the problems with these machines was that they were limited in the size of the jackpots they could offer because they could only accept one coin, plus the hoppers, still relying on those springs and gears, were limited in the number of coins they could pay out.

In the 60s the next generation of slots was introduced: the electromechanical. These machines still had a handle on the outside, but this time when you pulled it you activated an electric switch which started a motor to spin the reels. These machines increased the popularity of slots because they allowed multiple coin play and they also had electrically-powered hoppers that could pay out much larger jackpots.

In the 80s computer controlled slots were introduced. These new machines revolutionized the industry because everything was now controlled by a computer chip. These electronic marvels could offer progressive jackpots that were linked among different machines and it wasn't long before this new computer technology led to the introduction of a new game called video poker.

Today, the technology is so advanced that it allows slot machines that are hundreds of miles apart to be linked together by computer and offer jackpots that start at $10 million (Super Megabucks), or video poker to be played from five different decks at the same time (Five Deck Frenzy).

Although the technology constantly changes, one thing remains the same: the person responsible generally for the operation of the slot department is the slot manager. It is the slot manager who determines how the slot department will be laid out and how much the machines will be set to pay back.

As a slot player, you've probably had a few questions about how a slot department works: How do they decide where to put those slot machines out on the casino floor? Is winning purely luck? Are some machines really set to pay back more than others? And, if so, where do they put those better-paying machines? Well, the person with the answer to those questions would be the slot manager and I found two who were gracious enough to sit down for an interview in early 1998 to answer some questions about how their departments work and what goes into some of their business decisions.

The first stop was at the office of Rich Marino, Director of Slot Operations, at Luxor, the giant pyramid-shaped casino-resort in Las Vegas. Luxor is owned by Circus Circus, one of the largest gaming companies in the world and the hotel itself, with more than 4,400 rooms, is the world's third largest hotel.

Rich began his career working downtown at the Union Plaza in 1976 in the coin room pulling the buckets under the machines. He eventually became the shift manager and a few years later he moved to the Gold Strike which later merged with Circus Circus. After a one-year stint at the Elgin Riverboat in Illinois, Rich returned to Las Vegas to help open the Luxor casino and he had been there ever since.

Rich had more than 200 employees working for him in his slot department, including: change people, floor people, money runners, booth cashiers; supervisors, assistant shift managers and managers.

What are the job functions of the various people in your department?

Marino: A change person's main function is to provide our casino guests with change service without having to leave the machine. They also pay and verify jackpots on the machines. A booth cashier's function is to provide change and coin redemption service. Floor persons do minor repairs, fill empty machines, and verify jackpots. Supervisors verify the filling of machines and the payment of jackpots up to certain amounts. Assistant Shift Managers and Shift Managers verify larger jackpots. ...and manage all operations on their particular shift.

What goes into your decisions when you lay out the slot floor and are deciding where to put slot machines?

Marino: Traffic flow is the most important consideration when laying out a slot floor. Placing lower denomination machines in high traffic flow areas to insure that the property always looks busy. Also, I place the more popular machines in slower areas to draw people to those locations. I look for what types of machines people are playing and I also run reports continually: which locations are doing best, my top 10 machines, my types of machines, etc.

What is the most popular machine?

Marino: Wheel of Fortune is the most popular right now. IGT (International Game Technology) took its reel-spinning slot machine and added a second-feature spinning wheel on top that offers a bonus to players. They combined that with the popularity of the Wheel of Fortune game show and they now have the most successful machine on the market.

Actually, in the past 10 years, the slot industry has been kind of boring: just pull the handle and let the reels spin. Now, we have all these second-feature-type games with the Williams Games and the Vision IGT (International Game Technology) series. It makes it more exciting. It's not a local type of excitement, but a tourist type of excitement. Tourists like them a lot more than the locals like them.

I went to the gaming show recently and some of those newer slots seemed a little complicated.

Marino: In some cases I have to actually sit down and play those games before I can figure them out. Initially, I thought that the customers would reject them, but it's not happening. They are really taking to them. I believe a lot of the customers don't even know which combinations they're winning on. All they know is that they're having a good time and accumulating a lot of credits.

They actually don't know the winning combinations?

Marino: Yes, but they know they're having fun. They know there's money coming and they're winning credits and they're having a good time. That's the name of the game. The reality is that the casino has the edge. You know that and I know that and everybody knows that, but what you've got to do is let people have as much fun as they can, so that even if they don't win, they're still having fun. It's an entertainment experience. If you're sitting there and take out a $20 bill, and you're playing and that $20 bill is gone and you don't hit anything, you've got a negative experience, you know what I mean?

How about your decisions concerning the physical layout and where you want to place the machines?

Marino: What I try to do initially is create excitement by the front entrance of the casino so when a customer walks in they see people playing and having fun. I put popular nickel games up front because it seems the nickel games always fill up first. (Pulls out floor plan of the casino and points to various locations). As you can see I've located a couple of nickel banks up front and some Wheel of Fortune games next to them.

I try to draw the customers in and create a good flow through the casino. This is the entrance (pointing to a different area of the layout) from the Excalibur when you come over from the moving walkway that links the two properties. Here, I try to create the same scenario by putting Wheel of Fortunes on this wall and the Williams games adjacent to them. And, like I said, I try to create excitement in each area and I do that with the types of machines or denominations. The nickel games kind of shield the front areas and we also put them in the back areas because customers are going to find them there. They're going to find them no matter where you put them because they like playing nickel machines.

I'd like to address some common beliefs that players have about slot machines and here's the first one: "The casino can flip a switch to make the machines hold more." Or, "the machines are set tighter on the weekends." I've actually heard people say "there's a big convention coming this week and they're going to reset all the slots to make them tighter." Any truth to those kinds of thoughts?

Marino: There is no magic switch. The only time we change a machine is when we convert it to a newer or more popular model. And, of course, when you get a new model, then you would change the e-prom (the computer chip that controls the payback percentage) to that new model. The manufacturer initially sets all the percentages for the machines when ordered. I determine the hold percentages I want by the denomination of the machine. The hold percentage averages for the Las Vegas Strip are 11% for nickels, 6.5% for Quarters, 4.5% for dollars, and 3.5% for five dollars and above.

Also, gaming-wise to do that, it's not just going in and changing a chip. You have to go in and you actually have to take all of the money out of the machine. It's got to be returned to the cashier's cage, that money has to be counted and you have to assign a new number to that machine because that's a new machine once you change the e-prom. So, gaming regulations require you to change the statistics on the whole new machine. It's a whole day process to do that. It's not just to go in and change the chip and leave and say "okay, I've tightened them up for the weekend."

Another thing many players believe is that "the best paying machines are on the aisles."

Marino: Not true. The best machines are on the aisle? I'll tell you what, that's a perception people have because most of them like to play machines on the aisle. They'll walk up and play the machines on the end because they don't want to play with somebody next to them. If you've got a guy playing here, here, and here, you're not going to go right next to that guy. You're going to go to the end so there's nobody next to you. That's why we've gone to these round configurations. People don't like sitting next to each other. So, we're going more and more to the round ones because people really like that a lot and these games do a lot better than the normal straight rows of slot machines. That's why I try to break them up with rounds down the middle and slants.

But as far as the tighter and the looser machines, I set them up by model types. I mean, if I have a bank of quarter machines, I'll have a Double Diamond; a Red, White and Blue; and my percentages on those quarter machines are all the same. So, it doesn't matter which machine I put where.

Then you wouldn't have a situation where a high-paying machine would be sitting next to a low-paying machine?

Marino: No. If the machines were the same denomination on a particular bank the hold percentages would be virtually the same. In my dollar machines I order everything at between 4% and 5%. So, you're talking the difference between one percentage point and that's only because certain models are only available at certain percentages. I mean, I would never put an 8% dollar machine next to one at 4%. I don't do that here. Some places might do that, I don't know. I try to give everybody an equal shot no matter what.

So, there would be very little difference between a high machine and a low machine?

Marino: If I was going to set it up that way I would put the loosest machine in the middle as opposed to the end because they get the most play. That's why it appears to be looser to the customer because it gets more play and more action and more people are playing it and it cycles more. And, it gets into those better cycles more often.

Which brings us to the next question, "Do machines get 'hot' and pay out more frequently?"

Marino: Sure they get hot, they also get cold. Through the cycle of a machine it's percentaged to pay out a certain amount over a period of time based on the number of handle pulls the machine receives. However, the hot and cold cycles are random and indeterminable.

When you order a slot machine do you have to tell the manufacturer what you want it to pay?

Marino: Yes.

And, each manufacturer tells you the pre-approved percentages you can choose from?

Marino: That's correct. (goes to shelf, pulls down a book and opens it to a page). This book contains all the available hold percentages for these particular models and the denomination of a machine is what determines the hold percentage I would order for it.

This is what I order quarter machines at - 92.4% - which would be right around 7.5% holding for the house. If it's dollars, I order this one (around 95%) and for twenty-fives (around 97%) or hundreds (around 98%), it goes up, like that. If it's nickels, you start down here (around 89%). That's the way it works.

Now, over a period of time, this quarter machine is going to pay back 92.42% and it's going to hold around 7.5% for the house. And when I say over a period of time, that means over 10 million handle pulls.

10 million is the life cycle? On every machine?

Marino: 10 million is the numbers of handle pulls the manufacturer has determined it would take a particular machine to achieve that 7.5% hold calculation. Getting to that number though, may take a year. That means in January, that machine might be hot, or today it may be hot. So, I may be holding...it's a volatility index they call it...for the first two months of the cycle when that machine goes out on the floor, I may be in the negative. I may be paying out 400% or 500% on that game. But, the next month it may be tighter and at the end of that cycle, it's going to hold at 8%.

Let me show you something else here. I just put these games on the floor last week. These are the new vision games from IGT (International Game Technology). These have been on the floor approximately 14 days. What I do is an analysis: the coin in, jackpots filled, and it tells me my win per day, per unit and my payout percentage. Now, the first week, which is hardly anything to analyze, but this machine is doing its handle per day. This is what it's handling, this is what it's winning, this is what it's holding: 5.72%. It actually should be at 4.92%. So, it's over holding by .80%. It's holding too much.

So, you always have a variable there?

Marino:Right. There's a variance there. The next game on the row, okay, this one is not holding. It's half of what it should be holding.

That's half of what it should be holding, based on what the manufacturer said?

Marino:Right. It should be holding 5.2%, the manufacturer said, and it's only holding 2.75%, but it's only been on the floor for two weeks. When you see a machine not holding...we do a comparison at the end of each month of winners and losers. Then we look at the coin in and we see how long they've been on the floor. Most of the time, I'll look at a year-to-date number, or a lifetime number on the machine to see where they are actually at.

Will this tell you how many actual pulls were made on that machine?

Marino:Sure. You just divide, or you go to the machine itself and you could see exactly how many handle pulls. Normally, you just divide it by the number of coins in and you could tell the handle pulls. That's basically what we do, but we don't tighten them up, or loosen them up. Once they're out there, they're out there. The only time we do conversions is when we see a model not getting enough play. Then we say it's not popular and we try something else.

Do you ever have a problem, after a year, where a machine doesn't make money for you?

Marino:No, usually a machine will hold what it is percentaged to hold if it's had enough handle pulls. If they're supposed to hold 5%, they'll hold 5% after they've been on the floor for a while. Usually, when they don't make money, they're holding what they are supposed to hold, but it's not enough for the house average. What you would do is take your bottom 20% of your machines and convert those to more popular models.

But to go back to what you were asking before, the hot and the cold factor? That's definitely true. The machine can be hot today and colder than anything tomorrow. It will pay out 400% today to you and tomorrow it might take 400% from somebody else.

Okay, but there's no way to tell if it's going to stay hot, is there? It reminds me of when I talk to people about playing craps. They all say "just

find a 'hot' crap game." I say, "fine, you may find a 'hot' crap game, but all you know is what happened in the past. You don't know what's going to happen in the future."

Marino: Sure, It's the same as a "hot" slot machine, you just don't know what the next pull will bring.

Right. But people say, "well, if it's a 'hot' machine, it's going to keep paying out." People are under the assumption that it's going to keep paying out, and I tell them "no, it's purely luck."

Marino: You're right. They don't pay out forever. All it is, is luck. Being in the right place at the right time.

How about this one: "don't play a machine that just hit a jackpot?"

Marino: Well, it doesn't matter.

And that's because the odds remain constant on every pull of the handle?

Marino: That's right.

One last question. Do you have any suggestions for players?

Marino: Suggestions for players? The only suggestion I have is to just play the machine that you enjoy the most and that you have a good time at. I mean...I play a little bit. I go out with my wife and she'll play video poker machines. I'll play video poker with her, but I just play the machines that I enjoy playing. I'll play machines that I see paying back the best to the customer (by looking at the pay table). Those are the ones I'll look for, and locals do that. If you're a local customer, that's what you look for: the good video poker machines. Just like Jeff (referring to Jeff Compton, author of the *Las Vegas Advisor Guide to Slot Clubs*) will tell you. He's an expert at video poker machines.

Rich's answers were surprisingly candid and they certainly laid to rest some long-standing beliefs among slot players as to how slots are set up in a casino. For years slot players have always believed that some machines were set much higher than others within a casino. Rich dispelled this myth by pointing out that all of his machines within a particular denomination were set to pay back approximately the same amount. He pointed out that not all manufacturers offer the exact same percentages in their computer chips so there could be a difference of as high as 1% but you really won't find a situation where one quarter machine that's set to return 92% would be sitting next to another quarter machine set to return 82%.

If you look at the numbers from the Nevada Gaming Control Board regarding the returns on slot machines that are shown in this book it certainly corroborates what Rich was saying. After all, if the average $1 machine returns 95% how much of a difference could there be between the high and the low? Do you think half of the $1 machines are set at 99% and the other half are set at 91% in order to get that 95% average? Sorry, but it just doesn't work that way. Yes, there are differences among machines but, once again, the amount is minimal and it probably amounts to no more than 1%.

And what about the common belief that machines at the end of an aisle are set to return the most? Well, Rich killed that idea too. He explained that it just seems that end machines pay out more often simply because they're played more often.

This is somewhat akin to the "bad player" theory in blackjack. According to this theory, if there's a bad player at the blackjack table who constantly makes poor decisions it will somehow affect the order of the cards and cause the good players (who make correct playing decision) to lose more often. The truth is that the bad player really has no affect on the game because sometimes his decisions will hurt you and sometimes his decisions will help you. The problem is that you only tend to remember the situations where you lost because of his poor play and forget the times that you won because of his boneheaded moves.

This same theory can apply to slot machines at the end of an aisle. When you're playing in a casino, or just walking through, you'll only remember the times you saw people winning at machines, not losing. Since the end-of-the-aisle machines get more play, they will, of course, have more winners and people will tend to remember them as the better paying machines.

As far as constantly changing the payback percentages on the chips to make machines "looser" or "tighter" Rich pointed out that it's not quite that simple and that changes are rarely made because of all the extra work that's involved.

In the July 1998 issue of *Las Vegas Advisor* this same subject was covered in an interview with three different Las Vegas casino slot managers and two officials from the Nevada Gaming Control Board. The *Advisor* writer discovered that there actually are some slots where the percentages can be changed by flipping a switch, but it only applies to machines that are connected together in a "bank" where they all share the same centralized chip. The vast majority of the machines in a casino, however, are not capable of this function as they each have their own internal chip.

The *Advisor* story also went on to point out that Nevada law requires casinos to do paperwork whenever a chip is changed and it must be completed within 24 hours. Also, the casino must complete additional accounting paperwork for filing with the state. Evidently, the process is so time-consuming the story concluded that " no one we talked to even had a secondhand story of a Nevada casino that frequently changes chips."

Of course, Nevada is just one gaming jurisdiction in the U.S. and not every casino is going to work in the exact same manner. Or, will it? To get some perspective on how it's done in a different market I traveled to Atlantic City to interview Pete Ruchser, Director of Slot Operations at Harrah's.

Pete had more than 200 employees in his department and the returns on his machines at Harrah's were always among the best, if not the best, in the city. Pete started with Caesars in 1979, working in the cashier's cage and later became a manager. In 1984 he moved to Harrah's and through various promotions he eventually became the casino controller. In early 1994 the director of slots position became available and he had been in that position ever since.

Besides supervising the employees, what other responsibilities does your job include?

Ruchser: Well, I look at it as the basic four dimensions in the business. You have your product in front of your customers, the physical product: the slot machines, the way they're laid out on the floor, the gaming environment, the overall cleanliness of that environment, the signage in that environment, the mix of games that you have, and those types of things. Then, of course, you have the human resource aspect of that: the employees, the managers of the work force and how they interrelate with each other and other departments, and how they take care of their customers. And, obviously, there's the regulatory aspect of this, depending upon your jurisdiction. There's a little bit more importance placed on that, or emphasis, I should say than in some other jurisdictions, and that is how your operation complies with state and federal and any other regulations that you have to deal with. And, then the most important aspect of all of that is how it impacts on the customer, managing that customer base, and the customer service aspect of all of this. Those are the four dimensions and I try to keep all of those things in order.

When laying out your department, how do you decide where you want to put the machines?

Ruchser: Well, I have a lot of help with that. I have a slot performance manager who really is the product person in terms of knowing the ins and outs of the slot machines and how they work. He has a very good relationship with a lot of the vendors and his true focus is the gaming product itself. He has his thoughts on how that should be done. I have my thoughts on how that should be done and I get some input from the other side of the department, which is the service side. I also get a lot of feedback back from our marketing hosts, slot hosts, player development people, and generally, customers. I take all of that information and do the best I can with...very specific machine placement...or moving machines from place to place, or in terms of generally reconfiguring the casino and doing things such as making the slot aisles wider, or changing the direction and addressing things like that. So, there are a lot of different inputs that I have to digest.

Is there a standard where you would specifically place dollar machines and quarter machines? Or, is there some standard within the industry that says, you want to put the most popular games way back in the corner to draw people in?

Ruchser: There's probably some of that thinking out there. My experience with this property has been that, no, we don't necessarily look by denomination. If you go down on our floor you can see various points of entry, various points of egress, and quarters are not necessarily the furthest from any of those points of egress or entrance into the casino. We mix our denominations to make sure that there is a pretty decent selection of games and denomination of game type within various aspects of the casino. It really depends on what you're dealt with in terms of your four walls of your room and how you get in and out of your property. That would be my opinion.

How often do you change machine types or the mix in an area and what would be your primary reason for doing that?

Ruchser: Well, let's take the premise of looking overall at changing out within the course of a year. We have 2,500 slot machines and the life cycle of a machine can be anywhere between five and seven years. So, if you say five years, you're going to be looking at changing out some component of your floor anywhere between 15% to 20% of your total inventory on an annualized basis. So, you could change, whether through game modification, or actually taking a slot machine off the floor and inserting a new machine in its place, anywhere between 300 and 500 units per year. And, that is predominantly what we do. Obviously, it also depends on the machines total overall performance.

So, you're changing about 20% a year?

Ruchser: Sure. And, it depends on other considerations, you know, how old your slot product is with respect to the marketplace that you operate in. Also, it depends on how many new products come out. Some years there is this great influx of new technology that comes into the marketplace with new types of machines with different products and other years it's not quite as drastic, so you adjust your spending and mix accordingly.

I'd like to address some common beliefs that players have about slot machines and here's the first one: "The casino can flip a switch to make the machines hold more." Or, "the machines are set tighter on the weekends." I've actually heard people say "there's a big convention coming this week and they're going to reset all the slots to make them tighter." Any truth to those kinds of thoughts?

Ruchser: I have heard that before. They believe you sit up in your office and you flip a switch and you get a computer dial that says, "on the weekend hold 10% and in the middle of the week turn it down to 8%." That is absolutely, of course, impossible to happen. Also, it's illegal to happen in this state. I don't know anybody who is going to manipulate their game product based on short-term fluctualities in their business conditions.

Another thing many players believe is that "the best paying machines are on the aisles."

Ruchser: Customers aren't going to feel the hold percentage. You can have the same game program that is 95% on this machine in the middle of the aisle and it's 92% on the machine that is on the outside of the aisle and *theoretically* this game in here (in the middle of the aisle) is to the customer's advantage. Those hold percentages are calculated in the hundreds of thousands of cycles though and I don't know too many customers who have that type of a bankroll, or the time, to sit there and play through a cycle of a slot machine.

If you pull a handle or activate a button, you can get 10 handle pulls, or 10 decisions per minute. So, that's 600 per hour, barring that you don't have any coin jams and that you're constantly playing. Over a 24-hour period, that's 12,000-13,000 pulls; it's going to take you the better part of a month to get your slot machine cycle where you could say "yes, I've experienced one full cycle." And even then, you may not experience the actual hold percentage of that game versus the other game that you were playing side-by-side.

If someone comes in here and plays the dollar machines, are all of those machines set at relatively the same payback? Or, is there a big difference between the high and the low end?

Ruchser: In this marketplace our dollar reels in general are between 7% and

7.5% and somewhere between 8% and 8.5%. We may even have some as high as 8.8% or 8.9% depending on what type of program the manufacturer offers for that type of slot machine. So, there's a bandwidth in there.

So, even if someone did find a machine that was set higher and paid back more than another machine the difference would probably be marginal?

Ruchser: Yes. And, truly you don't know where, so to speak, that cycle is going to occur. You can sit there and have a 9% game and a 5% game and the customer can sit down and be just as lucky, if not luckier, on the 9% game than the 5% game.

How about players that believe a machines is "hot" and will pay out more frequently?"

Ruchser: Obviously, if you're sitting there and the perception is that the guy next to you is always winning, yes, in the terminology of the player, that other guy's machine is "hot." It (the slot) goes into its random number generator and if it selects a pay to come up and then three pulls later, it just happens to select another pay, and then three pulls later it selects another pay, yeah, that definition is "hot. " Especially, if you're sitting there next to that player and you're not getting anything.

But it's "hot' simply based on luck?

Ruchser: Right. Absolutely. It's a random number generator and it's the timing when you sit down at that machine and it just happens to sequence those reel stops.

Do you have days when machines pay out more than they take in?

Ruchser: Sure.

How do you track it?

Ruchser: We have a slot data system that tracks the coin in or wager into the machine, coin out, hand-paid jackpots, hopper fills, handle pulls. There's a wealth of data information in there.

You get a printout every day?

Ruchser: I can look at it daily if I want. I can look at each machine up to the minute of that day if I want to do that. Obviously, that is very time consuming. And, there are days when slot machines lose money. There's no doubt about it. And, it doesn't matter whether it's a low denomination game or a high denomination game. A quarter machine could get a couple of $250 pays during the day and obviously it's going to lose money that day. But, we don't look at analyzing our slot products on a day-to-day basis. The exception may be a new machine that we put on the floor for a test, to see if customers like it and in that case we'll look at it more closely to see how it does. We usually trial machines anywhere from 90 days to six months to get a sense of customer feedback and how the machine's performing. Unless of course, we believe it is performing incorrectly and there's a technical issue with the game, and that is brought to light relatively quickly, but that happens very, very, very infrequently.

Do you ever have a machine that has been in use for a few months and find out that it's paid out more than it's taken in?

Ruchser: We have had some games on the floor, some high denomination games, where after 60 days the games have lost money. We'll go in and do a diagnostics on the game to make sure it's correct and it's complying with its manufacturer's specifications and the state's regulations. If that is okay, then I'll leave the game on the floor if it's getting the appropriate amount of handle because the customers are playing it. But I'm not going to yank a machine off the floor after 30 or 60 days if it just happens to be something that customers are winning money on and the game is performing correctly. You know, that's just "the roll of the dice" so to speak. If it's a good product and the customers like it, we'll leave it out there for a while and see how it goes.

Do you have any suggestions for players?

Ruchser: That's like trying to give investment advice. My suggestion is to play if you enjoy yourself and if you no longer enjoy yourself, don't play, or take a break and do something else.

In terms of advisement for what games to play? That's totally a personal preference. There are so many products out there, it's like food. What you may enjoy, I may dislike. Also, in the randomness of this, I do not offer suggestions on what types of products people should play. I make the suggestion that you play what you enjoy and when you stop enjoying it, look for something else to do based on your experience. If you have any recommendations about what kind of games you would like to see, we're always more than happy to try and offer that or discuss it with the manufacturer, whatever the case may be.

The talk with Pete confirmed that there really isn't much difference between Las Vegas and Atlantic City as far as how frequently slot machine payback percentages are changed. Basically, they aren't. Once they're set, they stay that way because it's just too much trouble to keep changing it.

Actually, it's an even bigger problem to change payback percentages in New Jersey because casinos in that state aren't allowed to go into a machine and change a chip on their own. They must first notify the state's regulators that they want to make the change and then an Electronics Specialist from the Division of Gaming Enforcement must be present to supervise the changing of the chip. Gaming regulations aren't quite that strict in Nevada where casinos are free to change the chips on their own. However, even though Nevada casinos don't have to notify the state before changing a chip, they are required to make sure they only use a chip that has been previously approved by the state and they're also required to complete paperwork notifying regulators of the change.

Pete seemed to put more emphasis on the randomness of slot machines by saying that even if you play one machine that is programmed to pay back less than another you might actually win more on the lesser paying machine simply because of luck. Once again though, the fact that there really isn't much difference between the high and low paying machines within a particular denomination was made by Pete when he said that most of his $1 machines were programmed to pay back somewhere between 7% and 8.5%, depending on the manufacturer. Just a 1-1/2% spread between the high and the low.

And what have we learned from all of this? Well, besides seeing that casinos don't constantly change the paybacks on their machines so they can increase their winnings at a moments notice, hopefully, we've also learned that casinos are a business and the decision as to what the payback percentage on their slot machines should be is simply a function of that machine's cost to the casino.

If you think about it, most slot machines take up about the same amount of space and all of them probably require the same amount of electricity and routine maintenance. Now, if the operating costs are basically the same, then it only makes sense that a casino needs to take more out of a nickel machine, percentagewise, than a quarter machine in order to cover its costs. As an example, casinos know they need to keep 11% on a nickel machine because the profit on a five-coin pull is only about 3¢ (25¢ x .11), whereas a quarter machine can be set to keep only 8% because the profit on a three-coin play on that machine is 6¢ (75¢ x .08).

So, if you're looking for a better return from a slot machine it seems that the best thing you can do is play a higher denomination machine (assuming you can afford it). Just remember that nickel machines return the least, $100 machines return the most and plan your gambling budget accordingly.

Video Poker

by Steve Bourie

Okay, who knows the main difference between video poker and slot machines? C'mon now, raise your hands if you think you know it. If you said "a slot machine is a game of luck and video poker is a game of skill" then you are correct! When you play a slot machine there is no decision you can make which will affect the outcome of the game. You put in your money; pull the handle; and hope for the best. In video poker, however, it is your skill in playing the cards which definitely affects the outcome of the game.

Okay, who knows the other major difference between video poker and slot machines? Well, you're right again if you said "you never know what percentage a slot machine is set to pay back, but you can tell a video poker machine's payback percentage just by looking at it." Of course if you knew that answer then you also knew that video poker machines almost always offer you better returns than slot machines (provided you make the right playing decisions).

Now for those of you who didn't know the answers to those two questions, please read on. You others can skip the rest of this story as I am sure you're eager to get back to your favorite video poker machine.

First, let's cover the basics. Video poker has virtually the same rules as a game of five card draw poker. The only difference is that you have no opponent to beat and you can't lose more than your initial bet. First, you deposit from one to five coins in the machine to make your bet. You are then shown five cards on the video screen and your goal is to try to make the best poker hand possible from those cards. Since it is a draw game, you are given one opportunity to improve your hand. This is done by allowing you to discard from one, up to all five cards from your original hand. Of course, you don't have to discard any if you don't want to. After choosing which cards you want to keep (by pushing the button below each card), you then push the deal button and the machine will replace all of the other cards with new cards. Based on the resulting final hand the machine will then pay you according to the pay schedule posted on the machine. Naturally, the better your hand, the higher the amount the machine will pay you back.

That's pretty much how a video poker machine works from the outside, but what about the inside? Well, I had three specific questions about that so I contacted International Game Technology, which is the world's largest manufacturer of video poker machines (as well as slot machines), to see if they could provide some answers. Here's what they said:

#1: Are the cards dealt to you on a random basis?

IGT: Gaming regulations require that gaming devices must have random outcomes of game play results. In order to satisfy this requirement, games of all types use a random number generator (RNG) software algorithm to determine game outcome. While the game is in the idle state, i.e. waiting for someone to deposit a coin or push a play credit button, the RNG algorithm is called hundreds of times every second. The RNG has approximately 16,000,000,000,000,000,000 possible outcomes and, depending on the game type, there will be many billions of outcomes that map into any set of cards, or keno balls, or slot machine symbols. This ensures that all IGT games are completely random, just as if the cards were dealt from a perfectly shuffled deck.

#2: When does the shuffling actually stop?

IGT: On all game types, when the start, deal or bet button is pushed, the randomly selected outcome is determined. This result is determined solely by the RNG and is not dependent on any factors of game play, such as how many coins are bet, or on what happened in the last game played or on how many seconds you wait before deciding what cards to draw.

#3: Is there a draw card assigned to each dealt card?

IGT: No, IGT games operate as follows: the first five cards dealt are displayed and additional cards are taken from the top of the deck as needed. So, if you discard one card it doesn't matter which card you discard, the draw card will be the same.

According to IGT's first answer we know that all of the hands are generated randomly. Some people believe that the machine knows what cards it initially deals you and then it gives you bad draw cards so you won't have a winning hand. This isn't true. The deck is shuffled randomly and then all cards are dealt and drawn in order. By the way, the number with all the zeros is 16 quintillion. Don't feel ignorant if you didn't know it because neither did I. Of course, when our national debt gets that high, we'll all be familiar with it!

One other point must be made here regarding random outcomes in video poker machines. Please notice that the above answer stated *gaming regulations* require that the machines must have random outcomes. You should be aware that there are casinos operating in places that *do not* have gaming regulations. Examples are cruise ships which operate in international waters and some Indian reservations that are not subject to state regulations. You should also be aware that the technology exists for machines to be set so they do not act randomly. These machines are actually programmed to avoid giving the players better hands and they wind up giving the house a much bigger advantage. These machines are illegal in Nevada, New Jersey, Colorado and all other states that pattern their gaming regulations after those states. You may, however, come across them in unregulated casinos.

With the second answer we know that the RNG stops when you deposit the first coin, or when you push the bet or deal button. This means that the results will be the same whether we deposit one coin or the maximum coins. Some people think that the outcome will be different depending on how many coins are deposited. This is not true. If you put in one coin and get a royal flush, you would have gotten that same royal flush if you had put in five coins.

The last answer clears up some confusion about how the draw cards are dealt. Some people believe that the machine initially deals 10 cards: five up cards that you see, plus one other card under each of those cards as a draw card. This is not true. The draw card you receive is in the same order as if it were being dealt off the top of the deck. Example: You are dealt (10♣,J♣,Q♣,6♦,6♥). You discard (6♦,6♥) and draw (6♣,6♠). Had you kept (6♦,6♥) and discarded (10♣,J♣,Q♣) you would have had four sixes.

One final point you should keep in mind - IGT is not the only manufacturer of video poker machines. There are quite a few others and they may engineer their machines to work in a different manner. Their RNG may not stop in the same way and their draw cards may be dealt differently. IGT, however, is by far the largest and it is the type of machine you will most often encounter in a casino.

Now that you understand how a video poker machine works let's learn how to pick out the best paying ones. In the beginning of this story it was mentioned that "you can tell a video poker machine's payback percentage just by looking at it." That's true, but it takes a little bit of knowledge to know the difference among all the different types of machines. An example of some of the different machines available are: Tens or Better, Jacks or Better, Two Pairs or Better, Joker Poker and Deuces Wild. To make it even more confusing, not only are there different machines, but each of those machines can have a different pay schedule for the same hand.

Fortunately, every video poker machine's payback percentage can be mathematically calculated. Not only does this let you know which machines offer you the best return, but it also tells you the best playing decisions to make on that particular machine based on the odds of that combination occurring. The bad news, however, is that it's fairly impossible to do on your own so you'll have to either buy a book that lists all of the percentages and strategies or buy a computer program that does the work for you. Take a look at the tables on the next few pages and you'll see some different types of video poker games and their payback percentages (when played with maximum coin and perfect strategy). For those of you with a computer, *Bob Dancer Presents Win Poker* can determine the exact payback percentage for any video poker machine. It retails for $29.95 (see ad on page 68) and besides calculating percentages it will also allow you to play video poker on different types of machines and analyze hands to show you the expected return for each play. You can set the game to automatically show you the best decision each time or you can set it to just warn you if you make a wrong decision on your own. It's so simple that my 11-year-old son plays it and I'm confident he can play better than the average Las Vegas visitor. "I'm going for the flush, dad!"

If you have no desire to get quite that serious about learning video poker then I'll try to provide some general tips to help you out. First, you'll need to find the machines that offer you the highest returns. One of the best is the 9/6 Jacks or Better machine. Of course, you're probably wondering "what exactly is a 9/6 Jacks or Better machine?" Well, the Jacks or Better part refers to the fact that you won't win anything from the machine unless you have at least a pair of Jacks. The 9/6 part refers to the payback schedule on this kind of machine. As stated earlier, each machine can have a different payback schedule and there are at least 20 different kinds of payback schedules available on Jacks or Better machines. In Las Vegas the two most common Jacks or Better machines you will find are 8/5 and 9/6. Here's a comparison of their pay schedules (per coin, for five-coin play):

Hand	9/6	8/5
Royal Flush	800	800
Straight Flush	50	50
4-of-a-Kind	25	25
Full House	**9**	**8**
Flush	**6**	**5**
Straight	4	4
3-of-a-Kind	3	3
Two Pairs	2	2
One Pair J's	1	1

As you can see, the schedules are identical except for the better payoffs on the 9/6 machines for Flushes and Full Houses. The payback on a 9/6 machine is 99.5% with perfect play, while the 8/5 machines return 97.3% with perfect play. Of course, it doesn't make any sense to play an 8/5 machine if a 9/6 machine is available. Yet, in Las Vegas you'll see lots of people playing an 8/5 when a 9/6 can often be found in the same casino. The reason they do that is because they don't know any better; you do. Always look for the 9/6 machines. They can be found in every downtown Las Vegas casino and most, but not all, strip casinos. In other states, including New Jersey, they won't be found as easily. On a trip to Mississippi I found a few, but it took some searching and not every casino had them. If you can't find one be sure to double check with the Slot Host to see if they're offered.

One other common machine you will come across is an 8/5 Jacks or Better progressive. These feature the same 8/5 pay table as above except for the royal flush which pays a jackpot amount that is displayed on a meter above the machine. The jackpot will continue to build until someone hits a royal flush; then it will reset and start to build again. If the jackpot on a 25¢ machine is above $2,240 (for five coins) then you should play it. If it's below $2,240 then stick to the regular 9/6 machines.

Another good tip is to restrict your play to the same kind of machine all the time. Each video poker machine has its own particular strategy and what works best on a Jacks or Better machine is definitely much different from what works

Jacks or Better Pay Table Variations

(Per coin with maximum coin played and perfect strategy)

9/7 (at Stratosphere)

Royal Flush	800
Straight Flush	50
4-of-a-kind	25
Full House	9
Flush	7
Straight	4
3-of-a-kind	3
2 Pair	2
Jacks or Better	1
Payback	**100.8%**

9/6 with 4,700 coin jackpot

Royal Flush	940
Straight Flush	50
4-of-a-kind	25
Full House	9
Flush	6
Straight	4
3-of-a-kind	3
2 Pair	2
Jacks or Better	1
Payback	**99.90%**

9/6 with 4,000 coin jackpot

Royal Flush	800
Straight Flush	50
4-of-a-kind	25
Full House	9
Flush	6
Straight	4
3-of-a-kind	3
2 Pair	2
Jacks or Better	1
Payback	**99.54%**

8/5

Royal Flush	800
Straight Flush	50
4-of-a-kind	25
Full House	8
Flush	5
Straight	4
3-of-a-kind	3
2 Pair	2
Jacks or Better	1
Payback	**97.28%**

7/5

Royal Flush	800
Straight Flush	50
4-of-a-kind	25
Full House	7
Flush	5
Straight	4
3-of-a-kind	3
2 Pair	2
Jacks or Better	1
Payback	**96.15%**

6/5

Royal Flush	800
Straight Flush	50
4-of-a-kind	25
Full House	6
Flush	5
Straight	4
3-of-a-kind	3
2 Pair	2
Jacks or Better	1
Payback	**95.00%**

Bonus Poker Pay Table Variations

(Per coin with maximum coin played and perfect strategy)

7/5 Bonus

Royal Flush	800
Straight Flush	50
Four Aces	80
Four 2s 3s 4s	40
Four 5s-Ks	25
Full House	7
Flush	5
Straight	4
3-of-a-kind	3
2 Pair	2
Jacks or Better	1
Payback	**98.02%**

8/5 Bonus

Royal Flush	800
Straight Flush	50
Four Aces	80
Four 2s 3s 4s	40
Four 5s-Ks	25
Full House	8
Flush	5
Straight	4
3-of-a-kind	3
2 Pair	2
Jacks or Better	1
Payback	**99.17%**

9/6 Double Bonus

Royal Flush	800
Straight Flush	50
Four Aces	160
Four 2s 3s 4s	80
Four 5s-Ks	50
Full House	9
Flush	6
Straight	5
3-of-a-kind	3
2 Pair	1
Jacks or Better	1
Payback	**97.81%**

9/7 Double Bonus

Royal Flush	800
Straight Flush	50
Four Aces	160
Four 2s 3s 4s	80
Four 5s-Ks	50
Full House	9
Flush	7
Straight	5
3-of-a-kind	3
2 Pair	1
Jacks or Better	1
Payback	**99.11%**

10/7 Double Bonus

Royal Flush	800
Straight Flush	50
Four Aces	160
Four 2s 3s 4s	80
Four 5s-Ks	50
Full House	10
Flush	7
Straight	5
3-of-a-kind	3
2 Pair	1
Jacks or Better	1
Payback	**100.17%**

10/7 Triple Bonus

Royal Flush	800
Straight Flush	50
Four Aces	240
Four 5s-Ks	120
Four 2s 3s 4s	75
Full House	10
Flush	7
Straight	4
3-of-a-kind	3
2 Pair	1
Kings or Better	1
Payback	**98.52%**

Deuces Wild Pay Table Variations

(Per coin with maximum coin played and perfect strategy)

Short Pay		Full Pay	
Natural Royal Flush	800	Natural Royal Flush	800
Four Deuces	200	Four Deuces	200
Wild Royal Flush	25	Wild Royal Flush	25
5-of-a-kind	15	5-of-a-kind	15
Straight Flush	9	Straight Flush	9
4-of-a-kind	**4**	**4-of-a-kind**	**5**
Full House	3	Full House	3
Flush	2	Flush	2
Straight	2	Straight	2
3-of-a-kind	1	3-of-a-kind	1
Payback	**94.34%**	**Payback**	**100.76%**

best on a Deuces Wild machine. I usually only play 9/6 Jacks or Better machines because that is what I practice on and I automatically know the best decision to make all the time. Keep in mind that when you calculate the payback percentage for a video poker machine the number you arrive at is based on perfect play. As an example, a 9/6 Jacks or Better video poker machine has a 99.5 percent payback with perfect play. This means that, theoretically, it will return $99.50 for every $100 played in the machine, but only if the player makes the correct decision every time. If you make mistakes, and most players do, the return to the casino will be higher. If you play several different kinds of machines it becomes increasingly harder to remember the correct play to make and you will make mistakes. Therefore, it only makes sense to memorize the correct decisions for one kind of machine and to always play on that same kind of machine (of course, in order to learn those proper strategies, you may want to buy that book or software).

Now that you've decided which machines to play, you'll need some help with your playing strategy. Reproduced on the next two pages are charts that will give you an excellent simple strategy for both 9/6 and 8/5 video poker machines. These charts were derived from computer calculations using the *VP Tutor* program and will give you a near-perfect strategy for playing your hands. They aren't 100% perfect but they are close to it and will only be fractionally incorrect in some situations. The only difference between the two tables is shown in the poker hands that have been *italicized* in the 8/5 strategy tables.

To use any chart just look up your hand and play it in the manner that is closest to the top of the chart. For example: you are dealt (6♣,6♦,7♥,8♠,9♣). You keep (6♣,6♦) rather than (6♦,7♥,8♠,9♣) because a low pair (#16) is higher

Simple Strategy Table For 9/6 Jacks or Better

1. Royal Flush
2. Straight Flush
3. 4 of a kind
4. 4 card Royal Flush
5. Full House
6. Flush
7. 3 of a kind
8. Straight
9. 4 card Straight Flush
10. Two Pairs
11. 4 card inside Straight Flush
12. Pair of Jacks or higher
13. 3 card Royal Flush
14. 4 card Flush
15. 4 card straight with 3 high cards
16. Low Pair
17. 4 card Straight with 2 high cards
18. 4 card Straight with 1 high card
19. 3 card Inside Straight Flush with 2 high cards
20. 3 card Straight Flush with 1 high card
21. 4 card Straight with no high cards
22. 3 card Double Inside Straight Flush with 2 high cards
23. 3 card Inside Straight Flush with 1 high card
24. 3 card Straight Flush with no high cards
25. 4 card Inside Straight with 4 high cards
26. 2 card Royal Flush with no Ace or 10
27. 2 card Royal Flush with Ace and no 10
28. 3 card Double Inside Straight Flush with 1 high card
29. 3 card Inside Straight Flush with no high card
30. 4 card Inside Straight with 3 high cards
31. 3 high cards with no Ace
32. 2 high cards
33. 2 card Royal Flush with 10 and no Ace
34. 1 high card
35. 3 card Double Inside Straight Flush with no high card
36. All New Cards

Simple Strategy Table For 8/5 Jacks or Better

1. Royal Flush
2. Straight Flush
3. 4 of a kind
4. 4 card Royal Flush
5. Full House
6. Flush
7. 3 of a kind
8. Straight
9. 4 card Straight Flush
10. Two Pairs
11. 4 card inside Straight Flush
12. Pair of Jacks or higher
13. 3 card Royal Flush
14. 4 card Flush
15. 4 card straight with 3 high cards
16. Low Pair
17. 4 card Straight with 2 high cards
18. 4 card Straight with 1 high card
19. 3 card Inside Straight Flush with 2 high cards
20. 3 card Straight Flush with 1 high card
21. 4 card Straight with no high cards
22. 3 card Double Inside Straight Flush with 2 high cards
23. 3 card Inside Straight Flush with 1 high card
24. 3 card Straight Flush with no high cards
25. 4 card Inside Straight with 4 high cards
26. 2 card Royal Flush with no Ace or 10
27. 2 card Royal Flush with Ace and no 10
28. *3 high cards with no Ace*
29. *4 card Inside Straight with 3 high cards*
30. *3 card Double Inside Straight Flush with 1 high card*
31. *2 high cards*
32. *3 card Inside Straight Flush with no high card*
33. 2 card Royal Flush with 10 and no Ace
34. 1 high card
35. 3 card Double Inside Straight Flush with no high card
36. All New Cards

Basic Strategy For Full-Pay Deuces Wild

Generated by Tom Ski's *Video Poker Strategy Master*

With FOUR DEUCES

Four Deuces

With THREE DEUCES

Wild Royal
Five Tens-Aces
Three Deuces

With TWO DEUCES

Wild Royal
Five of a Kind
Straight Flush
Four of a Kind
4-Card Wild Royal
4-Card STFL, Open, 22-67suited to 22-9Tsuited
Two Deuces

With ONE DEUCE

Wild Royal
Five of a Kind
Straight Flush
Four of a Kind
4-Card Wild Royal
Full House
4-Card STFL, Open, 2-567suited to 2-9TJsuited
Three of a Kind
Flush
Straight
2-345suited, 2-456suited
4-Card STFL, 1 Gap, 6-Q High
4-Card STFL, 2 Gaps, 7-K High
2-A34suited, 2-A35suited, 2-A45suited
3-Card Wild Royal, Jack Hi
3-Card Wild Royal, Queen Hi
3-Card Wild Royal, King Hi
3-Card STFL, Open, 2-67suited to 2-9Tsuited
2-AKsuited, 2-AQsuited, 2-AJsuited, 2-ATsuited 0 Penalty Card
One Deuce

With NO DEUCE

Royal
4-Card Royal
Straight Flush
Four of a Kind
Full House
Three of a Kind
Flush
Straight
4-Card STFL, Open, 3456suited to 9TJQsuited
4-Card STFL, Inside
3-Card Royal
One Pair
4-Card Flush
4-Card ST, Open, but not 3456
3-Card STFL, Open, 567suited to 9TJsuited
3-Card STFL, 1 Gap, 7 to Q High
456suited
345suited
JTsuited
3-Card STFL, 2 Gaps, 7 to K Hi
QTsuited, QJsuited
346suited, 356suited
3456
4-Card ST, Inside, but not A345
Redraw

Note - Penalty cards are cards that interfere with drawing to a flush or straight. For example: with K♣, Q♣, 10♦, 7♠, 3♥ you keep K♣, Q♣ and there are no penalty cards. With K♣, Q♣, 4♦, 7♠, 3♣ you also keep K♣, Q♣but there is one penalty card (3♣) and when you discard it you are throwing away a card which could have helped you draw a flush. With K♣, Q♣, 10♦, 7♠, 3♣, you keep K♣, Q♣ but now there are two penalty cards (3♣, 10♦) because one card (3♣) could have helped you draw a flush and the other (10♦) could have helped you draw a straight. With Q♣, J♣, 10♦, 7♣, 3♣ there are three penalty cards (10♦, 7♣, 3♣). Two of them (7♣, 3♣) could have helped you draw a flush and the other (10♦) could have helped you draw a straight.

Perfect Strategy For Pick'Em Poker

Generated by Tom Ski's *Video Poker Strategy Master*

Three of a Kind
QJTsuited
KQJsuited, KQTsuited, KJTsuited
High Pair, 99-AA
Royal, Ace Hi
9TJsuited
89Tsuited
789suited
QJ9suited, QT9suited
Straight Flush, Open, 0 Hi, 345suited-678suited
JT8suited, J98suited, T97suited
KQ9suited, KJ9suited, KT9suited
T87suited, 986suited, 976suited
Straight Flush, 2 Gaps, 2 Hi Cards
Flush, 3 Hi Cards
Straight Flush, 1 Gap, 0 Hi Cards
9TJ or TJQ
Straight Flush, 2 Gaps, 1 Hi Card
Flush, 2 Hi Cards
Low Pair, 22-88
Straight Flush, 2 Gaps, 0 Hi Cards
Straight, 1 Gap, 3 Hi Cards
89T
Flush, 1 Hi Card
Straight, 2 Gaps, 3 Hi Cards
Straight, 1 Gap, 2 Hi Cards
789
Flush, 0 Hi Cards
3 Hi Cards
Straight, 2 Gaps, 2 Hi Cards
T87,986,976
Straight, Open, 0 Hi Cards 345-678
2 Hi Cards
Straight, 2 Gaps, 1 Hi Card
Straight, 1 Gap, 0 Hi Cards
1 Hi Card
Straight, 2 Gaps, 0 Hi Cards
0 Hi Cards

Important Note - High card is 9 or higher on Pick'Em.

on the chart than a four-card straight with no high cards (#21). Remember to always look for the highest possible choice on the chart when there are multiple ways to play your hand. As another example: you are dealt (8♣,8♦,J♥,Q♥,K♥). You keep (J♥,Q♥,K♥) rather than (8♣,8♦) because a three-card royal flush (#13) is higher on the chart than a low pair (#16). As a final, but radical, example of how to play your hand by the chart what would you do if you're dealt (6♥,10♥,J♥,Q♥,K♥)? Yes, you have to break up your flush by discarding the 6♥ and go for the royal flush because the four-card royal flush (#4) is higher on the chart than the pat flush (#6).

When looking at the 9/6 chart there are a few things that should seem rather obvious:

1) A low pair is relatively good. Of the 36 possible hands, a low pair is #16 which means there are 20 hands worse than a low pair. If you look at the 15 hands that are better than a low pair eight of them are pat hands that require no draw. Of the other seven hands, six of them are four card hands and the remaining hand is a three-card royal flush.

2) Don't hold three cards trying to get a straight or flush. Nowhere on the chart do you see that you should hold three cards to try for a straight or flush. In some instances you should hold three cards to try for a straight flush, but *never* a straight or flush.

3) Rarely draw to an inside straight. Inside straights (6,7,_,9,10% appear only twice on the chart and only in rather bad positions: #30 (with three high cards) and #25 (with four high cards). It is much easier to draw to an outside straight (_7,8,9,10_) where you can complete your straight by getting the card you need on either end. Open end straights appear four times on the chart and in much higher positions than inside straights: #21 (with no high cards), #18 (with one high card), #17 (with two high cards) and #15 (with three high cards).

4) Don't hold a kicker. A kicker is an unpaired card held with a pair. For example (8,8,K) or (K,K,9) are examples of hands where an extra card (the kicker) is held. *Never* hold a kicker because they add no value to your hand!

Following the 9/6 and 8/5 tables are strategy charts for full-pay Deuces Wild and Pick'Em. These were both generated by *Video Poker Strategy Master*, a great new software program by Tom Ski, which allows you to generate your own video poker strategy charts on your home computer. The full-pay Deuces game can only be found in Nevada casinos but Pick'Em Poker can be found in many different markets around the country.

For your information there are exactly 2,598,960 unique poker hands possible on a video poker machine (when played without a joker). On a 9/6 Jacks or Better machine a royal flush will occur about once every 40,000 hands; a straight flush about every 9,000 hands; four-of-a-kind about every 425 hands; a full house about every 87 hands; a flush about every 91 hands; a straight about every 89 hands; three-of-a-kind about every 14 hands; two pairs about every 8 hands; and a pair of Jacks or better about every 5 hands. The interesting thing

Other Video Poker Game Pay Tables

(Per coin with maximum coin played and perfect strategy)

Pick'Em Poker (five coin payout)

Royal Flush	6,000
Straight Flush	1,199
4-of-a-kind	600
Full House	90
Flush	75
Straight	55
3-of-a-kind	25
Two Pair	15
Pair 9's or Better	10
Payback	**99.95%**

All American Poker

Royal Flush	800
Straight Flush	200
4-of-a-kind	40
Full House	8
Flush	8
Straight	8
3-of-a-kind	3
Two Pair	1
Pair Jacks or Better	1
Payback	**100.72%**

Double Joker

Natural Royal Flush	800
Wild Royal Flush	100
5-of-a-kind	50
Straight Flush	25
4-of-a-kind	9
Full House	5
Flush	4
Straight	3
3-of-a-kind	2
2 Pair	1
Payback	**99.97%**

Deuces Deluxe

Natural Royal Flush	800
Four Deuces	200
Natural Straight Flush	50
Wild Royal Flush	25
5-of-a-kind	15
Natural 4-of-a-kind	10
Wild Stright Flush	9
Wild 4-of-a-kind	4
Full House	4
Flush	3
Straight	2
3-of-a-kind	1
Payback	**100.34%**

to note here is that both a flush and a straight are harder to get than a full house, yet a full house always has a higher payback than either of them. The majority of the time, about 55% to be exact, you will wind up with a losing hand on a 9/6 machine.

The next bit of advice concerns how many coins you should bet. You should always bet the maximum amount (on machines returning 100% or more) because it will allow you to earn bonus coins when you hit the royal flush. Example: For a royal flush on a 9/6 machine with one coin played you receive 250 coins; for two coins you get 500; for three coins you get 750; for four coins you get 1,000 and for five (maximum) coins you get 4,000 coins. This translates into a bonus of 2,750 coins! A royal flush can be expected once every 40,400 hands on a 9/6 machine; once every 40,200 hands on an 8/5 machine; and once every 32,700 hands on an 8/5 progressive. The odds are high, but the added bonus makes it worthwhile. If you can't afford to play the maximum coins on a positive machine then move down to a lower denomination machine.And, if you absolutely insist on playing less than the maximum, be sure to play only one coin at a time. It doesn't make any sense to play two, three or four coins, because you still won't be eligible for the bonus.

One important thing to keep in mind when you look at the total payback on these video poker machines is that those numbers always include a royal flush and the royal flush plays a *very* big factor in the total return. As a matter of fact, the royal flush is such a big factor on video poker machines that you are actually expected to lose until you get that royal flush. Yes, even by restricting your play to video poker machines with a more than 100% payback you are *still* expected to lose money until you hit a royal flush. Once you hit that royal flush it will bring your cash back up to that 100% level but until it happens you should be fully aware that you are statistically expected to lose money.

According to video poker expert Bob Dancer, "on a 25¢ Jacks or Better 9/6 machine you will lose at a rate of 2.5% while you are waiting for the royal to happen. Another way to look at this is quarter players who play 600 hands per hour can expect to lose about $18.75 per hour, on average, on any hour they do not hit a royal." You really have to keep in mind that there are no guarantees when you play video poker. Yes, you are expected to get a royal flush about once every 40,000 hands but there are no guarantees that it will happen and if you don't get that royal flush it could cost you dearly.

A final tip about playing video poker concerns slot clubs. Every major casino has a slot club and you should make it a point to join the slot club before you insert your first coin. It doesn't cost anything to join and as a member you will have the opportunity to earn complimentaries from the casinos in the form of cash, food, shows, drinks, rooms or other "freebies." When you join the club you'll be issued a card (similar to a credit card) that you insert in the machine before you start to play and it will track how much you bet, as well as how long you play. Naturally, the more money you gamble, the more freebies you'll earn. Just make sure you don't get carried away and bet more than you're comfortable with just to earn some extra comps. Ideally, you want to get comps for gambling that you were going to do anyway and not be pressured into betting more than you had planned. Many clubs will also give you cash back for your play and that amount should be added into the payback percentage on the kind of machine you'll be playing. For example: at The Golden Nugget in Las Vegas, the slot club rebates .67% in cash for your video poker play. By only playing 9/6 Jacks or Better machines with a return of 99.54% you can add the .67% rebate to get an adjusted figure of 100.21%. This means that you are, theoretically, playing at a game where you have a slight advantage, *plus* you're still eligible for other room and food discounts on top of your cash rebate.

Choosing Video Poker Games

by John Grochowski

Way back in the early 1990s when the nationwide expansion of gambling was at its beginning and riverboat casinos were new, I asked a riverboat slot director why there was so little video poker on his floor.

``Our guests aren't ready for it,'' he told me. ``When we opened, we didn't know what everybody was going to play. We assumed it would be about normal for the Las Vegas Strip. We opened with about 17 percent video poker, and they sat there empty. All anyone wanted to play was the slots. So we dropped to 9 or 10 percent video poker.''

Things have changed. Slot directors move to other jobs at other casinos, and player tastes change. The current slot director at that same riverboat told me in 2000 that he now has 18 percent video poker, and players can't get enough of it. If he was starting from scratch, he'd turn 20, maybe even 25 percent of his floor over to video poker. What happened?

Video poker, it seems, is an acquired taste. You can see that clearly in casino gambling's capital city. Las Vegas visitors who stick to the Strip will see video poker taking up roughly 15 percent of the slot floors -- a little more in some casinos, a little less than others. But get off the Strip and check out the places that cater to the locals, places such as the Fiesta and Santa Fe in northwest Las Vegas, or Sunset Station and The Reserve to the southeast in Henderson. There you'll see row after row after row of video poker, 50 percent or more of the slot floor.

The difference is in the experience of the players. What the Las Vegas locals know, and what regular players in newer gaming markets are learning, is that they get a better run for their money on video poker than on the slots. Whereas slots on the Las Vegas Strip return an average of a little more than 95 percent of coins played to dollar players and a little less than 93 percent to quarter players, even the bad video poker games, the ones that experts warn to stay away from, return 95 percent with expert play. The good machines return 99 percent, even 100 percent or more in the long run -- although even on those machines there will be more losing sessions than winners, balanced out in the long run by the odd royal flush.

Video poker does it with a high hit frequency, too. On most Jacks or Better-based games, about 45 percent of all hands bring some return. That's a percentage slots were unable to approach until the advent of multiline, multicoin video slots, and on those games many "winners" bring returns of less than the wagers.

Not every player has access to those 100-percent machines. In new gaming markets, where demand for a place to play frequently outstrips available space, slot directors are able to use games that will maximize their profit margins. They know they can use a Jacks or Better game that pays 7-for-1 on full houses and 5-for-1 on flushes instead of a full-pay game that returns 9-for-1 and 6-for-1, and they'll still get plenty of play. There are good machines out there, too, but it's up to the player to learn to tell the difference.

JACKS OR BETTER: In video poker, when the casino wants to change the long-term payback percentage of a game, it changes the pay table. Given the same strategy, players get winning hands no more or less frequently, but some hands pay a little more or a little less.

In Jacks or Better, the base game around which many video poker variations are built, the payoffs that usually are changed are full houses and flushes. We look for games that pay 9-for-1 on full houses and 6-for-1 on flushes, with the full pay table being 250-for-1 on royal flushes (jumping to 4,000 coins with a five-coin wager), 50-for-1 on straight flushes, 25-for-1 on four of a kind, 9-for-1 on full houses, 6-for-1 on flushes 4-for-1 on straights, 3-for-1 on three of a kind, 2-for-1 on two pair and 1-for-1 on pairs of Jacks or better.

For each unit that the payoff on full houses or flushes drops, we lose about 1.1 percent of our long-term payback. On an 8-5 Jacks or Better game, with one-unit drops in both spots on the pay table, our average return drops to 97.3 percent. Drop the full house payback again to 7-for-1, and a 7-5 machine drops to 96.2 percent.

Given better options, a video poker player in the know would walk away from that 7-5 game. In Las Vegas, he might even leave the casino and look for a better deal next door or across the street. That's tough to do on a riverboat, or in a Native American casino that's miles away from the next option. So a player who finds the best video poker in a casino is 7-5 Jacks or Better has a decision to make. Does he take up table games? Does he just go home and skip his night's entertainment? Or does he sigh, decide that at least a 96-percent game is better than he'd get on the slots, and play anyway? Most take the third option.

BONUS POKER: The "bonuses" in Bonus Poker are on certain fours of a kind. Four 2s, 3s or 4s will bring you 40-for-1 and four Aces will bring 80-for-1 instead of the 25-for-1 that is standard on Jacks or Better and on the remaining quads in Bonus Poker.

Other than that, the pay table is the same as in Jacks or Better, with reduced paybacks on full houses and flushes. We look for games that pay 8-for-1 on full houses and 5-for-1 on flushes. That's a 99.2 percent game with expert play. Bonus Poker games often have 7-5 and 6-5 versions, with overall returns dropping about 1.1 percent for each unit the flush payoff drops.

There are no major strategy differences between Bonus Poker and the versions of Jacks or Better that pay 5-for-1 on the flush. Learn to play 8-5 Jacks, and you're ready for Bonus Poker.

DOUBLE BONUS POKER: If everyone could play this game perfectly and played only the best available version, the casinos would be supporting us instead of the other way around. Double Bonus Poker, which in its full-pay version pays 10-for-1 on full houses, 7-for-1 on flushes and 5-for-1 on straights, returns 100.17 percent in the long run with expert play.

The full pay table is as follows: 250-for-1 on royal flushes (jumping to 4,000 coins with a five-coin wager), 50-for-1 on straight flushes, 160-for-1 on four Aces, 80-for-1 on four 2s, 3s and 4s, 50-for-1 on four of a kind, 10-for-1 on full houses, 7-for-1 on flushes, 5-for-1 on straights, 3-for-1 on three of a kind, 1-for-1 on two pair and 1-for-1 on pairs of Jacks or better.

A few important things to note: Two pair pays only 1-for-1 instead of the 2-for-1 Jacks or Better players get. More of the overall payback is tied up in the higher end of the pay table. With five coins wagered, four Aces bring an 800-coin jackpot. I've had more than one former slot player tell me that Double Bonus is the game that pried them away from the reels, with a realistic secondary jackpot worth walking away with making the difference.

Few play at expert level, and the casinos are in no danger of losing money. There are some tricky little moves in this game that average players miss. For example, if we're dealt a full house that includes three Aces, our best play is to break up the full house and go for the fourth Ace. We'd never do that in Jacks or Better or Bonus Poker. Also, the 7-for-1 payback on flushes dictates that we hold three parts of a flush. Given 10 of diamonds, 8 of clubs, 6 of diamonds, 4 of hearts, 2 of diamonds, in 10-7 Double Bonus we'd hold the three diamonds, whereas in Jacks or Better we'd discard all five.

To change the payback percentage, the casino changes payoffs on full houses, flushes and sometimes straights. It's common to see Double Bonus games with 9-7 (99.1 percent) and 9-6 (97.8 percent pay tables), and I sometimes see pay tables as low as 8-5-4, paying 8-for-1 on full houses, 5-for-1 on flushes and 4-for-1 on straights. The 8-5-4 game pays only 94.2 percent with expert play, making it problematic as to whether a video poker player is really any better off on that game than on the reel slots.

DOUBLE DOUBLE BONUS POKER: The big change as compared to Double Bonus is that there are extra bonuses available on some fours of a kind provided the fifth card is a certain denomination. If four Aces are accompanied by a 2, 3 or 4, the usual 160-for-1 jackpot jumps to 400-for-1 -- a 2,000-coin bonanza with five wagered. If four 2, 3s or 4s are accompanied by an Ace, 2, 3 or 4, the 80-for-1 payoff jumps to 160-for-1.

Straights drop back to 4-for-1 on all versions of this game. The full-pay Double Double Bonus game pays 9-for-1 on full houses and 6-for-1 on flushes, and returns 98.9 percent with expert play.

It's not unusual to see Double Double Bonus in an 8-5 format, leaving a 96.8 percent game, and I've even seen 7-5, a 95.7 percent pay table in the long run with expert play.

One quick strategy tip: Do not hold fifth-card kickers without already having the four of a kind. If you're dealt three Aces, a 2 and a 9, discard both the 2 and the 9. Give yourself two chances to draw the fourth Ace instead of just one.

DEUCES WILD: Someday, I'm going to write a book with nothing but Deuces Wild pay tables and strategy variations. There are countless versions of Deuces Wild. Most video poker books focus on strategy for full-pay Deuces Wild, which is available only in Nevada. The 100.8 percent payback with expert play is too strong for regulators' tastes in most gaming markets, and the game has never been licensed outside Nevada. It's a great game if you can find it. Most players can't.

Let's compare it to another game that video poker fans sometimes call ``Illinois Deuces.'' It doesn't say ``Illinois'' on the machine -- it just says Deuces Wild. Manufacturers and casino operators leave it to the player to tell the difference among pay tables, if they can.

The game isn't limited to Illinois. It's available nationwide. It just has that nickname because it rose to popularity in the early '90s at the Par-A-Dice casino in East Peoria, Illinois. Look at the following pay tables, and guess which one is the full-pay game, returning 100.8 percent, and which is Illinois Deuces, returning 98.9

Variation No. 1: Natural royal flush 250-for-1 (jumps to 4,000 coins for a five-coin bet); four 2s 200-for-1; royal flush with wild cards 25-for-1; five of a kind 15-for-1; straight flush 9-for-1; four of a kind 5-for-1; full house 3-for-1; flush 2-for-1; straight 2-for-1; three of a kind 1-for-1.

Variation No. 2: Natural royal flush 250-for-1 (jumps to 4,000 coins for a five-coin bet); four 2s 200-for-1; royal flush with wild cards 25-for-1; five of a kind 15-for-1; straight flush 9-for-1; four of a kind 4-for-1; full house 4-for-1; flush 3-for-1; straight 2-for-1; three of a kind 1-for-1.

The differences look minor, right? No. 1 pays 5-for-1 on four of a kind, while No. 2 pays only 4-for-1. But No. 2 pays 4-for-1 on full houses and 3-for-1 on flushes, but up a notch from the payouts on No. 1. So which is better? It's No. 1.

Some players fall into the trap of thinking that in poker, full houses and flushes are more common than four of a kind, so No. 2 must be the better game. That's exactly what the operators want you to think. In Deuces Wild, we get four of a kind more often than we get full houses and flushes combined. If you have two pair and one of the pair consists of 2s, you have four of a kind. If you have three 9s, an 8 and a 2, the wild deuces doesn't become an 8 to complete a full house, it takes the place of a 9 to give you four of a kind.

One major strategy difference comes when we're dealt two pairs. If we have two 9s and two 8s, strategy tables that focus on full-pay Deuces will tell you to keep only one pair. But in Illinois Deuces, where we get less for four of a kind and more for a full house, our best play is to keep both pairs and make a one-card draw for a full house. Let's try one more variation:

Variation No. 3: Natural royal flush 250-for-1 (jumps to 4,000 coins for a five-coin bet); four 2s 200-for-1; royal flush with wild cards 25-for-1; five of a kind 16-for-1; straight flush 13-for-1; four of a kind 4-for-1; full house 3-for-1; flush 2-for-1; straight 2-for-1; three of a kind 1-for-1.

Again, we have a Deuces variation that differs from full-pay in three places on the pay table. As in Illinois Deuces, four of a kind is reduced to 4-for-1, and we know that's important. Five of a kind goes up to 16-for-1 from the usual 15-for-1, and there's a big jump on straight flushes, to 13-for-1 from 9-for-1.

Those jumps aren't nearly enough to make up the difference. This game, nicknamed ``Colorado Deuces'' but available nationwide, returns only 96.8 percent with expert play.

There's no easy road map to all the variations of Deuces Wild. The key thing to remember is that changes on the low end of the pay table in Deuces Wild or any other video poker game have a greater effect than those higher on the pay table. With few exceptions such as four-of-a-kind in Deuces Wild, hands lower on the pay table occur more frequently than those higher up. An increase on full houses to 4-for-1 helps the player much more often than a bigger increase on straight flushes, and so makes a bigger difference in the long-term return.

So it goes with any video poker game. In Double Bonus, the four-of-a-kind bonuses, the enhanced payoffs on full houses, flushes and straights all are offset by one decrease low on the pay table -- the drop from 2-for-1 to 1-for-1 on two pair.

When you next find an unfamiliar pay table, be aware. Any boost high on the pay table might look attractive, but check out what you're giving up to get it.

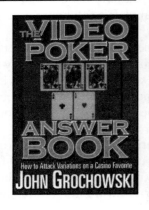

Deuces Wild

by Tom Ski

Playing video poker (VP) can be a great way spend a Las Vegas or Reno getaway. For many VP games, the house edge against you is less than 1%, and in some cases you can actually turn the tables around and have an edge over the house! How can this be you ask?

Well, the secret is beginning to get out that some video poker games, if played with the proper strategy, will actually return over 100% of the money played. The reason this situation exists is because the typical, unskilled player plays at a level about 2% below optimum. So if a game returns 101% with optimum play, then an unskilled player will only play at a 99% rate of return. Thus, the house will still make a profit. But with a little study of the proper strategy, it is not too difficult to play at more than a 100% rate of return.

Often I am asked what is the best game for someone just starting out to learn to play. The answer is simple: Deuces Wild. In Nevada only, it is common to find full-pay Deuces Wild machines at the 25-cent level that return 100.76% with optimal play. At an average playing speed of 600 hands per hour, a skilled player can win $5.71 per hour on such a machine in the long run. But this does not mean that at the end of each hour you will be $5.71 richer. Some hours you might lose $200, and others you might win $1,000. It just means that the your long term average over many thousands of hours of play will approach $5.71 per hour. In addition to this, many casinos have slot clubs that offer cash back and food or room comps for your play. Cash back can often add another $1.50 per hour to your win rate. Now this sure beats the typical VP or slot machine that gobbles up anywhere for $3 to $50 an hour of your hard earned money. The term 'full pay' for Deuces Wild refers to the game with this paytable:

Royal Flush	250
Four Deuces	200
Royal Flush with Deuce	25
Five of a Kind	15
Straight Flush	9
Four of a Kind	5
Full House	3
Flush	2
Straight	2
Three of a Kind	1

The paytable shows the numbers you should look for in the one coin bet column. However, in the five coin bet column, the royal flush should pay at least 4,000 coins. Always play maximum coins (usually five) as you will receive a payoff at the bonus rate of 800-for-1 vs. only 250-for-1 if you wager less than maximum number of coins. Also, be sure that all the pays match the table shown here. Many times you will see the payoff on four-of-a-kind reduced to four. You might think this does not mean much, but it chops a whopping 6%+ from the total return bringing it all the way down to the 95% level. Even if the pays are increased on other hands, (as they often are to lure the uninformed) the drop on four-of-a-kind cannot be overcome. Avoid all such games.

Now that you know one of the best games to play, its time to take a look at the strategy chart. You can find it listed on page 62. This is a listing generated from my *VP Strategy Master* software. A strategy chart is a list of the proper way to play a specific VP game. If the paytable changes, then so too will the strategy listing. This makes sense because if say the value of a flush were to increase, then one would be more inclined to hold flush draws since they now pay more.

To use the strategy chart for Deuces Wild, one must first look at the five cards that are dealt to you. Look and see how many deuces are in your hand, and then refer to the chart heading that corresponds to this number. Now, go down the list and hold the cards that fit the first matching rule.

For example: if you were dealt a pair of sevens and four to a flush with no deuce, you would consult the listing under 'Strategy No Deuce' and you will find the rule 'One Pair' just above the rule '4 Flush'. Thus holding the pair of sevens is the proper play. If you were dealt 2♥ 7♦ 8♦ 9♦ 7♣, you would consult the listing under 'Strategy One Deuce'. Going down this list, you will find the rule ' 4 STFL, Open, 2-567s to 2-9TJs' just above 'Three-of-a-Kind.' The cards 2♥ 7♦ 8♦ 9♦ match with the 4 STFL Open rule with three consecutive suited cards between 567s and 9TJs. (s=suited) Thus, you would drop the made three sevens and go for the one card draw to a straight flush.

One rule listed under the 'Strategy One Deuce' deserves special mention. The rule: 2-AKs,2-AQs,2-AJs,2-ATs, 0 Pen refers to any hand with two cards to a royal flush that include an ace and a deuce with 0 Penalty cards. A penalty card in this case is any other card in your hand that is the same suit as the royal cards, or one that could be used to make a straight with the two royal cards. For example, if dealt 2♣ A♦ J♦ 8♦ T♥, the 8♦ would be called a flush penalty and the T♥ would be called a straight penalty. By throwing these cards away, it becomes slightly less likely that you will make a flush or a straight on the draw as a secondary winning combination. This is because they are removed from play and cannot reappear. Because of this, the value of holding 2♣ A♦ J♦ is lowered enough to no longer make it the correct hold. Rather, the next matching rule should be used which is now to hold the deuce only. If all of this is a little confusing don't let it bother you. Simply choose to hold the deuce only every time and the loss in EV will be very small.

Now that you are armed with all this knowlege, it is time to begin playing. But what can you expect? Unfortunately, you will find that even though your expectation is to win $5.71 per hour, most likely you will find yourself losing most of the time. How can this be? Well, the reason is that if you do not hit the royal flush or four deuces, your return will only be 94.92%. At this rate, you will be losing $38.10 per hour on average. Ouch!

You will hit four deuces on average about once every 4,900 hand or about once per every eight hours of play. When you do hit them, it will be for $250, and this will often bail you out of a losing session. The royal will show up about once every 75 hours and be worth $1,000. These two key hands are required for you to fully realize the long run potential of the game.

Try not to get discouraged if you're having poor results and are tempted to play slots or another VP game that returns under 100%. As long as you are not playing over your head, and wish to continue to gamble, you should stick with the Deuces Wild. The table listed here shows your chances of long term success if you stick with playing Deuces Wild for various sized bankrolls.

Risk of Ruin	50%	25%	10%	5%	1%
Bankroll Size (no cash back)	$1,326	$2,652	$4,405	$5,732	$8,811
Bankroll Size (0.20% cash back)	$1,021	$2,042	$3,392	$4,414	$6,785

Under the 25% Risk of Ruin heading, you will see that if your gambling bankroll was $2,652, your chance of losing it all is only 25%. In other words, you have a 75% chance of never going broke and eventually approaching the long term return of $5.71 per hour for the game. If you play at a casino that offers 0.20% cash back ($1.50 per hour), your bankroll requirement for a 75% success rate falls to $2,042. If you wanted a 95% chance of never going broke, you would need $5,732 if there was no cash back, and $4,414 if there was cash back. Keep in mind, these bankroll requirements cover many hundreds of hours of play. A typical weekend visitor to Las Vegas will only play around 10-20 hours, and so the weekend bankroll requirement would only be around $500-$1,000.

Full-pay Deuces Wild should be around in the 25-cent denomination for a long time to come. In addition to being a great value for the visiting tourist, many Nevada locals enjoy playing the game. It provides hours of entertainment for the many retirees that have been attracted to the state for its warm climate and low taxes. The best place to find the full-pay Deuces Wild is in the many 'locals' casinos away from the Strip and dowtown. On the internet you can find a listing of full pay locations at http://www.vid-poker.com and then click on the full-pay locations link. For simplicy of strategy and the valued received, full-pay Deuces Wild is really a great game to play.

Tom Ski is an expert video poker theoretician and is a regular video poker columnist for "Poker Digest" magazine and "Video Poker Player" newsletter. His software program "Video Poker Strategy Master" is the only product of its kind that can generate extremely accurate strategies for almost any conventional VP game or paytable. You can email him at: tomskilv@yahoo.com. *Ordering information for his software can be found on page 78.*

Losing Money On Good Video Poker Games?

by Tom Ski

Many times players get frustrated while playing a good game that returns over 100% because they often find themselves losing anyway. It just doesn't seem to make sense that one can lose a lot of money on these so called "good games." Well, unfortunately, video poker is a very high variance game. A simple game like blackjack with mostly even money payoffs has a very low variance. An occasional double down win is about as big as it gets. But VP often offers a whopping 800-for-1 return for a royal flush. This and other longshot payoffs make many VP games exhibit variances that are 20 times greater than the variance of blackjack. If one fails to hit one of the big hands offered by their VP game of choice, then they will find themselves going through a lot of money.

The table that follows shows just how much one will lose per hour if a big hand(s) is not hit. The table assumes a play rate of 600 hands per hour on a single line five coin 25 cent game and proper playing strategy.

Game	Overall	No Royal	No 5 Kind	No Stfl.	No 4 Aces	No 4 Twos	No 4 Kind
Joker AK 4700	$7.50	($10.72)	($24.67)				
Deuces Wild	$5.71	($7.56)				($38.08)	
All-American	$5.40	($8.40)		($29.70)			($97.25)
10-7 Dbl. Bonus	$1.29	($11.23)		($15.50)	($39.35)		
9-5 Dbl. Joker	($0.22)	($13.57)	($29.17)				
Pick'em	($0.37)	($2.92)		($7.57)			($45.67)
9/6 Jacks	($3.45)	($18.30)		($22.42)			($66.75)

The Overall Column shows the long term hourly win/loss offered by the game. The No Royal Column shows what your loss rate will be if you never hit a royal but hit all other hands in their proper proportion. The No 5 Kind Column where applicable, shows the loss rate if no five-of-a-kind or higher hand is hit. The No Stfl. Column shows the loss rate if no straight flush or higher is hit. As you move to the right in the table, you will see the loss rate increase as more big hands are being removed from play.

From the table we can see in 10-7 DB, that one will lose $39.35 if four aces or higher is not hit. This in spite of the fact the game is a long term winner at $1.29 per hour. So in a typical four-hour session, a player will often lose close to $160 in this game if the big hands fail to show up.

The moral of the story is to not get discouraged by short term setbacks. Keep focused on the long run. If you only make a few gambling trips a year, think of each trip as just part of one long lifetime session. When it is all said and done, your final results will begin to approach the numbers shown in the Overall Column.

Tom Ski is an expert video poker theoretician and is a regular video poker columnist for "Poker Digest" magazine and "Video Poker Player" newsletter. His software program "Video Poker Strategy Master" is the only product of its kind that can generate extremely accurate strategies for almost any conventional VP game or paytable. You can email him at: tomskilv@yahoo.com. Ordering information for his software can be found on page 78.

Overdue For A Royal Flush?

by Tom Ski

Reflecting back on the times I used to play live poker on a regular basis, I recall being constantly bombarded with bad beat stories. Heck, I was even guilty of telling a few of them myself. But with video poker there are no bad beats. And better yet, you can't go on tilt! Oh, I suppose some players might do something foolish like drop a high pair to hold three to a royal when the situation is not right. Or jump up from playing quarters to dollars in a desperate attempt to get even when their bankroll is not large enough. But for the most part, I think psychologically, video poker is much less stressful than live poker. In addition, I think it is easier to become a winning video poker player than it is to become a winning live poker player.

Unfortunately, as in all forms of gambling, video poker players are not immune from unlucky streaks. Most notably, running bad by failing to hit any royal flushes is a frustrating experience. These rare gems only appear about once every 55 to 65 hours depending on one's playing speed and game type selection. Deuces Wild players will see them on average about once every 45,000 hands, 9/6 Jacks or Better players about once every 40,000 hands, and Double Bonus players about once every 48,000 hands. The use of different playing strategies for each game is the reason why the length of the royal cycles are different.

The following table shows the chances of not hitting any royals after a specific number of hands. The comment column makes references to royal cycles based on a royal cycle length of 40,000 hands.

Number of Hands	Chance	Comment
27,726	1-in-2	50-50 mark
40,000	1-in-2.7	1 cycle
80,000	1-in-7.4	2 cycles
120,000	1-in-20.1	3 cycles
160,000	1-in-54.6	4 cycles
200,000	1-in-148	5 cycles
240,000	1-in-403	6 cycles
280,000	1-in-1,096	7 cycles
320,000	1-in-2,980	8 cycles
360,000	1-in-8,103	9 cycles
400,000	1-in-22,026	10 cycles
600,000	1-in-3,269,017	15 cycles

It is relatively common to hear players anguish over not having hit a royal for 120,000 hands. The chances of running this bad are 1-in-20.1, which is about on par with someone making 3-of-a-kind on the last card in a poker hand to beat your high two pair. A feat that seems to happen all too often! I listed the 15 cycle drought because someone told me this was how bad they had been running. While possible, it is likely there was a little exaggerating going on. I recently hit four aces twice in an hour, and the lady next to me said how lucky I was, and that she had never even hit aces once in over 26 years of playing. If she had played just two hours a week, the chances of this would be 1-in-5... with the 5 having 140 digits after it!

Just as we can suffer from the cruel fortunes of lady luck, we can just as easily bask in the glory of a fabulous winning streak. The gambling literature is full of tales recalling daring risk takers who went on tremendous runs of good fortune. Some of these runs have even gone as far as to close down a casino due to "breaking the bank". My mother remembers visiting Las Vegas in 1956 and after settling in, walked down to the casino for a little action, only to find a sign stating that the casino was closed. She was told a high roller had gone on a hot streak and had "broke the bank." So for those that wish to pull off the same feat, here are a few numbers that will help you gauge your chances.

Assuming a royal cycle of 40,000 hands:

Hit 2 royals in the next 1,500 hands? 1-in-1476
Hit 2 royals in an eight hour day (6,000 total hands)? 1-in-103
Hit 3 royals in an eight hour day? 1-in-2,065
Hit 2 royals in one cycle? 1-in-5.4
Hit 3 royals in one cycle? 1-in-16.3
Hit 4 royals in one cycle? 1-in-65.2
Hit 5 royals in one cycle? 1-in-326
Hit 6 royals in one cycle? 1-in-1,957
Hit 7 royals in one cycle? 1-in-13,700
Hit 8 royals in one cycle? 1-in-109,601
Hit 9 royals in one cycle? 1-in-986,410
Hit 10 royals in one cycle? 1-in-9,864,101

By far, the luckiest run I ever went on involved hitting five jackpots in 1/5 of a jackpot cycle. The odds against running this good or better were over 444,913-to-1. Unfortunately, the casinos involved reacted by removing the games from the floor. I can't say that I blame them. Since then I have learned to be more discreet so as to keep good plays lasting longer. I hope other VP pros can learn from this as well, and avoid other such red flag behavior as locking up seats with team players and playing two machines at one time. Both of these activities will draw attention to the machines from casino management and likely result in them removing the games sooner than they would have otherwise.

All American Video Poker

by Dan Paymar

The original video poker guru, Lenny Frome, pointed out long ago that the payoffs for Jacks-or-Better didn't seem to jibe with the final hand probabilities. With optimum play, the full house flush and straight all have very nearly the same frequency of occurrence, yet the payoffs for the full pay game are 4-for-1, 6-for-1 and 9-for-1, respectively. Why not equalize the payoffs for hands with nearly the same probability? Well, All American does just that, and you can see the result in the payoff table below. The optimum strategy changes drastically, causing the probabilities of these three hands to be more as we would expect in live poker. It just goes to show that it's hard to predict the effects of payoff changes.

All American has never become popular even though its payback (a bit over 100.7%) and variance rival the very popular Deuces Wild. There are three reasons for this:

1. Most players tend to use common Jacks-or-Better strategy, which is definitely a losing proposition, yielding much less than 100% payback.

2. The strategy to get that 100.7% payback is unintuitive and necessarily quite complex.

3. There never have been a lot of these machines around (although quite a few Bally GameMaker machines include AA).

Here is the payoff schedule for the full pay game, and the final hand probabilities with optimum play:

Final Hand	Per-coin Payoff	Probability
Royal Flush	800	.0000230
Straight Flush	200	.0001418
Four-of-a-Kind	40	.002252
Full House	8	.01098
Flush	8	.01569
Straight	8	.01843
3-of-a Kind	3	.06884
Two Pair	1	.11961
Pair of Jacks	1	.18335
Zilch	0	.58067

If you are comparing this game to Jacks or Better, the enhanced paybacks on the Straight Flush, Flush and Straight more than make up for the reduction on Two Pair, but optimum strategy to achieve maximum payback is complex and not intuitive.

In many parts of the country, Kansas City in particular, All American may be the only attractive video poker game. AA has also shown up under other names, such as "Gator Bonus" and "Draw Deluxe," so it may be necessary to search for it by pay schedule rather than name.

Many recreational players find the game too difficult to play successfully, and casinos are reluctant to offer unpopular games. Perhaps to boost interest in the game, Bally has put AA on some GameMakers with quads paying 50-for-1 instead of 40-for-1. This adds 2.25% to the payback, making it one of the best video poker games available.

The following strategy is accurate for both versions and should allow you to take full advantage of this game. Successful play will require both practice (tutoring program suggested) and concentration, as there are several playable hands unique to this game that can be easily overlooked.

The hand rank table on the following page will yield about 100.71% payback with the previously noted payoff schedule, or about 102.96% if Four-of-a-Kind pays 50-for-1 (plus any slot club benefits, of course). As with any strategy, select the card combination that appears first in this table.

All American Strategy

Royal Flush
Straight Flush
Four-of-a-Kind
RF 4, SF 4
Full House
Flush
Straight
Straight Flush 4 Inside
Three-of-a-Kind
RF 3 (not A-high)
Two Pair
Flush 4 [See Note 1]
Straight 4 (3 high cards)
RF 3 (A, no 10)
Straight 4 (2 high cards)
High Pair
RF 3 (A-x-10)
Straight 4 (0 or 1 high cards)
Straight Flush 3, Straight Flush 3 Inside
Straight 4 Inside (3 or 4 high cards)
Straight Flush 3 Double Inside (2 high cards)
Straight 4 Inside (2 high cards)
Straight Flush 3 Double Inside (1 high card)
Straight 4 Inside (1 high card) [See Note 2]
Low Pair
Straight 4 inside (No high cards)
Straight Flush 3 Double Inside (No high cards) [SeeNote 3]
Q-J-10 unsuited
RF 2 (Q-J) [See Note 4]
K-Q-J unsuited
Flush 3 (2 high cards)
RF 2 (K-Q, K-J)
RF 2 (A-K, A-Q, A-J)
RF 2 (J-10, Q-10)
J-10-9 unsuited
Straight 3 inside (2 high cards) [See Note 6]
Q-J unsuited
Flush 3 (1 high card) [See Note 7]
A-K-Q or A-K-J (All unsuited)
J-9 suited

RF 2 (K-10)
K-Q or K-J (All unsuited) [See Note 8]
A-K, A-Q, A-J (All unsuited)
RF2 (A-10)
Q-9 or J-8 suited [See Note 9]
One Jack [See Note 9]
One A, K or Q
Straight 3 (No high cards)
Flush 3 (No high cards)
Straight Flush 2 (No high cards) [See Note 10]
Straight Flush 2 Inside (No high cards) [See Note 10]
Zilch (draw 5 cards)

Notes:

1. Hold Flush 4 over RF 3 (K-x-10) if the other discard is a 9 or higher.
2. Hold Straight 4i h1 over SF3 di h1 if there is a low pair present that is not a subset of the SF3.
3. Hold SF3 di h0 over Straight 4i h0 if SF3 is not a subset of the Straight 4.
4. Hold RF2 (Q-J) over Q-J-10 unsuited if no discard is of the same suit as the Q-J.
5. Hold Straight 3i h2 over RF2 (Q-10) if any discard is an 8 or is of the same suit as Q-10.
6. Hold Flush 3 h1 over RF2 (Q-10) if the RF2 is a subset of the Flush 4 and any discard is a 9 or A.
7. Hold K-J unsuited over J-9 suited if discarding an 8.
8. Hold Q-9 suited over A-Q unsuited if no discard is 8 or higher; Hold J-8 suited over A-J unsuited if no discard is 7 or higher.
9. Hold J over J-8 suited if any discard is 7 or higher; Hold J over RF2 (A-10) if no discard same suit as J; Hold J over A-J unsuited if no discard is the same suit as J or is a 7 or higher.
10. Not 2 low.

Some versions of All American pay only 100-for-1 or even 50-for-1 for a Straight Flush, or less than 40-for-1 for Quads. Any of these changes reduces the payback to less than 100%, so examine the pay schedule carefully before beginning play.

Dan Paymar is the author of the top-selling book "Video Poker - Optimum Play" and editor of "Video Poker Times" a bi-monthly newsletter on video poker. You can e-mail him at vptimes@lvcm.com or visit his web site at www.vegasplayer.com/video-poker.html Ordering information for his products can be found on pages 84 and 91.

Professional Video Poker

by Dan Paymar

Is it possible to make a living playing video poker? Yes, it is, and I know several people who do just that. In Las Vegas there are lots of video poker machines available that will yield over 100% payback with optimum play.

But how can such games exist? Wouldn't the casinos take them out or change them if they were losing money? Yes, of course they would. The key phrase is "optimum play." There are hundreds of thousands of visitors to Las Vegas every year, and lots of them play video poker. The vast majority are simply recreational players who never bother to learn to play well. Their errors result in about 2% to 4% lower payback than can be achieved by a skilled player on the same game. Since most of the players are losing and only a few are winning, the casino makes its profit on nearly every machine.

Well, we've established that the opportunity to be a long term winner at video poker really exists, but just how big is that opportunity? Let's start with the most common "over 100%" game, full pay Deuces Wild. (I don't have space here to define "full pay." For that and the winning strategy I suggest you get a copy of *Video Poker - Optimum Play*.) With optimum play, the maximum payback has been calculated at 100.762%, but only a computer could play that well. Still, you can easily learn my Precision Play rules and achieve a realistic 100.75% payback.

A pro would probably look for a fast machine and play 600 to 1000 hands per hour. Starting off, you won't be that fast, so let's assume you're playing 500 games per hour on a full pay $1 Deuces Wild machine. To get full payback you must play five coins, so at $5 per play you're wagering $2,500 per hour. At 100.75% payback, you can expect to gain an average of .75% of your wagers, or $18.75 per hour.

It would be nice if we could expect a $150 gain in each eight-hour session, but it won't happen like that. Eight hours at 500 plays per hour is only 4,000 plays, which is far short of the long term. But if you played eight hours a day, five days a week, you would play 200,000 games in about 10 weeks, so the fluctuations should average out over a few months. The million or so hands played in a year of full-time play would provide ample opportunity for the fluctuations to be smoothed out by averaging.

This is not a recommendation that you quit your job and play video poker for a living. Even if you do manage to win regularly, gambling can be quite boring and perhaps hazardous to your health to sit on a stool and stare at a video screen all day.

If you are considering playing video poker full time, first be sure you have enough money to pay all your bills and living expenses for at least six months, plus a separate gaming bankroll that can withstand the very large fluctuations inherent in nearly all games of chance. The suggested minimum for such a bankroll is enough for a 99% chance of hitting a natural royal flush. If your choice of machines is the standard full-pay $1 Deuces Wild, this would be about $12,000. But even this is no guarantee of success. We know of one "professional" who lost a $20,000 bankroll in six months playing $1 Deuces Wild.

As we have seen, there definitely are opportunities to make money playing video poker. The requirements include:

1. Be sure you have a big enough bankroll to withstand the wide fluctuations and minimize the chance of gambler's ruin (see the chapter on Probability of Ruin in *Video Poker - Optimum Play*, or better yet the Risk of Ruin articles in the *Video Poker Times*).

2. Search out a game that offers at least 100.5% payback along with a payoff schedule that isn't too heavy at the top end (such a game results in bigger bankroll fluctuations). Any cash rebate slot club should be included in the rated total payback.

3. Be sure you know the complete strategy for that game, and follow it carefully. Never play "hunches." If you are uncertain of a play, look it up in the book or cue card.

4. If it's a progressive machine, quit immediately when the most important jackpot resets, regardless of who hit it.

If you lack the bankroll for $1 machines, then start on quarter machines. Your expected win rate is cut by 75%, but so is your required bankroll.

In any case, if you are playing video poker or any other game regularly, the IRS will be interested in your gaming income. Since any jackpot of $1,200 or more will require identification for a W-2G gambling winnings report form, be sure to keep good records of all wins and losses for your tax return. Ask your accountant or tax attorney for tax advice.

Dan Paymar is the author of the top-selling book "Video Poker - Optimum Play" and editor of "Video Poker Times" a bi-monthly newsletter on video poker. You can e-mail him at vptimes@lvcm.com or visit his web site at www.vegasplayer.com/video-poker.html *Ordering information for his products can be found on pages 84 and 91.*

Optimum Play For Video Poker

by Dan Paymar

The term "optimum play" is used in many ads and by many writers and analysts when they really mean perfect play, that is, they are assuming that every play is made for the absolute highest expected value. Perfect play is presumed by most game analysis programs, so the resulting payback figure is the maximum achievable in the long run with computer-perfect play. Since most of us are only human, it is my contention that the term "optimum play" should have a somewhat different meaning.

Except for a few of the simpler games, perfect play is impossible for most of us, so the rated payback is really a target value to be approached by the best players. Unless you happen to have an unlimited bankroll and unlimited time, and you are able to play computer-perfect strategy, you will have to settle for only near perfect play on most of the attractive games. Moreover, you may even want to modify that if your time or bankroll is limited. My Precision Playvv rules will easily get you within a few hundredths of one percent of a game's rated payback.

In many cases, two or more possible ways of playing a hand have such close expected values that the discards may affect the decision. Some published strategies take many of these "penalty card" situations into account, but the only way that perfect play would be possible on many of the games would be to take a computer to the casino and evaluate every dealt hand before selecting which cards to hold. Even if this were allowed, however, the reduction in your playing speed would cost much more than the slight gain in expected payback.

Many video poker games are so complex that no matter how many details are included in playing rules or how many notes are attached to a hand rank table, it is nearly always possible to find yet another exception where a marginal decision is affected by the discards. So just how perfect is it desirable to make a playing strategy? In other words, what is optimum play?

This is actually a personal matter, depending upon your bankroll, skill level, available playing time and perhaps most importantly, your personal goals. For example, a playing strategy might be devised to:

1. Maximize the chances of a winning session,
2. Maximize the chances of a royal flush,
3. Maximize playing time on a given bankroll,
4. Maximize expected payback for money wagered, or
5. Maximize expected hourly win rate.

My book, *Video Poker - Optimum Play,* discusses each of these possible goals in detail, but for our purposes here I will assume that your goal is the same as mine; that is, to maximize your average long-term win rate without overplaying your bankroll. The objective of my book is to teach you to be such an optimum player.

Your expected win rate is equal to the product of your advantage, your bet size and your playing speed. For example, if you currently achieve 100.75% payback on Deuces Wild by following my Precision Play rules, then your advantage is 0.75%, or.0075 as a decimal fraction. If you play this game on a five-coin quarter machine at 500 hands per hour, then your expected average long-term win rate is .0075 x $1.25 x 500 = $4.69 per hour.

Now suppose you find a very detailed strategy that theoretically will yield the game's rated 100.762% payback. By necessity, that strategy will be significantly more complex, so you probably won't play quite as fast, say 480 hands per hour. Assuming you master the intricacies of the new strategy, your expected average win rate is now .00762 x $1.25 x 480 = $4.57 per hour.

Thus, that "better" strategy not only is harder to use but it has cost you twelve cents per hour! Even worse, you may not have really mastered the new strategy, and although you make fewer errors, the ones you do make may be more expensive. Thus, the 'perfect" strategy may actually cost you money. Was it worth the effort?

Many professional blackjack players try different multilevel counting systems but return to a simple single level count for the best expected win rate over the long run. For each dealt situation in blackjack there is only one perfect way to play it, the same as for video poker, yet each pro uses what he has found to be his own optimum strategy. Thus the pro will not always make the perfect play, but the difference in EV between the perfect play and his decision will be very small.

In conclusion, there is no single optimum strategy for any complex game. For each game, the optimum strategy is the one that yields the highest win rate *for you.* Precision Play is an excellent compromise between simplicity and perfection and will thus yield the highest win rate for most beginning to intermediate players.

Dan Paymar is the author of the top-selling book "Video Poker - Optimum Play" and editor of "Video Poker Times" a bi-monthly newsletter on video poker. You can e-mail him at vptimes@lvcm.com or visit his web site at www.vegasplayer.com/video-poker.html
Ordering information for his products can be found on pages 84 and 91.

10/7 Double Bonus Video Poker

by Skip Hughes

10/7 Double Bonus has become one of the most popular games for the smart player in the last few years. There are several reasons for this: The game is very common and can fairly easily be found in denominations from $.05 to $1 and even some higher denomination games exist.

The game can often be found in casinos that offer cash back, improving its basic (100.17%) return, especially during double or triple point promotions. It is now the best multi-deal game available as full pay Deuces Wild and Joker Poker have apparently disappeared from these machines. However, there are also real drawbacks to the game as well. One of these is the very high "variance" associated with the game. This means that you have to expect more severe win/loss swings than with other games and will thus need a higher bankroll. For instance, the quarter player playing "perfectly" would need a $2,652 bankroll to play Deuces Wild (with no cash back) with a 25% chance of losing his entire starting bankroll at some point. The same player playing quarter 10/7 with .2% cash back would need a $6,332 bankroll to have the same 25% "Risk Of Ruin."

The other problem associated with Double Bonus is that the computer perfect strategy is so full of complicated penalty card situations that it is very difficult for anyone to play the game anywhere close to perfection (no player plays any video poker game perfectly all the time - nobody.)

However, while I can't do much to reduce the variance of the game, except to suggest you play wherever the cash back is the best (another way to reduce the effect of variance in this game is to drop down in denomination and play the 5-play or 10- play machines), I can offer some relief from the 60-70 line strategy tables that reflect "perfect strategy."

It's pretty well known that playing a 10/7 game using regular Jacks or better strategy will yield a slightly higher return than playing 9/6 Jacks or Better with that strategy. - Somewhere in the neighborhood of 99.7%. To boost that percentage much closer to 100% add the following changes:

-Hold 3 ACES over ACES FULL
-Hold a 4 CD FLUSH over a 3 CD RF
-Hold TJQ OR JQK RF over pair of J-K
-Hold a 4 CD STRT over a LOW PAIR
-Hold a 3 CD FLUSH w/1 HC over 1 or 2 HC
-Hold a 4 CD INS STRT over a 3 CD Flush
-Hold a 3 CD Flush over DRAW 5

Playing this simplified strategy with .2% cash back will get you on an even basis over the long term, even with an occasional error. To get close to the 100.17% return without having to memorize dozens of penalty card situations, I have created the following strategy that makes the game quite a lot easier while sacrificing very little return.

10/7 DOUBLE BONUS STRATEGY

Royal Flush
4 of a Kind
Straight Flush
4 Card Royal
Three Aces
Full House
Flush
3 of a Kind (2 Through King)
Sraight
Any 4 Card Straight Flush
Two Pair
Pair of Aces
4 Card Flush (3 High Cards)
3 Card Royal (KQJ or QJT)
One Pair (Jacks through Kings)
4 Card Flush (2 High Cards)
3 Card Royal (All Others)
4 Card Flush (0 or 1 High Card)
4 Card Open Straight
One Pair (2 through 4)
3 Card Straight Flush (JT9 or QJ9)
One Pair (5 through 10)
3 Card Open Straight Flush (0 High Cards)
3 Card Inside Straight Flush (1 High Card)
4 Card Inside Straight (4 High Cards)
3 Card Double Inside Straight Flush (2 High Cards)
4 Card Inside Straight (3 High Cards)
2 Card Royal (QJ,KQ,KJ)
3 Card Double Inside Straight Flush (1 High Card)
3 Card Flush (2 High Cards)
3 Card Inside Straight Flush (0 High Cards)
2 Card Royal (AK,AQ,AJ)

4 Card Inside Straight (2 High Cards)
KQJ,QJT (Unsuited)
4 Card Inside Straight (1 High Card)
2 Card Royal (JT)
Two High Cards (QJ)
2 Card Royal (QT)
3 Card Flush (1 High Card)
3 Card Double Inside Straight Flush (0 High Cards)
Two High Cards (A-*,K-) (*Hold Ace alone if no suited discard)
2 Card Royal (KT)
One High Card
4 Card Inside Straight (0 High Cards)
3 Card Flush (0 High Cards)
Draw Five New Cards

Skip Hughes publishes a monthly newsletter with timely tips and information about playing video poker. See the ad below for ordering information.

Video Poker and Slot Clubs

by Jean Scott

Jean Scott is one of the country's most renowned and successful low rollers. She stays at casino-hotels in Nevada, New Jersey, Mississippi, and Illinois up to 120 nights a year and rarely pays for a room. She knows her way around the comp and slot club systems so well, she could eat free buffet or coffee shop meals three times a day for the rest of her life. She gets comped shows, hairdressing, manicures, massages, clothing, jewelry, even gifts for her grandkids. How does she do it? She belongs to slot clubs. She participates in promotions and drawings. She uses funbooks. She befriends slot hosts. The Las Vegas Advisor pegged her the Queen of Ku Pon in 1994 and in 1995, the CBS news magazine ***48 Hours*** *aired an entire hour-long segment revolving around her, in which Dan Rather dubbed her the Queen of Comps. She also appeared in a segment on* ***Hard Copy*** *about how to beat the casinos at the machines.*

Jean Scott has disclosed her valuable secrets in her book, ***The Frugal Gambler****. The following article, adapted from that book, takes a practical look at video poker.*

This is a nuts-and-bolts look at my game of choice: video poker. This is the game I use to get the things that I want from casinos. Since the freebie system in Las Vegas is designed to reward gamblers, you have to be a player if you expect to tap into the richest veins in the system. And to come out ahead, you have to play positive-expectation games. Blackjack is an obvious candidate, but I've found that I can do even better playing video poker. By playing the schedules that return 100% or more, and milking the benefits of good slot clubs, I can pretty much write my own ticket in Las Vegas. But it all comes back to playing the game well enough so I don't lose back everything I gain (like 99.9% of players do).

Of course, the most important aspect of winning at video poker is studying the game-learning how to pick the machines with greater-than-100% returns, then playing them optimally. You can accomplish this by studying the work of video poker experts like Dan Paymar, Bob Dancer and the late Lenny Frome.

After learning the playing skills, however, many find that the realities of actual play are a little daunting. In this section, I discuss a few of the more practical concerns of the average (and low-rolling) video poker player. I play a lot and I talk to a lot of other video poker players. They ask me questions about things like perfect play, low-roller bankroll requirements, when to change machines, and when it's proper to deviate from video poker's basic strategy. Here are a few answers.

When Full-Pay is Not Full-Pay - One of the most common questions that people ask me is, "Why would a casino offer a machine that pays more than 100%? Doesn't the casino have to have an edge on every game? How are they going to pay for all the lights?" (It's amazing how concerned people are about the casinos pay their light bills.)

The fact is, the casinos retain a healthy edge on machines that have the potential to pay back over 100%. How is that possible? Two reasons. First, the 100% payback is for max-coin play only (the bonus for a max-coin royal flush is worth 1.5%-2%). Secondly, the positive payout assumes the players employ a perfect playing strategy. Most regular players understand at least a little about video poker strategy, but perfect play is a tall order.

I've seen full-pay deuces wild machines in more than one casino with signs that say, "This machine pays back 98%." Now, I know that full-pay deuces returns 100.76%, so why are they advertising it as paying back 98%?. Here's why. The casino knows that in the past, when it's tallied all its wins and losses from that machine, the bottom line has been a profit of 2%. This is due to "short-coin" and sub-optimal play. Almost no one plays at a positive level, so the casino wins its 2%-or more.

A lot of 100%+ video poker machines-deuces wild and double bonus progressive, for example-have such strange strategies that if you don't know and abide by them, you could be playing at several percentage points below the 100%-return level. Some play so poorly they'd be better off playing slot machines.

How Much Money Will I Need? - This is another common question I'm asked, though a lot of people just assume I can do what I do in the casinos because I have all the money in the world. Everyone wants to know how much money is necessary to allow the percentages to bear out. My answer is, "Not too much." Let's not forget that we're talking about a low-roller playing quarter video poker and making $1.25 wagers here.

In his book, *Video Poker-Optimum Play*, Dan Paymar has a chart that's very useful. It's labeled "Bankroll Necessary to Hit a Jackpot." That chart indicates that if you're playing quarter deuces wild, you should have a bankroll of at least $2,850 to be 99% sure of hitting the royal flush before going broke. My own experiences confirm this. I've been playing video poker for more than six years, three to six hours a day, at least 100 days a year, and I've never needed a "bankroll" (the amount of actual money I have to gamble with) greater than $3,000. In other words, my longest losing streak never resulted in total losses greater than $3,000.

The one time that I came close to accumulating losses of $3,000 was the most inopportune time of all for Lady Luck to leave me. It was the week the *48 Hours* video crew was following me around. As chance would have it, I lost consistently during that week, nearly reaching a $3,000 loss point. (For the record, I recouped the money and redeemed myself when I won an $18,000 automobile in a drawing that *48 Hours* caught on camera and aired on national television.)

There's no guarantee that you'll hit the jackpot before exhausting a $3,000 stake, but 99% is good enough for me. If you have a partner and two of you are playing, you don't both have to have that much; between the two of you, you figure to hit the royal flush twice as fast. If you want to have a little more than the minimum bankroll, just in case, you might feel better with $4,000 or $5,000 for two players. I do.

"Well, I don't have $3,000 to lose," you might say. Neither do I! I mean, I have it, but I certainly don't want to lose it. This bankroll that I've been talking about is not $3,000 that I intend to lose permanently. I like to think of it as a gambling bankroll that I sometimes loan back to the casinos while I wait.

Slot Club Benefits - In the conversation above, I'm talking only about winning and losing on the machines themselves, which doesn't take into account the cash-back from slot clubs and promotions. This is where much of your profit (and your reserve in case of poor luck) will come from. When you take a 100%+ machine and add in slot club cash and promotional winnings, you are playing at well over 100%, and the profits add up fast. One of my goals is to play a good enough pay schedule, combined with a good enough slot club and a good enough promotion, so that if I never hit the royal, I'll still break even. When that's accomplished, the royal flushes represent pure profit.

Changing Machines - One thing that many people agonize over is when they should change machines. The answer is, it doesn't really matter. But it's amazing how many people refuse to believe it. The math, remember, is based on play over the long term, and it will take you 40,000 hands, on average, to hit a royal flush. So it's all the same whether you play 40,000 hands on one machine or 1,000 hands on 40 different machines or 100 hands on 400 machines.

Of course, in real life you could get zero royals in 80,000 hands or five royals in 20,000 hands. Still, it makes no difference how many machines it takes you to do it.

Do I ever change machines? Sure I change machines. I change machines if the seat's not comfortable, or the buttons are sticking, or the air-conditioning is blowing cold air on my neck, or the person playing next to me is a grouch or a smoker. And I don't mind admitting it, but I occasionally change machines just because I'm disgusted with the one I'm playing, when it hasn't given me anything good for a long while. Again, it doesn't have anything to do with the math. It's just that losing is making me angry and I want to walk around, clear my head, and start fresh in a different part of the casino.

Go ahead: hop from one machine to another. But as you do, remember that it's for a psychological feeling, not for a mathematical reason.

Deviating from Basic Strategy - People ask me if, on occasion, I ignore the strict rules of video poker's basic strategy. They want to know if I sometimes have a feeling or a hunch that something's going to happen, and whether or not I act on it. My answer is "NO, NO, NEVER." If you don't trust the strategy charts, which have been derived by mathematicians and computer scientists, then there's not much hope for you.

Think about it. When you buy a video poker strategy book for $20, you're purchasing the results of thousands of dollars worth of research conducted by high-priced experts. Once you own it, all you have to do is spend a few hours, at most, learning the strategy for your game.

And there's another benefit. Playing perfect strategy is actually comforting. It cushions the blow when you lose. And you will lose. Everyone who plays video poker loses more sessions than they win. But when you're in a losing session, or even a series of them, it's very comforting to know that the math is correct. You can say, "I may be losing now, but I know that I'm doing the right thing. I also know that I have a small edge, and that eventually I'll come out ahead.

Blackjack

by Steve Bourie

Blackjack is the most popular casino game in America and one of the biggest reasons for that is its relatively simple rules that are familiar to most casino visitors. Blackjack also has a reputation as being "beatable" and although that is true in some cases, the vast majority of players will always be playing the game with the house having a slight edge over them.

At most blackjack tables there are 7 boxes, or betting areas, on the table. This means that up to 7 people can play at that table and each player has their own box in front of them in which they'll place their bet. Now, before you take a seat at any blackjack table the first thing you should do is to take a look at the sign that's sitting on each table because it will tell you the minimum amount that you must bet on each hand. If you're a $5 player you certainly wouldn't want to sit at a table that has a $25 minimum so, once again, be sure to look before you sit down.

Once you're at the table you'll need chips to play with and you get them by giving your cash to the dealer who will exchange it for an equal amount of chips. Be careful, however, that you don't put your cash down into one of the betting boxes because the dealer might think you're playing it all on the next hand!

After everyone has placed their bets in their respective boxes the dealer will deal out 2 cards to each player. He will also deal 2 cards to himself; one of those cards will be face up and the other face down. Now, if you've ever read any brochures in a casino they'll tell you that the object of the game of blackjack is to get a total of cards as close to 21 as possible, without going over 21. However, that really isn't the object of the game. The true object is to beat the dealer and you do that by getting a total closer to 21 than the dealer, or by having the dealer bust by drawing cards that total more than 21.

The one thing that's strange about blackjack is that the rules can be slightly different at each casino and this is the only game where this happens. If you play baccarat, roulette or craps you'll find that the rules are virtually the same at every casino in the U.S. but that isn't the case with blackjack. For example, in Atlantic City all of the casinos use 6 or 8 decks of cards that are always dealt from a little rectangular box called a shoe and the cards are always dealt face up. In Las Vegas, some casinos will offer that same kind of game while others will offer games that use only 1 or 2 decks that are dealt directly from the dealer's hand and all of the cards will be dealt face down. To make it even stranger, some casinos in Las Vegas will offer both kinds of games in their

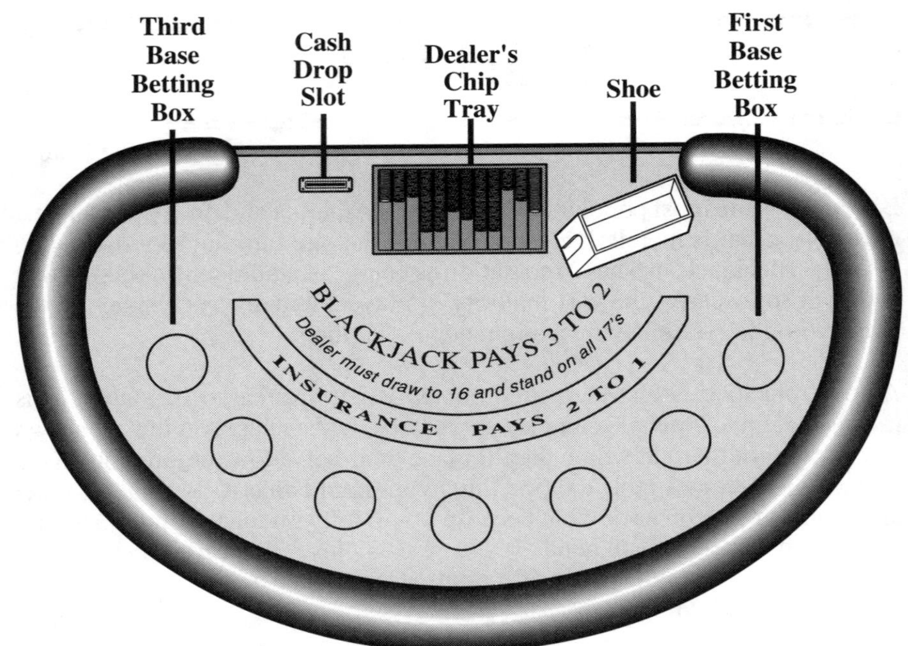

Typical Blackjack Table Layout

casinos and the rules will probably change when you move from one table to another. There can also be other rules variations concerning doubling down and splitting of pairs but we'll talk about those later. For now, just be aware that different casinos can have different blackjack rules and some of those rules will be good for you while others will be bad for you. Hopefully, after reading this story you'll know the good rules from the bad ones and which tables are the best ones to play at.

For our purposes, we'll assume we're playing in a casino that uses 6 decks of cards that are dealt out of a shoe and all of the player's cards are dealt face up. By the way, whenever you play blackjack in a casino where the cards are dealt face up don't touch the cards. In that kind of game the dealer is the only who is allowed to touch the cards and if you do happen to touch them they'll give you a warning not to do it again - so, don't touch the cards!

After the cards are dealt the players must determine the total of their hand by adding the value of their two cards together. All of the cards are counted at their face value except for the picture cards - jack, queen and king which all have a value of 10 - and the aces which can be counted as either 1 or 11. If you have an ace and any 10-value card you have a blackjack which is also called a natural and your hand is an automatic winner, unless the dealer also has a blackjack in which case the hands are tied. A tie is also called a ***push*** and when that happens it's a standoff and you neither win nor lose. All winning blackjacks are paid at 3-to-2, or one-and-a-half times your bet, so if you bet $5 and got a blackjack you would be paid $7.50

If the dealer has an ace as his up card the first thing he'll do is ask if anyone wants to buy ***insurance***. When you buy insurance you're betting that the dealer has a blackjack by having a 10 as his face down card. To make an insurance bet you would place your bet in the area just above your betting box that says "insurance pays 2-to-1" and you're only allowed to make an insurance bet of up to one-half the amount of your original bet. So, if you originally bet $10 you could only bet a maximum of $5 as your insurance bet. After all the insurance bets are made the dealer will check his face down card and if it's a 10 he'll turn it over and all of the insurance bets will be paid off at 2-to-1. If he doesn't have a 10 underneath, the dealer will then take away all of the losing insurance bets and the game will continue. By the way, according to basic strategy, insurance is a bad bet and you should never make an insurance bet.

If the dealer has a 10 as his up card the first thing he'll do is check to see if he has an ace underneath which would give him a blackjack. If he does have an ace he'll turn it face up and start collecting the losing bets that are out on the table. If he doesn't have an ace underneath the game will continue. In some casinos, however, the dealer won't check his hole card until after all of the hands are played out.

If the dealer doesn't have an ace or a 10 as his up card the game continues and the dealer will start with the player to his immediate left to see if they want another card. If a player wants another card they indicate that with a hand signal by tapping or scratching the table with their finger to show they want another card. Taking a card is also known as ***hitting*** or taking a hit. If a player doesn't want another card they would just wave their hand palm down over their cards. Not taking another card is known as ***standing***. The reason hand signals are used is because it eliminates any confusion on the part of the dealer as to exactly what the player wants and it also allows the security people to follow the game on the closed-circuit cameras that are hung from the ceiling throughout the casino.

Keep in mind that the hand signals will be slightly different if you're playing in a casino where the cards are dealt face down and you're allowed to pick them up. In that situation a player would signal that they wanted another card by scratching the table with the edges of the two cards they're holding. If they didn't want another card, they would simply place their two cards under the bet in their box.

In either case, if a player draws another card the value of that card is added to the total of the other cards and the player can continue to draw cards unless he gets a total of more than 21 in which case he busts and loses his bet.

When a player doesn't want any more cards, or stands, the dealer then moves on to the next player and after all of the players are finished then it's the dealer's turn to play. While each player can decide whether or not they want another card the dealer doesn't have that option and he must play by a fixed set of rules that require him to draw a card whenever his total is 16 or less and to stop when his total is 17 or more. If the dealer goes over 21 then he has busted and all of the players remaining in the game will be paid 1-to-1, or even money, on their bet.

If the dealer doesn't bust then each player's hand is compared to the dealer's. If the player's total is higher than the dealer's then they win and are paid even money. If the player's hand has a total that is lower than the dealer's hand then the player loses his bet. If the player and the dealer have the same total then it's a tie, or a push and neither hand wins. After all of the bets have been paid off, or taken by the dealer, a new round begins and new hands are dealt to all of the players.

When deciding how to play your hand there are also three other options available to you besides standing or hitting. The first is called ***doubling down*** and most casinos will allow a player to double their bet on their first two cards and draw only one more card. To do this you would place an amount equal to your original bet right next to it and then the dealer would give you one more card, sideways, to indicate that your bet was a double down. To double down in a game where the cards are dealt face down you would turn up your original two cards and tell the dealer you wanted to double down. Then, after you double your bet, the dealer would give you one more card face down. Some casinos may have restrictions on this bet and may only allow you to double down if the total of your 2 cards is 10 or 11, but it's always to your advantage if they allow you to double down on any two cards.

Another thing you can do is ***split*** your cards if you have a pair and then play each card as a separate hand. For example, if you had a pair of 8's you would place a bet equal to your original bet right next to it and tell the dealer you wanted to split your pair. The dealer would then separate your two 8's and give you one card on your first 8. Unlike doubling down, however, you are not limited to only getting one card and you can play your hand out normally. When you were finished with your first hand the dealer would then give you a card on your other 8 and you would play that hand out. Although I said that you weren't limited to just one card on your splits there is one instance where that will happen and that's when you split aces. Virtually all casinos will only give you one card on each ace when you split them. Also, if you get a 10-value card with your ace it will only count as 21 and not as a blackjack so you'll only get even money on that bet if you win. Besides splitting pairs you can also split all 10-value cards such as jack-king or 10-queen but it would be a very bad idea to do that because you would be breaking up a 20 which is a very strong hand and you should never split 10's. By the way, if you wanted to split a pair in a casino where the cards are dealt face down you would simply turn your original 2 cards face-up and then tell the dealer that you wanted to split them.

The last option you have is not available in most casinos but you may come across it in a few Las Vegas Strip casinos and it's called ***surrender***. With the surrender option you're allowed to lose half of your bet if you decide you don't want to play out your hand after looking at your first 2 cards. Let's say you're dealt a 10-6 for a total of 16 and the dealer has a 10 as his face-up card. A 16 is not a very strong hand, especially against a dealer's 10, so in this case it would be a good idea to surrender your hand and when the dealer came to your cards you would say "surrender." The dealer would then take half of your bet and remove your cards. Surrender is good for the player because in the long run you will lose less on the bad hands you're dealt and you should always try to play in a casino that offers the surrender option.

All right, we've covered the basics of how to play the game of blackjack and all of the possible options a player has, so the next question is how do you win? Well, the best way to win is to become a card counter, but for the average person that isn't always possible so let's start off by taking a look at basic blackjack strategy.

Computer studies have been done on the game of blackjack and millions of hands have been analyzed to come up with a basic formula for how to play your hand in any given situation. The main principle that these decisions are based on is the dealer's up card because, remember that the dealer has no say in whether or not he takes a card - he must play by the rules that require him to draw a card until he has a total of 17 or more. Now, according to these computer calculations the dealer will bust more often when his up card is a 2,3,4,5 or 6 and he will complete more hands when his up card is a 7,8,9,10-value card or an ace. Take a look at the following chart that shows how each up-card affects the dealer's chance of busting:

Chance The Dealer's Up Card Will Bust

2	35%
3	38%
4	40%
5	43%
6	42%
7	26%
8	24%
9	23%
10	21%
Ace	11%

As you can see, the dealer will bust most often when he has a 5 or 6 as his upcard and he will bust the least amount, approximately 11% of the time, when his upcard is an ace. This means it's to your advantage to stand more often when the dealer's upcard is a 2 through 6 and hope that the dealer will draw cards that make him bust. It also means that when the dealer's upcard is a 7 through ace he will complete more of his hands and in that situation you should draw cards until you have a total of 17 or more.

Now let's show you how to play your hands by using the basic strategy and we'll start off with the ***hard hand*** strategy and by hard hand I mean a 2-card total without an ace. A hand with an ace is known as a soft hand because the ace can be counted as either a 1 or an 11. So, if you had an ace-6 you would have a soft 17 hand and if you had a 10-6 you would have a hard 16 hand. Later on we'll take a look at how to play soft hands, but for now we'll concentrate on the hard hand totals. Oh yes, one more thing, the basic strategy I'm going to give you applies to casinos where they deal more than one deck at a time and the dealer stands on soft 17 which is the situation you'll find in the majority of casinos today. So, keep in mind that the strategy would be slightly different if you were playing against a single deck and it would also be slightly different if the dealer hit a soft 17.

Whenever your first 2 cards total 17 through 21, you should stand, no matter what the dealer's up card is.

If your cards total 16, you should stand if the dealer has a 2 through 6 as his upcard otherwise, draw a card. By the way, 16 is the worst hand you can have because you will bust more often with 16 than with any other hand. So, if that's the case then why would you want to ever hit a 16? Well, once again, those computer studies have shown that you should hit a 16 when the dealer has 7 through ace as his upcard because in the long run you will lose less often. This means that yes, 16 is a terrible hand, but you should hit it because if you don't you will lose even more often than when you do take a card.

If your cards total 15, you should also stand if the dealer has a 2 through 6 as his upcard otherwise, draw cards until your total is 17 or more.

The same rules from 15 and 16 also apply if your cards total 14. Stand if the dealer has a 2 through 6, otherwise draw cards until your total is 17 or more. The same rules also apply if your cards total 13. Stand if the dealer has a 2 through 6, otherwise draw cards until your total is 17 or more.

When your cards total 12 you should only stand when the dealer has a 4,5 or 6 as his upcard, remember - those are his 3 weakest cards and he will bust more often with those cards, so you don't want to take a chance on busting yourself. If the dealer's upcard is a 2 or a 3, then you should take just one card and stop on your total of 13 or more. Finally, if the dealer has a 7 through ace as his upcard then you should draw cards until your total is 17 or more.

When your cards total 11 you would always want to hit it because you can't bust, but before you ask for a card you should consider making a double down bet. If the casino allows you to double down then you should do that if the dealer has anything but an ace as his upcard. After you double down the dealer would give you just one additional card on that hand. If the dealer's upcard is an ace then you shouldn't double down. Instead, you should hit the hand and continue to draw until your total is 17 or more. If the casino doesn't allow you to double down then you should just hit your hand and then, depending on your total, play it by the rules I gave you for the hands that totaled 12 through 21. So, if you had an 11 and the dealer had a 5 as his upcard, you should take a card. Then let's say you draw an ace which gives you a total of 12. Well, as I said before, if you have a 12 against a dealer's 5 you should stand and that's how you should play that hand.

If your total is 10 you would, once again, want to double down unless the dealer showed an ace or a 10. If the dealer had an ace or a 10 as his upcard you should hit your hand and then use the standard rules for a hand valued at 12 through 21. So, if you had a 10 and the dealer had an 8 as his up card you would want to double down and take one more card. If you weren't allowed to double, then you would take a hit and let's say you got a 4 for a total of 14. You should then continue to hit your hand until your total is 17 or more.

If your total is 9 you would want to double down whenever the dealer was showing a 3,4,5 or 6 as his upcard. If the dealer had a 2 as his upcard, or if he had a 7 through ace as his upcard, you should hit your hand and then use the standard playing rules as discussed before. So, let's say you had a 9 and the dealer had a 4 as his upcard you would want to double down and take one more card. If you weren't allowed to double then you should take a hit and let's say you got a 2 for a total of 11, you would then take another hit and let's say you got an ace. That would give you a total of 12 and, as I showed you previously, you should stand on 12 against a dealer's 4.

Finally, if your total is 8 or less you should always take a card and then use the standard playing rules that we already discussed.

Now, let's take a look at splitting pairs, but keep in mind that the rules for splitting will change slightly depending on whether or not the casino will allow you to double down after you split your cards. Most multiple deck games allow you to double down after splitting so that's the situation we'll cover first and then I'll tell you about the changes if you're not allowed to double down after splitting.

Basic Strategy - Single Deck

Dealer stands on soft 17 • Double on any 2 cards • Double allowed after split

Your Hand	Dealer's Upcard									
	2	**3**	**4**	**5**	**6**	**7**	**8**	**9**	**10**	**A**
17	ALWAYS STAND ON HARD 17 (OR MORE)									
16	-	-	-	-	-	H	H	H	H*	H
15	-	-	-	-	-	H	H	H	H*	H
14	-	-	-	-	-	H	H	H	H	H
13	-	-	-	-	-	H	H	H	H	H
12	H	H	-	-	-	H	H	H	H	H
11	ALWAYS DOUBLE									
10	D	D	D	D	D	D	D	D	H	H
9	D	D	D	D	D	H	H	H	H	H
8	H	H	H	D	D	H	H	H	H	H
A,8	-	-	-	-	D	-	-	-	-	-
A,7	-	D	D	D	D	-	-	H	H	-
A,6	D	D	D	D	D	H	H	H	H	H
A,5	H	H	D	D	D	H	H	H	H	H
A,4	H	H	D	D	D	H	H	H	H	H
A,3	H	H	D	D	D	H	H	H	H	H
A,2	H	H	D	D	D	H	H	H	H	H
A,A	ALWAYS SPLIT									
10,10	ALWAYS STAND (NEVER SPLIT)									
9,9	Sp	Sp	Sp	Sp	Sp	-	Sp	Sp	-	-
8,8	ALWAYS SPLIT									
7,7	Sp	Sp	Sp	Sp	Sp	Sp	**Sp**	H	-*	H
6,6	Sp	Sp	Sp	Sp	Sp	**Sp**	H	H	H	H
5,5	NEVER SPLIT (PLAY AS 10 HAND)									
4,4	H	H	**Sp**	**Sp**	**Sp**	H	H	H	H	H
3,3	**Sp**	**Sp**	Sp	Sp	Sp	Sp	Sp	H	H	H
2,2	**Sp**	H	Sp	Sp	Sp	Sp	H	H	H	H

- =Stand H=Hit D=Double Sp=Split *= Surrender if allowed

shaded boxes show strategy changes from chart on next page

Basic Strategy - Single Deck

Dealer stands on soft 17 • Double on any 2 cards • Double NOT allowed after split

Your Hand	Dealer's Upcard									
	2	**3**	**4**	**5**	**6**	**7**	**8**	**9**	**10**	**A**
17	ALWAYS STAND ON HARD 17 (OR MORE)									
16	-	-	-	-	-	H	H	H	H*	H*
15	-	-	-	-	-	H	H	H	H*	H
14	-	-	-	-	-	H	H	H	H	H
13	-	-	-	-	-	H	H	H	H	H
12	H	H	-	-	-	H	H	H	H	H
11	ALWAYS DOUBLE									
10	D	D	D	D	D	D	D	D	H	H
9	D	D	D	D	D	H	H	H	H	H
8	H	H	H	D	D	H	H	H	H	H
A,8	-	-	-	-	D	-	-	-	-	-
A,7	-	D	D	D	D	-	-	H	H	-
A,6	D	D	D	D	D	H	H	H	H	H
A,5	H	H	D	D	D	H	H	H	H	H
A,4	H	H	D	D	D	H	H	H	H	H
A,3	H	H	D	D	D	H	H	H	H	H
A,2	H	H	D	D	D	H	H	H	H	H
A,A	ALWAYS SPLIT									
10,10	NEVER SPLIT (ALWAYS STAND)									
9,9	Sp	Sp	Sp	Sp	Sp	-	Sp	Sp	-	-
8,8	ALWAYS SPLIT									
7,7	Sp	Sp	Sp	Sp	Sp	Sp	H	H	-*	H
6,6	Sp	Sp	Sp	Sp	Sp	H	H	H	H	H
5,5	NEVER SPLIT (PLAY AS 10 HAND)									
4,4	NEVER SPLIT (PLAY AS 8 HAND)									
3,3	H	H	Sp	Sp	Sp	Sp	H	H	H	H
2,2	H	Sp	Sp	Sp	Sp	Sp	H	H	H	H

- =Stand   H=Hit   D=Double   Sp=Split   *= Surrender if allowed

Basic Strategy - Multiple Decks

Dealer stands on soft 17 • Double on any 2 cards • Double allowed after split

Your Hand	Dealer's Upcard									
	2	3	4	5	6	7	8	9	10	A
17	ALWAYS STAND ON 17 (OR MORE)									
16	-	-	-	-	-	H	H	H*	H*	H*
15	-	-	-	-	-	H	H	H	H*	H
14	-	-	-	-	-	H	H	H	H	H
13	-	-	-	-	-	H	H	H	H	H
12	H	H	-	-	-	H	H	H	H	H
11	D	D	D	D	D	D	D	D	D	H
10	D	D	D	D	D	D	D	D	H	H
9	H	D	D	D	D	H	H	H	H	H
8	ALWAYS HIT 8 (OR LESS)									
A,8	ALWAYS STAND ON SOFT 19 (OR MORE)									
A,7	-	D	D	D	D	-	-	H	H	H
A,6	H	D	D	D	D	H	H	H	H	H
A,5	H	H	D	D	D	H	H	H	H	H
A,4	H	H	D	D	D	H	H	H	H	H
A,3	H	H	H	D	D	H	H	H	H	H
A,2	H	H	H	D	D	H	H	H	H	H
A,A	ALWAYS SPLIT									
10,10	ALWAYS STAND (NEVER SPLIT)									
9,9	Sp	Sp	Sp	Sp	Sp	-	Sp	Sp	-	-
8,8	ALWAYS SPLIT									
7,7	Sp	Sp	Sp	Sp	Sp	Sp	H	H	H	H
6,6	Sp	Sp	Sp	Sp	Sp	H	H	H	H	H
5,5	D	D	D	D	D	D	D	D	H	H
4,4	H	H	H	Sp	Sp	H	H	H	H	H
3,3	Sp	Sp	Sp	Sp	Sp	Sp	H	H	H	H
2,2	Sp	Sp	Sp	Sp	Sp	Sp	H	H	H	H

- =Stand H=Hit D=Double Sp=Split *= Surrender if allowed

Basic Strategy - Multiple Decks

Dealer stands on soft 17 • Double on any 2 cards • Double NOT allowed after split

Your Hand	Dealer's Upcard									
	2	**3**	**4**	**5**	**6**	**7**	**8**	**9**	**10**	**A**
17	ALWAYS STAND ON HARD 17 (OR MORE)									
16	-	-	-	-	-	H	H	H*	H*	H*
15	-	-	-	-	-	H	H	H	H*	H
14	-	-	-	-	-	H	H	H	H	H
13	-	-	-	-	-	H	H	H	H	H
12	H	H	-	-	-	H	H	H	H	H
11	D	D	D	D	D	D	D	D	D	H
10	D	D	D	D	D	D	D	D	H	H
9	H	D	D	D	D	H	H	H	H	H
8	ALWAYS HIT 8 (OR LESS)									
A,8	ALWAYS STAND ON SOFT 19 (OR MORE)									
A,7	-	D	D	D	D	-	-	H	H	H
A,6	H	D	D	D	D	H	H	H	H	H
A,5	H	H	D	D	D	H	H	H	H	H
A,4	H	H	D	D	D	H	H	H	H	H
A,3	H	H	H	D	D	H	H	H	H	H
A,2	H	H	H	D	D	H	H	H	H	H
A,A	ALWAYS SPLIT									
10,10	ALWAYS STAND (NEVER SPLIT)									
9,9	Sp	Sp	Sp	Sp	Sp	-	Sp	Sp	-	-
8,8	ALWAYS SPLIT									
7,7	Sp	Sp	Sp	Sp	Sp	Sp	H	H	H	H
6,6	**H**	Sp	Sp	Sp	Sp	H	H	H	H	H
5,5	NEVER SPLIT (PLAY AS 10 HAND)									
4,4	H	H	H	**H**	**H**	H	H	H	H	H
3,3	**H**	**H**	Sp	Sp	Sp	Sp	H	H	H	H
2,2	**H**	**H**	Sp	Sp	Sp	Sp	H	H	H	H

- =Stand H=Hit D=Double Sp=Split *= Surrender if allowed

shaded boxes show strategy changes from chart on previous page

As I said earlier, when your first two cards are the same most casinos will allow you to split them and play them as two separate hands so let's go over the basic strategy rules on when you should do this.

The first thing you should remember is that you always split aces and 8's. The reason you split aces is obvious because if you get a 10 on either hand you'll have a perfect 21, but remember that you won't get paid for a blackjack at 3-to-2, instead it'll be counted as a regular 21 and you'll be paid at even money. If you have a pair of 8's you have 16 which is a terrible hand and you can always improve it by splitting your 8's and playing them as separate hands.

The next thing to remember about splitting pairs is that you never split 5's or 10's. Once again, the reasons should be rather obvious, you don't want to split 10's because 20 is a great hand and you don't want to split 5's because 10 is a great hand to draw to. Instead, you would want to double down on that 10, unless the dealer was showing a 10 or an ace as his upcard.

2's, 3's and 7's should only be split when the dealer is showing a 2 through 7 as his upcard. Split 4's only when the dealer has a 5 or 6 as his upcard (remember 5 and 6 are his weakest cards!), 6's should be split whenever the dealer is showing a 2 through 6 and finally, you should always split 9's unless the dealer is showing a 7, 10 or ace. The reason you don't want to split 9's against a 10 or an ace should be rather obvious, but the reason you don't want to split them against a 7 is in case the dealer has a 10 as his hole card because in that case your 18 would beat out his 17.

If the casino will not allow you to double down after splitting then you should make the following three changes: For 2's and 3's only split them against a 4,5,6 or 7; never split 4's; and for a pair of 6's only split them against a 3,4,5 or 6. Everything else should be played the same.

Now, let's take a look at how to play ***soft hands*** and remember a soft hand is any hand that contains an ace that can be counted as 1 or 11. For a soft hand of 19 or more you should always stand.

For soft 18 against a 2,7 or 8 you should always stand. If the dealer shows a 9, 10 or an ace you should always take a hit and for a soft 18 against a 3,4,5 or 6 you should double down, but if the casino won't allow you to double then you should just stand.

For soft 17 you should always take a hit, but if the casino allows you to double down, then you should double against a dealer's 3,4,5 or 6.

For soft 16 or a soft 15 you should always take a hit, but if the casino allows you to double down then you should double against a dealer's 4,5 or 6.

For soft 14 you should always take a hit, but if the casino allows you to double down then you should double against a dealer's 5 or 6.

Finally, for a soft 13 you should always take a hit, but if the casino allows you to double down then you should double against a dealer's 5 or 6.

The last thing we need to cover is surrender which, as noted before, isn't offered in many casinos but it is an option that does work in your favor and if available, you should play in a casino that offers it. The surrender rules are very simple to remember and only apply to hard totals of 15 or 16. If you have a hard 16 you should surrender it whenever the dealer has a 9, 10 or ace as his upcard and if you have a hard 15 you should surrender it whenever the dealer has a 10 as his upcard. That's all there is to surrender.

Now that you know how to play the game and you have an understanding of the basic strategy let's take a quick look at how the rules variations can affect the game of blackjack. As noted before, various computer studies have been made on blackjack and these studies have shown that each rule change can either hurt or help the player by a certain amount. For example, a single-deck game where you can double on any first 2 cards (but not after splitting pairs), the dealer stands on soft 17 and no surrender is allowed has no advantage for the casino when using the basic strategy. That's right, in a game with those rules in effect the game is dead even and neither the casino nor the player has an edge!

Take a look at the following chart and you'll see how some rules changes can hurt you or help you as a player. Minus signs in front mean that the casino gains the edge by that particular amount while plus signs mean that you gain the edge by that amount.

RULES THAT HURT YOU		RULES THAT HELP YOU	
Two decks	-0.32%	Double after split	+0.13%
Four decks	-0.49%	Late surrender	+0.06%
Six decks	-0.54%	Resplit Aces	+0.14%
Eight decks	-0.57%	Double anytime	+0.20%
Dealer hits soft 17	-0.20%		
No soft doubling	-0.14%		

As you can see, it's always to your advantage to play against as few decks as possible. The house edge goes up substantially as you go from 1 deck to 2, but the change is less dramatic when you go from 2 to 4, or from 4 to 6, and it's barely noticeable when you go from 6 to 8. You can also see that you would prefer not to play in a casino where the dealer hits a soft 17 because that gives the dealer a slight edge. You would also want to play in a casino where you're allowed to double down on your soft hands or else you would be giving another added edge to the casino.

You can also see from these charts that you would want to play in a casino where you were allowed to double down after splitting cards and you would also want to play in a casino that offered surrender. The other two rules variations that help the player are somewhat rare but they were put in to show you how these rules changes can affect your odds in the game. Some casinos will allow you to resplit aces again if you draw an ace to one of your original aces and this works to your advantage. Also, some casinos will allow you to double down on any number of cards rather than just the first two. In other words, if you got a 2- 4-3-2 as your first four cards you would then be allowed to double down on your total of 11 before receiving your 5th card. If they allow you to do this then, once again, you have a rule that works in your favor.

The point of showing you these charts is to help you understand that when you have a choice of places to play you should always choose the casino that offers the best rules. So, if you find a single-deck game with good rules you could be playing an even game by using the basic strategy, or at worst be giving the casino an edge of less than one-half of 1%.

Now, there is one way that you can actually have the edge working in your favor when you play blackjack and that's by becoming a card counter. As I said before, card counting is not for the average person but I do think it's important that you understand the concept of card counting and if you think you'd like to learn more about counting cards then it's something you can follow up on later.

Many people think that to be a card counter you have to have a photographic memory and remember every single card that's been played. Fortunately, it's not quite that difficult. Actually, the main concept behind card counting is the assumption that the dealer will bust more often when there are a lot of 10's in the deck and that he will complete more hands when there are a lot of smaller cards in the deck. Now, if you stop to think about it, it makes sense doesn't it? After all, the dealer has to play by set rules that make him take a card until he has a total of 17 or more. If there are a lot of 2's, 3's and 4's in the deck the dealer won't bust very often when he draws cards, but if there are a lot of 10's in the deck then chances are he will bust more often when he is forced to draw cards.

The card counter tries to take advantage of this fact by keeping a running total of the cards that have been played to give him an idea of what kind of cards remain in the deck. If there are a lot of 10 cards remaining in the deck then the counter will bet more money because the odds are slightly in his favor. Of course, if there are a lot of small cards remaining then the counter would only make a small bet because the odds would be slightly in favor of the dealer. Another thing that the card counter can do is to change his basic strategy to take advantage of the differences in the deck.

There are at least a dozen different card counting systems but let's take a quick look at a relatively simple one (it's also the most popular) and it's called the high-low count. With this system you assign a value of +1 to all 2's, 3's, 4's, 5's and 6's, while all 10's, Jacks, Queens, Kings and Aces are assigned a value of -1. The remaining cards: 7, 8 and 9 have no value and are not counted.

+1 = 2, 3, 4, 5, 6
-1 = 10, J, Q, K, A

When you look at these numbers you'll see that there are an equal number of cards in each group: there are five cards valued at +1 and five cards valued at -1. This means that they balance each other out and if you go through the deck and add them all together the end result will always be a total of exactly zero.

What a card counter does is to keep a running total of all the cards as they're played out and whenever the total has a plus value he knows that a lot of small cards have appeared and the remaining deck is rich in 10's which is good for the player. But, if the total is a minus value then the counter knows that a lot of 10-value cards have appeared and the remaining deck must be rich in low cards which is bad for the player. To give you an example of how to count let's say the following cards have been dealt on the first hand from a single deck:

2, 3, 3, 4, 5, 5, 5, 6, = +8
J, K, Q, A, = -4
Total = +4

As you can see, there were eight plus-value cards and four minus-value cards which resulted in a total count of +4. This means that there are now four more 10-value cards than low cards remaining in the deck and the advantage is with the player. Naturally, the higher the plus count, the more advantageous it is for the player and counters would be proportionally increasing their bets as the count got higher. The card counter would also be using the same basic strategy we spoke about previously, except for certain instances where a slight change would be called for.

On the other hand, if the count is negative, a card counter will always bet the minimum amount. Of course, they would prefer not to bet at all, but the casinos don't like you to sit at their tables and not bet so the counter has to bet something and the minimum is the least they can get by with.

There is one more important thing to explain about card counting and it's called the ***true count***. The true count is a measure of the count per deck rather than a ***running count*** of all the cards that have been played and to get the true count you simply divide the running count by the number of decks remaining to be played. As an illustration, let's say you're playing in a 6-deck game and the count is +9. You look at the shoe and estimate that 3 decks remain to be played. You then divide the count of +9 by 3 to get +3 which is the true count. As another example, let's say you're in an 8-deck game with a count of +12 and there are 6 decks left to be played. You divide +12 by 6 to get +2 which is the true count. To put it another way, a +2 count in a double-deck game with 1 deck left to be played is the same as a +4 count in a 4-deck game with 2 decks left to be played, which is the same as a +6 count is a 6-deck game with 3 decks left to be played, which is the same as a +12 count in an 8-deck game with 6 decks left to be played.

For the card counter it is crucial to always take the running count and then divide it by the number of decks remaining in order to get the true count because all betting and playing decisions are based on the true count rather than the running count.

Of course, if you're playing in a single-deck game the running count and the true count are initially the same. The more you get into the deck, however, the more weight is given to the running count because there is less than one deck remaining. So, if the running count was +3 and only a 1/2-deck remained you would calculate the true count by dividing +3 by 1/2 (which is the same as multiplying by 2/1, or 2) to get a true count of +6. As another example, if the running count was +2 and about 2/3 of the deck remained you would divide +2 by 2/3 (the same as multi-plying by 3/2 or, 1 and 1/2) to get +3.

As you can see, the count becomes much more meaningful as you get closer to the last cards in the deck and that's why casinos never deal down to the end. Instead, the dealer will insert a plastic card about 2/3 or 3/4 of the way in the deck and when that card is reached the dealer will finish that particular round and then shuffle the cards. How far into the deck(s) that plastic card is inserted is known as the ***penetration point*** and card counters always look for a dealer that offers good penetration. The card counter knows that the further into the deck(s) the plastic card is placed the more meaningful the true count will be and the more advantageous it will be for the card counter.

So, now that you know how those card counters keep track of the cards, what kind of advantage do you think they have over the casino? Well, not too much. Depending on the number of decks used, the rules in force, and the skill of the counter, it could be as much as 2% but that would be at the high end. Probably 1% would be closer to the actual truth. This means that for every $1,000 in bets that are made the card counter will win $10. Not exactly a huge amount but there are people out there who do make a living playing the game.

If you would like to learn more about blackjack, as well as more about card counting, be sure to take a look at the some of the ads in this book for ordering information on some very helpful books, newsletters, videos and computer software.

Blackjack 101

by Henry Tamburin

The casino's edge over a typical unskilled player is 5 to 10 percent. Which means, over an extended period of time, the player has a high probability of losing money. That's unfortunate because blackjack players can significantly reduce the edge against them if they learn which are the best games to play and how to play each hand. Read on and learn how to beat the casinos at their own game, in this Blackjack 101 short course.

First things first. If you don't know the basic rules of casino blackjack you shouldn't be playing in a casino. This sounds trivial but you'd be surprised how many players play this game without a clue as to the objective of the game. Many honestly believe the goal is to get as close to 21 as possible. Others believe the best strategy is to follow the strategy of the dealer - after all he seems to be winning all the time.

To put it in simple terms the objective is to either beat the dealer by having your hand total higher than the dealer, or to have the dealer bust when your total is 21 or less.You want to try, if possible, not to exceed a total of 21.The reason for this has to do with how the casino creates its edge to begin with. It's real simple: you as a player go first and if your hand totals more than 21, guess what? That's right you lose, even if the dealer subsequently goes over 21 with his hand. Pretty neat rule for the house and something to keep in mind as a player.

OK let's get back to the rules. If you don't know what double down or pair splitting or insurance or surrender is all about, you better get a good book on blackjack and learn the basics before you risk any money in the casinos. At the very least pick up the free gaming guides in the casinos that explain all this.

All blackjack games are not created equal. Casino managers have a certain amount of latitude to modify the rules as they see fit. It's important you understand which rules are more favorable for the house and which ones favor the player.

Here is a rundown of the good rules for the player:

- double down allowed on any two cards
- double down allowed after pair splitting
- multiple pair splitting allowed (even better if allowed with aces)
- dealer stands on soft 17
- the least number of decks the better (single or double is better than 4, which is better than 6, which is better than 8)
- surrender allowed

Rule number one, if you are serious about winning, is: **given a choice, always play blackjack at the casino which offers the best rules**. You'll need every edge you can get and this one is important. So study the rules and go seek out the better games.

Your next task to cut the casino's edge is to learn the basic playing strategy. These strategies are developed by computer analysis of the game and represent mathematically correct strategy for each given playing situation. You won't win every hand following the basic strategy simply because in some situations no matter what hand you have the dealer's chances of beating you are very high. However, the basic strategy will allow you to make the best play to minimize your losses in unfavorable situations and, more importantly, allow you to maximize your profits when the advantage on a particular hand is in your favor.

You can find the basic strategy in most blackjack texts, including my *Blackjack: Take the Money and Run,* and it involves learning about 25 rules as to when to hit, stand, double, split or surrender. What I've done is to condense and simplify the most important strategy decisions into a set of nine easy-to-learn rules specifically for the casual player. Think of it as your first venue into learning winning blackjack playing strategies.

Memorize and use the rules below when you play blackjack and you will reduce the casino's edge to about one percent. Learn the complete basic strategy and you'll reduce the casino's advantage even more to about one-half of a percent (and I hope you commit to the latter).

Simplified Blackjack Playing Strategy

Your Hand	Playing Strategy vs Dealer's Up card
12 thru 16	stand on 2 thru 6, hit on 7 thru ace
17 thru 21	stand, except always hit soft 17 (A,6)
10 or 11	double on 2 through 9
soft 13 thru 17	always hit (except double all against 5,6)
soft 18 thru 21	always stand (except double soft 18 against 5,6)
8,8 and ace,ace	always split
5,5 and 10,10	never split
2,2;3,3;6,6;7,7;9,9	split on 2 thru 7 (except stand on 9,9 vs 7)
Never Take Insurance	

Do not, I repeat, do not play blackjack in a casino until you at least learn the above condensed basic strategy and, better yet, the complete strategy. If you insist on playing without learning the basic strategy, I suggest you stay home and instead just mail a check to the casino. Over time the results will be the same.

Henry Tamburin is the author of "Blackjack: Take the Money and Run," "Reference Guide To Casino Gambling" and several other books. He is also featured in the blackjack instructional video "Blackjack - Deal Me In." Ordering information for his products can be found on page 178.

Single Deck vs. Multiple-Deck Blackjack

By Henry Tamburin

If you walk into a casino to play blackjack and notice several single and six deck blackjack games which one would you play? I'm sure your first inclination is the single deck game because somewhere you remember reading that "*a single deck game is a better game for players.*" Yet do you know why? And is it always a better game for players than multiple deck games? Let's see.

Many blackjack theoreticians have determined that the number of decks of cards has a great influence on the casino's edge over a typical basic strategy player. The following graph shows the effect the number of decks has on the casino's edge (typical Las Vegas Strip rules). As the number of decks increases (left to right on the bottom axis), so does the casino's edge (vertical axis). But notice the line in the graph is not straight. It rises rather steeply when you go from a one to two deck game then starts to gradually taper off as the number of decks increases. The biggest increase in the casino's edge occurs when you go from one to two decks where the casino edge increases from a player's advantage of 0.01% to a casino's advantage of -0.32% or an increase of 0.33%. With more than 6 decks the increase in the casino's edge becomes very small and levels out to about 0.6%. This is one reason why you never see more then 8 decks being used on a blackjack table because even if the casino's would be able to deal a game with one hundred decks of cards their edge would be about the same as an eight deck game.

Number of Decks	Casino's Edge *	Difference
1	+0.01	-
2	-0.32	0.33
3	-0.43	0.11
4	-0.49	0.06
5	-0.52	0.03
6	-0.54	0.02
7	-0.56	0.02
8	-0.57	0.01

*From *Casino Operations Management* by Jim Kilby and Jim Fox

When you first think about it, it's hard for players to understand why the casino's edge increases when more decks of cards are put into play. There are in fact several reasons for this.

"There are more blackjacks in single deck games vs. multiple deck games"

You're probably wondering how this can be since the percentage of aces and tens in a single deck game is the same as in 2, 4, 6, or 8 deck game. That's true but the effect of removing a card from a single deck game affects the percentages of the remaining cards to a *much greater* extent in a single deck game vs. a multiple deck game.

Suppose you shuffled a single deck of cards and wanted to know what your chances that the first card you select from the shuffled deck will be an ace and the second card a ten, jack, queen or king to give you a blackjack hand. This is easy to figure out. There are 4 aces in a single deck of cards and the chance of drawing one of those aces is just the ratio of 4 over 52. Once you draw the ace you've got only 51 cards left to draw a ten-value card. There are 16 ten-value cards in a deck of cards so the chance of drawing a ten-value card as the second card is the ratio of 16 over 51. If you multiply these two ratios you arrive at the probability of drawing an ace then a ten from a 52-card deck is 2.41%

$$4/52 \times 16/51 = 2.41\%$$

You could have just as easily drawn the ten-value card first then the ace. Therefore the overall probability of getting a blackjack in a single deck game is twice 2.41% or 4.82%. This translates into ***1 blackjack out of every 20.72 hands*** dealt to you. That's an important statistic because when you play blackjack and not getting a blackjack hand at least once out of every 21 hands don't be surprised if you are not winning.

The following chart summarizes the probabilities of getting a blackjack for 2, 4, 6 and 8 deck games using similar calculations. Note that a player will on average get *fewer blackjacks* as the number of decks increases. In fact you'll only be *98% as successful* drawing a blackjack in an 8-deck game compared to a single deck game which makes the single deck game better.

PROBABILTY OF GETTING BLACKJACK
vs NUMBER OF DECKS OF CARDS

# Decks	Probability
1	1 in every 20.72 hands
2	1 in every 20.93 hands
4	1 in every 21.02 hands
6	1 in every 21.07 hands
8	1 in every 21.07 hands

Although getting more blackjacks is good for the player, it's even better when you get a blackjack and the dealer doesn't. Which brings me to the second reason why the casino's edge *increases* when the number of decks of cards increases.

"The dealer's chances of duplicating our blackjack <u>decreases</u> as the number of decks decreases"

When you get a blackjack and the dealer doesn't, you get paid at 3 to 2. But if the dealer also has a blackjack, it is a tie and you win nothing. Therefore, the *less* chance the dealer has of getting a blackjack, the more times you will be paid the bonus 3 to 2 payoff and your earnings potential will increase.

Once a player gats a blackjack the probability of the dealer drawing an ace followed by a ten value card is:

Probability of getting an ace is 3/50
Probability of getting a ten value card is 15/49

When you multiply the above ratios then double the result to take into consideration the reverse (drawing a ten first then the ace) you arrive at the overall probability of the dealer getting a blackjack is *once in every 27.25 hands*. The corresponding probabilities for 2, 4, 6 and 8 decks are summarized in the table below.

PROBABILITY OF DEALER GETTING BLACKJACK AFTER PLAYER GETS A BLACKJACK vs. NUMBER OF DECKS

Number of Decks	Probability
1	1 in every 27.22 hands
2	1 in every 23.74 hands
4	1 in every 22.34 hands
6	1 in every 21.92 hands
8	1 in every 21.71 hands

Blackjack pushes are about 20% more likely in a 6 or 8 deck game, compared to a single deck game, which reduces our earnings potential. This makes the single deck game a much better game.

The third reason why the casino's edge increases when more decks are put into play is:

"When you double down, you are more likely to get the card you want in a single deck game compared to a multiple deck game"

The mathematical basis for this is the same as the above namely *the effects of card removal is much more pronounced in single deck games vs. multiple deck games*.

Take the case of a player drawing a 6 and a 5 against a dealer's 5 upcard. The player is looking for a ten-value card to give him a 21. In a single-deck game the chance of the player getting a ten value card after the players 6 and 5 and dealer's 5 are removed from the deck is the ratio 16 over 49 or 32.6% chance of getting a ten. In a six-deck game the probability becomes 96 over 309 or 31.07% chance of getting a ten. A player is 5% less likely to reach 21 in a 6-deck game compared to a single deck game. Or to put it another way, you are *more likely* to be successful doubling down in a single-deck game compared to a multiple-deck game making a single deck game the better game.

The number of decks of cards also affects the casino's edge on the insurance bet in blackjack.

"As the number of decks increase, the casino's advantage on the insurance bet increases"

When the dealer's upcard is an ace, the dealer will offer players the option of making an insurance bet equal to half of the players bet on the hand. The player wins the insurance bet at 2 to 1 odds if the dealer's downcard is a ten-value card giving him a blackjack. If the dealer's downcard is not a ten-value card, then the players insurance bet is lost.

It's easy to calculate the casino's advantage on the insurance bet. In a single deck game the probability that the dealer's downcard will be a ten value card is 16 over 51 (one card is already removed from the deck, the dealer's ace). The probability that the dealer's downcard will be a non-ten-value card is 35 over 51. To compute the casino's edge you multiply the corresponding probabilities by the payoff (+2 when you win and -1 when you lose) and add up the result.

$$(16/51 \times +2) + (35/51 \times -1) = -5.8\%$$

The casinos edge on the insurance bet for a 6-deck game is:

$$(96/311 \times +2) + (215/311 \times -1) = -7.4\%$$

Taking insurance is a bad bet in a single deck game (casino's edge 5.8%) but it becomes an even worse bet in a 6-deck game (casino's edge 7.4%).

On the surface it appears that a single deck game is a better game then a 6 six deck game but be careful because the casinos can and often do change the rules in a single deck game to increase their edge.

Presently the best single-deck blackjack rules in the country are offered at the Slots A Fun Casino in Las Vegas, the Cypress Bayou Casino in Charenton,

Louisiana, and the SunCruz Hollywood Cruise ship out of Dania, Florida. The playing rules are: the dealer stands on soft 17, the players can double down after pair splitting, and resplits allowed. The casino's edge in this game is a negative .13%, which means a basic strategy player has a slight edge over the casino *without* card counting. If a casino eliminates the rule that lets a player double down after pair splitting the casino's edge would change from -0.13% to -0.01%. The player would still have the edge but only a tiny one. By simply making the dealer hit rather than stand on soft 17, the casino's edge increases to 0.18%. Another way a casino can increase their edge more is to restrict player doubling to 9 and 10. The worst rule from the player's perspective is when casinos pay even money on blackjacks.

The following table summarizes the casino's edge for various single deck blackjack games currently offered in casinos throughout the country. It shows you how the casinos can increase their advantage in single deck games by altering the playing rules.

CASINO'S EDGE IN SINGLE DECK GAMES vs. PLAYING RULES

DAS = Double after pair splitting.
Stand 17 = Dealer stands on soft 17
Hit 17 = dealer hits soft 17
LS = late surrender
RSA = resplit aces

RULES	CASINO'S EDGE
Stand 17, DAS	-0.13%
Stand 17	-0.01%
Hit 17, DAS, LS	+0.02%
Hit 17, DAS	+0.06%
Hit 17, LS	+0.10%
Hit 17, Resplit aces allowed	+0.15%
Hit 17	+0.18%
Hit 17, No resplits	+0.22%
Stand 17, LS, Double only on 10	+0.23%
Stand 17, Double only on 10	+0.25%
Stand 17, Double only on 10. No resplits	+0.29%
Hit 17, Double only on 9	+0.32%
Hit 17, LS, Double only on 10	+0.41%
Hit 17, Double on 10 only	+0.44%
Stand 17, DAS, RSA, BJ pay even money	+2.6%

In most casinos a single deck game with one poor rule such as the dealer hitting soft 17 is still better then most 6 or 8 deck games. But be careful. The Bellagio in Las Vegas, for example, offers a very favorable six-deck game where the casino's edge is only 0.26% making it very competitive to some single deck games. There are also many favorable double deck games, sometimes in the same casino that offers the basic strategy player a lower casino edge. A case in point is the Copa Casino in Gulfport. At their single deck games the dealer stands on soft 17, late surrender is allowed but you can only double on 10 giving a casino's edge of 0.23%. At their double deck games the dealer also stands on soft 17 but there is no restriction on doubling and players can double after pair splitting and late surrender resulting in a casino's edge of 0.14%. This is *39%* lower than the casino's edge in the single deck game.

For the most part, single deck games are a better game for the basic strategy player. But be smart and check the playing rules to be sure that the casino hasn't negated the inherent low casino edge of single deck games with a bunch of unfavorable rules.

Henry Tamburin is one of America's most popular casino gaming writers and best-selling authors. For more of his winning advice visit his web site for casino players at www.smartgaming.com. Ordering information for his books and videos can be found on page 178.

Rating Blackjack Games

by Arnold Snyder

We'll consider three distinct types of players in developing a rating system for blackjack games. These players are: gamblers, basic strategy players, and card counters.

For gamblers, the best games will be those which contain the fewest number of decks, with single decks being the best, and also the fewest player options. All other factors being equal, if you go from a single-deck game to a two-deck game, you will lose about 0.3% more of all the money you bet in the long run. A four-deck game will cost about 0.5% more than a single-decker. A six-deck or eight-deck shoe will cost about 0.6% more than a single-deck game.

In dollars and cents, assuming 100 hands per hour at $5 per hand, each 0.1% is equal to about 50¢ per hour. So a more practical way to look at it (at this betting level) is that the two-decker costs you an extra $1.50 per hour. The four-decker costs an extra $2.50 per hour. And the six or eight-decker will cost you an extra $3.00 per hour.

The Gambler's Considerations

Since we're defining the gambler as a player type who does not stick to perfect basic strategy, we can't really say what the total cost per hour of playing blackjack will be for this player. We'd have to precisely analyze those plays in which s/he was varying from basic strategy to make this determination.

As a general consideration, non-basic strategy players do better with fewer options because there are fewer opportunities to misplay hands. For example, it would be better for this type of player to play in games in which doubling down is limited to totals of hard 10 and 11 only. This is because totals of 10 and 11 are the most valuable double downs to make and it is usually correct to double down on these hands. If doubling down is allowed on any two cards, players who don't know basic strategy may frequently make costly errors.

The Basic Strategy Player

The second type of player, the basic strategy player, would also prefer the game with the fewest number of decks, but this player differs from the gambler in that s/he will find it most advantageous to play in games with the most player options allowed.

The most valuable options are: early surrender, doubling down on any two cards, and doubling after splits. Of slightly lesser value are regular (late) surrender and resplitting aces. Any restrictive rules, such as no resplitting pairs, will hurt the basic strategy player who knows how to take advantage of the rule(s).

Card Counters

For card counters only, two other factors are of prime importance in rating games: deck penetration and betting spread. By deck penetration, we mean how many of the cards will be dealt between shuffles. In a four-deck game, a dealer who deals out 3-1/2 decks will be far superior, from a card counters perspective, to a dealer who deals out only 2-1/2 decks between shuffles.

By betting spread, we mean how widely the player may vary their minimum and maximum bets. A table which allows a spread from $2 to $5 will prove more profitable to a counter than one which allows a spread from $3 to $5. Multi-action tables are better yet. If you can spread from one hand of $2 to three hands of $5 (or $15 total action), this would be even more to a card coun-ter's advantage.

Note that deck penetration will have no effect whatsoever in the long run for players who are not card counters. Likewise, multi-action games, which allow a counter a greater betting spread, may tend to cause non-counters to overbet, and even to misplay hands.

So, before you pick the game, consider which player type you are. Non-counters should pick games in which they will lose the least. Card counters should pick the games where they will win the most.

Continuous Shuffling Machines in Blackjack

by Henry Tamburin

Ever since Edward Thorp published his ground breaking card counting system in 1962, skillful blackjack players have been able to get the edge over the casino by keeping track of specific cards as they are dealt by the dealer. Now a new innovation, touted as "a card counter's worst nightmare" claims to once and for all eliminate the advantage that card counters possess. The product is a new continuous multi-deck shuffler dubbed "The King" by its developer Shuffle Master Inc. of Las Vegas.

So what does this device do that threatens to make card counting obsolete? And does it have any effect on the casual blackjack player who is not card counting? Read on for the answers.

What makes this shuffler different from other automatic shufflers is that it completely randomizes the cards from a round of play with the other cards in the shuffler and then completely randomizes the delivery of the shuffled cards to the shoe. Here's how this "double randomization" process works.

After a round is over, the dealer inserts the cards into the shuffler. The cards are then randomized using an elevator system. The discards are placed on the elevator and then randomly placed into one of 19 elevator stops or shelves. The shuffler then randomly selects a shelf of cards and delivers those cards to the dealing shoe. These cards become the next group of cards dealt. The result, according to the folks at Shuffle Master, is "complete and total unpredictability."

How do these new shufflers wipe out the card counter's advantage? Card counters keep track of high and low value cards from one round to the next. They know when the remaining decks of cards in the playing shoe contain an excess of high value cards over low value cards. When this occurs the edge shifts in their favor and they increase their bets. Typically a skilled counter can gain a 1.0 to 1.5% advantage over the casino with this technique.

Essentially this new shuffler "immediately" recycles and deals cards from a 4-deck shoe on every round. More importantly, because any card can be delivered to a shelf and any shelf of cards can be delivered to the shoe, every discard re-inserted immediately following a hand has a chance to appear in the next round. The net result of this technology is that a card counter's advantage is eliminated.

How confident is Shuffle Master of the integrity of their new shuffler? This past summer they offering $100,000 to anyone who can show through mathematical analysis and/or computer simulation how a player can gain the advantage using the new shuffler.

There is no question that this new shuffler is going to be hard to beat. Not only does it thwart card counters but also a system used by players called "shuffle tracking" where skilled players have been able to track a group of cards through the dealer's shuffling routine and know when these cards will be dispensed from the shoe. This knowledge obviously gives the shuffle tracker a big advantage over the casino. However, the "random in, random out" process of shuffling from a totally enclosed continuous shuffler makes shuffle tracking obsolete.

The continuous shuffler will not alter the odds of the game for the casual blackjack player who does not count cards. But because more hands are dealt per hour with the shuffler, a casual player's bankroll won't last as long. That's another reason why casinos like the shuffler. The game is faster and as long as they have the edge over the average blackjack player, the casino's stand to win more money per hour. In other words, if you are a casual blackjack player, the more hands you play, the more money you will lose.

Dealers who have used the new shuffler have given it mixed reviews. Some of the negatives are that it doesn't give them a break from the physically tiresome monotonous task of dealing. One dealer mentioned to me that she often likes to carry on a casual conversation with players while she shuffles the cards but with the new shuffler "it's all business all the time."

It would seem that the continuous shuffler has lots of benefits for the casinos but none for the player. It eliminates card counting and shuffle tracking for the skilled player and results in higher hourly loss rates for the casual player. Maybe that's why Shuffle Master named the new continuous shuffler "The King."

Henry Tamburin is one of America's most popular casino gaming writers and best-selling authors. For more of his winning advice visit his web site for casino players at www.smartgaming.com. Ordering information for his books and videos can be found on page 178.

Craps

by Steve Bourie

At first glance the game of craps looks a little intimidating because of all the various bets you can make but actually the game itself is very simple, so first let me explain the game without any reference to the betting.

Everyone at the craps table gets a turn to roll the dice, but you don't have to roll if you don't want to. The dice are passed around the table clockwise and if it's your turn to roll you simply take two dice and roll them to the opposite end of the table. This is your first roll of the dice which is also called the "come-out" roll. If you roll a 7 or 11 that's called a "natural" and you win, plus you get to roll again. If you roll a 2,3 or 12 those are all called "craps" and you lose, but you still get to roll again. The only other possible numbers you can roll are 4,5,6,8,9 or 10 and if one of those numbers shows up, then that number becomes your "point" and the object of the game is to roll that number again before you roll a 7.

If a 7 shows up before your "point" number does then you lose and the dice move on to the next shooter. If your "point" number shows up before a 7 does, then you have made a "pass." You then win your bet and you get to roll again. That's all there is to the game of craps.

Now that you know how to play the game, let's find out about the different kinds of bets you can make. Two of the best bets you'll find on the craps table are in the areas marked "pass" and "don't pass". When you bet on the "pass" line you're betting that the shooter will win. To make a pass line bet you put your bet right in front of you on the pass line. Pass line bets are paid even-money and the house edge on a pass line bet is 1.41% You can also bet on the "don't pass" line in which case you're betting that the shooter will lose. To make a don't pass bet you put your bet in front of you in the don't pass area. Don't pass bets are also paid even-money and the house edge on them is 1.40%

In reality, the odds are always 1.41% against the shooter and in favor of the "don't pass" bettor by that same amount. Of course, if you're a "don't pass" bettor the casinos don't want to give you a bet where you have an edge so they have a rule in effect on "don't pass" bets where on the come out roll if the shooter throws a 12, you don't win. You don't lose either, the bet is just considered a "push," or tie, and nothing happens. In some casinos they may make 2 instead of 12 the number that's a push. Just look on the don't pass line and you'll you see the word "bar" and then the number that the casino considers a push. In our illustration it says bar 12, so in this casino your bet on the don't pass line will be a push if the come-out roll is a 12. This rule is what gives the casino its advantage on don't pass bets and it doesn't matter whether the casino bars the 2 or 12 the result is the same 1.40% advantage for the house.

All right, let's say you put $10 on the pass line and you roll the dice. If you roll 7 or 11 you win $10 and if you roll 2,3 or 12 you lose $10. So, what happens if you roll any of the other numbers? Well, as I said before, that number becomes your point and you have to roll that number again before you roll a 7 in order to win your pass line bet.

Once your point is established the dealer at each end of the table will move a marker into the box that corresponds to your point number to let everyone at the table know what your point is. The marker that's used has two different sides. One side is black with the word "off" and the other side is white with the word "on." Before any point is established the marker is kept in the Don't Come box with the black side facing up until you roll a point number and then the dealer turns it over to the white side and moves it inside the box that contains your point number.

For example let's say your come-out roll is a 4. The dealer simply turns the marker over to the white side that says "on" and places it in the 4 box. This let's everyone know that 4 is your point and that you will continue to roll the dice, no matter how long it takes, until you roll a 4, which will make you a winner, or a 7, which will make you a loser.

Now, keep in mind that once your point is established you can't remove your pass line bet until you either win, by throwing your point, or lose, by rolling a 7. The reason for this is that on the come out roll the pass line bettor has the advantage because there are 8 ways to win (by rolling a 7 or 11) and only 4 ways to lose (by rolling a 2, 3 or 12). If a point number is rolled, no matter what number it is, there are then more ways to lose than to win and that's why the bet can't be removed. If you were allowed to remove your bet everyone would just wait for the come-out roll and if they didn't win they would take their bet back which would give them a big advantage over the house and, as you know, casinos don't like that, so that's why you can't remove your bet.

As previously noted, the pass line is one of the best bets you'll find, but there is a way to make it even better because once your point number is established the casino will allow you to make another bet that will be paid off at the true odds. This is a very good bet to make because the casino has no advantage on this bet.

In this instance, since your point was 4, the true odds are 2-to-1 and that's what your bet will be paid off at: $2 for every $1 you bet. This is called an "odds bet," "taking the free odds" or "betting behind the line" and to make this bet you simply put your chips directly behind your pass line bet. There is a limit to how much you're allowed to bet and for many years most casinos allowed a maximum of 2 times the amount of your pass line bet. Nowadays, however, many casinos offer 5 times odds and some casinos are even allowing up to 100 times odds. In Las Vegas, Casino Royale and Sam's Town are two casinos that offer 100 times odds.

Typical craps table layout

Because the casino has no advantage on these bets you are effectively lowering the house edge on your total pass line bet by taking advantage of these free odds bets. For example, the normal house edge on a pass line bet is 1.41% but if you also make a single odds bet along with your pass line bet you will lower the house edge on your total pass line bets to .85%. If the casino offers double odds then the edge on your bets is lowered to .61% With triple odds the edge is lowered to .47% and if you were to play in a casino that allowed 10 times odds the edge would be lowered to only .18% which means that, statistically speaking, over time, that casino would only make 18¢ out of every $100 you bet on that table. As you can see, the more the casino allows you to bet behind the line, the more it lowers their edge, so it's always a good idea to take advantage of this bet. By the way, free odds bets, unlike regular pass line bets, can be removed or reduced, at any time.

All right, let's make our free odds bet on our point number of 4 by putting $20 behind the line. Then we continue to roll until we either roll a 4 or a 7. If a 4 came up we would get even money on the pass line bet, plus 2-to-1 on the free odds bet, for a total win of $50. But, if we rolled a 7, we would lose both the pass line bet and the free odds bet for a total loss of $30.

In this example we used 4 as our point number, but there are 5 other numbers that could appear and here are the true odds for all of the possible point numbers: the 4 and 10 are 2-to-1; the 5 and 9 are 3-to-2; and the 6 and 8 are 6-to-5. You'll notice that the numbers appear in pairs and that's because each paired combination has the same probability of occurring.

7 = 6 ways 1+6,6+1,2+5,5+2,3+4,4+3
6 = 5 ways 1+5,5+1,2+4,4+2,3+3
8 = 5 ways 2+6,6+2,3+5,5+3,4+4

As you can see there are 6 ways to make a 7 and only 5 ways to make a 6 or 8. Therefore, the true odds are 6-to-5.

7 = 6 ways 1+6,6+1,2+5,5+2,3+4,4+3
4 = 3 ways 1+3,3+1,2+2
10 = 3 ways 4+6,6+4,5+5

There are 6 ways to make a 7 and only 3 ways to make a 4 or 10, so the true odds are 6-to-3, which is the same as 2-to-1;

7 = 6 ways 1+6,6+1,2+5,5+2,3+4,4+3
5 = 4 ways 1+4,4+1,2+3,3+2
9 = 4 ways 3+6,6+3,4+5,5+4

and finally, there are 6 ways to make a 7, but just 4 ways to make a 5 or 9, so the true odds here are 6-to-4 which is the same as 3-to-2.

It's important that you remember these numbers, because 1.- you want to make sure that you're paid the right amount when you do win and 2.- you want to make sure that when you make your odds bets you make them in amounts that are paid off evenly.

As an example, if your point is 5 and you have $5 on the pass line, you wouldn't want to bet $5 behind the line because at 3-to-2 odds the casino would have to pay you $7.50 and they don't deal in change. When making the odds bet on the 5 or 9 you should always bet in even amounts and in the situation just mentioned most casinos would allow you to add an extra $1 so you would have $6 out and they could pay you $9, if you won. The only other situation where this occurs is on the 6 and 8 where the payoff is 6-to-5. So, in that instance you want to make your bets in multiples of $5. Also, if your pass line bet is $15, most casinos will allow you to bet $25 behind the line because, if you win, it's quicker for them to pay you $30, rather than dealing in $1 chips to give you $18 for $15. When situations like this exist, it's good to take advantage of them and bet the full amount you're allowed because that helps to lower the casino edge even more.

We've spent all this time talking about pass line betting, so what about don't pass betting? Well, everything applied to pass line betting works pretty much just the opposite for don't pass betting. If you put $10 on don't pass you would win on the come out roll if the shooter rolled a 2 or 3, you would tie if the shooter rolled a 12, and you would lose if the shooter rolled a 7 or 11. If any other number comes up then that becomes the shooter's point number and if he rolls a 7 before he rolls that same point number, you will win. If he rolls his point number before he rolls a 7, you will lose.

Don't pass bettors are also allowed to make free odds bets to back up their original bets, however, because the odds are in their favor they must lay odds rather than take odds. This means that if the point is 4 or 10, the don't pass bettor must lay 2-to-1, or bet $10 to win $5; on 5 or 9 he must lay 3-to-2, or bet $6 to win $4; and on 6 or 8 he must lay 6-to-5, or bet $6 to win $5. By taking advantage of these free odds bets the casino advantage is slightly lowered on the total don't pass bets to .68% with single odds; .46% with double odds; .34% with triple odds and .12% with 10 times odds. If you want to you can remove, or reduce the amount of your free odds, bet at any time. To make a free odds bet on don't pass you should place your odds bet right next to your original bet and then put a chip on top to connect the two bets. Keep in mind that when you make a free odds bet on don't pass the casino will allow you to make your bet based on the payoff, rather than the original amount of your don't pass bet. In other words, if the casino offered double odds, the point was 4 and you had $10 on don't pass, you would be allowed to bet $40 because you would only win $20 which was double the amount of your original $10 bet. Since you have to put out more money than you'll be getting back, laying odds is not very popular at the craps table and you'll find that the vast majority of craps players would rather bet with the shooter and take the odds. Statistically speaking, it makes no difference whether you are laying or taking the odds because they both have a zero advantage for the house.

One last point about don't pass betting is that once the point is established, the casino will allow you to remove your don't pass bet if you want to - but don't do it! As noted before, on the come out roll the pass line bettor has the advantage because there are 8 rolls that can win and only 4 that can lose, but once the point is established, there are more ways the shooter can lose than win, so at that point the don't pass bettor has the advantage and it would be foolish to remove your bet.

Now, let's take a look at the area marked come and don't come. Since you already know how to bet pass and don't pass, you should easily understand come and don't come because they're the exact same bets as pass and don't pass, except for the fact that you bet them after the point has already been established.

Let's say that the shooter's point is 6 and you make a come bet by putting a $5 chip anywhere in the come box. Well, that's just like making a pass line bet, except that the shooter's next roll becomes the come-out roll for your bet. If the shooter rolls a 7 or 11, you win. If a 2,3, or 12 is rolled you lose, and if anything else comes up then that becomes your point and the shooter must roll that number again before rolling a 7 in order for you to win. In this example if the shooter rolled a 4 the dealer would move your $5 come bet up into the center of the 4 box and it would stay there until either a 4 was rolled, which would make you a winner, or a 7 was rolled which would make you a loser. The house edge on a come bet is the same 1.41% as on a pass line bet. You are allowed free odds on your come bet and you make that bet by giving your chips to the dealer and telling him you want to take the odds. The dealer will then place those chips slightly off center on top of your come bet to show that it's a free odds bet. By the way, if you win, the dealer will put your winnings back in the come bet area so be sure to pick them up off the table or else it will be considered a new come bet.

One other point to note here is that when you make a come bet your bet is always working on every roll, even a come-out roll. However, when you take the odds on your come bets they are never working on the come-out roll. That may sound a little confusing, but here's what it means. In our example the shooter's initial point was 6 and then we made a $5 come bet. The shooter then rolled a 4 which became the point for our come bet. The dealer then moved our $5 come bet to the middle of the 4 box at the top of the table. We then gave $10 to the dealer and said we wanted to take the odds on the 4. On the next roll the shooter rolls a 6 which means he made a pass by rolling his original point number. The next roll will then become the shooter's come-out roll and the odds bet on our 4 will not be working. If the shooter rolls a 7 the pass line bettors will win and we will lose our $5 come bet because he rolled a 7 before rolling a 4. The dealer will then return our $10 odds bet because it wasn't working on the come-out roll. Now, if you want to, you can request that your odds bet be working on the come-out roll by telling the dealer. Then he'll put a marker on top of your bet to show that your odds bet is in effect on the come-out roll. Naturally, don't come betting is the same as don't pass betting, except again for the fact that the bet isn't made until after the point is established. In this case let's say the point is 5 and you make a don't come bet by placing a $5 chip in the don't come box. Well, once again, that's just like making a don't pass bet except that the shooter's next roll becomes the come-out roll for your bet. If the shooter rolls a 2 or 3, you win. If a 7 or 11 is rolled, you lose. If a 12 is rolled it's a standoff and if anything else comes up then that becomes your point and the shooter must seven-out, or roll a 7, before rolling that point number again in order for you to win. In this example if the shooter rolled a 10 the dealer would move your $5 don't come bet into the upper part of the 10 box and it would stay there until either a 7 was rolled, which would make you a winner, or a 10 was rolled which would make you a loser. The house edge on a don't come bet is the same 1.40% as on a don't pass bet and you can make a free odds bet on your don't come bet by giving your chips to the dealer and telling him you want to lay the odds. The dealer will then place those chips next to and on top of your don't come bet to show that it's a free odds bet. The final point to note here is that don't come bets, as well as the free odds bets on them, are always working - even on the come-out roll.

Now let's talk about place betting and that refers to the 6 numbers you see in the area at the top of the table: 4,5,6,8,9 and 10. Anytime during a roll you can make a bet that one of those numbers will appear before a 7 and if it does you will receive a payoff that is slightly less than the true odds. For example: the true odds are 2-to-1 that a 4 or 10 will appear before a 7. However, if you make a place bet on the 4 or 10 you will only be paid off at 9-to-5 and that works out to a casino advantage of 6.67%

The true odds of a 5 or 9 appearing before a 7 are 3-to-2, but on a place bet you would only receive a payoff of 7-to-5 which works out to a casino edge of 4.0%. Finally, on the 6 and 8 the true odds are 6-to-5 that one of those numbers will appear before a 7, but on a place bet you would only be paid off at 7-to-6 which means the casino would have an edge of 1.52% on this bet.

As you can see, making a place bet on the 6 or 8 gives the casino its lowest edge and this means that a place bet on the 6 or 8 is one of the best bets you will find on the craps table.

When you want to make a place bet you aren't allowed to put the bet down yourself, you have to let the dealer do it for you. To do this you would just drop your chips down onto the table and tell the dealer what bet you wanted to make. For example you could put three $5 chips down and say "Place the 4,5 and 9." The dealer would then put $5 on the edge of the 4 box, $5 on the edge of the 5 box and $5 on the edge of the 9 box. You'll notice that when the dealer puts your bets on the edge of the boxes they will always be placed in an area that corresponds to where you're standing at the table and this helps the dealer to remember who placed that bet.

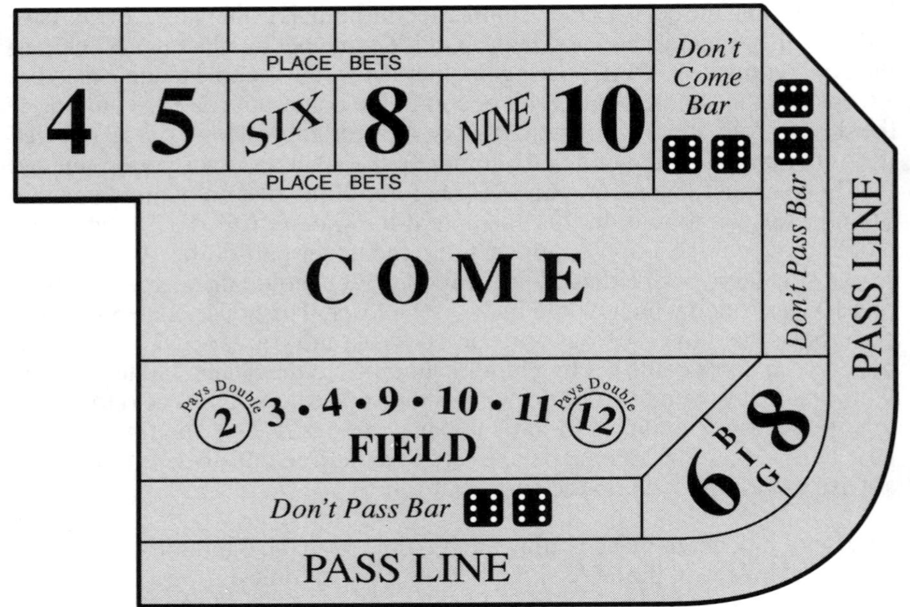

Enlargement of right side of craps layout

When making a place bet you don't have to bet more than one number and you don't have to bet the same amount on each number. You should, however, make sure that you always bet in multiples of $5 whenever you bet on the 4,5,9 or 10 and in multiples of $6 whenever you bet the 6 and 8. This will allow you to always get the full payoff on your bet. If, for example, you bet $3 on the 6 and you won you would only get back even-money, or $3, rather than the $3.50 which your bet should have paid and this results in an even bigger advantage for the casino. Another thing about place bets is that, unlike pass line bets, you can remove your place bets at any time and you do that by telling the dealer you want your bet down and he will take your chips off the table and return them to you. You could also tell the dealer that you didn't want your bet to be working on any particular roll or rolls and you do this by saying for example "off on the 5." The dealer would then put a little button on top of your bet that said "off" and he would remove it when you told him you wanted that number working again.

When we spoke about come bets before I mentioned that come bets are always working on every roll, but that's not the case with place bets because place bets are never working on the come-out roll. If you wanted to, however, you could ask for your place bet to be working on the come out roll by telling the dealer you wanted it working and he would place a button on top of your bet that said "on" to show that your bet was working on the come-out roll.

One last point about place bets is that when you win the dealer will want to know what you want to do for your next bet and you have three choices: if you want to make the same bet just say "same bet" and the dealer will give you your winning chips and leave your original place bet on the table. If you don't want to bet again, just say "take it down" and the dealer will return your place bet along with your winnings. And if you want to double your bet just say "press it" and the dealer will add your winning chips to your other place bet and return any extra chips to you. For example, if you won a $10 place bet on the 5 the dealer would have to give you back $14 in winning chips. If you said "press it" the dealer would add $10 to your place bet and return the remaining $4 in chips to you.

Besides, place betting there is also another way to bet that one of the point numbers will show up before a 7 does and that's called buying a number. A buy bet is basically the same as a place bet except you have to pay a commission of 5% of the amount of your bet and then if you win, the casino will pay you at the true odds. When making a buy bet you should always remember to bet at least $20 because 5% of $20 is $1 and that's the minimum amount the casino will charge you. The reason for the $1 minimum is because that's the smallest denomination chip they have at the craps table and they won't make change for anything under $1. The casino edge on any buy bet for $20 works out to 4.76% so let's take a look at a chart that shows the difference between buying and placing the point numbers.

Point Number	Casino Edge Buy Bet	Casino Edge Place Bet
4 or 10	4.76%	6.67%
5 or 9	4.76%	4.00%
6 or 8	4.76%	1.52%

As you can see the only numbers that you would want to buy rather than place are the 4 and 10 because the 4.76% edge on a buy bet is lower than the 6.67% edge on a place bet. For 5 and 9 the 4.76% edge on a buy bet is slightly worse than the 4.00% edge on a place bet and for the 6 and 8 the 4.76% is a hefty three times higher than the 1.52% edge on the place bet.

To buy the 4 or 10 you would just put your chips down on the layout and tell the dealer what bet you wanted to make. For example, if you put down $21 and said "buy the 10." The dealer will then keep the $1 chip for the house and put your $20 in the same area as the place bets but he'll put a button on top that says "buy" to let him know that you bought the number rather than placed it. Buy bets, just like place bets, can be removed at any time and are always off on the come-out roll. Also, if you do remove your buy bet you will get your 5% commission back.

Besides buy bets where you're betting with the shooter and hoping that a point number will appear before a 7 does, there are also lay bets where you're doing just the opposite - you're betting against the shooter and hoping that a 7 will appear before a point number does.

Lay bets are also paid at the true odds and you have to pay a 5% a commission of the amount you will win rather than the amount you're betting. Once again, when making a lay bet you should always remember to make them based on a minimum payoff of $20 because 5% of $20 is $1 and that's the minimum amount the casino will charge you.

Lay Number	Payoff	Casino Edge
4 or 10	$40 for $20	2.44%
5 or 9	$30 for $20	3.23%
6 or 8	$24 for $20	4.00%

For 4 and 10 you'll have to lay $40 to win $20 and the casino edge is 2.44%; for the 5 and 9 you'll have to lay $30 to win $20 and the casino edge is 3.23%; and for the 6 and 8 you'll have to lay $24 to win $20. The casino edge on that bet is 4.00%.

To make a lay bet you would just put your chips down on the layout and tell the dealer what you wanted to bet. For example, if you put down $41 and said "lay the 10." The dealer would then keep the $1 chip for the house and put your $40 in the same area as the don't come bets but he'll put a button on top that says "buy" to let him know that it's a lay bet. Lay bets, unlike buy bets, are always working on come-out rolls. Lay bets are, however, similar to buy bets in that they can be removed at any time and if you do remove your lay bet you will also receive your 5% commission back.

There are only a few other bets left located on the ends of the table to discuss and two of them are the big 6 and the big 8 which are both very bad bets. To bet the big 6 you place a chip in the big 6 box and then if the shooter rolls a 6 before rolling a 7 you win even money, or $1 for every $1 you bet. To bet the big 8 the same rules would apply: you put your bet in the box and then hope that the shooter rolls an 8 before rolling a 7 so you could win even money on your bet. The big 6 and big 8 can both be bet at any time and both are always working, even on the come-out roll. The casino edge on both the big 6 and the big 8 is 9.1%, which is the biggest edge we've seen so far. But, if you think back about some of the other bets we discussed doesn't this bet sound familiar? It should. This bet is the exact same as a place bet on the 6 or 8, but instead of getting paid off at 7-to-6 we're only getting paid off at even-money! Why would you want to bet the big 6 or big 8 at a house edge of more than 9% instead of making a place bet on the 6 or 8 at a house edge of only 1.5%? The answer is you wouldn't - so don't ever make this bet because it's a sucker bet that's only for people who don't know what they're doing.

The last bet we have to discuss on the player's side of the table is the field bet which is a one-roll bet that will pay even money if a 3,4,9,10 or 11 is rolled and 2-to-1 if a 2 or 12 is rolled. To make a field bet you would just place your chip anywhere in the field box and at first glance it doesn't seem like a bad bet. After all, there are 7 numbers you can win on and only 4 numbers you can lose on!

The only problem is that there are 20 ways to roll the 4 losing numbers and only 16 ways to roll the 7 winning numbers and even after factoring in the double payoff for the 2 and 12 the casino winds up with a hefty 5.6% advantage. In some casinos they pay 3-to-1 on the 2 (or the 12) which cuts the casino edge in half to a more manageable 2.8%, but as you've seen there are still much better bets you can make. By the way, if you win on a field bet the dealer will put your winning chips right next to your bet so it's your responsibility to pick them up, or else they'll be considered a new bet!

Now, let's take a look at some of the long-shots, or proposition bets in the center of the table. When you look at these bets one of the first things you'll notice is that, unlike the bets on the other side of the table, the winning payoffs are clearly labeled. The reason they do that is so you can see those big payoffs and want to bet them, but as you'll see, although the payoffs are high, so are the casino advantages.

All of the proposition bets are controlled by the stickman and he is the person who must make those bets for you. So, if you wanted to make a $1 bet on "any craps" you would throw a $1 chip to the center of the table and say "$1 any craps" and the stickmen would place that bet in the proper area for you. Then if you won, the stickman would tell the dealer at your end of the table to pay you. You should also be aware that they will only pay you your winnings and keep your original bet in place. If you don't want to make the same bet again, you should tell the stickman that you want your bet down and it will be returned to you.

There are only four proposition bets that are not one-roll bets and they are known as the "hardways." They are the hard 4, hard 6, hard 8 and hard 10. To roll a number the hardway means that the number must be rolled as doubles. For example 3 and 3 is a hard 6, but a roll of 4-2, or 5-1 are both called an easy 6, because they are easier to roll than double 3's.

To win a bet on hard 10 the shooter has to roll two 5's before rolling a 7 or an easy 10 such as 6-4 or 4-6. To win a bet on hard 4 the shooter has to roll two 2's before rolling a 7 or an easy 4 such as 3-1 or 1-3. The true odds of rolling a hard 4 or hard 10 are 8-to-1, but the casino will only pay you 7-to-1 which works out to a casino advantage of 11.1% on both of these bets.

To win a bet on hard 6 the shooter must roll two 3's before rolling a 7 or an easy 6 such as 5-1, 1-5; or 4-2, 2-4. To win a bet on hard 8 the shooter must roll two 4's before rolling a 7 or an easy 8 such as 6-2, 2-6 or 5-3, 3-5. The true odds of rolling a hard 6 or hard 8 are 10-to-1, but the casino will only pay you 9-to-1 which works out to a casino advantage of 9.1% on both of these bets.

As noted before, all of the other proposition bets are one-roll bets which means that the next roll of the dice will decide whether you win or lose. As you'll see, the house edge on all of these bets is very high and they should all be avoided.

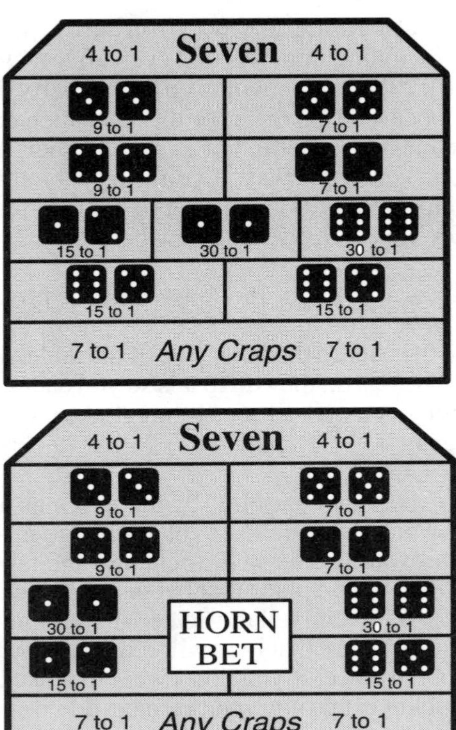

Two different types of proposition bets layouts

For the any craps bet you will win if a 2,3,or 12 is thrown on the next roll and lose if any other number comes up. The true odds are 8-to-1 but the casino will only pay you at 7-to-1 which gives them an edge of 11.1% on this bet and you'll notice that the stickman can put your bet either in the any craps box or, more likely, he'll put it on the circled marked "C" which stands for craps. The reason your bet will be placed in the "C" circle is that it's put in the circle that corresponds to where you're standing at the table and it makes it easier for the stickman to know who that bet belongs to.

For a craps 2 bet you win if the next roll is a 2 and lose if any other number shows up. The true odds are 35-to-1 but the casino will only pay you 30-to-1 which means that the edge on this bet is 13.9% In some casinos the odds for this bet will be shown as 30-for-1 which is actually the same as 29-to-1 and this results in an even bigger edge of 16.7% for the casino

A craps 12 bet works the same as a craps 2 bet, except that now you will only win if a 12 is thrown. Again, the true odds are 35-to-1 but you will only be paid at 30-to-1 which means the casino edge on this bet is the same 13.9% as in the last craps 2 bet. Also if the bet is shown on the layout as 30-for-1 the casino edge is raised to 16.7%

For a craps 3 bet you will only win if the next throw is a 3. The true odds are 17-to-1, but the casino will only pay you 15-to-1 which results in a casino advantage of 11.1% Once again, in some casinos the payoff will be shown as 15-for-1 which is the same as 14-to-1 and the house edge in that casino is an even higher 16.7%

The 11 bet is similar to the craps 3 bet, except that now the only number you can win on is 11. The true odds of rolling an 11 are 17-to-1, but the casino will only pay you 15-to-1 which gives them an 11.1% advantage. Additionally, if the payoff is shown on the layout as 15-for-1 rather than 15-to-1 the casino edge will be even higher at 16.7% By the way, because 11 sounds so much like 7 you will always hear 11 referred to at the table as "yo" or "yo-leven" to eliminate any confusion as to what number you are referring to. So, if you wanted to bet $5 on 11 you would throw a $5 chip to the stickman and say "$5 yo" and then he will either place it in the 11 box or place it on top of the "E" circle that corresponds to where you're standing at the table.

With a horn bet you are betting on the 2,3,11 and 12 all at once. A horn bet has to be made in multiples of $4 because you're making 4 bets at one time and you'll win if any one of those 4 numbers shows up on the next roll. You'll be paid off at the odds for the number that came in and you'll lose the rest of your chips. For example, if you make an $8 horn bet, this is the same as betting $2 on the 2, $2 on the 3, $2 on the 11 and $2 on the 12. If the number 2 came in you would get paid off at 30-to-1 so you would get back $60 in winnings and the casino would keep the $6 that you lost for the three $2 bets on the 3,11 and 12. The only advantage of a horn bet is that it allows you to make 4 bad bets at once rather than one at a time.

The last proposition bet we have to look at is also the worst bet on the craps table and it's the any 7 bet. With this bet you win if a 7 is rolled and lose if any other number comes up. The true odds are 5-to-1, but the casino will only pay you at 4-to-1 which gives them an edge of 16.7%

So there you have it! We've gone over all the possible bets you can make and now it's time to tell you how to win at the game of craps. Unfortunately, as you've seen, craps is a negative expectation game which means that every bet you make has a built-in advantage for the house. Actually, there is one bet that the casino has no advantage on and do you remember the name of that one? That's right it's the free odds bet and it's great that the casino has no advantage on that bet but the only way you're allowed to make that bet is to first make a negative expectation bet on pass/don't pass or come/don't come, so in essence, there are no bets you can make where you have an advantage over the house and in the long run the game of craps is unbeatable.

So, if that's the case then how do you win? Well, in reality there is only one way to win in craps and that way is to get lucky! Of course, this is easier said than done, but you will find it much easier to come out a winner if you only stick to the bets that offer the casino its lowest edge and those are the only bets you should ever make.

If you want to bet with the shooter I suggest you make a pass line bet, back it up with the free odds and then make a maximum of two come bets that are also both backed up with free odds. For example if double odds are allowed, you could start with a $5 pass line bet and say a 4 is rolled. You would then put $10 behind the line on your 4 and make a $5 come bet. If the shooter then rolled an 8 you would take $10 in odds on your come bet on the 8 and make another $5 come bet. If the shooter then rolled a 5 you would take $10 in odds on your come bet on the 5 and then stop betting. The idea here is that you always want to have a maximum of three numbers working and once you do, you shouldn't make anymore bets until one of your come numbers hits, in which case you would make another come bet, or if your pass line bet wins and then you would follow that up with another pass line bet. The important thing to remember is not to make more than two come bets because you don't want to have too much out on the table if the shooter rolls a 7. By using this betting system you'll only be giving the casino an edge of around .60% on all of your bets and with just a little bit of luck you can easily walk away a winner.

If you wanted to be a little more aggressive with this betting system there are some modifications you could make such as making a maximum of three come bets rather than two, or you could add place bets on the 6 and 8. Remember that a place bet on either the 6 or 8 only gives the casino a 1.52% advantage and that makes them both the next best bets after pass/don't pass and come/don't come. To add the place bets you would start off the same as before, but after you've made your second come bet you would look at the 6 and 8 and if they weren't covered you would then make a $6 place bet on whichever one was open or on both. By adding the place bets on the 6 and 8 you would always have at least three numbers in action and you could have as many as five covered at one time.

One final option with this system is to gradually increase the amount of your pass line and come bets by 50%, or by doubling them, and then backing them up with full odds, but I would only suggest you do this if you've been winning for awhile because it could get very expensive if the table was cold and no one was rolling many numbers. Of course, if the table got real cold you could always change your strategy by betting against the shooter and the strategy for that is basically just the opposite of the one I just told you about.

To bet against the shooter you would start with a $5 don't pass bet which you would back up with single free odds and then bet a maximum of two don't come bets that are both backed up with single odds. The reason you don't want to back up your bets with double odds is because when you're betting against the shooter you have to lay the odds which means you're putting up more money than you'll be getting back and, once again, it could get very expensive if a shooter got on a hot roll and made quite a few passes.

For an example of this system let's say you start with a $5 don't pass bet and a 4 is rolled. You would then lay the odds by putting $10 next to your $5 don't pass bet and then make a $5 don't come bet. If the shooter then rolled an 8 you would lay $6 in odds on your don't come bet on the 8 and make another $5 don't come bet. If the shooter then rolled a 5 you would lay $9 in odds on your come bet on the 5 and then stop betting. The idea here is that you always want to have a maximum of three numbers working and once you do, you shouldn't make anymore bets until one of your don't come numbers wins, in which case you would make another don't come bet, or if your don't pass bet wins and then you would follow that up with another don't pass bet. Once again, the important thing to remember is not to make more than two don't come bets because you don't want to have too much out on the table if the shooter gets hot and starts to roll a lot of numbers. With this system you'll always have a maximum of three numbers in action and you'll only be giving the casino an edge of about .80% on all of your bets. Some options to bet more aggressively with this system are to increase your free odds bets to double odds rather than single odds and also to make three don't come bets, rather than stopping at two. The choice is up to you but remember that because you must lay the odds and put out more money than you'll be getting back you could lose a substantial amount rather quickly if the roller got hot and made a lot of point numbers.

Now, one last point I want to make about betting craps is that the bankroll you'll need is going to be much bigger than the bankroll you'll need for playing any other casino game. If you're betting with the shooter you'll have one $5 pass line bet with double odds and two come bets with double odds which means that you could have as much as $45 on the table that could be wiped out with the roll of a 7. If you're betting against the shooter you'll have $5 on don't pass with single odds and two don't come bets with single odds which means you could have as much as $44 on the table that could be wiped out if the shooter got on a "hot" roll and made a lot of numbers. As I said before, you need to have an adequate bankroll to be able to ride out the losing streaks that can happen and you need to be able to hold on until things turn around and you start to win.

So how much of a bankroll is enough? Well, I would say about 7 times the maximum amount of money you'll have out on the table is adequate and 10 times would be even better. In both of our examples then you should have a bankroll of at least $300. If you don't have that much money to put out on the table then you might want to consider having lees money out on the table by making only one come or don't come bet rather than two or maybe even just limiting your bets to pass and don't pass along with the free odds.

Just remember that it doesn't matter whether you want to bet with the shooter or against the shooter - both of these systems will give you the best chance of winning because they allow the casino only the slightest edge and with a little bit of luck you can easily come out a winner. Good luck!

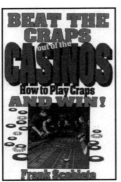

Craps and Comps

by Larry Edell

Most people look at craps as a negative expectation game and, even though playing is a lot of fun, they maintain that in the long run, you always lose at craps. There is, however, one way that you can almost always win at craps - but you have to take full advantage of the extra "perks" offered by the casinos - called "comps," or complimentaries to do it. And now, with some casinos offering "double comps," craps is quickly becoming one of the most profitable games ever for the knowledgeable player!

The first thing to consider before playing craps is your choice of casino. You should choose one that gives you credit for "spread" instead of "bet." For example, if you wager $10 pass, $12 6 & 8 and $5 field, you will be counted as a $10 player at "individual bet" casinos, but at the casinos that give you credit for "spread," you will be a $40 player - and get lots more comps!

It is also important to play where you get maximum odds on pass/come and don't pass/ don't come bets. If you normally play at the $25 level and make a pass line bet and take 2X odds you will have $75 in play. If you win, for example, on a four point you will get back $25 for your flat bet and $100 for your odds or a total of $125.

However if you play at a $5 minimum 20X odds casino, you can make a pass line bet for $5, take $70 in odds, and get back $5 for the flat bet and $140 for the odds, a total of $145! You bet the same amount of money but win $20 more!

You should try to find a casino that gives you at least 5X odds and comp credit on those odds. Just call your favorites on their 800 numbers and ask for a "casino host" - he's in charge of comps and he will be happy to answer any questions for you! Be sure to ask him about a credit application - having credit at a casino means you're a serious player, and it will improve your comp status.

When you play for four hours a day with $25 bets, the casino will usually give you a comped room. If you play at the $50 level you could get free room, food, shows and beverages! Now let's look a little closer at this. The value of a good meal or show for two is at least $50, and sometimes quite a bit more. If you eat twice a day for three days and see two shows, this means you will have $350 in comps! Plus, if your hotel's weekend rate is $150 per night and you stay there for two nights, this gives you $300 for the rooms and $350 for the meals and shows - a total of $650 EXTRA for just playing craps the way you normally would! Following is a chart listing some of the comps available at typical casinos:

AverageBet	Hours Per Day	Complimentaries Extended
$25	4	room only
$50	4	room & limited food/beverage
$75	4	unlimited food & beverage
$100	4	RFB & $150 airfare reimbursement
$125	4	RFB & $250 airfare reimbursement
$150	4	RFB & $400 airfare reimbursement
$175	4	RFB & $575 airfare reimbursement
$200	4	RFB & $750 airfare reimbursement

Double comps is a fairly new development, brought on by the intense competition between the larger hotels such as Hilton, Starwood, Holiday Inn, and others. When you stay at casinos owned by the larger chains, you can get "frequent visitor" points, and use these points for free stays at other hotels in the chain. In order to apply for this, you would call the hotel first on their 800 number, and request an application form, which you usually can fax back to save time. You'll usually receive a temporary number right away, and then, a few weeks later, a permanent card similar to your comp card. When you arrive at the hotel just present this card when you check in. As in gambling comps, the rewards vary - some hotels will give you a free room for five complete stays and some for any five days - a big difference!

Let's see now what a real difference comps can make. Let's say you don't have a comp card and bring $1,000 (along with your family) to play pass line with two come bets. At the end of the three day weekend you're ahead $100 playing craps, because you stuck to your system and played very conservatively. But, you've also spent $400 on food, $100 on drinks, $100 on two shows, and $300 on two nights lodging. So $900 was spent for food ($400), drinks ($100), shows ($100), and lodging ($300).

You left with $1,000 and came home with only $100, even though you won! Now let's say you have a comp card, and bring $1,000 with you, and play pass line and two come bets. You still play conservatively and win $100 over a three day weekend. But this time, you get a free room, two free shows, and all your food and drinks free, so you save all of these expenses. Instead of going home with $100, you go home with $1,100 - You not only made money but gave your family a terrific free vacation! And if you go to a hotel that offers "double comps" you've got some credit for a future stay also!

So remember- Before you play, you should plan on maximizing your comps by utilizing four methods - (1) Choose a casino for comp credits based on spread, not bet. (2) Get maximum odds and credit for those odds. (3) Apply For Casino Credit, and, (4) Join the casino's frequent visitor program so you get "double comps." And, as always, good luck at the tables!

Larry Edell is the publisher of "The Crapshooter," the only newsletter devoted to the game of craps. See page 142 ordering information.

Craps Bets - Good, Bad & Ugly

by Henry Tamburin

Craps is a unique casino game because it contains some of the best, and also some of the worst, casino bets. It's important you know the difference if you are serious about winning.

The Good Bets

The best bets on the craps layout are the ones in which the casino's edge is 1.5% or less. Play smart and you can lower that edge to under 0.5%. A game this close over the short term can be beat!

The best bets are: pass line and don't pass, come and don't come, the odds bet, and a place bet on the 6 or 8. The casino's edge for the basic pass line or come bet (and opposite don't pass and don't come) is 1.4%. The place bet on the 6 and 8 is 1.5%. Although we can't lower the house edge on the place bet we can lower it on the pass and come (and opposite don't pass and don't come) by making the odds bet.

Nowadays, because of fierce casino competition for craps players, casinos allow players to make an odds bet equal to double, triple, five, 10 and even 100 times the amount of their pass line bet. Thus, a player who wagers $3 on the pass line could wager a maximum of $300 in odds! The casino's edge on this bet is reduced to about 0.021% Folks, it just doesn't get any lower than this unless you want to learn how to card count in blackjack. The following table shows the relationship of the casino's edge with the amount of odds.

Casino's Edge

pass line	1.4%
single odds	0.8%
double odds	0.6%
triple odds	0.5%
5 times odds	0.3%
10 times odds	0.2%
20 times odds	0.1%
100 times odds	0.02%

One caveat, however, if you decide to bet 5, 10, 20 or more times odds. Although this will reduce the casino's edge, it also will increase the amount of money you have on the layout. One roll of 7 and you'll lose the pass line and odds. Therefore, you need to have more of a bankroll when you start betting large amounts in odds. Or, you can start off betting single odds and then when you win, keep the size of the pass line bet the same but increase your odds bet to double. Win again and increase to triple odds and so forth. This technique for getting more money on the layout during a hot roll on a bet where the casino has no advantage is thoroughly explained in my book, *Craps: Take The Money and Run.*

The Bad Bets

These craps bets have a casino edge from 2.4 to 6.7%. Although this is not intolerable why make bets with this high of a casino edge when you can make the good bets with a lot lower casino edge?

The bad bets include (casino edge in parenthesis): lay 4 or 10 (2.4%); lay 5 or 9 (3.2%); place 5 or 9 (4.0%); lay 6 or 8 (4.0%); buy bets (4.8%); field (5.6%); and place 4 or 10 (6.7%).

The Ugly Bets

Now we come to the ugly or what I also call the sucker bets of craps. Why? Because here are the bets which command a casino's edge from 9.0% up to a stratospheric 16.7%. If you like throwing your money away, here are the bets for you: big 6 and 8 (9.1%); hardway 6 or 8 (9.1%); hardway 4 and 10 (11.1%); any craps (11.1%); 11 or 3 proposition (11.1%); 2 or 12 proposition (13.9%); and any seven (16.7%). You can also throw the hop bets, horn bets, world bets, and insurance type bets into this category of sucker bets.

It's no secret that to be a winner in craps you must make only those bets that have a low casino edge, increase your bet size as you win consecutive bets to take advantage of a hot roll, and learn when to take the money and run. This is the basics of winning craps play and to start, make only the best bets on the craps table and stay away from those bad and ugly bets. It is the key to being a consistent winning craps player.

Henry Tamburin is the author of the book "Craps: Take The Money and Run" and is featured in the video "Craps - Rolling To Win." You can visit his web site at http://www.smartgaming.com. Ordering information for his series of books and videos can be found on page 178.

Roulette

by Steve Bourie

Virtually all American casinos use a double-zero roulette wheel which has pockets numbered from 1 to 36, plus 0 and 00 for a total of 38 pockets. This is in contrast to Europe where a single-zero wheel is used and the game has always been the most popular in the casino.

There are usually six seats at the roulette table and to help the dealer differentiate what each player is betting every player is assigned a different color chip which they purchase right at the table. Each table has its own minimum chip values and that information is usually posted on a sign at the table. As an example let's say a table has a $1 minimum chip value. This means that when you give the dealer your money the colored chips he gives you in return must have a minimum value of $1 each. So, if you gave the dealer $50 he would ask what value you wanted on the chips and if you said $1 he would give you 50 colored chips.

If you prefer, you could say you wanted the chips valued at $2 each and he would just give you 25 chips rather than 50. You can make the value of your colored chips anything you want and you'll notice that when the dealer gives you your chips he'll put one of your chips on the railing near the wheel with a marker on top to let him know the value of your chips. Later on when you're done playing at that table you must exchange your colored chips for regular chips before leaving. The colored chips have no value anywhere else in the casino so don't leave the table with them.

Besides the minimum chip value, there is also a minimum amount that must be bet on each spin of the wheel. Once again, the minimums are probably posted on a sign at the table and if it says $2 minimum inside and $5 minimum outside this means that if you are betting on any of the 38 numbers that pay 35-to-1 the total of all your bets must be $2. You could make two different $1 bets or one $2 bet, it doesn't matter except that the total of all your bets on the numbers must be at least $2. The $5 minimum outside means that any of the outside bets that pay 2-to-1, or even money, require that you bet $5 each time. On the outside bets you can't make a $3 bet and a $2 bet to meet the minimums - you have to bet at least $5 every time. After you've exchanged your cash for colored chips you're ready to place your first bet so, let's see what your options are:

You can make a ***straight*** bet where you only bet on one number and if it comes in you'll be paid 35-to-1. The casino advantage on this bet is 5.26% and by the time you're done with this roulette section I'm sure you'll be very familiar with that number.

Another choice you have is to do a ***split***. This is where you put a chip on the line that separates two numbers. If either number comes up you'll be paid at 17-to-1. The casino advantage on this bet is 5.26%.

If you put a chip in an area that splits 4 numbers this is called a ***corner*** bet and if any one of those 4 numbers comes in you will be paid off at 8-to-1. The casino advantage on this bet is 5.26%.

If you put a chip at the beginning of a row of 3 numbers, this is called a ***street*** bet and if any one of those 3 numbers shows up you will be paid off at 11-to-1. The casino advantage on this bet is 5.26%.

You can also put a chip on the line between two streets so that you have a ***double street*** covered and if any one of those 6 numbers come in you'll be paid off at 5-to-1. The casino advantage on this bet is?... you guessed it...5.26%.

The only other bet you can make on the inside numbers is the ***5- number*** bet where you place one chip in the upper left corner of the number 1 box. If any one of those 5 numbers comes in you'll be paid off at 6-to-1 and what do you think the casino advantage is on this bet? Nope, I gotcha... it's 7.89%. Actually, this is the worst possible bet on the roulette table and the only bet you'll come across that doesn't have a 5.26% house edge on the double-zero roulette wheel. You should never make this bet.

One quick word here about "to" and "for" when discussing odds. Whenever the odds are stated as "to" this means that in addition to the stated payoff you also receive your original bet back. In other words, if you won your single number bet in roulette you would receive 35-to-1, which is a 35-chip payoff, plus you'd still keep your original one-chip bet, so you end up with 36 chips. Now if the odds are stated as "for" that means you do not receive back your original bet. If the odds in your single number bet were 35-*for*-1 you would still receive a 35-chip payoff but the casino would keep your original one-chip bet so you would only end up with 35 chips. The only place in a casino where the odds are always stated as "for" is in video poker. You might also come across it on a couple of craps bets where the odds are stated as "for-one" rather than "to-one" in order to give the casino a slightly better edge.

Now, getting back to our roulette examples, let's look at all of the outside bets that you can make and keep in mind that the house edge on all of these outside bets is...do you remember the number?...that's right...5.26%.

There are three bets you can make that will pay you even money, or 1-to-1, which means that if you win, you will get back one dollar for every dollar you bet:

Red or black - If you put a chip on red then a red number must come up in order for you to win. If the ball lands on a black number, 0 or 00 - you lose. The same thing goes for black - you lose if it comes in red, 0 or 00 and you win if the ball lands on a black number.

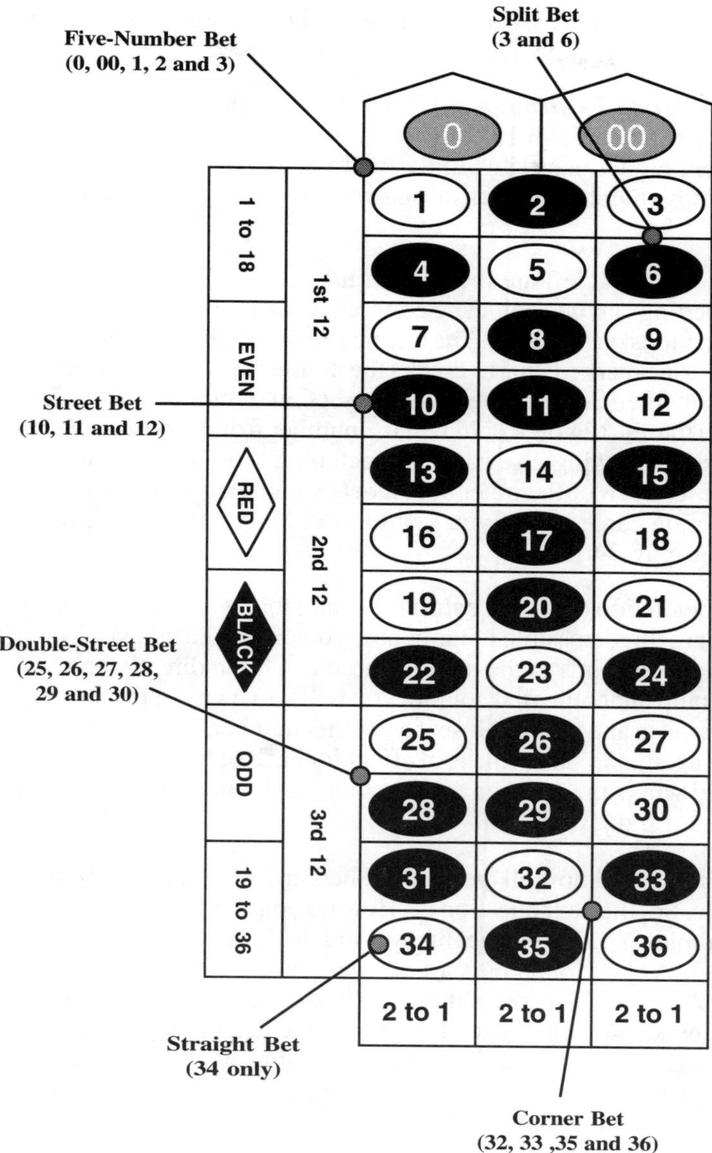

Typical felt layout for placing bets on American double-zero roulette wheel

Odd or even **-** If you put a chip on odd then the ball must land on an odd number in order for you to win. If it lands on 0, 00, or an even number - you lose. If you bet on even, you win if an even number shows up and lose if the ball lands on 0, 00 or an odd number.

1 through 18 and 19 through 36 **-** If you bet on 1 through 18, then you win if a number from 1 through 18 comes in and you lose if the ball lands on 0, 00 or a number higher than 18. Similarly, if you bet on 19 through 36, you win if one of those numbers comes in and you lose on 0, 00 or any number lower than 19.

The only other bets left are the ***dozens*** and columns bets. If you look at the roulette betting layout you can see three areas that each correspond to 12-number sections on the table. The one marked 1st 12 covers the numbers from 1 to 12, the one marked 2nd 12 covers the numbers from 13 to 24 and the other one that's marked 3rd 12 covers the last section of numbers from 25 to 36. If you bet on the 1st 12 you would win if a number from 1 to 12 came in and you would lose if anything else came in, including 0 or 00. The same principle holds true for each of the other dozen bets where you would win if a number in that section came in and you would lose if anything else showed up. All dozens bets pay 2-to-1.

The last bet to look at is the ***column*** bet and that is also a bet that pays 2-to-1. There are three possible column bets you can make and you'll notice that each area corresponds to the numbers in the column directly above it. So, if you put a chip under the first column you will win if any of the numbers in that column come in and you will lose if any other number, including 0 or 00 shows up. Once again, the same rule is in effect for each of the other columns where you would win if the number appears in the column above your bet and you would lose if it doesn't.

All right, now you know all the possible bets and you know how to make them at the table. So, the next question is "How do you win?" and the answer to that is very simple - You have to get lucky! And that's the ONLY way you can win at roulette. As you found out earlier, every bet, except for the 5-number bet, which I'm sure you'll never make, has a house edge of?...that's right...5.26%. So, feel free to put your chips all over the table and then just hope that you're lucky enough to have one of your numbers come up. You see, it just doesn't matter what you do because you'll always have that same house edge of 5.26% working against you on every bet you make.

Now, you may have heard of a system for roulette where you should place your bets only on the numbers that are evenly spaced out around the wheel. For example, if you wanted to play only four numbers, you could bet on 1,2,31 and 32 because when you looked at a roulette wheel, you would notice that if you divided it into four equal parts, you would have a number that appears in each of the four sections. So, is this a good system? Well, actually it's no better and no worse than any other roulette system. The fact is that it's purely a matter of chance where the ball happens to land and it makes no difference whether the numbers you choose are right next to each other or evenly spaced out on the wheel. Each number has an equal chance to occur on every spin of the wheel and the house edge always remains at 5.26%.

You can probably tell that I wouldn't recommend roulette as a good game to play because there are other games that offer much better odds, but if you really insist on playing the game I have three good suggestions for you. #1 - Go to Atlantic City! In Atlantic City if you make an even-money outside bet, like red or black, odd or even, 1 through 18 or 19 through 36 and if 0 or 00 come up, the state gaming regulations allow the casino to take only half of your bet. Because you only lose half of your bet this also lowers the casino edge on these outside bets in half to 2.63%. This rule is only in effect for even-money bets so keep in mind that on all other bets the house edge still remains at that very high 5.26%.

The second suggestion I have for you also involves some travel and here it is: Go to Europe! The game of roulette began in Europe and many casinos over there use a single-zero wheel which makes it a much better game because the house edge on a single-zero roulette wheel is only 2.70%. To make it even better, they have a rule called "en prison" which is similar to the Atlantic City casino rule. If you make an even-money outside bet and the ball lands on 0 you don't lose right away. Instead, your bet is "imprisoned" and you have to let it ride on the next spin. Then, if your bet wins, you can remove it from the table. Because of this rule, the casino edge on this bet is cut in half to 1.35% which makes it one of the best bets in the casino and almost four times better than the same bet when it's made on a standard double-zero roulette wheel in the United States.

Now, if you're not into traveling and you don't think you can make it to Atlantic City or Europe, then you'll just have to settle for suggestion #3 which is: Win quickly! Naturally, this is easier said than done, but in reality, if you want to win at roulette the best suggestion I can give you is that you try to win quickly and then walk away from the table because the longer you continue to bet the longer that big 5.26% house edge will keep eating away at your bankroll. One major principle of gambling is that in order to win you must only play the games that have the lowest casino edge and, unfortunately, roulette is not one of them.

Before closing out this look at roulette, let's take a minute to examine one of the most famous betting systems of all time and the one that many people frequently like to use on roulette. It's called the Martingale system and it is basically a simple system of doubling your bet whenever you lose. The theory behind it is that sooner or later you'll have to win and thus, you will always come out ahead. As an example, let's say you're playing roulette and you bet $1 on red, if you lose you double your next bet to $2 and if you lose that then you double your next bet to $4 and if you lose that you double your next bet to $8 and so forth until you eventually win. Now, when you finally do win you will end up with a profit equal to your original bet, which in this case is $1. If you started the same system with a $5 bet, you would have to bet $10 after your first loss, $20 after your second loss and so forth, but whenever you won you would end up with a $5 profit.

In theory, this sounds like a good idea but in reality it's a terrible system because eventually you will be forced to risk a great amount of money for a very small profit. Let's face it, even if you only wanted to make a $1 profit on each spin of the wheel, sooner or later you will hit a major losing streak where you will have to bet an awful lot of money just to make that $1 profit. For example, if you go eight spins without a winner, you would have to bet $256 on the next spin and if that lost then you'd have to bet $512. Would you really want to risk that kind of money just to make $1? I don't think so. You may think that the odds are highly unlikely that you would lose that many bets in a row, but eventually it will happen and when it does you will suffer some astronomical losses. One other problem with this system is that eventually you won't be able to double your bet because you will have reached the casino maximum, which in most casinos is $500 on roulette. Just keep in mind that the Martingale system works best when it's played for fun on paper and not for real money in a casino. If it was truly a winning system it would have bankrupted the world's casinos years ago.

Baccarat

by Steve Bourie

When you think of Baccarat you probably think of a game that's played by the casino's wealthiest players who sit at a private table and can afford to bet tens of thousands of dollars on the flip of a card and you know what? You're right! The game of Baccarat has always had a reputation as being for the richest gamblers and that usually scared off the average player, but nowadays more and more people are discovering that Baccarat is really a good game for the small stakes player because 1.-it has a relatively small advantage for the casino and 2.-it's very simple to play.

The mini-Baccarat table is the kind of Baccarat table you're most likely to find in the standard American casino and the game is played pretty much the same as regular Baccarat except that in the mini version all of the hands are dealt out by the dealer and the players never touch the cards. Other than that, the rules are virtually the same. Oh yes, one other difference you'll find is that the betting minimums will always be lower on mini-Baccarat and it's usually pretty easy to find a table with a $5 minimum.

Now, as I said before the game of Baccarat is very simple to play and that's because the only decision you have to make is what bet you want to make from the three that are available: player, banker or tie. After the players make their bets the game begins and two 2-card hands are dealt from a shoe that contains 8 decks of cards. One hand is dealt for the banker and another hand is dealt for the player. The values of the two cards in each hand are added together and the object of the game is to have a total as close to 9 as possible. After the values of the first two cards in each hand are totaled, a third card can be drawn by either the player, the banker or both. But, the decision as to whether or not a third card should be drawn is not decided by the dealer or the players - it is only decided by the rules of the game.

Actually the name Baccarat comes from the Italian word for zero and as you'll see there are lots of zeros in this game because when you add the cards together all of the 10's and all of the face cards are counted as zeros, while all of the other cards from ace though 9 are counted at their face value. So, a hand of Jack, 6 has a total of 6; 10,4 has a total of 4; king, 7 has a total of 7; and ace, queen which would be a great hand in blackjack, only has a total of 1. The other thing about adding the cards together is that no total can be higher than 9. So, if a total is 10 or higher you have to subtract 10 to determine its value. For example, 8,8 totals 16 but you subtract 10 and your total is 6; 9,5 has a total of 4; 8,3 has a total of 1; and 5,5 has a total of 0.

Once again, the object of the game of Baccarat is to have a total as close to 9 as possible, so after the first two cards are dealt if either the player or banker hand has a total of 9 then that's called a “natural” and that hand is the winner. If neither hand has a total of 9 then the next best possible hand is a total of 8 (which is also called a “natural”) and that hand would be the winner. If both the player and the banker end up with the same total then it's a tie and neither hand wins.

Now, if neither hand has an 8 or a 9 then the rules of the game have to be consulted to decide whether or not a third card is drawn. Once that's done, the values of the cards are added together again and whichever hand is closest to a total of 9 is the winner. If both hands end up with the same total then it's a tie and neither hand wins.

If you want to bet on the player hand just put your money in the area marked "player" and if you win you'll be paid off at even-money, or $1 for every $1 you bet. The casino advantage on the player bet is 1.36%. If you want to bet on the banker hand you would place your bet in the area marked "banker" and if you win, you'll also be paid off at even-money, but you'll have to pay a 5% commission on the amount you win. So, if you won $10 on your bet, you would owe a 50¢ commission to the house. The 5% commission is only required if you win and not if you lose. The dealer will keep track of the amount you owe by putting an equal amount in a small area on the table that corresponds to your seat number at the table. So, if you're sitting at seat #3 and won $10 on the bank hand the dealer would pay you $10 and then put 50¢ in the #3 box. This lets him know how much you owe the casino in commissions and when you get up to leave the table you'll have to pay the dealer whatever amount is in that box. After adjusting for that 5% commission the casino advantage on the banker bet is 1.17%

Finally, if you want to bet on a tie you would place your bet in the area marked "tie" and if you win you'll be paid off at 8-to-1, or $8 for every $1 you bet. The big payoff sounds nice but actually this is a terrible bet because the casino advantage is a very high 14.1% and this bet should never be made.

As you've seen, the casino advantage in Baccarat is very low (except for the tie bet) and the rules are set in advance so no decisions are made by either the players or the dealer about how to play the cards. This means that, unlike blackjack where you have to decide whether or not you want another card, you have no decisions to make and no skill is involved. This also means that Baccarat is purely a guessing game, so even if you've never played the game before you can sit at a table and play just as well as anyone who's played the game for 20 years! This is the only game in the casino where this can happen and that's why I tell people that Baccarat is an especially good game for the beginning player because you need no special knowledge to take advantage of those low casino edge bets.

The only part of Baccarat that gets a little confusing is trying to understand the rules concerning the draw of a third card, but remember, the rules are always the same at every table and they'll usually have a printed copy of the rules at

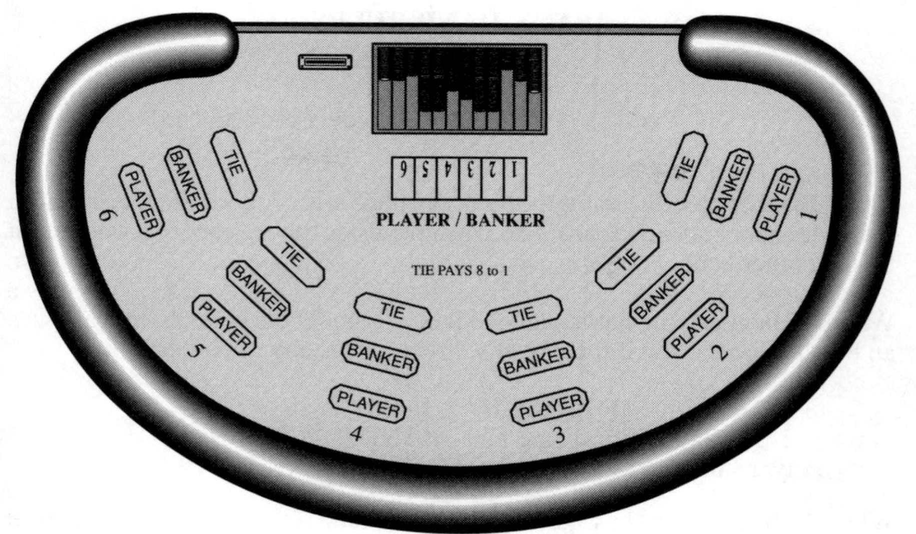

A Sample Mini-Baccarat Table Layout

the table and will give you a copy if you ask for it. After playing the game for awhile you'll start to remember the rules on your own, but until then here's a rundown on how it works:

As noted before, if the first two cards in either hand total 8 or 9, then the game is over and the highest total wins. If the totals are both 8 or both 9 then it's a tie and neither hand wins. For any other total the rules have to be consulted and it's always the player hand that goes first. If the player hand has a total of 6 or 7, it must stand. The only other totals it can possibly have are 0,1,2,3,4 or 5 and for all of those totals it must draw a card.

PLAYER HAND RULES

8,9	STANDS (Natural)
6,7	STANDS
0,1,2,3,4,5	DRAWS

There, that wasn't too hard to understand was it? If the player hand has a total of 6 or 7 it stands and for anything else it has to draw a card. Well, that was the easy part because now it gets a little complicated.

After the player hand is finished the banker hand must take its turn and if its first 2 cards total 0,1 or 2 it must draw a card. If its two cards total 7 it must stand and if the total is 6 it will stand, but only if the player hand did not take a card.

BANK HAND RULES

8,9	STANDS (Natural)
0,1,2	DRAWS
6	STANDS (If player took no card)
7	STANDS

The only other possible totals the bank can have are 3,4,5 or 6 and the decision as to whether or not a 3rd card is drawn depends on the 3rd card that was drawn by the player hand.

When the banker hand has a total of 3 it must stand if the player's 3rd card was an 8 and it must draw if the player's 3rd card was any other card.

IF BANK HAS 3 and

Player's third card is 8 - BANK STANDS
Player's third card is 1,2,3,4,5,6,7,9,10 - BANK DRAWS

When the banker hand has a total of 4 it must stand if the player's 3rd card was a 1,8,9, or 10 and it must draw if the player's 3rd card was any other card.

IF BANK HAS 4 and

Player's third card is 1,8,9,10 - BANK STANDS
Player's third card is 2,3,4,5,6,7 - BANK DRAWS

When the banker hand has a total of 5 it must stand if the player's 3rd card was a 4,5,6 or 7 and it must draw if the player's 3rd card was any other card.

IF BANK HAS 5 and

Player's third card is 4,5,6,7 - BANK STANDS
Player's third card is 1,2,3,8,9,10 - BANK DRAWS

When the banker hand has a total of 6 it must stand if the player's 3rd card was a 6 or 7 and it must draw if the player's 3rd card was any other card.

IF BANK HAS 6 and

Player's third card is 6 or 7 - BANK STANDS
Player's third card is 1,2,3,4,5,8,9,10 - BANK DRAWS

There you have it - those are the rules of Baccarat concerning the draw of a third card. As you saw they were a little complicated, but remember that you don't have to memorize the rules yourself because the dealer will know them and play each hand by those rules, but you can always ask for a copy of the rules at the table to follow along.

Now let's try some sample hands: The player hand has queen,9 for a total of 9 and the banker hand has 4,4 for a total of 8. Which hand wins? Both hands are naturals, but the player hand total of 9 is higher than the banker hand total of 8, so the player hand is the winner.

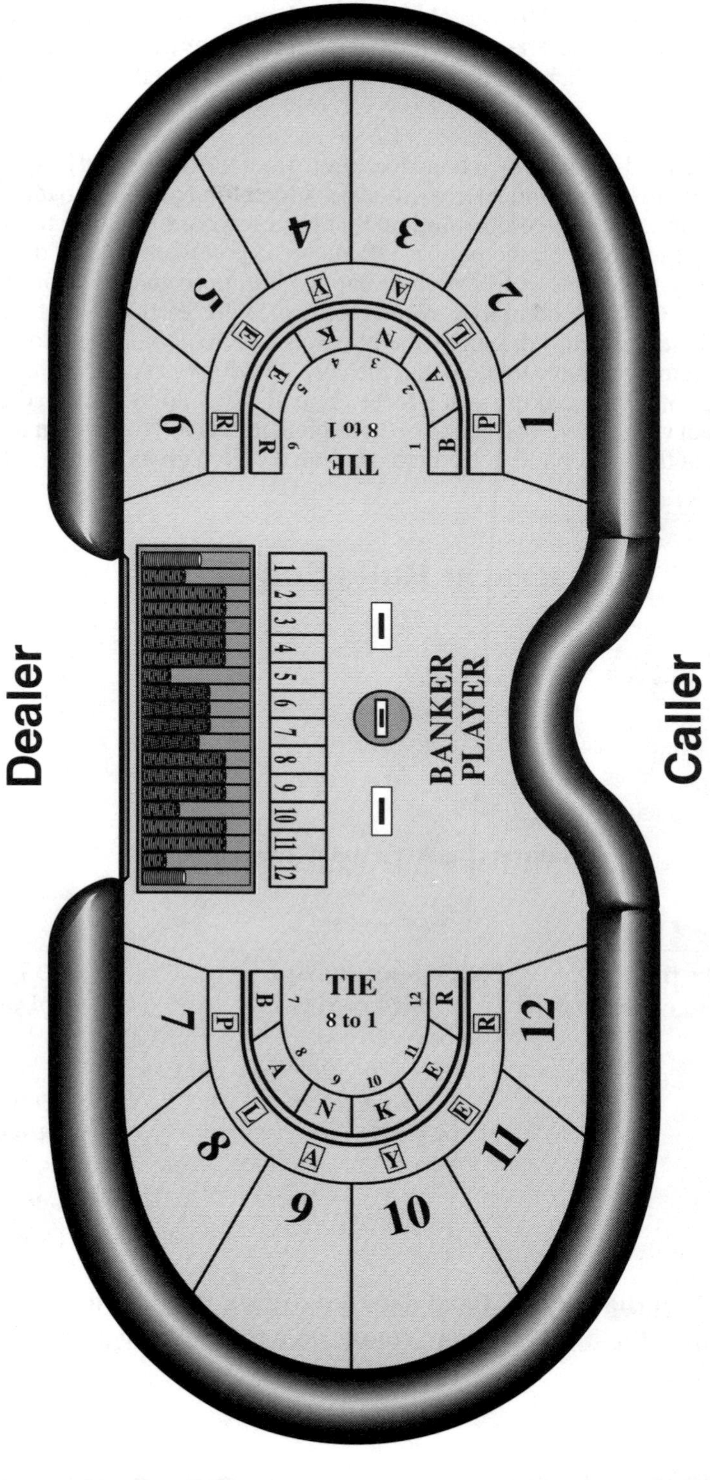

Dealer

Caller

A 12-Seat Baccarat Table Layout

If the player hand has 4,2 for a total of 6 and the banker hand has ace, jack which totals 1, what happens? The player hand must stand on its 6 and the banker hand must always draw when it has a total of 0,1 or 2. Let's say the bank draws a 7 and wins 7 to 6.

What happens when the player hand has king, 5 and the bank hand has 2,4? The player hand must draw and let's say it gets a 7 for a total of 2. The banker hand has a total of 6 and if it could stand on that total it would win because its 6 is higher than the 2 held by the player. Of course, if you were betting on banker that's exactly what you would want to happen but, unfortunately for you, the rules require the bank hand to draw another card whenever its first two cards total 6 and the third card drawn by the player is a 7. So now, instead of having a winning hand you have to hope that the card you draw isn't a 5, which would give you a total of 1 making you a loser. You also wouldn't want to draw a 6 because that would give you a total of 2 which would give you a tie. In this case let's say that the bank hand goes on to draw an 8 which gives it a total of 3 and it wins 3 to 2.

Baccarat Rules Summary

Player Hand

When the first two cards total	
0-1-2-3-4-5	**Draws**
6-7	**Stands**
8-9	**Natural (Banker cannot draw)**

Banker Hand

When the first player's two cards total	DRAWS when player's third card is	STANDS when third card is
0-1-2	**Always Draws**	
3	**1-2-3-4-5-6-7-9-0**	**8**
4	**2-3-4-5-6-7**	**1-8-9-0**
5	**4-5-6-7**	**1-2-3-8-9-0**
6	**6-7**	**1-2-3-4-5-8-9-0**
7		**Stands**
8-9		**Stands (Natural)**

If the Player's hand does not draw a third card, then the Banker's hand stands on a total of 6 or more.

If the player hand has 3,ace for a total of 4 and the banker hand has 8,7 for a total of 5, what happens? The player hand must draw and say it gets a 9 for a total of 3. Once again, the banker hand would like to stand on its total because it would win, but the rules have to be consulted first and in this case when the banker's first 2 cards total 5 and the player's third card drawn is a 9 the banker hand must stand, so the banker hand wins 5 to 3.

Finally, let's say the player hand has 4,3 for a total of 7 and the banker hand has 6,10 for a total of 6. The player hand must always stand on totals of 6 or 7 and the banker hand must also stand on its total of 6 because the player hand didn't take a third card. The player hand wins this one 7 to 6.

All right, now that you know how to play Baccarat we come to the important question which is - how do you win? Well, as I said before, if you bet on player you'll only be giving the casino a 1.36% edge and if you bet on banker you'll be giving the casino an even more modest edge of just 1.17%. While both of these are pretty low edges to give the casino you're still stuck with the fact that the casino will always have an edge over you and in the long run the game of Baccarat is unbeatable. So, if that's the case then how do you win? Well, the answer to that is very simple - You have to get lucky! And that's the ONLY way you can win at Baccarat. Of course, this is easier said than done, but fortunately, in the game of Baccarat, you have the option of making two bets that require no skill and both offer the casino a very low edge especially when you compare them to roulette where the house has a 5.26% advantage on a double-zero wheel and slot machines where the edge is about 8% to 10% I always stress the point that when you gamble in a casino you have to play the games that have the lowest casino edge in order to have the best chance of winning and with that in mind you can see that Baccarat is not that bad a game to play for the recreational gambler.

Now let's take a quick look at one of the most common systems for betting on Baccarat. One thing that many Baccarat players seem to have in common is a belief in streaks and the casinos accommodate these players by providing scorecards at the table that can be used to track the results of each hand. Many players like to bet on whatever won the last hand in the belief that it will continue to come in and they hope for a long streak.

The thinking for these players is that since Baccarat is purely a guessing game it's just like guessing the outcome of a coin toss and chances are that a coin won't alternately come up heads, tails, heads, tails, heads, tails but rather that there will be streaks where the same result will come in for awhile. So, is this a good system? Well, actually, it's no better and no worse than any other system because no matter what you do you'll still have the same casino edge going against you on every bet you make: 1.36% on the player and 1.17% on the banker. The one good thing about a system like this though is that you don't have to sit there and guess what you want to play each time. Instead, you go into the game knowing how you're going to play and you don't have to blame yourself if your guess is wrong, instead you get to blame it on your system!

Blackjack Books by Stanford Wong

One of the World's Leading Experts on Winning at Blackjack

Professional Blackjack - This is the 1994 revision of a classic first published in 1975. In addition to teaching card counting by means of two simple, but powerful methods, this edition includes: strategies for playing new rules such as over/under, simulation results to replace all the "best guesses" of earlier editions, plus tables of expectations. 352 pages; **$19.95**

Basic Blackjack - What blackjack neophytes need is basic strategy. It must be mastered before one goes on to card counting. *Basic Blackjack* has the most complete explanation of basic strategy available anywhere.

Example: In early 1993, blackjack players of Ramada Express in Laughlin were pleasantly surprised to find the casino had decided to pay 3:2 on five-card hands at blackjack. Those customers who had *Basic Blackjack* had only to turn to table 21 to find basic strategy for exploiting this rule.

Basic Blackjack also contains the best of *Winning Without Counting*, an out-of-print book on getting an edge at blackjack without counting cards that initially sold for $200 per copy. 224 pages; **$14.95**

Shipping Charges: $3 for first book and $1 for each additional book

Send Check or Money Order To:
Casino Vacations • P.O. Box 703
Dania, FL • 33004

Credit Card Orders Call Toll-Free:
(800) 741-1596
order online at:
www.americancasinoguide.com

The Baccarat Battle Book by Frank Scoblete

For the first time ever, Frank shows players how to "push the house" to reduce the casino's commission on the Bank bet from five percent to four percent. Frank shows how manipulating the pace of the game can bring more in comps for less risk. He also explains and analyzes many of the most famous betting systems and shows why they leave much to be desired. Then he shows how to utilize his special variations of these systems to reduce the player's exposure to the house edge.

Frank describes the Seven Deadly Sins of Gambling and how to avoid them. Finally, Frank describes his 13 Baccarat Battle Rules for Successful Play. If you play baccarat or want to play baccarat, don't go to the casino until you've read **The Baccarat Battle Book**! 214 Pages **$12.95** + $3 shipping ($1 extra shipping for each additonal book). For credit card orders call toll-free **(800) 741-1596.** Or send check or money order to:

Casino Vacations • P.O. Box 703 • Dania, FL 33004
order online at: **www.americancasinoguide.com**

How Good Are Those "Other" Games?

by Frank Scoblete

When I was a kid I had a friend, Billy, who came from a very large family on his mother's side. I never saw any of his relatives from his father's side. One day I asked him about it. "Oh, I never see those people from the 'other' side. I don't even know most of the people from the 'other' side." He emphasized the word "other" every time he spoke of them. Finally, I caught a glimpse of one of them one day and, you know what, she looked kind of "otherly."

I guess we all have our "others" in this life and the casinos are no different. You have the machines, you have poker, blackjack, craps, and roulette -- those are the standard fares from casino-gambling-times primordial; but then you have all those "other" games. Most "other" games are mutated versions of the traditional games; some evolved naturally, but most have been genetically engineered to look somewhat similar to their forebears with one major difference - they can usually take your money faster either because the house edge is higher or the game is speedier or some combination of both.

In the years that I have been writing about casino gambling, I have seen many "other" games such as Two Up, a coin flipping game; Casino War, the kid's game where high card wins; Russian Roulette, not the gun kind, the card version; Pokette, a combination of roulette and poker; Sic Bo, which is a dice game like Chuck-A-Luck which is a dice game like Mini-Just Dice which is a dice game like Heads and Tails which is a dice game like Sic Bo. I have played countless versions of blackjack: Red and Black, Multiple Action, Jackpot Blackjack, Bonus Blackjack, Over-Under 13 Blackjack, Royal Match and Double Exposure Blackjack. I have also played Red Dog, the casino version of acey-deucy; CrapJack, a combination of blackjack and craps;
BacCraps, a combination of baccarat and craps; Pai Gow, tiles and poker version; Super Pan Nine, the gambling game, not the Chinese combination dinner platter; Hickok's Six Card, a deadly poker variant named after a guy who died playing poker (is it any wonder this game expired?); Double Down Stud, the table game, not the porno movie; Fast Action Hold'em, a poker mutant; Bahamian Baccarat, that's mini-bac without the commission on the Bank bet, and the ubiquitous Big Wheel.

With the exception of the Pai Gow tiles or its poker variation, none of the above games have really caught the fancy of the casino gaming public. Many don't even exist anymore. They are dinosaur dead. However, some games have indeed hung/caught on, establishing niches in many, if not most, casinos and casino venues; and these few survivors have become the official "other" games in the casino pantheon. They are Let It Ride, Caribbean Stud, Three Card Poker, Spanish 21 and the aforementioned Pai Gow poker.

All are mutants of older games but not one has evolved naturally over time, rather each was deliberately created in the laboratory of mad-gambling scientists with one view in mind -- to take our money in as pleasant a way as possible. In fact, all of these "other" games range from decent to very good based on their respective house edges and speeds. So how good are these "other" games? If we judge based on a combination of speed and house edge, we can determine how many average bets we will lose in an hour of playing these games in the long run.

SPANISH 21 - Spanish 21 is the newest table game to generate some heat in casino circles. No wonder. Played with the correct basic strategy, called the Armada Strategy, players can face a house edge of around .8 percent -- which means for every $100 wagered at this game, you can expect to lose a mere 80 cents. Not bad. Of course, Spanish 21 earns much more for the casinos owing to the fact that most players do not know that a completely different basic strategy is called for. Instead, the Spanish 21 players use the basic strategy for regular blackjack, with some homespun variations on occasion, and wind up giving the casinos edges of two, three, four or more percent. Such edges, coupled with the relatively fast speed of the game (anywhere from 60 to 100 hands an hour) can cause players to wind up like the Spanish Armada, in the drink.

Spanish 21 is played exactly like regular blackjack with this difference -- all the 10-spot cards have been removed. The Kings, Queens and Jacks remain. To make up for the reduction in total blackjacks because of the removal of the 10-spots, the casino gives many exciting bonus hands such as:

a. Five-card 21 pays 3 to 2.
b. Six-card 21 pays 2 to 1.
c. Seven (or more)-card 21 pays 3 to 1.
d. A three-card hand of 6-7-8 composed of mixed suits pays 3 to 2.
e. A three-card hand of 6-7-8 composed of the same suit pays 2 to 1.
f. A three-card hand of 6-7-8 composed of all spades pays 3 to 1.
g. A 7-7-7 hand composed of mixed suits pays 3 to 2.
h. A 7-7-7 hand composed of the same suit pays 2 to 1.
i. A 7-7-7 hand composed of all spades pays 3 to 1.
j. A player may surrender the original bet but save the double-down bet. This rule does not apply if the hand is busted. This rule is called the Double-Down Rescue.
k. There is a Jackpot bonus of $1,000 paid to any player who has 7-7-7

of the same suit if the dealer is also showing a 7 (of any suit). When this occurs, all other players at the table receive a bonus of $50. Some casinos make the jackpot $1,000 per five dollars wagered up to a maximum of $5,000 for a $25 or higher bet. This option will appeal to those players who like the idea that a bad run can be dramatically turned around with a quick hit of luck.

Summary: Very Good Game
Loss Per Hour: Approximately one-half average bets.
Qualifier: Must play Armada Strategy.
Playing Tip: Slow the pace whenever possible.

CARIBBEAN STUD - Caribbean Stud sailed to the mainland from the islands, circa the 1980s, and has gotten a very strong foothold on the casino beach fronts. It is a game with a relatively high house edge of 5.3 percent, but as I wrote in *Bold Card Play: Best Strategies for Caribbean Stud, Let It Ride and Three Card Poker* (see ad on page 168), there is another way to figure the house edge at Caribbean Stud that brings it down to 2.6 percent because it includes the total amount bet and not just the initial wager. Caribbean Stud is a moderately paced game of between 45 and 55 decisions per hour.

There are two main wagers in Caribbean Stud -- the "ante" and the "bet." The "bet" area looks like a treasure chest just bursting with gold coins. The "ante" is the rectangular area. Atop the "ante" on the layout is a side bet - the jackpot - that is made by dropping a one-dollar chip in the jackpot slot. When a player opts to place a jackpot bet, he becomes eligible to hit the progressive jackpot (or a percentage thereof) that increases with each hand played. The side jackpot bet is strictly optional and does not influence the winning and losing of hands. To open, the players put a bet in the "ante" square and, if they wish, they can make the one-dollar jackpot bet. The dealer deals five cards face down to each player. The dealer then deals himself five cards, the last one face up. The players now have two choices to make: 1. they can play out their hands, or 2. they can surrender their hands and lose their "antes."

If they decide to play out their hands, they must place a bet that is "double" their "ante" in the "bet" square. Once the players have made their respective decisions, they put all their cards face down on the table. The dealer will now scoop up the "ante" bets from all the players who dropped out. This done, the dealer turns over his remaining four cards and makes the best poker hand possible out of them.

The dealer must "qualify" with an Ace-King hand for the game to be fully decided. If he fails to have a hand that is A-K or better, he pays off the "antes" and pushes on the "bets." The player then takes back the "bet" wager. If the dealer qualifies with a hand of Ace-King (or better), then all the players' hands are judged against it. If the player cannot beat the dealer's hand, the player loses both his "ante" and his "bet." If the player beats the dealer, the "ante" is paid off at even money, while the "bet" is usually paid off at the following house odds:

Winning Hand	Bonus Payout Table
Ace-King	1 to 1
One Pair	1 to 1
Two Pair	2 to 1
Three-of-a-kind	3 to 1
Straight	4 to 1
Flush	5 to 1
Full House	7 to 1
Four-of-a-kind	20 to 1
Straight Flush	50 to 1
Royal Flush	100 to 1

If the dealer fails to qualify, you don't win the bet bonus -- no matter how good your hand is. You also can't win a bonus if the dealer beats your hand.

The jackpot side bet is paid off independently, so you can lose to the dealer and still collect on the jackpot bet. The following is a typical jackpot pay scale:

Hand	Progressive Bonus
one pair	none
two pair	none
three of a kind	none
straight	none
flush	$50
full house	$75
four of a kind	$100
straight flush	10 percent of the progressive jackpot
royal flush	100 percent of the progressive jackpot

Summary: Good Game
Loss per hour: Approximately one average bet.
Qualifier: Raise on Ace-King-Jack-8-3 or better.
Playing Hint: Don't make jackpot side bet.

LET IT RIDE - A game that started fast out of the starting gates and seems to have just gotten more and more popular in the few short years it has existed is Shuffle Master's Let It Ride, another poker variant. The house edge is approximately 2.8 percent with the proper basic strategy (see ad on page 168 for my book *Bold Card Play Strategy: Best Strategies for Caribbean Stud, Let It Ride and Three Card Poker*) .

In front of each player are three betting squares labeled "1" and "2" and "$." The player places a bet in each square. The object of the game is to make the best poker hand that is a pair of 10s or better with your three cards and two community cards. You are "not" playing to beat the dealer as in Caribbean Stud, merely to get a good hand that pays a bonus according to a set payoff schedule. This bonus schedule applies to all hands. If, at the end of play, you have three bets working, you will receive the bonus on all three bets. If you only have one bet working, you will only receive the bonus on that one bet.

The dealer gives each player three cards and puts two cards face down as "community" cards. The players now look at their three-card hands. The players can now decide to withdraw their number "1" bet or let it ride. To let a bet ride, a player must put his three cards face down under his wager or behind his number "1" bet. To withdraw the number "1" bet, the player must scratch the felt to indicate to the dealer that the bet is to be returned. Players are not allowed to touch their chips once they are on the layout so the players cannot take back their bets themselves. The dealer will push the bet back if the player so desires.

Once the players have decided what to do with bet number "1" and the dealer has returned all withdrawals from play, the dealer now turns over the first of the two community cards. Again the players can decide whether to take off their number "2" bet or let that bet ride.

An important point to note is that the player who allows his number "1" bet to ride does not have to let his number "2" bet ride. Each bet is handled separately and there is a distinct strategy for each round of play. The "$" bet cannot be taken down.

Finally, the dealer turns over the second community card and the players are paid off according to the payoff schedule, or their losing bets are collected as the case may be. Some casinos have begun to offer a "Bonus" jackpot for an additional side bet, as is done with Caribbean Stud. You place this bet at the beginning of the round and it is not returnable as are bets number "1" and number "2."

Payoff Schedule For Let It Ride

Hand	Payoff
Pair of Tens	1 to 1
Pair of Jacks	1 to 1
Pair of Queens	1 to 1
Pair of Kings	1 to 1
Pair of Aces	1 to 1
Two Pair	2 to 1
Three-of-a-kind	3 to 1
Straight	5 to 1
Flush	8 to 1
Full House	11 to 1
Four-of-a-kind	50 to 1
Straight Flush	200 to 1
Royal Flush	1,000 to 1

Summary: Fair/Good Game
Loss per hour: Approximately one and a half average bets.
Qualifier: Must use proper Bold Card Play basic strategy.
Playing Tip: Only bet pair of 10s or better.

PAI GOW POKER - In negative expectation games, slow is good. Pai Gow Poker is deliciously slow, sometimes no more than 40 hands in an hour are actually played to completion. If you play according to the house way of setting the cards, you will face an approximately 2.5 percent casino edge.

Pai Gow Poker is a poker variation of the Chinese tile game. The game begins when one player is designated as the "dealer/banker." He must bank the bets of the other players. If no player wants to assume this role, the casino will bank the game. It is played with a standard deck of 52 cards with one joker added that can be used as an ace.

Before the deal, three dice are shaken and displayed to determine the order of the deal. Each player is then dealt seven cards with which he must make two hands based on poker rankings -- a back hand of five cards and a front hand of two cards. The five-card hand must outrank the two-card hand.

To win, you have to defeat the banker on both your front and back hands. To lose, the banker must defeat you on both as well. A "copy" or push goes to the banker. The house takes a five percent commission on all winning player hands and, since you win approximately 50 percent of the time, the house edge is a 2.5 percent.

Summary: Good Game
Loss Per Hour: Approximately one average bet.
Qualifier: You must play correct hand-making strategy. (You can find this in my book "Guerrilla Gambling: How to Beat the Casinos at Their Own Games!")
Playing Tip: When in doubt, let the house set your hand.

THREE CARD POKER - Another relatively new game that is gaining adherents throughout the country is Three-Card Poker, developed by poker pro Derek Webb. It is a very simple poker variant that has a very simple basic strategy, the objective of which is to beat the dealer's three-card hand. There is also an added incentive in attempting to win bonuses for certain premium hands.

The player can bet on three propositions called "Ante", "Play" and the independent "Pair Plus." The dealer deals the player three cards and himself three cards. If a player has opted to place an Ante bet, when he looks at his three cards he must decide whether to stay in the game or fold. To stay, he must place a bet equal to his Ante bet in the Play square. Now the dealer turns over his three cards. If the player beats the dealer's three-card hand, the player wins the Ante bet at even money. The Play bet pays a bonus for certain premium hands such as a straight flush, three of a kind, a straight and a flush. The Play pays even money for a pair.

The Pair Plus bet is a side bet that can be made without placing an Ante bet. If the player has a Pair Plus, which is two of a kind or better, he receives an additional payout. Many of these payouts are greater than one to one.

Unlike Caribbean Stud, where a dealer not qualifying for play cancels winning player hands, in Three Card Poker a non-qualifying dealer is a benefit to the players. What qualifies a dealer? Simply, if the dealer does not have at least a queen high or better hand, the players win on all their bets.

The house has a moderate edge on Three Card Poker when proper strategy is employed. The Ante and Play hands face a 2.14 percent house edge, while the Pair Plus bet comes in at 2.32 percent for the house (there is no strategy for Pair Plus). A conservative strategy would call for making only the Ante and Play wagers until one had a comfortable win before making several exploratory Pair Plus bets. If luck kept shinning on you when you did so, then continue to play all three propositions. For truly small bankrolls, you could play the Pair Plus without placing the Ante or Play wagers.

Three Card Poker Bonus Payout Schedule

Hand	Ante Bonus Payout	Pair Plus Payout
Straight Flush	5 to 1	40 to 1
Three of a Kind	4 to 1	30 to 1
Straight	1 to 1	6 to 1
Flush	0	4 to 1
Pair	0	1 to 1
High Card	0	Player loses

Winning Ante wagers are paid 1 to 1.
Winning Play wagers are paid 1 to 1.

Summary: Fair Game
Loss Per Hour: Approximately two average bets.
Qualifier: Best to avoid Pair Plus unless you're way ahead.
Playing Tip: Bet Play on your queen or better, otherwise fold.

There are probably a few good reasons why these "other" games have caught on. They offer the players choices to make that do affect their expectation, while simultaneously offering the players an opportunity to win big bonuses if Lady Luck smiles on them. Unlike my friend Billy's family, some of these "others" might be worth getting to know.

Award-winning author Frank Scoblete is the number one best-selling gaming author in the world. His books, videos and audio cassettes on casinogambling have sold over a million copies. He also publishes his own quarterly magazine, "The New Chance and Circumtance," and has his own website www.scoblete.com.in association with RGT Online. See ads for his books on pages 142, 152, 160 and below.

Got Milk? Why Internet Casinos Pay (Usually)

by Bill Haywood

Although the first Internet casino opened almost five years ago, and the Internet gambling industry today is estimated to be a $1.5 billion industry, Haywood has written a book that is the first comprehensive study of this industry, and it is written from the perspective of the player who wants to make money from these online casinos. Writing under the pseudonym "Yikes" in the Spring '99 Blackjack Forum, Haywood penned: "Milking the Matchplays: Beating the Online Casinos," the first article ever written on playing in web casinos for a profit. If you missed Bill'sarticle, which describes his basic method of play (a form of cyber comp hustling), the point is to collect the 10%-20% and higher deposit bonuses, while racking up more than the minimum in action, the minimum generally being deposit, plus bonus. The following article is taken from the first chapter of his book.

Flamers on the net are not shy in their skepticism of virtual gambling. Here's the usual response: "Give your credit card number to an offshore Internet bookie? HaHaHaHaHaHaHaHa!" Most cyber casinos are located on Caribbean islands and if they decide to keep your money, they can. It has happened more than once.

It is sensible to be leery, especially considering the ignoble roots of the gambling den. Gambling, as well as other businesses, was very different in the olden days, back before the automated, incorporated society. Once upon a time, shoemakers took pride in protecting their friends' feet, food came from gardens not drive-up windows, and the ancestors of HMOs took pride in saving lives. Gambling has become corporatized, but the predecessors of Internet casinos never went through the community-minded stage. Early casino bosses were thugs and scoundrels in flashy clothes. They now have changed - into business suits. The casino today is akin to what Marxists call "primitive accumulation," or organized plunder by powerful institutions.

The savvy player's decision to exploit eCasino weaknesses is not based on trust, or belief that some abstract "they" would never allow cyber-stealing. It comes from a cold-eyed look at the nature of the industry, and the trickster's impulse to beat the big guys at their own game.

The eCasinos pay winnings out of self-interest. Their checks clear for the same reason that nickel bags contain heroin and not baking powder: so people will keep coming back. It is the exhilaration of a win that turns dabblers into gamblers, and that is the foundation of games of chance. Although blatant ripoffs can never be ruled out, there have been surprisingly few. Just as the occasional gas station will have a dishonest meter, there are still plenty that do not. In research for my book (BeatWebCasinos.Com, soon to be published by RGE), I played at dozens of Internet casinos. Not one refused to give back money I had deposited. There have been problems — and they will be detailed in this book — but in the main they pay. Now let's look at some of the reasons why honest casinos would be more profitable than rogues.

Beef vs. Dairy - The gambling industry is split between two different business philosophies, which in this article will be referred to as "beef" and "dairy." The beef side of the industry wants all your money right now. They do not expect to ever see the gambler again, so they devour the entire carcass immediately and leave the bones in the sun. Dairy casinos are different — they know that thriving, happy cows are the best milkers. They want you healthy for your entire productive lifespan (and then the ride to the glue factory will be comped by the house). Dairy executives do not even call it gambling; they use the nicer sounding "gaming." Gambling has a terrible reputation for ruining lives. Gaming is the clean, corporate, modern pastime. They want a pasteurized image as sparkling as a stainless steel bulk tank just before milking time. Dairy eCasinos tend to offer better odds so you can play longer and have more fun. They also tend to be bigger operations than the beef rustlers.

There are powerful economic agents seeking an orderly, trustworthy gambling industry that is hooked into every home. Dairy methods are better suited for this than beef. A look at the economics of online gambling suggests why: there is too much money to be made for operators to blow it by ripping people off.

Note first of all how much cheaper cyber casinos are. Land gambling is a very labor intensive business; for every person they hire, they pay another to watch him, and another to spy on her. They build cavernous structures, fill them with lightbulbs and pay an army of guys to shine them and mail the electric bills. The first cyber casino went online on August 18, 1995. It had 17 employees and cost $1.5 million to start. There is not a parking ramp in Atlantic City that could be built for that paltry sum. But don't stop reading, we haven't gotten to the exciting figures yet. Take the cost of comps, that is, the complimentary rooms and meals handed out to make people feel good about losing. The land industry standard is that a full 40-percent of what you lose is eligible to come back in the form of comps. The online expense is nothing like that. The eCasinos are experimenting with comps, but it's hard when there's no buffet. ECasinos not only spend less to get a dollar, they get more dollars from the player. In casino accounting, the "hold" is what a player leaves behind at the end of the day. The land betting hold is generally considered to be 40 percent. You walk in with $100, bet it over and over running up hundreds in action, until you leave with $60 left.

Statistics on Internet gambling are scarce, but there is every reason to believe that the cyber hold is higher. Michael Flint of I-national Gaming says most people who log-on to his cyber dens lose their whole deposit. Flint guesses that the occasional win brings the average hold down to 60 percent. In Australia, the Lasseters company has both land and Internet gambling. CEO Peter Bridge says the average loss per session on land is $44. On computer: $200. Since expenses are low, the extra hold goes right to the bottom line. And if eCasinos get busy, they do not have to build a Taj Mahal annex. Once established, extra Internet capacity is a trivial expense. Offshore taxes are generally lower too.

There is so much money to be made online that the Internet domain name "blackjack.com" was sold in June, 1999 for $460,000. Half a million for the right to name the street where the virtual casino was going up! The price of established eCasinos is also impressive - a September 1999 want ad asked $6 million cash for a place claiming a $420k monthly win. Another asked $10 million up front. Not bad for a business that can fit in a dentist's office. Starnet, an industry leader in leasing eCasino software, claims that the April 1999 "handle" (the total amount bet, not the hold) for all of its licensees was $100 million.

That's a lot, but they're just getting started. The whole Internet is still getting started. In 1999, there were about 147 million users of the web world wide, expected to be 194 million two years later. Another source predicts 350 million users by 2003. Even the poorest countries have rich communities that are eager to bet online.

There is also still tremendous growth potential among those already online, because most people are not yet making cash transactions over the web (only one fifth do). Gambling - on the Internet in particular - has many souls still to be persuaded. A study by Cyber Dialogue found that of adults already online, only two percent are willing to have anything to do with online gambling. That is two percent of more than 65 million Americans online. Compare that to 20 percent of a nation of 260 million who gamble regularly on land. If the industry attains a good reputation, the potential for growth is enormous. Reputation is built one player at a time by promptly paying her for that first, timid step into a cyber gambling den.

The nature of the Internet gambling industry has important implications for savvy players to exploit matchplays. Since fixed costs are so low, Internet casinos are hemorrhaging money. What do they do when their pockets burst? They throw money our way in the form of promotions. Since one crap game is pretty much the same as another, the eCasino has to use other means to pull customers in. (In all fairness, marketing budgets can be staggering. This will weed out the less limber eCasinos.) Competition to attract players is good for us; it is the source of the deposit bonuses for which this article lives.

More often than not, management considers bonuses to be a one-time formality necessitated by competition and industry custom. They are simply making too much money to worry about us chiselers. If you have a conveyer belt of money coming at you, do you run along the side catching bills that fly off, or do you wait at the end with a great big box? Currently, bonus hustling is still beneath the radar of the industry. Internet gambling execs fret about hackers, credit card fraud, players reneging on debts and minors sneaking in, but not about promotional bonuses. They are aware that some people cash out quickly, and generally they will not give the bonus unless a certain minimum amount has been wagered, but that is the extent of their worries. Not once did the issue come up at the Internet gambling conference in Vancouver, British Columbia in June 1999. I asked a marketing employee at Starnet Software what they do about people who bet and run. "Oh, they have to play their full deposit" was the clipped answer. The issue just did not register, despite his being a client marketing consultant for one of the two biggest software franchisers.

Michael Flint of I-national said flatly that he doesn't believe that people would go to the trouble of downloading five megabytes of software just for the bonus. Such salutary attitudes may or may not change as the industry matures, but for right now high cash flow plus low costs equals meal time for us foxes along the conveyor belt. Besides creating some interesting opportunities for the sly, the profitability of Internet gambling creates powerful incentives to offer honest games and prompt payouts.

Consider this, who makes more money in the long run, a cheater at cards or the manufacturer of cards? The card shark gets a score here and there, but the manufacturer sells the most cards if they are believed to be unmarked. The "cards" in our case is the software that companies sell for consumers to gamble on. More will bet if the games are trusted. The software designers driving the industry understand this, and they are powerful agents for a commercial form of integrity. Alchemists like Microgaming or Boss Media hold the formula for turning copper wire into gold. When they license their software to a casino owner, they typically keep 30 percent of the win every blessed month. Global Games Corporation takes 50 percent.

The software companies generally keep close control over their franchisees, often providing all the technical support and cash handling as part of a package. Starnet has been aggressively discounting franchises for as low as $10,000, attracting many small-fry proprietors who would be a greater risk for trouble, except that all transactions go through Starnet. These small licensees rent what is known as a "turnkey" package. The big company does almost everything; the eCasino owner just has to turn the key in the lock when he arrives at work. (However, most owners do write the checks for winnings and usually control the button that gives you a bonus.) Since the only real function of the micro-franchisee is to attract web traffic, they should not even be considered owners. They are independent marketing reps for the Starnets who actually run the casinos. Those who promote well will succeed. Others will fail, but at no risk to the software company. The Starnets thus gather about them the most energetic eCasino marketers without suffering any liability for the ones who fail. The game designers make their money from the industry volume as a whole - they are less tempted to stiff someone who runs up a surprise $30k win at craps. It's for the poor web owner to carry most of that risk.

Software companies make their money not when one casino does well, but when all their licensees do. Granted this is more true of the bigger, older outfits - some early gerry-rigged java games were very fly-by-night, but for trend-setters there is strong incentive for self-policing the industry. Major firms dig into the backgrounds of license applicants. "Our name goes on them, but their name goes on us," explains Avron Marcus of Microgaming.

One thing in particular they do not want their brand name associated with is money laundering. David Prue of Tropika says they particularly worry about Russian mobsters who like to set up an eCasino, then lose $100,000 a week to themselves. The dirty money bet by "players" then comes out as honest winnings of the casino. Major software companies do not want their brand besmirched by such activities. Would you want to place bets with the Russian mob? Probably not, so Tropika reports that it does thorough investigations of potential licensees. And the mysterious types with wide ties who drop by asking about a franchise?

"As soon as you say to somebody they've got to clear an RCMP (Royal Canadian Mounted Police) and Interpol background check," says Prugh, "we don't hear from them again. That has happened on many occasions."

After the software is licensed, the big firms keep a tight rein on it. The servers of licensees remain hooked to the franchiser's mainframe for various purposes, including monitoring — that is, if they have their own servers. Only the head office can make most changes in program configurations. Even if a casino owner is intent on introducing cheating sub-routines into the program, he cannot get at the source code because it is encrypted. At least that's what a Microgaming exec told me. Do I believe him? Yes, because he's dairy, not beef. Two lessees of Starnet said the same thing. Encryption is the industry standard in dairy software.

Many of the software designers, such as Online Gaming Systems (OTCBB:OGAM) are publically traded companies, some have even qualified to get onto the Nasdaq board. Publicly traded companies have to follow the rules of the Securities and Exchange Commission (SEC), which requires independent audits. Compared to private holdings, their books are open to the world. For the ambitious companies, the future is not in screwing a few credit card holders, but in attracting the pools of investment capital. Stock prices are vulnerable to wild swings based on the flimsiest rumors, so like any company they are sensitive to scandal and lawsuits. The wise farmer worries not just about tainted milk, but the mere whiff of it. If a company issues stock, that is a good sign that their business is selling lots of software, not ventilating the players.

The software kings and the casino owners have distinct interests, and this has created some interesting clashes. A fascinating case involved a defunct casino known as Tradewinds, which licensed its software from Atlantic International Entertainment (AIEE, now Online Gaming Systems). Tradewinds was started by a greeting card shop owner who had no background in casino management.

A savvy player noticed that his blackjack game had generous rules for surrender and doubling down, did not shuffle every hand and could be beaten with precision play. The player deposited $20k, then racked up an impressive $70k in wins. The owner lacked the background to understand what was happening, so he assumed the player was a computer hacker who had discovered a bug. The casino froze both the winnings and the initial $20k. Undeterred, the player eventually complained to the software firm, telling AIEE frankly that the game had generous rules and he beat it fair and square. AIEE investigated and determined that there was no software bug; the game was vulnerable because of the rules and configurations that the owner selected. AIEE demanded that Tradewinds pay the $90k or have the software turned off. Tradewinds refused. The player never got a cent, but the owner lost his casino. (The URL link for Tradewinds now takes you to a place called Go Online Sports Book and Sharkey's Casino.)

Two lessons here. One, never win so much that a proprietor is tempted to go out of business rather than pay. Two, and more importantly, is that it was the software manufacturer who shut down the place. The U.S. police did not care, the alleged regulatory authorities in Costa Rica did not care, but AIEE pulled the plug. The company was reportedly about to go public with a stock offering, so it was being especially careful. But the principle remains: software companies are dairy industry leaders!

Although Internet casinos are far cheaper than physical ones, they still cost enough to screen out your average basement computer larcenist. Already the market is crowded enough that it takes several million dollars in startup costs for a website to stand out. The software needs to be flashy, and a license from a sovereign government ranges from $25k in Dominica to $350k in Australia. The major firms will lease software only to government licensees, so the unlicenced places use java programs that are noticeably cruddy.

Casino credit card processors have all kinds of software safeguards in place. Generally, eCasinos do not even get your credit card number. Your money goes to a third party credit card processor, who then forwards the credits minus your number to the casino. Sure, nothing is certain. But your credit card is probably safer with major eCasinos than with the kid swiping it at the gas station. Also notable: outfits like Goldchip or Mpact commonly process credit cards for a variety of online casinos. Like the software programmers, they are milkers, not butchers. They benefit from volume and the overall health of the industry.

Cash processors and software designers cannot strong-arm casinos that they do not license, but they can encourage governments to do so through regulation and law enforcement. Traditionally business is thought to be hostile to regulation, but the gambling industry lives to be regulated. Take Nevada, the closest thing to a republic by and for the casino. The state's economic health rests on gambling and it protects its reputation aggressively. To sell slot machines in Nevada, a manufacturer has to have the model tested. Not only do the Nevada machines have to have fair and verifiably random number generators, but the manufacturer must certify that all their machines sold anywhere in the world work the same way. Nevada does not want a cheating machine on a Gulf Coast island to tar the reputation of similar models in Vegas. That is forward-thinking dairy philosophy taken to its furthest.

If anything, Internet casinos are even more eager for regulation than the landlubbers. Recall the statistic about how only two percent of adults online will stick so much as their cursor in a web slot? Credibility is the single biggest obstacle the industry faces. The solution is to accept regulation in return for government sanction.

Sue Schneider of the Interactive Gaming Council (IGC), the Internet gambling industry group, dreams of a time when federal and state governments will regulate eCasinos "the way they license and supervise land-based casinos. Customers will know what they're getting.... Why risk your hard earned cash at www.flybynight.org when you can do the same thing at www.licensed-and-regulated.com?"

The IGC is not waiting around for American sanction; the group is working internationally on a model regulatory code. So far, 25 governments have set up net gambling licensing, and the IGC wants such laws to spread as far and as uniformly as possible. Many of the first Internet casinos got licenses in the Caribbean, but more and more are considering Australia, despite the fact that the casino rate for taxes down under is 50 percent. They need regulation and legitimacy and are "quite willing to pay for that with taxes because they are facing a colossal problem," according to David Post of the Cyberspace Law Institute.

"They want everybody to know that there's no cheating.... You won't see the industry explode until that happens." Once a solid regulatory foundation has been established, look for the really big players like Harrah's, Caesars, and even Microsoft to sweep in.

In the meantime, the IGC is trying to fill the "regulatory void" until governments take over. In the autumn of 1999, the IGC launched its seal of approval program and mediation service. IGC members pledge to follow a code of responsible dairy practices and get to sport a little seal of approval on their websites. Although the IGC's commitment is not to the consumers' pocket books, rather to the industry's reputation, membership in the group is a good sign when you are evaluating casinos.

A look at some of the statistics and players of online gambling shows that beef-dairy is not just a cutesy metaphor; there is powerful evidence that the most important players are insisting on an honest game. Besides the software and ecash firms, there are the consortiums that own strings of major websites. They all want a clean parlor. Tending toward the beef trade are the small, single proprietor Internet casinos. They do not have the capital for the fanciest software. They cannot afford to offer jackpots of hundreds of thousands of dollars. They cannot buy respectability in the form of a government license. The beef operations will be increasingly squeezed in future years by the big guys. The beef casinos are the places you want to avoid. If you can identify them, you can have a happy career of bonus hustling in the dairy casinos. On the whole, eCasinos will pay, because they know we got milk. Which software companies?

The best and easiest way to protect yourself from cyber ripoffs is to only play sites using major software brands. If you cannot identify the software, do not play. Two of the most reliable software companies are Microgaming and Starnet. They are the industry leaders with the most franchisees and the most to gain from a clean industry. You can play quite a few eCasinos before running out of these two. Identifying them is straight forward. In the case of Microgaming, many websites mention up front that they use Microgaming, so that is easy enough. If not, then after downloading and installing the program, use Explorer file manager to locate the file casino.exe. Right click on it and go down to properties, pick the "version" tab and you should see the words MicroGaming Systems.

Starnet software is recognizable by the distinctive, vertical placement of the buttons on the blackjack game. The java version has similar placement. If the website lists this phone number (888) 685-7619 for tech support, that's Starnet. Starnet sites generally process credit cards through EFS, Electronic Financial Services, a Starnet subsidiary. The EFS "ATM" machine is notable for using "V-Chips." Starnet is also developing a seal of approval, which may turn up on its casino websites. Other software brands that I have had a fair amount of good experience with: Cryptologic, Chartwell, Gambling Systems, Boss, Perplexa and Xirtrix. There are two types of software: the java programs that you can play right away, and then the ones that require downloading a substantial program and installing it on your hard-drive. Generally, the downloaded programs are much more complex, and hence represent a bigger (and presumably more reliable) company behind it than the java versions. Nonetheless, there are good java companies; play only the ones with lush graphics. If the software is elaborate, then the designer is more likely to be in the business of selling software, not rip-off joints.

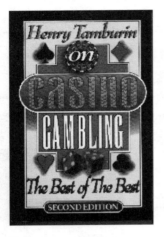

A Few Last Words

by Steve Bourie

When I sit down to put this book together each year I try to make sure that everything in here will help to make you a better and more knowledgeable gambler when you go to a casino.

I try to include stories that will help you understand how casinos operate, how to choose the best casino games and also how to play those games in the best way possible.

My philosophy with this book is that gambling in a casino is fun and for about 99% of the people who visit casinos that statement is true. The vast majority of people who gamble in casinos are recreational players who enjoy the fun and excitement of gambling. They know that they won't always win and they also realize that over the long term they will most likely have more losing sessions than winning ones. They also understand that any losses they incur will be the price they pay for their fun and they only gamble with money they can afford to lose. In other words, they realize that casino gambling is a form of entertainment, just like going to a movie or an amusement park, and they are willing to pay a price for that entertainment. Unfortunately, there are also some people who go to casinos and become problem gamblers.

According to Gamblers Anonymous you may be a problem gambler if you answer yes to at least seven of the following 20 questions:

1. Do you lose time from work due to gambling?
2. Does gambling make your home life unhappy?
3. Does gambling affect your reputation?
4. Do you ever feel remorse after gambling?
5. Do you ever gamble to get money with which to pay debts or to otherwise solve financial difficulties?
6. Does gambling cause a decrease in your ambition or efficiency?
7. After losing, do you feel you must return as soon as possible and win back your losses?
8. After a win, do you have a strong urge to return and win more?
9. Do you often gamble until your last dollar is gone?
10. Do you ever borrow to finance your gambling?
11. Do you ever sell anything to finance your gambling?

12. Are you reluctant to use your "gambling money" for other expenses?
13. Does gambling make you careless about the welfare of your family?
14. Do you ever gamble longer than you planned?
15. Do you ever gamble to escape worry or trouble?
16. Do you ever commit, or consider committing, an illegal act to finance yourgambling?
17. Does gambling cause you to have difficulty sleeping?
18. Do arguments, disappointments, or frustrations create within you an urge to gamble?
19. Do you have an urge to celebrate good fortune by a few hours of gambling?
20. Do you ever consider self-destruction as a result of your gambling?

If you believe you might have a gambling problem you should be aware that help is available from The National Council on Problem Gaming, Inc. It is the foremost advocacy organization in the country for problem gamblers and is headquartered in Washington, D.C. It was formed in 1972 as a non-profit agency to promote public education and awareness about gambling problems and operates a 24-hour nationwide help line at 1-800-522-4700. Anyone calling that number will be provided with the appropriate referral resources for help with their gambling problem.

I sincerely hope that none of you reading this book will ever have a need to call that number but it was an issue that I felt should be addressed.

ARIZONA

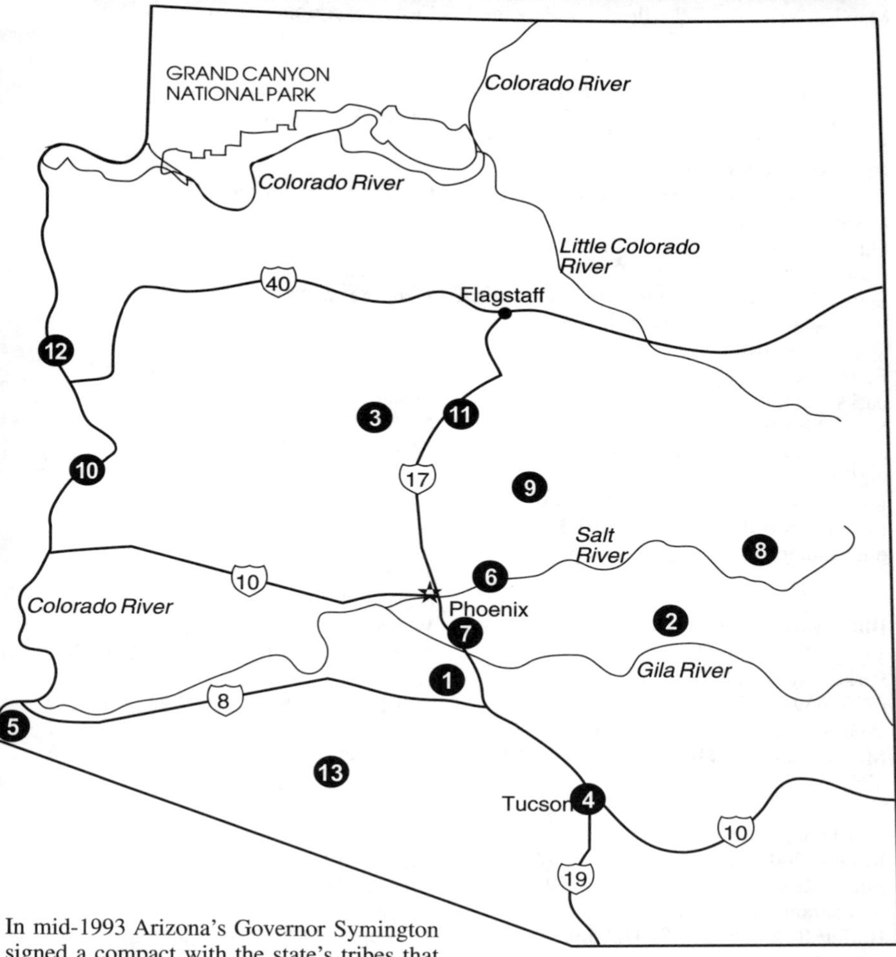

In mid-1993 Arizona's Governor Symington signed a compact with the state's tribes that allowed them to offer slot machines on their reservations.

The compact doesn't allow for any table games but some casinos offer video versions of blackjack, craps and roulette. The Arizona tribes aren't required to release information on their slot machine percentage paybacks, however, according to the Arizona Department of Gaming, the terms of the compact require each tribes' machines to return the following minimum and maximum paybacks: video poker and video blackjack - 83% to 100%, slot machines - 80% to 100%, keno - 75% to 100%. Each tribe is free to set its machines to pay back anywhere within those limits.

All Arizona casinos have slots, video poker and video keno. Optional games include: video blackjack (VBJ), video craps (VC), video roulette (VR), poker (P), keno (K), bingo (BG) and simulcasting (S). The minimum gambling age is 18 (21 if liquor is served) and all casinos are open 24 hours. For more information on Arizona call the state's Office of Tourism at (800) 842-8257.

Apache Gold Casino Resort
P.O. Box 1210
San Carlos, Arizona 85550
(520) 475-7800
Map Location: **#2** (90 miles E. of Phoenix)

Toll-Free Number: (800) APACHE-8
Rooms: 147 Price Range: $55-$95
Suites: 10 Price Range: $75-$150
Restaurants: 1 Liquor: Yes
Buffets: B-$6.93 (Sat/Sun) L-$8.55
D-$10.70/$15.00 (Fri-Sat)
Casino Size: 10,000 Square Feet
Other Games: P, K, BG, S, VR
Casino Marketing: (800) APACHE-8
Senior Discount: 10% room discount for AAA and AARP members. 15% for Player's Club members
Fun Book: Available through local motels, RV parks and the chamber of commerce
Special Features: Hotel is Best Western. Stay and Play Packages (Sun-Thu) include two free buffets. Lounge serves beer and wine. 18-hole golf course. Driving range. Pro shop. Convenience store. RV Park w/full hookups and dump station.

Blue Water Casino
119 W. Riverside Drive
Parker, Arizona 85344
(520) 669-7777
Web Site: www.bluewaterfun.com
Map Location: **#10** (160 miles W. of Phoenix)

Toll-Free Number: (800) 747-8777
Rooms: 200 Price Range: $81-$109
Suites: 25 Price Range: $219-$249
Restaurants: 1 Liquor: Yes
Buffet: B- $5.95 L:$6.95 D: $8.95
Other Games: P, K, BG (Tue-Sun)
Senior Discount: 10% discount for AAA and AARP members.

Bucky's Casino & Resort
530 E. Merritt
Prescott, Arizona 86301
(520) 776-1666
Web Site: www.buckyscasino.com
Map Location: **#3** (91 miles S.W. of Flagstaff, Junction of Hwy. 69 & Hwy. 89)

Toll-Free Number: (800) SLOTS-44
Room Reservations: (800) 967-4637
Rooms: 81 Price Range: $59-$159
Suites: 80 Price Range: $139-$179
Restaurants: 2 (1 open 24 hours) Liquor: Yes
Other Games: VBJ, P, K, BG
Casino Marketing: (520) 771-0580
Special Features: Located in Prescott Resort Hotel. Free on-site shuttle service. Gas station with RV dump and mini-mart. Room discount for AAA and AARP members.

Casino Arizona - Salt River
524 N. 92nd Street
Scottsdale, Arizona 85256
(480) 850-7777
Web Site: www.casinoaz.com
Map Location: **#6** (15 miles N.E. of Phoenix)

Toll-Free Number: (877) 7-24-HOUR
Restaurants: 1 Liquor: Yes
Buffets: L/D-$6.00
Other Games: P, BG

Casino Arizona - Indian Bend
9700 E. Indian Bend
Scottsdale, Arizona 85256
(480) 850-7777
Web Site: www.casinoaz.com
Map Location: **#6** (15 miles N.E. of Phoenix)

Toll-Free Number: (877) 7-24-HOUR
Restaurants: 1 Liquor: Yes
Buffet: $5.00 (11am-11pm)
Other Games: BG

Casino of the Sun
7406 S. Camino De Oeste
Tucson, Arizona 85746
(520) 883-1700
Web Site: www.casinosun.com
Map Location: **#4**

Toll-Free Number: (800) 344-9435
Restaurants: 2 (1 open 24 hours) Liquor: No
Buffets: L-$5.95 D-$6.95
Other Games: VBJ, BG
Senior Discount: Food discounts available
Special Features: Smoke shop. Gift shop.

Cliff Castle Casino & Hotel Lodge
353 Middle Verde Road
Camp Verde, Arizona 86322
(520) 567-9031
Web Site: www.cliffcastle.com
Map Location: **#11** (50 miles S. of Flagstaff)

Toll-Free Number: (800) 381-SLOT
Room Reservation Number: (800) 524-6343
Rooms: 89 Price Range: $59-$89
Suites: 2 Price Range: $79-$89
Restaurants: 3 Liquor: Yes
Buffets: B-$7.50 (Sat-Sun) L/D-$7.50
Other Games: VBJ, VC, VR, P
Special Features: Casino is located in Cliff Castle Lodge.

Cocopah Casino & Bingo
15136 S. Avenue B
Somerton, Arizona 85350
(520) 726-8066
Map Location: **#5** (13 miles S.W. of Yuma)

Toll-Free Number: (800) 23-SLOTS
Restaurants: 1 Snack Bar Liquor: No
Other Games: VBJ, BG
Special Features: Nonsmoking gaming areas. $1 breakfast special from 3am-10am.

Desert Diamond Casino
7350 S. Old Nogales Highway
Tucson, Arizona 85734
(520) 294-7777
Map Location: **#4**

Restaurants: 1 Liquor: No
Casino Size: 45,000 Square Feet
Other Games: VBJ, VC, P, K, BG

Fort McDowell Casino
P.O. Box 18359
Fountain Hills, Arizona 85269
(602) 837-1424
Web Site: www.fortmcdowellcasino.com
Map Location: **#6** (25 miles N.E. of Phoenix)

Toll-Free Number: (800) THE-FORT
Restaurants: 3 (1 open 24 hours) Liquor: No
Buffets: B-$2.95 L-$6.95 D-$8.95 (Mon/Thu/Sun)/$11.95 (Fri/Sat)/$12.95 (Tue)
Other Games: P, K, BG, S, VBJ
Special Features: Fortune club members get buffet discounts. Free valley-wide transportation (reservations required).

Gila River Casino - Vee Quiva
6443 N. Komatke Lane
Laveen, Arizona 85339
(520) 796-7777
Map Location: **#7** (10 miles S.W. of Phoenix)

Toll-Free Number: (800) WIN-GILA
Restaurants: 2 (1 open 24 hours) Liquor: No
Buffets: B-$3.99 L-$5.00 D-$8.00
Casino Size: 30,000 Square Feet
Other Games: P, K, BG

Gila River Casino - Wild Horse
5512 W. Wild Horse Pass
Chandler, Arizona 85226
(520) 796-7727
Map Location: **#7** (25 miles S.E. of Phoenix)

Toll-Free Number: (800) WIN-GILA
Restaurants: 1 (open 24 hours) Liquor: No
Buffets: B-$3.99 L-$5.00 D-$8.00
Casino Size: 60,000 Square Feet
Other Games: VC, VR, P, K, BG

Golden Hasan Casino
PO Box 10
Ajo, Arizona 85321
(520) 362-2746
Map Location: **#13** (125 miles S.W. of Phoenix)

Restaurants: 1 Snack Bar
Hours: 12pm-12am/11am-1am (Fri-Sat)

Harrah's Ak Chin Casino
15406 Maricopa Road
Maricopa, Arizona 85239
(602) 802-5000
Web Site: www.harrahs.com
Map Location: **#1** (25 miles S. of Phoenix)

Toll-Free Number: (800) HARRAHS
Restaurants: 4 (1 open 24 hours) Liquor: Yes
Buffets: B-$5.50 L-$7.99 (Fri/Sat) D-$10.99
Casino Size: 30,000 Square Feet
Other Games: VBJ, VC, VR, P, BG
Fun Book: Only given to bus groups
Special Features: Two bars. Live entertainment. Native-American crafts store and smoke shop.

Hon-Dah Casino
P.O. Box 3250
Pinetop, Arizona 85935
(520) 369-0299
Web Site: www.hon-dah.com
Map Location: **#8** (190 miles N.E. of Phoenix)

Toll-Free Number: (800) WAY-UP-HI
Rooms: 100 Price Range: $79-$99
Suites: 28 Price Range: $150-$180
Restaurants: 1 (open 24 hours) Liquor: Yes
Buffets: B-$3.95 L-$4.95
D-$6.95 (Sun-Thu)/$11.95 (Fri-Sat)
Other Games: VBJ, P, BG (Sun/Mon)
Fun Book: Available through local motels and chamber of commerce
Special Features: 120-space full-service RV park. Convenience store. Gas station.

Mazatzal Casino
P.O. Box 1820
Hwy. 87, Milemarker 251
Payson, Arizona 85547
(520) 474-6044
Web Site: www.777play.com
Map Location: **#9** (90 miles N.E. of Phoenix)

Toll-Free Number: (800) 777-7529
Restaurants: 2 (1 open 24 hours) Liquor: Yes
Casino Size: 35,000 Square Feet
Other Games: VBJ, P, K, BG
Senior Discount: 10% off food, if 55, or older
Fun Book: Only given to groups or with Stay & Play packages
Special Features: Offers Stay & Play packages with local motels that include: discounted room price, Fun Books, breakfast for two in restaurant, plus free shuttle to and from motel. Sports bar. Video arcade. Gift shop. Nonsmoking gaming area.

Paradise Casino
450 Quechan Drive
Yuma, Arizona 85364
(760) 572-7777
Web Site: www.paradisecasinoyuma.com
Map Location: **#5** (244 miles W. of Tucson)

Toll-Free Number: (888) 777-4946
Restaurants: 1 (open 24 hours) Liquor: Yes
Buffets: L-$4.25
Casino Marketing: (760) 572-2463
Other Games: P, K, BG
Senior Discount: 10% off food, if 65, or older
Special Features: Cappuccino bar.

Spirit Mountain Casino
8555 South Highway 95
Mohave Valley, Arizona 86440
(520) 346-2000
Map Location: **#12** (15 miles S. of Bullhead City)

Restaurants: 1 Snack Bar Liquor: Yes
Casino Size: 12,000 Square Feet
Other Games: Video Let It Ride
Special Features: Adjacent to 120-space full-service RV park. Convenience store. Gas station.

Yavapai Casino
1501 E. Highway 69
Prescott, Arizona 86301
(520) 445-5767
Web Site: www.buckyscasino.com
Map Location: **#3** (91 miles S.W. of Flagstaff)

Toll-Free Number: (800) SLOTS-44
Restaurants: 1 Snack Bar Liquor: No
Other Games: BG
Special Features: Located across the street from Bucky's Casino. Free shuttle bus service.

CALIFORNIA

On March 7,2000 California voters approved a state-wide referendum that legally allowed the state's Indian tribes to begin offering electronic gaming machines, blackjack, and other house-banked card games. The games of craps and roulette are not permitted.

Most California card rooms also offer some form of player-banked blackjack but, because they are prohibited by law from playing blackjack, the game is played to 22 rather than 21. For a listing of California card rooms visit our web site at: www.americancasinoguide.com.

Unless otherwise noted, all California Indian casinos are open 24 hours and offer: slots, video poker, and video keno. Optional games offered include: blackjack (BJ), poker (P), pai gow poker (PGP), Caribbean stud poker (CSP), three card poker (TCP), bingo (BG), casino war (CW) and simulcasting (S). The minimum gambling age is 18 (21 if alcohol is served).

Although most of the casinos have toll-free numbers be aware that many of those numbers will only work for calls made within California. Also, many of these casinos are in out-of-the-way locations, so it is advisable to call ahead for directions.

For more information on visiting California call the state's department of tourism at (800) 862-2543.

Barona Casino
1000 Wildcat Canyon Road
Lakeside, California 92040
(619) 443-2300
Web Site: www.barona.com
Map Location: **#1** (15 miles N.E. of San Diego)

Toll-Free Number: (888) 7-BARONA
Restaurants: 2 Liquor: No
Buffets: B-$3.99 (Sat-Sun) L-$6.99 D-$7.99
Other Games: BJ, BG (Fri-Sun), S, PGP, CW
Special Features: Groups of 8 or more receive a discount book that includes: 50% off buffet, 15% off gift shop and $5 in video machine play. Golf course.

Black Bart Casino
P.O. Box 1177
Willits, California 95490
(707) 459-7330
Map Location: **#11** (160 miles N.W. of Sacramento)

Restaurants: 1 Deli Liquor: No
Hours: 8am-2am/24 hours (Fri/Sat)
Casino Size: 3,000 Square Feet
Other Games: Slots Only

Cache Creek Indian Bingo & Casino
14455 Highway 16
Brooks, California 95606
(530) 796-3118
Web Site: www.cachecreek.com
Map Location: **#2** (35 miles N.W. of Sacramento)

Toll-Free Number: (800) 452-8181
Restaurants: 2 Liquor: No
Buffets: B-$5.95 (Sat-Sun)
D-$5.95/$9.95 (Fri)
Casino Size: 18,000 Square Feet
Other Games: BJ, P, BG (Thu-Mon), PGP

Cahuilla Creek Restaurant & Casino
PO Box 390845
Anza, California 92539
(909) 763-1200
Map Location: **#19** (30 miles S. of Palm Springs)

Restaurants: 1 Liquor: Yes
Buffets: Brunch-$6.95 (Thu/Sun)
Hours: 8am-11pm/1am (Fri/Sat)
Other Games: BJ, P, BG (Fri-Mon)
Senior Discount: 10% off food, if 55, or older
Special Features: Free supervised children's play area.

Casino Morongo
49750 Seminole Drive
Cabazon, California 92230
(909) 849-3080
Web Site: www.casinomorongo.com
Map Location: **#3** (90 miles E. of Los Angeles)

Toll-Free Number: (800) 252-4499
Restaurants: 2 Liquor: Yes
Casino Size: 85,000 Square Feet
Other Games: BJ, P, CSP, TCP, BG (Thu-Mon)

Cher-Ae Heights Casino
P.O. Box 635
Trinidad, California 95570
(707) 677-3611
Map Location: **#4** (25 miles N. of Eureka)

Toll-Free Number: (800) 684-BINGO
Restaurants: 1 Snack Bar Liquor: No
Other Games: BJ, P, BG (Wed-Sun)

Chicken Ranch Bingo
16929 Chicken Ranch Road
Jamestown, California 95327
(209) 984-3000
Map Location: **#5** (100 miles S.E. of Sacramento)

Toll-Free Number: (800) 752-4646
Restaurants: 1 Snack Bar Liquor: No
Hours: 10am-Midnight
Casino Size: 35,000 Square Feet
Other Games: BG (Thu-Sun)

Chumash Casino
3400 East Highway 246
Santa Ynez, California 93460
(805) 686-0855
Map Location: **#13** (40 miles N.W. of Santa Barbara)

Toll-Free Number: (800) 728-9997
Restaurants: 1 Liquor: No
Other Games: BJ, P, PGP, BG (Wed/Fri-Sun)

Colusa Casino & Bingo
P.O. Box 1267
Colusa, California 95932
(530) 458-8844
Web Site: www.colusacasino.com
Map Location: **#6** (75 miles N. of Sacramento)

Toll-Free Number: (800) 655-U-WIN
Restaurants: 1 Snack Bar Liquor: No
Other Games: BJ, P, BG (Tue/Fri-Sun)
Fun Book: Need coupon from local area businesses

Eagle Mountain Casino
P.O. Box 1659
Porterville, California 93258
(559) 788-6220
Web Site: www.eaglemtncasino.com
Map Location: **#21** (60 miles S.E. of Fresno)

Toll-Free Number: (800) 903-3353
Restaurants: 2 Liquor: No
Buffets: L-$5.95 D-$7.95
Casino Size: 9,600 Square Feet
Other Games: BJ, BG

Elk Valley Casino
2500 Howland Hill Road
Crescent City, California 95531
(707) 464-1020
Map Location: **#7** (84 miles N. of Eureka)

Toll-Free Number: (888) 574-2744
Restaurants: 1 Snack Bar Liquor: No
Casino Size: 19,000 Square Feet
Other Games: BJ, P, BG (Fri-Mon)
Senior Discount: Lunch discount every Tue, if 55, or older
Special Features: Weekly poker tournaments.

Fantasy Springs Casino
82-245 Indio Springs Drive
Indio, California 92203
(760) 342-5000
Web Site: www.cabazonindians.com
Map Location: **#8** (125 miles E. of Los Angeles)

Toll-Free Number: (800) 827-2WIN
Restaurants: 2 (1 open 24 hours) Liquor: Yes
Casino Size: 95,000 Square Feet
Other Games: BJ, P, PGP, CSP, BG, S
Fun Book: Go to Fan Club desk
Senior Discount: Bingo discount on Monday, if 55, or older
Special Features: Nightly free entertainment

Feather Falls Casino
3 Alverda Drive
Oroville, California 95966
(530) 533-3885
Wb Site: www.featherfallscasino.com
Map Location: **#22** (100 miles N. of Sacramento)

Toll-Free Number: (877) OK-BINGO
Restaurants: 1 Liquor: Yes
Buffets: B-$4.95 (Sun) D-$7.95 (Fri)
Casino Size: 38,000 Square Feet
Other Games: BJ, BG (Wed-Sun)
Senior Discount: $2 off Sunday brunch, if 55, or older

Gold Country Casino
4020 Olive Highway
Oroville, California 95966
(530) 538-4560
Web Site: www.gold-country-casino.com
Map Location: **#22** (100 miles N. of Sacramento)

Toll-Free Number: (800) 334-9400
Restaurants: 1 Snack Bar Liquor: No
Other Games: BJ, P, BG
Senior Discount: Free continental breakfast, $5 gaming token, prize drawings, on Tue/Thu from 6am-noon, if 55, or older

Golden Bear Casino
54 E. Klamath Beach Road
Klamath, California 95546
(707) 482-5501
Map Location: **#7** (70 miles N. of Eureka)

Restaurants: 1 Snack Bar Liquor: No
Hours: 8am-10pm/12am (Fri/Sat)
Other Games: Slots Only

Harrah's Rincon Casino
33750 Valley Center Road
Valley Center, California 92082
(760) 751-2949
Web Site: www.harrahs.com
Map Location: **#20** (35 miles N.E. of San Diego)

EXPECTED TO OPEN BY EARLY 2001
Special Features: 45,000-square-foot permanent casino and 300-room hotel expected to open by December 2001.

Havasu Landing Casino & Resort
P.O. Box 1707
Havasu Lake, California 92363
(760) 858-4593
Web Site: www.havasulanding.com
Map Location: **#18** (200 miles E. of Los Angeles)

Toll Free Number: (800) 307-3610
Restaurants: 1 Liquor: Yes
Hours: 8:30am-Mid/2am (Fri/Sat)
Other Games: Video BJ
Special Features: Campground rentals (800) 307-3610. Mobile homes on lake available for daily rental (760) 858-5410.

Hopland Sho-Ka-Wah Casino
13101 Nakomis Road
Hopland, California 95449
(707) 744-1395
Web Site: www.shokawah.com
Map Location: **#23** (100 miles N. of San Francisco)

Restaurants: 1 Liquor: No
Other Games: BJ, BG

Jackson Rancheria Casino & Hotel
12222 New York Ranch Road
Jackson, California 95642
(209) 223-1677
Web Site: www.jacksoncasino.com
Map Location: **#9** (60 miles S.E. of Sacramento)

Toll-Free Number: (800) 822-WINN
Rooms: 99 Price Range: $59-$74
Suites: 4 Price Range: $149-$239
Restaurants: 2 Liquor: No
Buffets: D-$12.50
Other Games: BJ, P, LIR, BG (Tue/Wed/Fri-Sun)

Konocti Vista Casino
2755 Mission Rancheria Road
Lakeport, California 95453
(707) 262-1900
Web Site: www.kvcasino.com
Map Location: **#23** (120 miles N. of San Francisco)

Toll-Free Number: (800) FUN-1950
Restaurants: 1 Snack Bar Liquor: No
Other Games: BJ, P, PGP

Lucky Bear Casino
P.O. Box 1348
Hoopa, California 95546
(530) 625-4048
Map Location: **#24** (30 miles N.E. of Eureka)

Restaurants: 1 Snack Bar Liquor: No
Hours: 10am-Mid/2am (Fri/Sat)
Other Games: P, BG

Lucky 7 Casino
350 N. Indian Road
Smith River, California 95567
(707) 487-7777
Map Location: **#7** (100 miles N. of Eureka)

Restaurants: 1 Snack Bar Liquor: No
Other Games: BJ
Casino Size: 3,600 Square Feet

Mono Wind Casino
37302 Rancheria Lane, Box 1060
Auberry, California 93602
(559) 855-4350
Map Location: **#25** (30 miles N.E. of Fresno)

Restaurants: 1 Snack Bar Liquor: No
Other Games: BJ, PGP, BG
Senior Discount: $2 off in restaurant, if 55, or older

Paiute Palace Casino
PO Box 1325
Bishop, California 93514
(760) 873-4150
Web Site: www.paiute.com
Map Location: **#26** (130 miles N.E. of Fresno)

Toll-Free Number: (888) 3-PAIUTE
Restaurants: 1 Liquor: No
Other Games: BJ, P, CSP, BG (Mon/Fri/Sun)
Fun Book: Ask at cashier cage
Senior Discount: 10% off in restaurant, if 55, or older

Palace Indian Gaming Center
17225 Jersey Avenue
Lemoore, California 93245
(559) 924-7751
Web Site: www.thepalace.net
Map Location: **#10** (50 miles S. of Fresno)

Toll-Free Number: (800) 942-6886
Restaurants: 2 (1 open 24 hours) Liquor: No
Casino Size: 17,500 Square Feet
Other Games: Video BJ, BG (Thu-Mon)

Paradise Casino
350 Picacho Road
Winterhaven, California 92283
(760) 572-7777
Web Site: www.paradisecasinoyuma.com
Map Location: **#27** (150 miles E. of San Diego)

Toll-Free Number: (888) 777-4946
Restaurants: 1 Liquor: Yes
Buffets: L/D-$4.25
Other Games: P, BG, Keno

Pechanga Entertainment Center
45000 Pala Road
Temecula, California 92592
(909) 693-1819
Web Site: www.pechanga.com
Map Location: **#28** (50 miles N. of San Diego)

Toll-Free Number: (888) PECHANGA
Restaurants: 2 (1 open 24 hours) Liquor: No
Buffets: B-$6.95 (Sat)/$8.95 (Sun) L-$4.95 D-$6.95
Other Games: BJ, P, CSP, BG
Special Features: 170-space RV park with full hook-ups. Live entertainment and headliner acts.

Pit River Casino
20265 Tamarack Avenue
Burney, California 96013
(530) 335-2334
Map Location: **#29** (190 miles N. of Sacramento)

Toll-Free Number: (888) 245-2992
Restaurants: 1 Snack Bar Liquor: No
Hours: 10am-Midnight Daily
Other Games: BJ, P, BG

Red Fox Casino & Bingo
300 Cahto Drive
Laytonville, California 95454
(707) 984-6800
Map Location: **#30** (150 miles N.W. of Sacramento)

Toll-Free Number: (888) 4-RED-FOX
Restaurants: 1 Snack Bar Liquor: No
Hours: 10am-Mid/2am (Fri/Sat)

Robinson Rancheria Bingo & Casino
1545 E. Highway 20
Nice, California 95464
(707)275-9000
Map Location: **#11** (100 miles N.W. of Sacramento)

Toll-Free Number: (800) 809-3636
Restaurants: 1 Liquor: No
Casino Size: 37,500 Square Feet
Other Games: BJ, P, PGP, BG
Senior Discount: Free lunch buffet and $10 matchplay Mondays 9am-4pm, if 55, or older

San Manuel Indian Bingo & Casino
5797 North Victoria Avenue
Highland, California 92346
(909) 864-5050
Web Site: www.sanmanuel.com
Map Location: **#12** (65 miles E. of Los Angeles)

Toll-Free Number: (800) 359-2464
Restaurants: 2 Snack Bars Liquor: No
Casino Size: 75,000 Square Feet
Other Games: BJ, P, BG
Senior Discount: $10 bingo buy-in on Fridays, if 55, or older
Special Features: Live entertainment weekly.

Shodakai Casino
PO Box 320
Calpella, California 94581
(707) 485-0700
Map Location: **#23** (115 miles N. of San Francisco)

Toll-Free Number: (800) 332-9683
Restaurants: 1 Snack Bar Liquor: No
Other Games: BJ, P, BG (Fri-Mon)

Soboba Casino
23333 Soboba Road
San Jacinto, California 92583
(909) 654-2883
Web Site: www.soboba.net
Map Location: **#3** (90 miles E. of Los Angeles)

Toll-Free Number: (888) 772-SOBOBA
Restaurants: 2 Liquor: Yes
Buffets: B-$4.99 (Only Sun)
Casino Size: 52,000 Square Feet
Other Games: BJ, P, PGP

Spa Casino
140 N. Indian Canyon Drive
Palm Springs, California 92262
(760) 323-5865
Web Site: www.aguacaliente.org
Map Location: **#3** (115 miles E. of Los Angeles)

Toll-Free Number: (800) 258-2WIN
Room Reservations: (800) 854-1279
Rooms: 230 Price Range: $69-$129
Restaurants: 2 (1 open 24 hours) Liquor: Yes
Casino Size: 15,000 Square Feet
Other Games: BJ, CSP, LIR
Special Features: Hotel offers hot mineral spa with massages and facials. 10% room discount for seniors and AAA members.

Spotlight 29 Casino
46200 Harrison Place
Coachella, California 92236
(760) 775-5566
Web Site: www.spotlight29casino.com
Map Location: **#8** (130 miles E. of Los Angeles)

Toll-Free Number: (800) 841-6666
Restaurants: 1 Liquor: Yes
Buffets: Brunch-$8.79 (Sun) L-$4.79 D-$7.29
Other Games: BJ, MB, P, PGP, CSP

Susanville Casino
900 Skyline Drive
Susanville, California 96130
(530) 252-1100
Map Location: **#31** (160 Miles N.E. of Sacramento)

Restaurants: 1 Snack Bar Liquor: No
Hours: 11am-Mid/2am (Fri/Sat)
Other Games: BJ, P, BG (Wed-Sun)
Senior Discount: 15% off in deli, if 55, or older

Sycuan Casino
5469 Dehesa Road
El Cajon, California 92019
(619) 445-6002
Web Site: www.sycuancasino.com
Map Location: **#14** (10 miles E. of San Diego)

Toll-Free Number: (800) 279-2826
Restaurants: 1 Liquor: No
Buffets: L-$7.95 D-$7.95
Casino Size: 73,000 Square Feet
Other Games: BJ, B, MB, P, PGP, BG, S
Fun Book: Ask at slot club
Senior Discount: $5 discount on $15 bingo packs on Sun/Thu.

Table Mountain Casino & Bingo
8184 Table Mountain Road
Friant, California 93626
(559) 822-2485
Map Location: **#15** (15 miles N. of Fresno)

Toll-Free Number: (800) 541-3637
Restaurants: 3 (1 open 24 hours) Liquor: No
Buffets: L-$5.95 D-$7.95 (Only Mon)
Other Games: BJ, P, PGP, BG (Thu-Sun)

Twin Pines Casino
22223 Highway 29 at Rancheria Road
Middletown, California 95461
(707) 987-0197
Web Site: www.twinpine.com
Map Location: **#32** (70 miles W. of Sacramento)

Toll-Free Number: (800) 564-4872
Restaurants: 1 Snack Bar Liquor: No
Other Games: BJ, PGP, BG, Keno
Senior Discount: $10 video match play 10am-7pm Wednesdays, if 55, or older
Special Features: Daycare facility.

Viejas Casino & Turf Club
5000 Willows Road
Alpine, California 91901
(619) 445-5400
Web Site: www.viejas.com
Map Location: **#16** (25 miles E. of San Diego)

Toll-Free Number: (800) 84-POKER
Restaurants: 4 (1 open 24 hours) Liquor: Yes
Buffets: L-$6.99/$9.99 (Sun) D-$8.99
Other Games: BJ, P, PGP, BG, S
Special Features: Outlet shopping center.

Win-River Casino
2100 Redding Rancheria Road
Redding, California 96001
(530) 243-3377
Web Site: www.win-river.com
Map Location: **#17** (163 miles N. of Sacramento)

Toll-Free Number: (800) 280-8946
Restaurants: 1 Snack Bar Liquor: No
Casino Size: 37,000 Square Feet
Other Games: BJ, P, BG (Thu-Sun)

COLORADO

Colorado offers "limited gaming" in the mountain towns of Black Hawk, Central City and Cripple Creek. There are also two Indian casinos (which abide by Colorado's limited gaming rules) in Ignacio and Towaoc. Gambling is limited in two aspects: one, only electronic games (including slots, video poker, video blackjack and video keno) and the table games of poker, blackjack, let it ride and 3-card poker are allowed. Two, a single wager cannot exceed $5.

The rules for poker are such that a raise is considered a separate bet. Three raises per round are allowed. On the last round, two players may go "head-to-head" with an unlimited number of raises. Nine varieties of poker are approved for casino play. Texas Hold 'Em, 7-Card Stud and Omaha are the most popular choices.

Blackjack wagers are limited to a $5 maximum, with most casinos allowing a $2 or $3 minimum bet. However, doubles and splits are considered separate bets. Colorado casinos employ Vegas Strip rules and most allow doubling after splits. Since pairs may be split three times (to make up to four hands) it is theoretically possible to bet $40 on what began as a single $5 wager.

Multiple action blackjack is also available in Colorado. Multiple action allows a player to place up to three bets (of up to $5 each) on a single blackjack hand. This hand is then played for three rounds against the same dealer upcard. Several Colorado casinos offer multiple action blackjack.

Here's information, as supplied by Colorado's Division of Gaming, showing the slot machine payback percentages for each city's casinos for the one year period from July 1, 1999 through June 30, 2000:

	Black Hawk	Central City	Cripple Creek
5¢ Slots	93.33%	92.60%	**93.64%**
25¢ Slots	94.29%	94.02%	**94.36%**
$1 Slots	95.23%	95.02%	**95.33%**
$5 Slots	**96.14%**	94.58%	94.98%
All	**94.55%**	94.01%	94.54%

These numbers reflect the percentage of money returned on each denomination of machine and encompass all electronic machines including video poker and video keno. The best returns for each category are highlighted in bold print and you can see that Black Hawk offered the best returns on $5 machines, while Cripple Creek offered the best returns in all other denominations.

Colorado gaming regulations do not allow the casinos to be open 24 hours. The maximum hours they can be open are from 8am until 2am.

The two major free gaming oriented magazines are *The Gambler* and the *Rocky Mountain News Gaming Guide*. Both are free, and available in most casinos in Colorado. Look in them for ads for casino coupons or fun books. The *Denver Post* Weekend section (published every Friday) also contains coupons and fun book offers for the casinos in Black Hawk and Central City.

For more information on visiting Black Hawk call (303) 582-5221, for Central City information call (800) 542-2999 and for Cripple Creek information call (877) 858-GOLD. For general information on Colorado call the state's tourism board at (800) 433-2656.

Black Hawk

Map Location: #1 (35 miles west of Denver. Take U.S. 6 through Golden to Hwy 119. Take Hwy 119 to Black Hawk. Another route is I-70 West to exit 244. Turn right onto Hwy. 6. Take Hwy 6 to 119 and into Black Hawk.)

The Lodge at Black Hawk and the Isle of Capri are the only two casinos with hotel rooms in that city. The next closest lodging is at Harvey's Wagon Wheel Casino, 3/4-mile up Gregory St. in Central City (see Central City listings for particulars). Another alternative is the Gold Dust Lodge, located on Hwy. 119 about 1.5 miles from Black Hawk casinos. The Gold Dust features 23 remodeled rooms with private baths, TV and telephones.

Fitzgeralds, a nationally-known gaming company, has a casino in downtown Black Hawk.

The casinos in Black Hawk and Central City are located one mile apart. The Black Hawk Shuttle Service provides free transportation around Black Hawk and Harvey's runs a free shuttle service from Black Hawk to Central City.

There are a few bus tour programs such as Ace Express, People's Choice and Casino Transportation, Inc. (CTI) operating between the metropolitan Denver area and Black Hawk/ Central City. These programs are bargain priced ($10, or less) and usually affiliated with one or two casinos that will reimburse a portion of the tour charge and also provide coupons or fun books. Check the "Weekend" section of the Friday *Denver Post* and *Rocky Mountain News* for bus tour ads and for casino ads that feature coupons.

Most Black Hawk casinos offer free parking but some have "captive" parking lots where parking is free, but the parking ticket must be validated hourly. Failure to validate, or leaving the casino, will generate a parking fee of as high as $3 per hour. Black Hawk also has a large public lot called Miner's Mesa that offers free parking and a free shuttle into town.

Black Hawk Station
141 Gregory Street
Black Hawk, Colorado 80422
(303) 582-5582
Web Site: www.blackhawkstationcasino.com

Restaurants: 1 (snack bar)
Other Games: Blackjack

Bull Durham Saloon & Casino
110 Main Street
(303) 582-0810

Restaurants: 1 (snack bar)
Other Games: Blackjack
Fun Book: Coupons often given out at door
Special Features: Free drinks for $1 slot and table players.

Bullwhackers Black Hawk Casino
101 Gregory Street
(303) 764-1600
Web Site: www.bullwhackers.com

Toll-Free Number: (800) GAM-BULL
Restaurants: 1
Casino Size: 36,000 Square Feet
Other Games: Blackjack, Poker, Let It Ride, 3-Card Poker
Senior Discount: 2x slot club points on Tues.
Special Features: Cash back slot club. Video arcade. Free (with validation) parking lot.

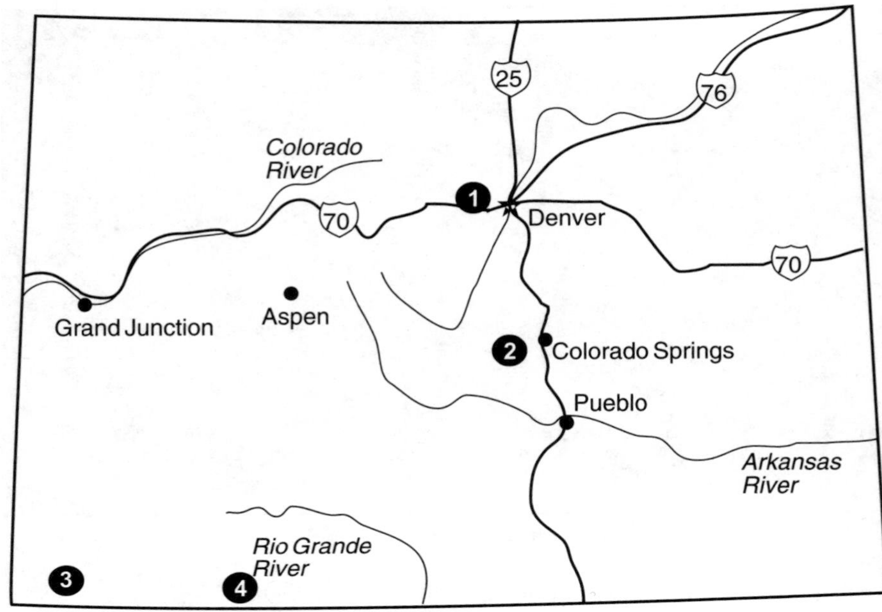

Bullwhackers Silver Hawk
100 Chase Street
(303) 764-1400
Web Site: www.bullwhackers.com

Toll-Free Number: (800) GAM-BULL
Restaurants: 1
Casino Size: 12,000 Square Feet
Other Games: Blackjack
Special Features: Cash back slot club. Video arcade. Free parking (with validation). Frequent in-casino promotions.

Canyon Casino
131 Main Street
(303) 777-1111

Restaurants: 1
Other Games: Blackjack, Let It Ride,
3-Card Poker
Special Features: Free on-site parking (with validation). Cash back slot club. Ongoing promotions.

Colorado Central Station Casino
340 Main Street
(303) 582-3000
Web Site: www.coloradocentralstation.com

Restaurants: 2
Buffet: B-$4.30 L-$7.95 D-$9.95
Other Games: Blackjack, Poker, Let It Ride
Fun Book: Available through group and bus tour program. Coupons sometimes handed out at door.
Special Features: Free valet parking (with validation). Cash back slot club. Live entertainment. Burger King restaurant. Receive 50% buffet discount with slot club card.

Eureka! Casino
211 Gregory Street
(303) 582-1040

Restaurants: 1
Special Features: 50¢ strawberry margarita. $1 shrimp cocktail. Lucky Dragon Chinese restaurant.

Fitzgeralds Casino
101 Main Street
(303) 582-6162
Web Site: www.fitzgeralds.com

Toll-Free Number: (800) 538-5825
Restaurants: 1
Other Games: Blackjack
Special Features: Cash back slot club. Covered parking. Frequent in-casino promotions.

Gilpin Hotel Casino
111 Main Street
(303) 582-1133
Web Site:
wwwthegilpinhotelcasino.citysearch.com

Restaurants: 2
Buffets: B-$3.98 (Mon-Sat)/$19.90 (Sun)
D-$15.54 (Fri)
Other Games: Blackjack
Casino Marketing: (303) 278-1114
Special Features: Live entertainment. Cash back slot club. Closed-circuit showings of sports events. Frequent slot tournaments. Free valet parking (with validation). 50% buffet discount with slot club card.

Golden Gates Casino
261 Main Street
(303) 582-1650
Web Site: www.goldengatescasino.com

Restaurants: 1
Other Games: Blackjack, 3-Card Poker
Special Features: Free valet parking (with validation).

Isle of Capri Casino - Black Hawk
401 Main Street
(303) 998-7777
Web Site: www.isleofcapricasino.com

Toll-Free Number (800) 843-4753 (Press-6)
Rooms: 112 Price Range: $89-$129
Suites: 125 Price Range: $139-$175
Restaurants: 3 (1 open 24 hours)
Buffets: B-$5.77 L-$7.77 D-$11.77
Hours: 8am-2am
Other Games: Blackjack, LIR
Senior Discount: Various, if 50, or older.
Special Features: Colorado's largest casino and newest casino hotel.

Jazz Alley Casino
321 Main Street
(303) 582-1125

Restaurants: 1
Other Games: Blackjack, 3-Card Poker
Senior Discount: Free lunch 11am-2pm on
Wed. after earning 10 points on VIP Card
Fun Books: Handed out at the front entrance.
Special Features: Cash back slot club. Frequent food promotions in restaurant. Free valet parking (with validation). $10 cash back when you take CTI shuttle (278-4838), or $15 cashback, when you ride the Coach USA shuttle (421-2780) after earning 10 points on VIP card.

The Lodge Casino at Black Hawk
240 Main Street
(303) 582-1771

Toll-Free Number: (877) 711-1177
Rooms: 47 Price Range: $75-$199
Suites: 3 Price Range: $250-$499
Restaurants: 3
Buffets: B-$5.49 L-$7.49
D-$10.99/$19.95 (Fri)
Other Games: Blackjack, Poker, Let It Ride,
3-Card Poker
Special Features: 2-for-1 Friday dinner buffet coupons for slot club members. $10 off room rate with slot club card, or to AAA, or AARP members.

Mardi Gras Casino
333 Main Street
(303) 582-5600
Web Site: www. mardigrasbh.com

Restaurants: 2
Other Games: Blackjack, Poker, 3-Card Poker
Special Features: Free on-site parking. Receive $5 voucher usable on your next trip when you park in garage. Slot club.

Red Dolly Casino
530 Gregory Street
(303) 582-1100

Restaurants: 1
Casino Size: 7,000 Square Feet
Special Features: Free on-site parking (with validation). 10-ounce top sirloin steak dinner for $3.95. 20-ounce steak dinner for $5.95.

Richman Casino
101 Richman Street
(303) 582-0400

Restaurants: 1 snack bar
Other Games: Blackjack, 3-card poker
Special Features: Free valet parking (with validation).

Riviera Black Hawk Casino
444 Main Street
(303) 582-1000

Buffet: L-$6.99 D-$7.99
Other Games: Blackjack, Poker

Wild Card Saloon & Casino
112 Main Street
(303) 582-3412

Restaurants: 1 (snack bar)
Special Features: Convenience store located in casino.

Central City

Map location: **#1** (same as Black Hawk). Central City is located one mile from Black Hawk. Turn left at the third stoplight on Hwy. 119 and proceed up Gregory Street.

Harvey's Wagon Wheel Hotel/Casino is the only hotel in Central City but there are also a few bed & breakfasts: the Gregory Inn (7 rooms, $55 to $155, 303-582-5561), Chateau L'acadienne (3 rooms, $60 to $94, 303-582-5209) and the High Street Inn (3 rooms, $75 to $85, 303-582-0622).

Some casinos (Teller House, Bonanza) have captive parking lots. There are also several small private parking lots in the immediate area which usually charge $5. Some casinos will reimburse this fee after a one-hour stay in their casino. Public Parking is also provided free of charge at lots B, C and D. For Central City tourism information call (800) 542-2999.

Central Palace Casino
132 Lawrence Street
(303) 477-7117

Toll-Free Number: (800) 822-7466
Restaurants: 1
Buffets: $6.95
Other Games: Blackjack

Doc Holliday Casino
101 Main Street
(303) 582-1400

Restaurants: 1
Casino Size: 5,000 Square Feet
Fun Book: Only given to tour groups
Special Features: Single-deck blackjack. Video arcade. Taco Bell Express restaurant.

Dostal Alley Saloon & Gaming Emporium
1 Dostal Alley
(303) 582-1610

Famous Bonanza/Lucky Strike/Easy Street
107 Main Street
(303) 582-5914
Web Site: www.famousbonanza.com

Restaurants: 1
Other Games: Blackjack, 3-Card Poker
Special Features: Restaurant features Mexican specialities. Video arcade. All you can eat pasta special (Mon-Thu), prime rib dinner special for $4.95 (Fri-Sun).

Harvey's Wagon Wheel Hotel/Casino
321 Gregory Street
(303) 582-0800
Web Site: www.harveys.com

Toll-Free Number: (800) 924-6646
Room Reservations: (800) HARVEYS
Rooms: 118 Price Range $69-$129
Suites: 6 Price Range $140-$175
Restaurants: 2
Other Games: Blackjack, Poker, Let It Ride, 3-Card Poker
Fun Book: Available through slot club.
Special Features: Tony Roma's restaurant. Cash back slot club. "Infinity Mine" collapses every 30 minutes. Bus program from several Denver locations. Free valet and self parking. 10% room discount to slot club members.

Cripple Creek

Map Location: **#2** (47 miles west of Colorado Springs. Take exit 141 at Colorado Springs off I-25. Go west on Hwy. 24 to the town of Divide. Turn left onto Hwy. 67 and go 18 miles to Cripple Creek.)

Cripple Creek has several hotel/casinos the largest of which is the Double Eagle Hotel & Casino. There is also a 67-room Holiday Inn Express, located 1/4-mile from the casinos, which offers rates of $49 (Winter) to $99 (Summer) per night. Free shuttle service is provided to and from the casinos. For reservations, call 1-800-HOLIDAY.

Many Cripple Creek casinos hand out coupons and fun books at their doors. Also check the ads in the *Colorado Springs Gazette*, the *Pueblo Chieftain* and the free tourist magazines.

There are five casinos that sponsor their own shuttle service from Colorado Springs and Pueblo. It's called the Ramblin' Express and the round-trip fare is about $20 per person, however, you are also given a coupon book which contains a variety of offers that are valid at the five sponsoring casinos.

Most Cripple Creek parking lots charge a fee of $3 to $5 which is usually reimbursed by the casino. Check at the lot for each particular casino's parking rules. For Cripple Creek tourism information call (877) 858-GOLD.

Black Diamond/Silver Spur Casinos
425 E. Bennett Avenue
Cripple Creek, Co 80813
(719) 689-2898

Restaurants: 1 (snack bar)
Casino Size: 3,300 Square Feet
Other Games: Blackjack
Fun Book: Coupons handed out at front door
Special Features: **Black Diamond** and **Silver Spur** are adjacent casinos that are interconnected. Free drinks for players. $1 daily drink specials. 99¢ shrimp cocktail. Real gold vein in wall (upstairs). Live entertainment at Silver Spur Theater.

Brass Ass Casino
264 E. Bennett Avenue
(719) 689-2104

Restaurants: 1 (snack bar)
Special Features: Free hot dogs and popcorn. Associated with Midnight Rose and J.P McGill's.

Bronco Billy's Sports Bar & Casino
233 E. Bennett Avenue
(719) 689-2142
Web Site: www.broncobillyscasino.com

Toll Free Number: (877) 989-2142
Restaurants: 2
Other Games: Blackjack, 3-Card Poker
Casino Size: 21,000 Square Feet
Fun Book: Ask at cashier's cage
Special Features: Includes **Buffalo Billy's** casino with sports theater and weekend steakhouse. 122" video wall with over 60 satellite tv's tuned to sports. 49¢ breakfast from 8am to 11am. Full-service restaurant with $6.95 t-bone steak special from 2pm daily. Double jackpots at top two minutes of every hour and 12am-1:30am every night.

Colorado Grande Gaming Parlor
300 E. Bennett Avenue
(719) 689-3517
Web Site: www.anchorgaming.com

Restaurants: 1
Senior Discount: Free lunch on Tuesday with AARP card and active slot club card
Special Features: Cash back slot club.

Creeker's Casino
272 E. Bennett Avenue
(719) 689-3239
Web Site: www.creekerscasino.com

Restaurants: 1
Buffets: L/D-$6.95 (Sun)/$11.95 (Fri) $12.95 (Sat)
Special Features: Cash back slot club. Associated with Double Eagle Hotel and Casino. Free pizza for players. Arcade.

Double Eagle Hotel & Casino
442 E. Bennett Avenue
(719) 689-5000
Web Site: www.decasino.com

Toll-Free Reservations: (800) 711-7234
Rooms: 151 Price Range: $59-$119
Suites: 8 Price Range: $119-$160
Restaurants: 1
Buffets: B-$5.95 L-$8.95
D-$9.95/$13.95 (Fri)
Other Games: Blackjack, Poker, Let It Ride
Fun Book: Ask at the slot club
Special Features: Valet parking. Free self-parking. Free live entertainment. Video arcade. Bus service from Colorado Springs, Pueblo and Denver.

Gold Rush Hotel & Casino/Gold Digger's Casino
209 E. Bennett Avenue
(719) 689-2646

Toll-Free Number: (800) 235-8239
Rooms: 14 Price Range: $49-$79
Restaurants: 2
Other Games: Blackjack, Let It Ride, Poker
Senior Discount: Various, if 50, or older
Special Features: Gold Digger's and Gold Rush are adjacent properties interconnected to form one casino. All rooms have TV, telephone and private bath. Golden Grille restaurant. Video arcade located next to casino. $2.99 New York steak special. 10% room discount to seniors and AAA members.

Imperial Casino Hotel
123 N. Third Street
(719) 689-2922

Toll-Free Number: (800) 235-2922
Rooms: 29 Price Range: $45-$85
Suites: 2 Price Range: $100-$145
Restaurants: 2
Other Games: Blackjack, Poker
Fun Book: Coupons handed out at door
Special Features: 9 rooms available with private bath. Live entertainment.

J.P. McGill's
232 E. Bennett Avenue
(719) 689-2497

Restaurants: 1
Special Features : Associated with Midnight Rose Hotel and Casino.

Johnny Nolon's Casino
301 E. Bennett Avenue
(719) 689-2080

Restaurants: 2
Special Features: Full-service restaurant with nightly specials and Subway sandwich shop.

Midnight Rose Hotel & Casino
256 E. Bennett Avenue
(719) 689-2865
Web Site: www.midnightrose.com

Toll-Free Number: (800) 635-5825
Rooms: 19 Price Range: $39-$89
Restaurants: 2
Buffet: L-$5.99 D-$6.99/$7.99 (Fri-Sun)
Other Games: Blackjack, Poker, Let It Ride
Fun Book: Ask at cashier's cage
Special Features: All rooms have TV, phone and private bath. Wendy's, Pizza Hut, Baskin Robbins and video arcade downstairs. Full-service restaurant (with daily specials) upstairs. Ramblin' Express shuttle service from Colorado Springs, Pueblo, Canon City and Castle Rock.

Palace Hotel & Casino
172 E. Bennett Avenue
(719) 689-2993

Rooms: 16 Price Range: $19-$69
Restaurants: 1
Special Features: 3 rooms available with private bath.

Uncle Sam's Casino
251 E. Bennett Avenue
(719) 689-2222

Special Features: Free soup and sandwich given to players.

Virgin Mule
259 E. Bennett Avenue
(719) 689-2734

Restaurants: 1 snack bar

Wild West Casino
443 E. Bennett Avenue
(719) 689-4180

Restaurants: 1
Special Features: Mexican restaurant.

Womacks/Legends Hotel & Casino
200-220 E. Bennett Avenue
(719) 689-0333
Web Site: www.womacks.com

Toll-Free Number: (888) 966-2257
Rooms: 8 Price Range: $39-$79
Restaurants: 1
Other Games: Blackjack, Let It Ride, Poker
Special Features: All rooms with private bath and satellite tv (no telephone). Womacks and Legends are adjacent properties interconnected to form one casino. Cash back slot club. Free parking. Free drinks.

Indian Casinos

Sky Ute Casino and Lodge
14826 Highway 172 N./P.O. Box 340
Ignacio, Colorado 81137
(970) 563-3000
Web Site: www.skyutecasino.com
Map Location: **#4** (345 miles S.W. of Denver, 20 miles S.E. of Durango)

Toll-Free Number: (800) 876-7017
Rooms: 36 Price Range: $45-$69
Restaurants: 1 Liquor: Yes
Buffets: B-$4.99 (Sat-Sun) L-$6.99
D-$8.99/$12.99 (Fri-Sat)
Hours: 24 Hours Daily
Other Games: Blackjack, Poker,
Bingo (Wed/Thu/Sun)
Senior Discount: 10% room and restaurant discount, if 65, or older
Special Features: Liquor is not served in casino, only in the restaurant. Southern Ute Cultural Center and Museum is located next to casino.

Ute Mountain Casino & RV Park
3 Weeminuche Drive/P.O. Drawer V
Towaoc, Colorado 81334
(970) 565-8800
Web Site: www.utemountaincasino.com
Map Location: **#3** (425 miles S.W. of Denver, 11 miles S. of Cortez on Hwys. 160/166)

Toll-Free Number: (800) 258-8007
Restaurants: 1 Liquor: No
Buffets: B-$4.50 (Sat-Sun) L-$5.95
D-$7.75/$10.95 (Fri)
Casino Size: 32,000 Square Feet
Hours: 8am-4am Daily
Other Games: Blackjack, Poker, Let It Ride,
Keno, Bingo (Fri-Tue)
Fun Book: Given at local motels/RV parks
Senior Discount: 15% restaurant discount, if 55, or older.
Special Features: 84-space RV Park. Ute Tribal Park tours available.

CONNECTICUT

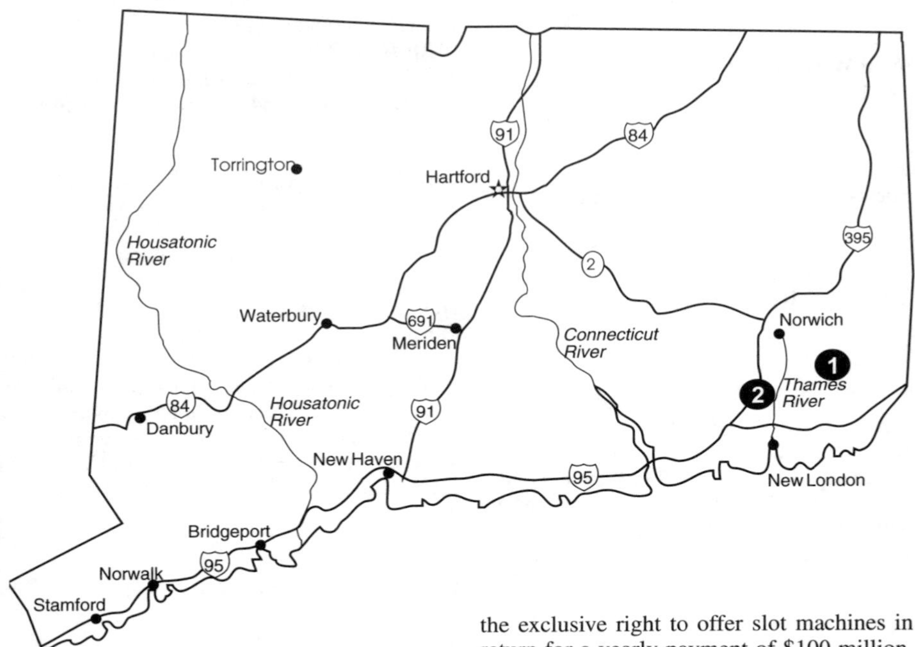

Foxwoods was New England's first casino. It is also the largest casino in the world and according to *Business Week* it is "the most profitable gambling operation in the U.S., if not the world." The slot machines alone bring in more than $2 million a day in gross profit.

The Mashantucket Pequot Tribe which operates Foxwoods had to sue the state to allow the casino to open. They argued that since the state legally permitted "Las Vegas Nights," where low-stakes casino games were operated to benefit charities, then the tribe should be entitled to do the same. Eventually, they won their case before the U.S. Supreme Court and began construction of their casino which was financed by a Malaysian conglomerate (after 22 U.S. lenders turned down their loan requests).

When the casino first opened in February 1992, slot machines were not permitted. In January 1993 a deal was made between Governor Weicker and the Pequots which gave the tribe the exclusive right to offer slot machines in return for a yearly payment of $100 million, or 25% of the gross slot revenue - whichever is greater. The agreement was subject to cancellation, however, if the state allowed slot machines anywhere else in Connecticut.

In early 1994 the Mohegan tribe signed a compact with the state that allows them to offer casino gambling at their reservation in Uncasville (map location #2). The Pequots gave permission for the Mohegans to have slot machines in their casino and in return the state lowered the Pequots yearly payment requirements to $80 million, or 25% of the gross revenue - whichever is greater. The same payment schedule also applies to the Mohegans. The payment schedules are subject to cancellation, however, if the state legalizes any other form of casino gambling. The Mohegan casino opened in October 1996.

The minimum gambling age at both properties is 18 for bingo and 21 for the casino. Both casinos are also open 24 hours. For information on visiting Connecticut call the state's Vacation Center at (800) 282-6863.

Foxwoods is the world's largest casino with over 300,000 square feet of gaming space. The property features three hotels, 24 food outlets, three regular casinos, a smoke-free casino, a slots-only casino, a simulcast facility a 3,200-seat bingo and a total of more than 5,000 electronic gaming machines.

The games offered at Foxwoods are: blackjack, craps, roulette, baccarat, mini-baccarat, big six wheel, bingo, poker, pai gow poker, Caribbean stud poker, let it ride, keno, pull tabs, red dog, casino war and chuck-a-luck. There is also a simulcast facility with pari-mutuel betting.

Foxwoods Resort Casino
Route 2
Ledyard, Connecticut 06339
(860) 312-3000
Web Site: www.foxwoods.com
Map Location: **#1** (45 miles S.E. of Hartford; 12 miles N. of I-95 at Mystic). From I-95 take exit 92 to Rt. 2-West, casino is 7 miles ahead. From I-395 take exit 79A to Rt. 2A follow to Rt. 2-East, casino is 2 miles ahead.

Toll-Free Number: (800) PLAY-BIG
Hotel Reservations: (800) FOXWOODS
Rooms: 1,416 Price Range: $140-$325
Suites: 198 Price Range: $175-$1,500
Restaurants: 24 (3 open 24 hours)
Buffets: B-$7.95 L-$12.95 D-$12.95
Casino Size: 314,492 Square Feet
Casino Marketing: (800) 99-SLOTS
Senior Discount: 10% room discount for AAA and AARP members
Special Features: Three hotels with pool, spa, health club and beauty salon. Turbo Ride: a 48-seat computer-controlled large-screen-movie adventure ride. Cinedrome nightclub. 1,500-seat theatrical showroom with headliner entertainment. Gift shops. "Wampum Card" earns complimentaries for players.

The following information is from Connecticut's Division of Special Revenue regarding Foxwoods' slot payback percentages for the fiscal year ending June 30, 2000:

Denomination	Payback %
5¢	89.23
25¢	90.71
50¢	91.26
$1.00	92.00
$5.00	94.76
$10.00	94.75
$25.00	95.42
$100.00	95.93
Average	**91.78**

These figures reflect the total percentages returned by each denomination of slot machine from July 1, 1999 through June 30, 2000. Foxwoods' total win on its slot machines during that year was slightly less than $757 million and of that amount 25%, or about $189 million, was paid to the state.

Keep in mind that the casino doesn't pay any tax on its table games and therefore it isn't required to report the profits on that part of its operation. A rough estimate of the table game wins, however, is possible. Since the average casino generates about 65% of its profits from its slot machines, it can be estimated that Foxwoods' total combined (slots and table games) win is about $1.16 billion. After subtracting the slot winnings of $757 million this leaves a table games win of about $403 million.

The games offered at Mohegan Sun are: blackjack, craps, roulette, baccarat, mini-baccarat, wheel of fortune, bingo, poker, pai gow poker, Caribbean stud poker, let it ride, Spanish 21, casino war and keno.

Mohegan Sun Casino
1 Mohegan Sun Boulevard
Uncasville, Connecticut 06382
(860) 204-8000
Map Location: **#2**
Web Site: www.mohegansun.com

Toll-Free Number: (888) 226-7711
Restaurants: 20 (2 open 24 hours)
Buffets: B-$7.95 L-$11.95 D-$11.95
Casino Size: 180,000 Square Feet
Casino Marketing: (888) 226-7711
Special Features: Restaurants include: three fine dining, New York-style deli, buffet, coffee shop and a food court with specialty food outlets. 6,000-square-foot Kid's Quest - supervised children's activity center. On-site gas station. Free nightly entertainment in the Wolf Den Showroom with headline performers.

Here's information from Connecticut's Division of Special Revenue regarding Mohegan Sun's slot payback percentages for the fiscal year ending June 30, 2000:

Denomination	Payback %
25¢	90.86
50¢	91.03
$1.00	92.06
$5.00	94.51
$10.00	95.10
$25.00	95.41
$100.00	94.08
$500.00	86.76
Average	**91.97**

These figures reflect the total percentages returned by each denomination of slot machine from July 1, 1999 through June 30, 2000. Mohegan Sun's total win on its slot machines during that period was slightly more than $529 million and of that amount 25%, or about $132 million, was paid to the state.

DELAWARE

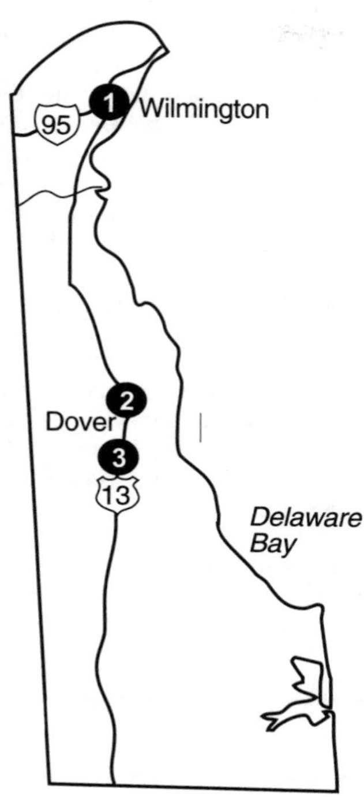

Delaware's three pari-mutuel facilities all feature slot machines. Technically, the machines are video lottery terminals (VLT's) because they are operated in conjunction with the Delaware Lottery. Unlike VLT's in other states, however, Delaware's machines pay out in cash. The VLT's also play other games including: video poker, video keno and video blackjack.

According to figures from the Delaware Lottery for the six-month period from January 1, 2000 through June 25, 2000 the average VLT return at Delaware Park was 92.50%, at Dover Downs it was 91.50% and at Midway Slots & Simulcast it was 90.12%.

The minimum gambling age is 21, For more information on visiting Delaware call the state's tourism office at (800) 441-8846.

Delaware Park Racetrack & Slots
777 Delaware Park Boulevard
Wilmington, Delaware 19804
(302) 994-2521
Web Site: www.delpark.com
Map Location: **#1**

Toll-Free Number: (800) 41-SLOTS
Hours: 8am-2am/1pm-2am (Sun)
Restaurants: 8
Buffets: L/D-$9.95 (Fridays)
Special Features: Live thoroughbred racing April through November. Daily simulcasting of horse racing.

Dover Downs Slots
1131 N. DuPont Highway
Dover, Delaware 19901
(302) 674-4600
Web Site: www.doverdowns.com
Map Location: **#2**

Toll-Free Number: (800) 711-5882
Hours: 8am-2am/1pm-2am (Sun)
Restaurants: 2
Buffets: B-$6.95 (Sat) L-$7.45 D-$8.95
Casino Size: 64,000 Square Feet
Special Features: Live harness racing November through April. Daily simulcasting of horse racing. Live entertainment, concerts and dinner shows.

Midway Slots & Simulcast
Delaware State Fairgrounds
U.S. 13 South
Harrington, Delaware 19952
(302) 398-4920
Web Site: www.midwayslots.com
Map Location: **#3** (20 miles S. of Dover)

Toll-Free Number: (888) 88-SLOTS
Hours: 8am-2am/1pm-2am (Sun)
Restaurants: 2
Buffets: L/D-$8.99
Senior Discount: Various, if 50, or older
Special Features: Live harness racing September through November at Harrington Raceway. Daily simulcasting of horse racing.

FLORIDA

Florida does not have legalized casino gambling. It does, however, have a thriving day-cruise industry which offers gamblers the opportunity to board ships that cruise offshore where casino gambling is legal. From the east coast the boats sail three miles out into the Atlantic Ocean and from the west coast the boats travel nine miles out into the Gulf of Mexico.

There are a variety of boats in operation ranging from Port Canaveral's 1,800-passenger Ambassador II cruise ship all the way down to the yacht-sized SunCruz Casino boat in Key Largo which carries 150 passengers.

Generally, you will find that the larger ships have more of a variety of things to do besides the gambling, but the cost will be a little higher because of added port/service charges. Most of the ships that sail from the major ports, such as Port Everglades and the Port of Miami, will add port/service charges to the quoted cruise price. Usually, there is also a charge to park your car at those locations. Since late 1994 many smaller ships have begun operations and because they don't dock at the large ports they usually don't have port/service charges added to their cruise prices. Also, most of them offer free parking. You will find that almost all of the ships are constantly running price specials so don't be surprised if you call and are quoted a price lower than the regular brochure rates listed here.

All ships offer: slots, video poker, blackjack, craps, roulette and Caribbean stud poker. Some casinos also offer: baccarat (B), mini-baccarat (MB), sports book (SB), poker (P), pai gow poker (PGP), let it ride (LIR) and bingo (BG). Each boat sets its own minimum gambling age: on some boats it's 21 and on others it's 18. The minimum drinking age on all boats is 21.

The nearest Caribbean casinos are in the Bahamas. There is one on Grand Bahama Island: The Casino at Bahamia (800) 223-1818 which operates a 727 jet charter service with two flights daily from the Fort Lauderdale airport. One flight leaves at 9am and returns at 5:15pm. The other flight leaves at 6:30pm and returns at 12:45am. Grand Bahama Island is 90 miles from Fort Lauderdale and the flight takes 20 minutes. The cost is $79 (plus taxes of $43) which includes round-trip taxi transportation between the airport and the casino. Look in the coupon section in the back of this book for a special free trip offer to Casino at Bahamia.

The other two casinos are in the Bahamian capital of Nassau which is on New Providence Island: Nassau Marriott Resort & Crystal Palace Casino (800) 222-7466 and Atlantis, Paradise Island (800) 321-3000.

There is daily scheduled jet service on several airlines to the Nassau airport from both Miami and Fort Lauderdale. Nassau is 150 miles from Miami and the flying time is approximately 45 minutes.

For Florida visitor information call (904) 488-5607. For information on the Florida Keys or Key West call (800) 352-5397.

Crystal River

Map Location: **#16** (90 miles N. of Tampa)

SunCruz Casino - Crystal River
(727) 848-3423
Web Site: www.suncruzcasino.com

Reservation Number: (800) 474-DICE
Gambling Age: 18
Ship's Registry: U.S.A.
Food Service: A la Carte Menu
Schedule:
11:00am - 6:00pm (Mon-Wed)
9:00am - 4:00pm (Thu-Sun)
5:00pm - 12:00am (Thu-Sun)
Price: $5
Port Charges: Included
Parking: Free
Casino Size: 3,000 Square Feet
Other Games: LIR
Special Features: 150-passenger *SunCruz IV* departs from the Barge Canal off U.S. 19 in Inglis, 8 miles north of Crystal River. Must be 18, or older, to board.

Daytona Beach

Map Location: **#12**

SunCruz Casino - Daytona
4884 Front Street
Ponce Inlet, Florida 32127
(904) 322-9000
Web Site: www.suncruzcasino.com

Reservation Number: (800) 474-DICE
Gambling Age: 18
Ship's Registry: U.S.A.
Food Service: A la Carte Menu
Schedule:
11:00am - 4:00pm (Mon-Fri)
12:00pm - 5:00pm (Sat/Sun)
7:00pm - 12:00am (Sun-Thu)
7:00pm - 12:30am (Fri/Sat)
Price: $10
Port Charges: Included
Parking: Free
Casino Size: 18,000 Square Feet
Other Games: MB, P, LIR, CSP
Special Features: 560-passenger *SunCruz III* departs from Ponce Inlet near Down the Hatch restaurant. Free boarding cocktail and hors d'oeuvres while in port. Must be 18, or older, to board.

Fernandina Beach

Map Location: **#17** (35 miles N.of Jacksonville)

Stardancer Casino - Fernandina Beach
500 S. Front Street
Fernandina Beach, Florida 32034
(904) 491-8877

Reservation Number: (877) WIN-3711
Gambling Age: 21
Ship's Registry: U.S.A.
Buffets: L-$6 D-$8.50
Schedule:
12:30am - 5:30pm
7:30pm - 12:30am
Price: $20
Port Charges: Included
Parking: Free
Special Features: 299-passenger *Stardancer* sails from port located on Amelia Island.

Fort Lauderdale

Map Location: **#2**

New SeaEscape
2701 W. Oakland Park Boulevard
Fort Lauderdale, Florida 33311
(954) 453-2200
Web Site: www.seaescape.com

Reservation Number: (877) SEA-ESCAPE
Gambling Age: 18
Ship's Registry: Bahamas
Food Service: Buffet Included
Schedule:
10:00am - 4:00pm (Tue-Sat)
11:00am - 4:30pm (Sun)
7:30pm - 12:30am (Mon-Thu)
7:30pm - 1:30am (Fri/Sat)
6:30pm- 11:30pm (Sun)
Prices: Day- $29.95/$34.95 (Sun)
Eve- $29.95 (Mon-Thu) /$39.95 (Fri/Sat)
Port Charges: Included
Other Games: MB, P, PGP, LIR, BG, PG
Senior Discount: $5 off regular fare on any cruise, if 55, or older
Special Features: 1,050-passenger *Island Adventure* sails from Port Everglades in Fort Lauderdale. All prices are for advance purchase tickets only - $10 surcharge on tickets purchased at pier. Showroom with live entertainment on each cruise. Full-service dinner upgrade available. Private cabin rentals available. Children's prices offered on all cruises. Call for reservation to poker room. Ship makes one cruise to Bimini, Bahamas once each month.

SunCruz Casino - Hollywood
647 E. Dania Beach Boulevard
Dania, Florida 33004
(954) 929-3800
Web Site: www.suncruzcasino.com

Reservation Number: (800) 474-DICE
Gambling Age: 18
Ship's Registry: U.S.A.
Food Service: $5 lunch buffet, $7 dinner buffet and a la carte menu available.
Schedule:
11:00am - 4:15pm (Mon-Fri)
12:00pm - 5:30pm (Sat/Sun)
7:30pm - 12:30am (Sun-Thu)
7:30pm - 1:15am (Fri/Sat/holidays)
Price: $10

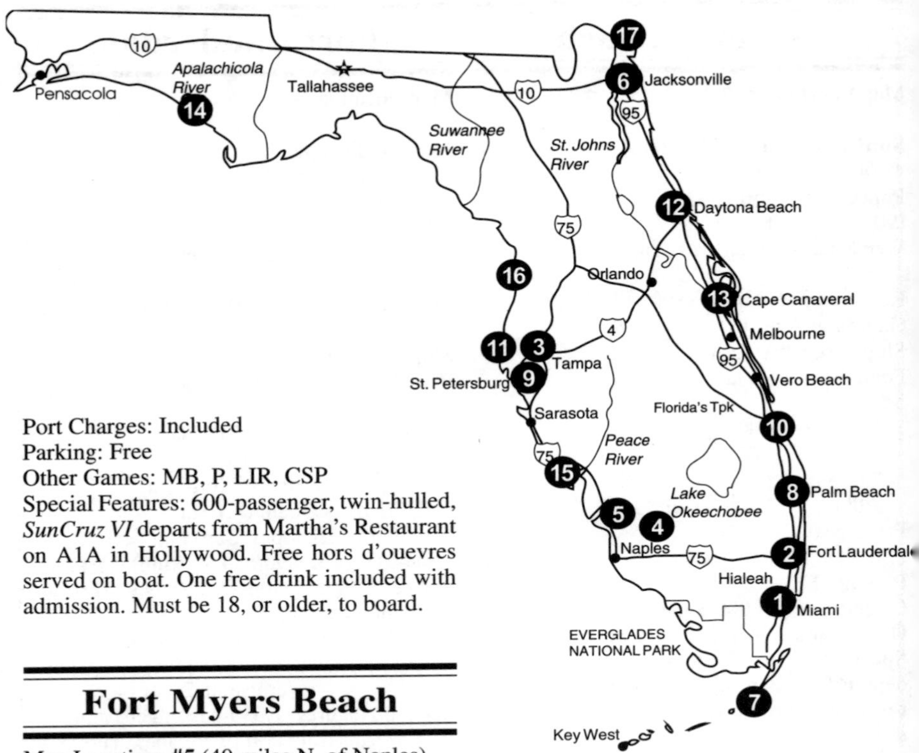

Port Charges: Included
Parking: Free
Other Games: MB, P, LIR, CSP
Special Features: 600-passenger, twin-hulled, *SunCruz VI* departs from Martha's Restaurant on A1A in Hollywood. Free hors d'ouevres served on boat. One free drink included with admission. Must be 18, or older, to board.

Fort Myers Beach

Map Location: **#5** (40 miles N. of Naples)

Big M Casino
450 Harbor Court
Fort Myers Beach, Florida 33931
(941) 765-7529
Web Site: www.bigmcasino.com

Toll-Free Number: (888) 373-3521
Gambling Age: 21
Ship's Registry: U.S.A.
Buffets: L-$7.95 D-$11.95
Schedule:
11:00am - 4:30pm (Daily)
6:00pm -11:30pm (Daily)
Prices: $15.00/$20.00 (Sat evening)
Port Charges: Included
Parking: Free Valet Parking
Other Games: LIR
Special Features: 400-passenger *Big M* sails from Moss Marina next to Snug Harbor on Fort Myers Beach. Must be 21, or older, to board.

Stardancer Casino - Fort Myers Beach
645 San Carlos Boulevard
Fort Myers Beach, Florida 33931
(941) 463-5000

Reservation Number: (800) 688-PLAY
Gambling Age: 21
Ship's Registry: Panama
Food Service: Included
Schedule:
10:30am - 4:30pm (Daily)
6:30pm -12:30am (Mon-Thu)
6:30pm - 1:00am (Fri/Sat)
Prices: $30/$35 (Fri/Sat Eve)
Port Charges: None
Parking: Free
Other Games: P
Special Features: Boat was purchased by Stardancer at press time and all listed information is subject to change by them. 340-passenger *Stardancer* sails from Snug Harbor on Fort Myers Beach. Must be 21, or older, to board.

The IGT Card Casino Chip Program

Because of the intense competition among South Florida's casino boats some of them are involved a special promotional program that can provide some great savings to casino-goers. The program involves the *In Good Taste* (IGT) credit card which offers a 25% discount on gambling chips purchased with the card.

The IGT card has been around for more than 25 years and originally started as a discount credit card for use only at restaurants. You can still use the card for a 25% discount at restaurants but it now offers that same discount in other areas including: airline travel, hotel lodging, cruises, Las Vegas and Biloxi casino gambling vacations, florists, dry cleaners, magazine subscriptions and more.

Whenever you make a purchase with the IGT card you receive a 25% discount when you are billed. They do not, however, give a discount on the tax or tip. As an example, let's say you charge a $100 dinner on the card, plus $6 tax and a $15 tip for a total of $121. When you get your bill from IGT you will be charged $75 for the dinner ($100 less 25%), plus $6 tax and the $15 tip for a total of $96. Upon receipt of the bill you also have the option of paying it by check or charging it to your Visa, MasterCard or Discover card.

As of August 2000 there were four casino boats in South Florida participating in the IGT program. On the Casino Princesa in Miami you can purchase up to $125 in special chips on the IGT card. You will only be billed $93.75 by IGT which means you are starting off $31.25 ahead. You can receive all $125 worth of chips in $5 or $25 denominations. These special chips can only be played on table games and cannot be cashed - they must be played. If you win your bet you will be paid with regular chips and the special IGT chips will continue to remain in play until your bet loses. You are allowed to participate in the IGT program on the boat a maximum of once a week.

The SunCruz boats in Hollywood, Key Largo and Riviera Beach also participate in the IGT program but they will all allow you to buy up to $250 in chips. All three boats will also give you the choice of receiving $100 in $5 chips, or $250 in $25 chips. If you opt for the $5 chips you will be required to bet a minimum of $10 each time. The rest of the program is pretty much the same with IGT billing you $75 for the $100 in chips, or $187.50 for the $250 in chips, meaning you are starting off either $25 or $62.50 ahead.

The Riviera Beach location limits you to once per week for the program while the Key Largo and Hollywood locations are a little more restrictive because they limit you to just one visit per month.

IGT also has the chip program in place at the Majesty Casino Cruise ship in Freeprt, New York. On this boat you are allowed to purchase $250 in IGT chips once a week.

The IGT program is truly a powerful program because you are starting off with a 25% edge against the house. Lest you forget, it is supposed to be the other way around! On rare occasions some Las Vegas casinos have special chip programs similar to this where you can get maybe a 5% edge at best - $1,050 in special chips for $1,000 - but never as high as 25% like this program offers; it's very advantageous for the players. How come it works in South Florida? Three probable reasons:

1 - Competition. There are quite a few boats to choose from so the boats have to offer something extra to get people in their casinos.

2 - Bad players. The average South Florida casino-goer is a recreational gambler and not very knowledgeable. The casino edge against these players is much higher than knowledgable gamblers who know the proper playing strategies.

3 - Time. You're stuck on a boat for 3-1/2 hours with nowhere to go. It probably takes no more than 30 minutes to go through the IGT chips and end up with all regular chips. If you were in a land-based casino you could simply walk out and take your money home but on a casino boat you still have another three hours to go before it heads back to shore. With all that time on your hands you have nothing left to do but gamble.

Now, if you're a perfect basic strategy blackjack player the biggest casino edge on any of these boats is about one-half of one percent, so you should have an excellent chance of coming out a winner with the IGT program.

The usual cost for a one year IGT membership is $48 but we have made arrangements with them for a free 6-month membership for our readers who live in certain metropolitan areas. If you're not from those areas you can still save by getting a one-year membership for only $24 - a 50% discount off the regular membership fee. Be sure to look in the coupon section in the back of this book for full details on this great money-saving program..

Scouting Report - South Florida Casino Boats

New SeaEscape - The six-deck blackjack games on this boat have the following rules: dealer hits soft 17, double down on any first two cards, resplit any pair (except aces), double after split allowed and late surrender offered. The casino edge in this game against a perfect basic strategy player is .54%. The craps game offers a maximum of 2X odds.

Only 25¢ video poker machines are offered. There are some Game Maker Jacks or Better machines with 6/5 (95% return) and 7/5 (96.15% return) pay tables which can be found in the showroom area. This is in contrast to the unusually good 10/7 Double Bonus (100.17% return) machines located in the main casino. Some 7/5 Double Bonus (98.02% return) machines are also available in the main casino.

SunCruz, Hollywood - This boat offers both six-deck ($25 minimum) and eight-deck ($5 minimum) blackjack games with the following rules: dealer stands on soft 17, double down on any first two cards, resplit any pair (except aces), double after split allowed and late surrender offered. The casino edge in this game against a perfect basic strategy player is .34% against six decks and .37% with eight decks in play. They also offer a single-deck game that has those same rules, with the exception of late surrender. Because of those generous rules, the advantage in this game is actually in favor of the perfect basic strategy player by .13%. The minimum bet on this game is $100 and because of that high minimum the table isn't always open. They will, however, open a table for anyone who requests that particular game.

The Sun Cruz craps game offers a maximum of 5X odds. For video poker players there are some 25¢ Jacks or Better machines with 6/5 (95% return) and 7/5 (96.15% return) and 8/5 (97.28% return) pay tables. At the $1 level there are 8/5 Jacks or Better (97.28% return) and also some 7/5 Bonus (98.02% return) games.

Fort Pierce

Map Location: **#10**

Midnight Gambler
1 Avenue A, Dock A
Fort Pierce, Florida 34950
(561) 464-8694

Reservation Number: (561) 464-8694
Gambling Age: 21
Ship's Registry: Australia
Food Service: A la Carte Snack Bar
Schedule:
11:00am - 4:30pm (Daily)
7:00pm -12:00am (Daily)
Price: Free
Port Charges: None
Parking: Free
Special Features: Operates seasonally from December through April. 275-passenger *Midnight Gambler* sails from pier A at Port of Fort Pierce. Must be 21, or older, to board.

Jacksonville

Map Location: **#6**

La Cruise Casino
4738 Ocean Street
Atlantic Beach, Florida 32233
(904) 241-7200

Reservation Number: (800) 752-1778
Gambling Age: 18
Ship's Registry: Panama
Food Service: A la Carte Snack Bar
Schedule:
11:00am - 4:00pm (Tue-Thu/Sat)
4:15pm - 6:00pm (Sun)
7:00pm -12:00am (Tue-Sat)
Price: $18
Port Charges: Included
Parking: Free
Other Games: P, CSP, SB, B6
Senior Discount: $13 for Wed am cruises, plus $5 in tokens, if 50, or older
Special Features: 450-passenger *La Cruise* sails from Mayport Village. $10 seafood buffet offered in land-based pavilion on every cruise. Must be 18, or older, to board.

Key Largo

Map Location: **#7** (50 miles S. of Miami)

SunCruz Casino - Key Largo
99701 Overseas Highway
Key Largo, Florida 33037
(305) 451-0000
Web Site: www.suncruzcasino.com

Reservation Number: (800) 474-DICE
Gambling Age: 18
Ship's Registry: U.S.A.
Food Service: A la Carte Snack Bar
Shuttle Schedule:
Departs/Returns 2:00pm/2:30 (daily)
Departs/Returns 5:00pm/5:30 (daily)
Departs/Returns 7:00pm/7:30 (daily)
Departs/Returns 9:30pm/9:30 (daily)
Departs/Returns 11:00pm/11:30 (daily)
Returns 12:45am (Sun-Thu)
Returns 1:15am (Fri/Sat)
Prices: $10
Port Charges: Included
Parking: Free
Other Games: SB
Special Features: 150-passenger *SunCruz I* departs from the Holiday Inn dock in Key Largo. The boat then stays offshore and a water taxi shuttles passengers back and forth according to the above schedule. Free hors d'ouevres served on boat. One free drink included with admission. Must be 18, or older, to board.

Miami

Map Location: **#1**

Casino Princesa
100 S. Biscayne Boulevard
Miami, Florida 33131
(305) 379-LUCK
Web Site: www.casinoprincesa.com

Reservation Number: (305) 379-LUCK
Gambling Age: 21
Ship's Registry: U.S.A.
Food Service: Buffet Included
12:30pm - 5:30pm (Daily)
7:30pm -12:30am (Daily)
1:00am - 5:00am (Fri-Sat-Sun)

Prices: $22.95 Day/$22.95 Eve/$17.95 (1am)
Port Charges: Included
Parking: $5 Valet Parking
Casino Size: 10,000 Square Feet
Other Games: MB, P, LIR
Fun Book: Visit their web site at
www.baysidemarketplace.com
Special Features: 600-passenger *Casino Princesa* sails from Bayside Marketplace in downtown Miami. $5 parking fee reimbursed with $5 match play. Must be 21, or older, to board.

Royal Star Casino Cruise
1120 Port Boulevard,
Terminal 12, 2nd Floor
Miami, Florida 33132
(305) 373-STAR
Web Site: www.royalstarcasinocruise.com

Reservation Number: (305) 379-LUCK
Gambling Age: 21
Ship's Registry: U.S.A.
Food Service: Buffet Included
12:30pm - 5:30pm (Tue-Sun)
7:30pm -12:30am (Mon-Sun)
Prices: $10.00
Port Charges: Included
Parking: $4
Other Games: MB, P, LIR, PGP, CSP
Special Features: $4 parking fee refunded in matchplay or tokens Must be 21, or older, to board.

Stardancer Casino - Miami Beach
1280 5th Street
Miami Beach, Florida 33139
(305) 538-8300

Reservation Number: (877) STARR-21
Gambling Age: 21
Ship's Registry: Panama
Buffets: L-$10 D-$10
Schedule:
4:15pm - 5:30pm (Daily)
7:30pm -12:30am (Mon-Thu)
7:30pm - 1:00am (Thu-Sun)
Prices: $10 Day/$12 Eve/$15 (Fri/Sat Eve)
Port Charges: Included
Parking: Free
Other Games: MB, S21
Special Features: 500-passenger *Europa Sun* sails from Miami Beach Marina. Shortest ride to international waters. Must be 21, or older, to board.

Palm Beach

Map Location: **#8**

Contessa Cruise & Casino
1201 U.S. Highway 1 #250
North Palm Beach, Florida 33408
(561) 622-6744

CLOSED AT PRESS TIME - EXPECTED TO REOPEN BY DECEMBER 2000
Reservation Number: (888) 711-8946
Gambling Age: 21
Ship's Registry: Panama
Buffets: Included
Schedule:
1:00pm - 7:00pm (Sun)
2:00pm - 8:00pm (Mon-Wed)
9:30am - 4:15pm (Thu/Sat)
4:30pm - 10:30pm (Thu/Fri/Sat)
Price: $25 Day/$29 (Fri/Sat Eve)
Port Charges: Included
Parking: Free
Casino Size: 20,000 Square Feet
Other Games: MB, P, LIR
Special Features: 420-passenger, *Contessa* departs from Port of Palm Beach. $10 for valet parking but it's reimbursed with chips in the casino. Must be 21, or older, to board.

Palm Beach Princess
777 East Port Road
Riviera Beach, Florida 33404
(561) 845-7447
Web Site: www.pbcasino.com

Reservation Number: (800) 841-7447
Gambling Age: 18
Ship's Registry: Panama
Food Service: Buffet Included
Schedule & Prices:
12:30pm - 5:30pm (Mon-Fri) $25
12:30pm- 5:30pm (Sat) $30
11:00am - 5:00pm (Sun) $30
7:00pm - 12:30am (Mon-Thu) $25
7:00pm - 1:00am (Fri/Sat) $30
6:00pm - 11:00pm (Sun) $25
Port Charges: Included
Parking: $5
Casino Size: 15,000 Square Feet
Other Games: SB, LIR, P, Oasis Stud Poker
Senior Discount: $5 off full fare, if 55, or older
Special Features: 800-passenger *Palm Beach*

Princess sails from the Port of Palm Beach. Private cabin rentals available. Swimming pool. Lounge with live entertainment, cabaret shows, games and dancing. Children only allowed on day cruises. Must be 18, or older, to board on evening cruises.

SunCruz Casino - Palm Beach
111 East 14th Street
Riviera Beach, Florida 33404
(561) 863-9555
Web Site: www.suncruzcasino.com

Reservation Number: (800) 474-DICE
Gambling Age: 18
Ship's Registry: U.S.A.
Buffets: L-$5.00 D-$7.00
Schedule:
11:00pm-4:00pm
12:00pm-5pm (Sat/Sun)
7:00pm-12:00 am (Sun-Thu)
7:00pm-12:30am (Fri/Sat)
Price: Price changes monthly and can vary from free to $17. Call to inquire.
Port Charges: Included
Parking: Free
Other Games: LIR
Special Features: 450-passenger, *SunCruz X* departs from Riviera Beach Marina. One free cocktail included with admission. Must be 18 or older to board. A la carte food menu also available.

Port Canaveral

Map Location: **#13** (60 miles S. of Daytona Beach)

SunCruz Casino - Port Canaveral
620 Glen Cheeks Drive
Port Canaveral, Florida 32920
(407) 799-3511
Web Site: www.suncruzcasino.com

Toll-Free Number: (800) 474-DICE
Gambling Age: 18
Ship's Registry: U.S.A.
Buffets: L/D-$5.00
Schedule
9:00am - 4:15pm (Mon/Wed/Thu/Sat)
1:00pm-6:30pm (Sun)
4:15pm - 6:00pm (Mon-Thu)
4:15pm - 6:30pm (Fri/Sat)
7:00pm - 12:00am (Mon-Thu)
7:30pm - 1:00am (Fri/Sat)
7:30pm - 12:00am (Sun)
Price: Varies monthly. Call to inquire.
Port Charges: Included
Parking: Free
Other Games: MB, P
Special Features: 1,000-passenger, *SunCruz VIII* departs from Port Canaveral. One free drink and hors d'ouevres included with admission. Must be 18 or older to board. A la carte food menu also available.

Sterling Casino Lines
Terminal 2B
Cape Canaveral, Florida 32920
(407) 783-2212
Web Site: www.sterlingcasinolines.com

Reservation Number: (800) ROLL-7-11
Gambling Age: 21
Ship's Registry: Bahamas
Buffets: Included
Schedule:
11:00am - 4:00pm (Daily)
7:00pm - 12:00am (Daily)
Port Charges: Included
Parking: Free
Casino Size: 75,000 Square Feet
Other Games: CSP
Special Features: 1,800-passenger, *Ambassador II* departs from terminal 2 at Port Canaveral. Free live entertainment in the lounge. Must be 21, or older, to board.

Port Richey

Map Location: **#11** (15 miles N.W. of Tampa)

SunCruz Casino - Port Richey
8715 Port Richey Village Loop
Port Richey, Florida 34668
(813) 848-3423
Web Site: www.suncruzcasino.com

Reservation Number: (800) 474-DICE
Gambling Age: 18
Ship's Registry: U.S.A.
Food Service: A la carte menu
Schedule: 9am,11am,12:30pm,4pm,7pm
Price: $5
Port Charges: Included
Parking: Free
Other Games: P, SB, LIR
Special Features: Two different boats: *SunCruz II* a 350-passenger boat and *SunCruz IX* another 350-passenger boat depart from behind Hooter's Restaurant. Sometimes the boat is anchored offshore and a water taxi shuttles passengers back and forth. Must be 18 or older to board. A la carte food menu also available.

St. Petersburg

Map Location: **#9**

SunCruz Casino - John's Pass
12788 Kingfish Drive
Treasure Island, Florida 33706
(727) 895-3325
Web Site: www.suncruzcasino.com

Reservation Number: (800) 474-DICE
Gambling Age: 18
Ship's Registry: U.S.A.
Buffets: L-$5 D-$7
Schedule:
11:30am - 5:00pm (Mon-Fri)
11:30am - 5:30pm (Sat/Sun)
7:00pm -12:30am (Sun-Thu)
7:00pm - 1:00am (Fri/Sat)
Prices: $10
Port Charges: Included
Parking: Free
Other Games: MB, SB, P, LIR
Special Features: 590-passenger *SunCruz V* sails from Kingfish Wharf at John's Pass on Treasure Island. Must be 18 or older to sail.

SunCruz Casino - Clearwater
198 Seminole Street
Clearwater, Florida 33755
(727) 895-3325
Web Site: www.suncruzcasino.com

Reservation Number: (800) 474-DICE
Gambling Age: 18
Ship's Registry: U.S.A.
Buffets: L-$5 D-$7
Schedule:
11:00am - 5:00pm (Mon-Fri)
11:30am - 5:30pm (Sat)
4:15pm - 4:15pm (Sun)
7:00pm -12:30am (Mon-Thu)
7:00pm - 1:00am (Fri/Sat)
Prices: $10
Port Charges: Included
Parking: Free
Other Games: MB, SB, P, LIR
Special Features: 470-passenger *SunCruz XI* sails from Clearwater Bay Marina. Must be 18 or older to sail. A la carte food menu also available.

Stardancer Casino - Madeira Beach
150 153rd Avenue
Madeira Beach, Florida 33708
(813) 393-2885

Reservation Number: (800) 688-PLAY
Gambling Age: 21
Ship's Registry: U.S.A.
Food Service: A la carte menu
Buffet: D-$10
Daily Schedule:
11:30am - 5:30pm
7:00pm - 1:00am
Prices: Free
Port Charge: Included
Parking: Free
Other Games: MB, P, SB, Lotto
Special Features: 440-passenger *Europa Sky* sails from John's Pass Village in Madeira Beach. Must be 21, or older, to board.

Indian Casinos

Florida has four Indian gaming locations. The Seminoles have three and the fourth is on the Miccosukee reservation.

There is no state-tribal compact in effect in Florida and the state has gone to court to shut down the Indian gaming operations. In turn, the Seminole tribe has made a formal appeal to Secretary of the Interior Bruce Babbitt to allow full-scale casino gambling on their reservations. Until the matter is fully resolved, federal officials have not allowed the state to shut down any Tribes' gambling operations.

All Indian casinos offer high-stakes bingo, video pull tabs and poker games with a maximum pot of $10. All are open 24 hours and the minimum gambling age is 18.

Miccosukee Indian Gaming
500 S.W. 177 Avenue
Miami, Florida 33194
(305) 222-4600
Map Location: **#1**
Web Site: www.miccosukee.com

Toll-Free Number: (800) 741-4600
Room Reservations: (877) 242-6464
Rooms: 256 Price Range: $69-$129
Suites: 46 Price Range: $129-$189
Restaurants: 2 (1 open 24 hours) Liquor: Yes
Buffets: B-$8.95 L/D-$11.95
Special Features: Live entertainment and dancing nightly in Cypress Lounge. Pay-per-view boxing events shown free of charge.

Hollywood Seminole Gaming
4150 N. State Road 7
Hollywood, Florida 33021
(954) 961-3220
Web Site: www.seminoletribe.com/gaming
Map Location: **#2** (5 miles S. of Fort Lauderdale)

Toll-Free Number: (800) 323-5452
Restaurants: 3 Snack Bars Liquor: Yes
Casino Size: 73,500 Square Feet
Special Features: Have announced plans for a major expansion including hotel facilities.

Seminole Indian Casino
5223 N. Orient Road
Tampa, Florida 33610
(813) 621-1302
Map Location: **#3**
Web Site: www.casino-tampa.com

Toll-Free Number: (800) 282-7016
Restaurants: 1 Cafeteria Liquor: Yes

Seminole Indian Casino
506 South 1st Street
Immokalee, Florida 33934
(941) 658-1313
Map Location: **#4** (35 miles N.E. of Naples)

Toll-Free Number: (800) 218-0007
Restaurants: 2 (1 open 24 hours) Liquor: Yes
Casino Size: 43,000 Square Feet
Special Features: Live entertainment nightly from 6pm.

GEORGIA

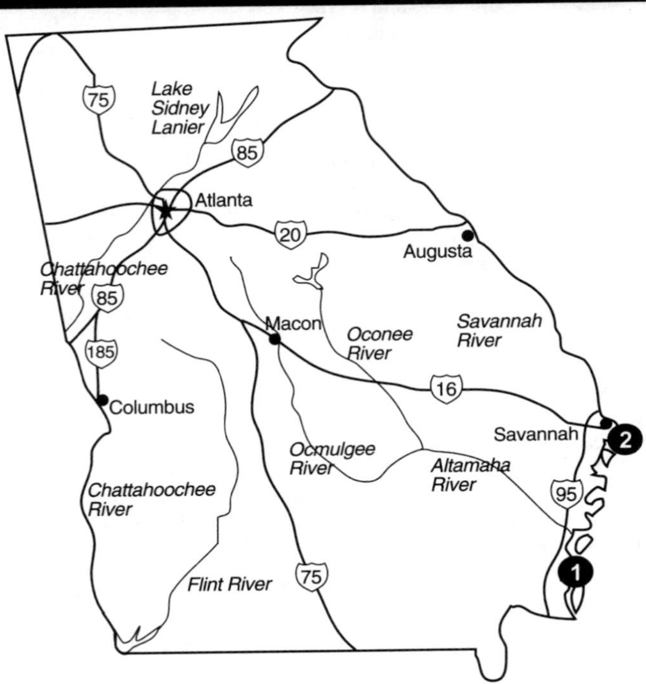

There are two gambling cruise ship operations in Georgia and both sail three miles out into international waters where casino gambling is permitted.

For information on visiting Georgia call the state's tourism department at (800) 847-4842.

Atlantic Star Cruise Lines
P.O. Box 2117
Tybee Island, Georgia 31328
(912) 786-7827
Map Location: **#2** (20 miles E. of Savannah)

Reservation Number: (912) 786-7827
Gambling Age: 21 Ship's Registry: U.S.
Buffets: Included
Schedule:
1:00pm - 5:00pm (Sat/Sun)
7:00pm - 11:00pm (Mon/Wed-Sat)
Prices: $9.95 for all cruises
Port Charges: Included Parking: Free
Games Offered: Blackjack, Craps, Slots
Special Features: 100-passenger *Atlantic Star* sails from Lazaretto Creek Marina on Tybee Island. No one under 21 permitted to board.

Golden Isles Emerald Princess
One St. Andrews Court
Brunswick, Georgia 31520
(912) 265-3558
Web Site: www.emeraldprincesscasino.com
Map Location: **#1** (75 miles S. of Savannah)

Reservation Number: (800) 842-0115
Gambling Age: 18 Ship's Registry: Panama
Buffets: Included
Schedule & Prices:
11:00am - 4:00pm (Sat) $19.98
1:00pm - 6:00pm (Sun) $17.50
7:00pm - 12:00am (Tue) $25.00
7:00pm - 12:00am (Wed/Thu)$15.90
7:00pm - 1:00am (Fri) $25.00
7:00pm - 1:00am (Sat) $35.00
Port Charges: Included Parking: Free
Games Offered: Blackjack, Craps, Roulette, Caribbean Stud Poker, Sports Book
Special Features: 400-passenger *Emerald Princess* sails from Brunswick Landing Marina in downtown Brunswick. Children only permitted on day cruises, they must be 8 or older and pay full fare. Packages with hotel accommodations are available.

IDAHO

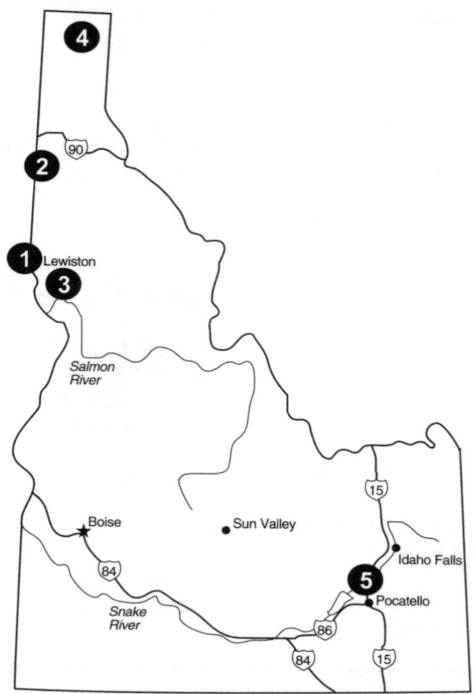

Idaho has five Indian casinos that offer electronic pull-tab machines and other video games. The machines don't pay out in cash. Instead they print out a receipt which must be cashed by a floor attendant or taken to the cashier's cage. Some casinos also offer bingo.

According to David High in the attorney general's office the terms of the compact between the tribes and the state do not require any minimum payback percentage that the gaming machines must return to the public.

The minimum gambling age at all casinos is 18. For Idaho tourism information call (800) 635-7820

Clearwater River Casino
7463 North & South Highway 95
Lewiston, Idaho 83501
(208) 746-5733
Map Location: **#1** (250 miles N. of Boise)
Web Site: www.crcasino.com

Toll-Free Number: (877) 678-7423
Restaurants: 1 Snack Bar Liquor: No
Hours: 24 Hours Daily
Casino Size: 30,000 Square Feet
Other Games: Bingo (Wed-Mon), Simulcasting
Senior Discount: Sunday Bingo discount, if 55, or older

Coeur D'Alene Tribal Bingo/Casino
U.S. Highway 95/P.O. Box 236
Worley, Idaho 83876
(208) 686-5106
Map Location: **#2** (350 miles N. of Boise)
Web Site: www.cdacasino.com

Toll-Free Number: (800) 523-BINGO
Restaurants: 1 Deli Liquor: No
Buffet: D-$6.95(Mon)/$7.95(Tue-Wed)
$5.75(Thu)/$13.95(Fri)/$12.95(Sat)
$9.95(Sun)
Hours: 24 Hours Daily
Casino Size: 30,000 Square Feet
Other Games: Bingo (Fri-Sun), Simulcasting
Senior Discount: 10% off bingo, if 55, or older
Special Features: Double jackpots at select times on Mondays.

It'se Ye-Ye Bingo & Casino
404 Main Street
Kamiah, Idaho 83536
(208) 935-1019
Web Site: www.crcasino.com
Map Location: **#3** (225 miles N. of Boise)

Toll-Free Number: (877) 678-7423
Restaurants: No Food Liquor: No
Hours: 24 Hours Daily
Casino Size: 2,300 Square Feet
Other Games: Bingo (Thu-Sat)

Kootenai River Inn & Casino
Kootenai River Plaza
Bonners Ferry, Idaho 83805
(208 267 8511
Map Location: **#4** (450 miles N. of Boise)

Toll-Free Number: (800) 346-5668
Rooms: 47 Price Range: $75-$111
Suites: 4 Price Range $225.00
Restaurants: 1 Liquor: Yes
Buffets: B-$8.95 (Sun)
Hours: 24 Hours Daily
Casino Size: 30,000 Square Feet
Other Games: Bingo (Wed/Fri/Sun)
Special Features: Hotel affiliated with Best Western.

Shoshone-Bannock High Stakes Casino
P.O. Box 868
Fort Hall, Idaho 83203
(208) 237-8778
Web Site:www.sho-ban.com
Map Location: **#5** (5 miles N. of Pocatello)

Toll-Free Number: (800) 497-4231
Restaurants: 1 Snack Bar Liquor: No
Hours: 8am-12am (Mon-Thu)/10pm (Sun)
24 Hours (Fri/Sat)
Casino Size: 15,000 Square Feet
Other Games: Bingo (Fri-Sun/Tue)

ILLINOIS

Illinois was the second state to legalize riverboat casinos. There are 10 licenses issued for the entire state and each licensee is allowed to have up to two boats. In July 1997 the Silver Eagle (map location **#4**) closed and this left only nine boats in operation. In June 1999, however, the Silver Eagle reapplied with the Gaming Board to move its boat to Rosemont, which is located in Cook County, about a 10-minute-drive from O'Hare International Airport. The Gaming Board was expected to approve the move but a lawsuit to block the licensing move was later filed by another business group and as of August 2000 the issue had not yet been decided by the courts.

Riverboat casinos began operating in Illinois in September 1991 with the launching of the first boat: the Alton Belle. All boats were originally required to cruise but in June 1999 the Governor signed a bill permitting dockside gambling. Unlike Mississippi, however, the casinos are not open 24 hours.

Here's information from the Illinois Gaming Board on each casino's average slot payback percentage for the 1999 calendar year beginning January 1, 1999 and ending December 31, 1999:

CASINO	PAYBACK %
Casino Queen	95.0
Grand Victoria	94.7
Alton Belle	94.6
Hollywood	94.2
Empress	94.2
Harrah's	94.1
Players	93.8
Par-A-Dice	93.5
Rock Island	93.3

These figures reflect the total percentages returned by each casino for all of their electronic machines. As you can see, the Casino Queen returned the most to its slot machine players, while the Rock Island riverboat returned the least. Although these numbers are only for 1999, they pretty much remain the same from year-to-year with Casino Queen at the top, Rock Island at the bottom and the others somewhere in between.

Unless otherwise noted, all casinos offer: slots, video poker, blackjack, craps, roulette and Caribbean stud poker. Some casinos also offer: let it ride (LIR), baccarat (B), mini-baccarat (MB) and poker (P). The minimum gambling age is 21.

For more information on Illinois casinos contact the state's Bureau of Tourism at (800) 223-0121.

Alton Belle Riverboat Casino
219 Piasa Street
Alton, Illinois 62002
(618) 474-7500
Web Site: www.argosycasinos.com
Map Location: **#1** (260 miles S.W. of Chicago. 25 miles N. of St. Louis, MO)

Reservation Number: (800) 336-SLOT
Restaurants: 2
Buffets: B-$6.39 L-$7.47/$11.77(Sun) D-$11.77
Valet Parking: $5
Casino Hours: 8am-4am/6am (Fri-Sat)
Casino Size: 19,300 Square Feet
Other Games: LIR
Casino Marketing: (800) 500-VIP1
Fun Book: Only given to groups
Special Features: 1,200-passenger modern yacht on the Mississippi River.

Casino Queen
200 S. Front Street
E. St. Louis, Illinois 62201
(618) 874-5000
Web Site: www.casinoqueen.com
Map Location: **#6** (290 miles S.W. of Chicago)

Reservation Number: (800) 777-0777
Rooms: 150 Price Range: $99-$149
Buffets: B-$3.95 L-$7.95
D-$11.95/$14.95 (Tue/Sat)
Valet Parking: $3
Casino Hours: 9am-6:30am
Casino Size: 27,500 Square Feet
Other Games: MB, LIR
Senior Discount: Free admission Wednesdays until 3 p.m., if 50 or older. Also receive free danish, coffee, juice, 2-for-1 break fast or lunch and 35% off in gift shop.
Special Features: 2,500-passenger, old-fashioned, paddlewheeler docked on the Mississippi river. 92-space RV park. Sports Bar with 27 tv's and live entertainment on weekends. MetroLink light-rail station at doorstep. 10% room discount to AAA members.

Empress Casino Hotel Joliet
2300 Empress Drive
Joliet, Illinois 60436
(815) 744-9400
Web Site: www.empresscasino.com
Map Location: **#2** (43 miles S.W. of Chicago)

Reservation Number: (888) 4-EMPRESS
Rooms: 85 Price Range: $40-$120
Suites: 17 Price Range: $80-$140
Restaurants: 3
Buffets: B-$3.95 L-$6.95 D-$9.95
Valet Parking: $5/Free with Empress Card
Casino Hours: 8:30am-6:30am
Casino Size: 16,800 Square Feet - *Empress I*
Casino Size: 19,400 Square Feet - *Empress II*
Other Games: LIR, MB, P
Senior discount: Mondays receive a $1.99 breakfast buffet and double points before 10:30am, if 55 or older and a member of the slot club.
Special Features: 1,000-passenger *Empress I* and 1,500-passenger *Empress II* are modern yachts on the Des Plaines River. Off track betting parlor located in land-based pavilion. Rooms are at on-property Empress Hotel. 15% discount on meals, gift shop purchases and lodging when you show Empress card. 80-space RV park.

Grand Victoria Casino
250 S. Grove Avenue
Elgin, Illinois 60120
(847) 888-1000
Web Site: www.grandvictoria-elgin.com
Map Location: **#9** (41 miles N.W. of Chicago)

Reservation Number: (847) 888-1000
Restaurants: 3
Buffets: L-$10.71 D-$17.15/$19.29 (Fri-Sun)
Valet Parking: $2/$4 (Fri-Sun)
Casino Hours: 8:30am-6:00am
Casino Size: 29,850 Square Feet
Other Games: B, MB
Casino Marketing: (847) 468-7000
Fun Book: Only given to groups
Special Features: 1,200-passenger paddle wheeler-replica on the Fox River. Live entertainment (Wed-Sun).

Harrah's Joliet Casino
150 N. Scott Street
Joliet, Illinois 60431
(815) 774-2610
Web Site: www.harrahs.com
Map Location: **#2** (43 miles S.W. of Chicago)

Reservation Number: (800) HARRAHS
Rooms: 204 Price Range: $69-$159
Suites: 81 Price Range: $300
Restaurants: 2
Buffets: B-$6.99 L-$7.99
D-$12.99/$18.99 (Fri-Sat)
Valet Parking: $5
Casino Hours: 8:30am-6:30am
Size: 13,440 Square Feet - *Southern Star II*
Size: 17,000 Square Feet - *Northern Star*
Other Games: MB, P
Casino Marketing: (800) HARRAHS
Special Features: Complimentary soda and juice. *Northern Star* is a 1,000-passenger modern mega-yacht. *Southern Star II* is an 1880s stern wheeler replica. Both boats are on the Des Plaines River. Pavilion houses 210-seat buffet, steakhouse, sports bar and lounge with live entertainment. 10% room discount with a slot club card. The hotel has four large suites which can only be reserved through the casino.

The Best Places To Play In The Chicago Area

by John Grochowski

Gaming in Chicago is a work in progress. It's the first major American city outside traditional gaming states to have a large number of legal casinos within the metropolitan area. You can't hop in the car in New York or Los Angeles and arrive at any of eight casinos within 45 minutes. You can in Chicago, both to riverboats in Illinois and vessels in harbor off Lake Michigan in Indiana. However, though those casinos are easy distances from Chicago, they are far-flung relative to each other.

This is not Las Vegas, or Atlantic City, or even Tunica County. With the exception of Trump and Majestic Star in Gary, Indiana, which share a land-based pavilion, there is no casino-hopping on foot. Casinos are not walking distance from each other. Some are more than an hour apart by car. What that means to a customer searching for a good game is that the pressure isn't as intense on casinos to provide one. There's no worry that you're going to walk out and try the game next door. You'll find no single-deck blackjack in the Chicago area, and 100-percent video poker machines are few and far between. Nevertheless, there are some opportunities to pick and choose among the games. Here are the ones to look for:

Roulette: Unfortunately, all roulette wheels in the Chicago-area casinos are standard American double-zero versions.

Craps: The face of Chicago-area craps changed in 1999 when Horseshoe Gam -ing took over the Empress Casinos in Joliet, Illinois, and Hammond, Indiana. Both ran games with 100x odds as a spring- and-summer special, then settled on 20x odds as their standard game. No one else in the area offers more than 10x odds. Worth a mention is the Par-A-Dice casino, about a three-hour drive away in East Peoria, which offers $1 line bets at some light traffic times.

Caribbean Stud: Trump and Majestic Star allow $2.50 minimum antes. Other area casinos have only $5 and $10 minimum tables. That doesn't cut the house edge on the main ante-bet combination; it just allows the player to risk less money while facing the same disadvantage of about 5.2% of the ante. However, it dramatically reduces the break-even point on the $1 side bet on the progressive jackpot. With a $5 ante, the point at which the progressive wager becomes an even bet is a jackpot of about $340,000. With a $2.50 ante, that break-even point drops below $200,000.

Blackjack: Most of the games use either six or eight decks. For a basic strategy player, the best sets of rules are in force in Joliet, both at Empress aboard Empress I and Empress II and at Harrah's aboard Northern Star and Southern Star. Both use six decks. The dealer stands on all 17s, the player may double down on any first two cards, including after splits, and may resplit Aces. The house edge on the game is .33% against a basic strategy player. The ability to resplit aces sets the Joliet game apart from the rest of the area. Trump comes close with an eight-deck game with the same basic rules with two exceptions: The player may not resplit aces, but late surrender is offered. That leaves a house edge of .36 percent.

The only two-deck tables in the area are at Majestic Star in Gary and Hollywood Casino in Aurora, Illinois. Majestic Star has the better game, with the dealer standing on all 17s and double downs permitted on any first two cards. That makes it a .38 percent game, but is available only to $25 players. Take a longer drive to Par-A-Dice, and you can get the same game with a $10 minimum. The Hollywood 2-deck game is much tougher -- dealer hits soft 17, double downs are permitted on 9, 10 and 11 only, and the player may not double after splits or resplit pairs. The house edge is .68 percent.

Video Poker: The only 100 percent-plus game in the area is 10-7 Double Bonus Poker, and that's available only at the $1 level at Empress Joliet, both on Empress I and Empress II. Some machines add a progressive jackpot on the royal flush, enhancing the 100.17 percent payback to experts on the basic game.

However, there are many 99-percent-plus games in the area. Majestic Star, which had been the weakest video poker casino in the area, has made a big upgrade in its dollar inventory. It now has 9/6 Jacks or Better, a 99.5 percent game with expert play, and 20/10/6/5 Joker's Wild two pair or better with a 5,000-coin royal flush jackpot. That's a 99.9 percent game with expert play, and by far the best Joker game in the region.

Hollywood in Aurora and Grand Victoria in Elgin, Illinois, also have 9/6 Jacks or Better for dollar players, and Grand Victoria also has a bank of $5 9/6 games. Harrah's Joliet checks in with $1 9/7 Double Bonus Poker, a 99.1 percent game, along with a fast-moving progressive jackpot on royal flushes that frequently takes the theoretical return over the 100-percent mark.

For quarter players, the best single-line game is 8-5 Bonus Poker, a 99.2 percent game, at Harrah's in East Chicago, Indiana.

The advent of Triple Play and Five Play Poker has brought many decent games to the area. It's easy to find Triple Play and Five Play games with 9/6 Jacks or Better and a good version of Deuces Wild. It's not Las Vegas-style full-pay Deuces, but it's a 99.7 percent game. Four-of-a-kind paybacks are lowered to 4-for-1 while full houses are enhanced to 4-for-1 and flushes to 3-for-1, just as in the game known as Illinois Deuces. However, five of a kind also is enhanced to 16-for-1 and straight flushes to 10-for-1. Players can find those games on Triple Play/Five Play quarter machines at Trump and Hollywood and on dollar machines at Harrah's Joliet, Empress Joliet and Grand Victoria.

John Grochowski is the gaming columnist for the "Chicago Sun-Times" and also a contributing writer to "Casino Executive Magazine." For ordering information on two of John's books: "The Casino Answer Book" and "The Slot Machine Answer Book" be sure to look for his ad on page 52. For information on his new "Video Poker Answer Book" turn to page 78.

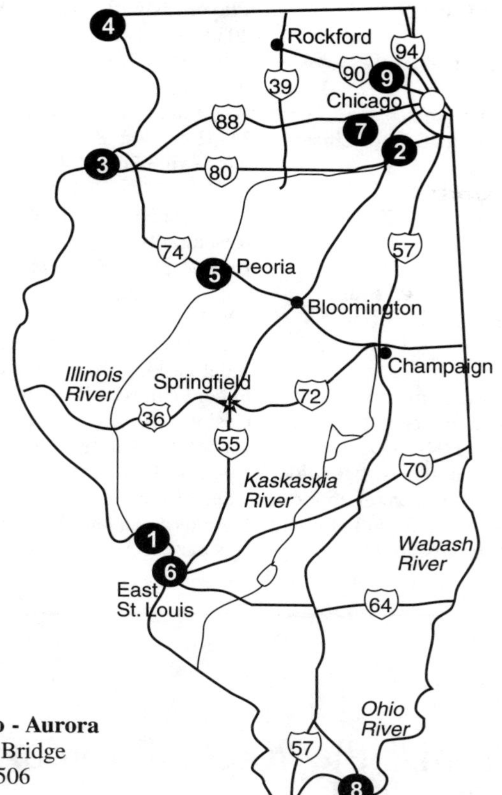

Hollywood Casino - Aurora
1 New York Street Bridge
Aurora, Illinois 60506
(630) 801-7000
Web Site: www.hollywoodcasino.com
Map Location: **#7** (41 miles W. of Chicago)

Toll Free Number: (800) 888-7777
Restaurants: 5
Buffets: B-$4.99 L-$7.99
D-$11.99/$14.99 (Fri/Sun)
Valet Parking: $2/$4 (Fri-Sat)/Free with Marquee or Screen Card
Casino I Hours: 8:30am-6:30am
Casino II Hours: 10:30am-2am
Size: 21,000 Square Feet - *City of Lights I*
Size: 11,000 Square Feet - *City of Lights II*
Other Games: B, MB, (P on City of Lights I)
Casino Marketing: (630) 801-7203
Senior Discount: 2-for-1 breakfast or lunch buffet on Thursday, if 55 or older. Must have slot club card.
Special Features: 1,200-passenger *City of Lights I* and 675-passenger *City of Lights II* are paddlewheel-replica boats on the Fox River. All restaurants are in land-based pavilion. Headliner entertainment offered at nearby Paramount Arts Center.

Jumer's Casino Rock Island
1735 First Avenue
Rock Island, Illinois 61201
(309) 793-4200
Web Site: www.jumers.com
Map Location: **#3** (170 miles W. of Chicago)

Reservation Number: (800) 477-7747
Restaurants: 1 on boat adjacent to casino
Buffets: L-$5.95 D-$8.95
Valet Parking: Free
Casino Hours: 7am-1am/3am (Fri-Sat)
Casino Size: 8,100 Square Feet
Casino Marketing: (800) 477-7747
Senior Discount: Free buffet if you play a minimum of $50 in slots or buy in for at least $50 and play for a minimum of 50 minutes on table games, if 50, or older.
Special Features: 1,200-passenger old-fashioned paddlewheel boat on the Mississippi River. Free hors d'oeuvres, coffee, juice and soft drinks. $1 mixed drinks. Restaurant is on *Effie Afton* which is docked next to the casino.

Par-A-Dice Riverboat Casino
21 Blackjack Boulevard
East Peoria, Illinois 61611
(309) 698-7711
Web Site: www.par-a-dice.com
Map Location: **#5** (170 miles S.W. of Chicago)

Toll-Free Number: (800) 727-2342
Room reservations: (800) 547-0711
Rooms: 208 Price Range: $79-$99
Suites 12 Price Range: $175-$250
Buffets: B-$4.95 L-$7.95/ $8.95 (Sun)
D-$10.95/ $12.95 (Fri/Sat)/$8.95 (Sun)
Valet Parking: $5
Casino Hours: 8:30am-4:30am
Casino Size: 26,116 Square Feet
Casino Marketing: (309) 694-5899
Senior Discount: 25% off buffet, if 55, or older
Special Features: 1,600-passenger modern boat on the Illinois River. 2 restaurants and banquet facilities. All rooms are at on-property Hampton Inn.

Players Island Casino - Metropolis
203 S. Ferry Street
Metropolis, Illinois 62960
(618) 524-2628
Web Site: www.playersisland.com
Map Location: **#8** (Across from Paducah, KY. Take exit 37 on I-24)

Toll-Free Number: (800) 935-7700
Restaurants: 2
Buffets: B-$4.99 L-$6.99/$7.99 (Sat/Sun)
D-$10.99/ $12.99 (Sat/Sun)/$15.99 (Wed)
Hours: 9am-5am/7am (Fri-Sat)
Valet Parking: Not Offered
Other Games: MB, LIR, P
Casino Size: 22,150 Square Feet
Casino Marketing: (800) 929-5905
Special Features: 1,300-passenger side wheeler-replica on the Ohio River. Both restaurants are in land-based pavilion. Casino offers packages through local hotels.

INDIANA

Although the governor vetoed riverboats for his state, the Indiana legislature voted to override him and in June 1993 Indiana became the sixth state to legalize riverboat gambling.

The terms of Indiana's law originally allowed for 11 riverboats in the state: five on Lake Michigan, one on Patoka Lake (map location **#1**) and five along the Ohio River. It was later discovered that the U.S. Army Corps of Engineers owned the rights to Patoka Lake and they would not allow a riverboat on that body of water. In order to move the location for that 11th riverboat a new law will have to be passed by the Indiana legislature.

As of August 2000 there were nine riverboat casinos in operation. The 10th riverboat, Belterra Casino, was expected to open by November 2000 in Florence (map location **#10**).

All Indiana riverboats are required to cruise and there are no bet or loss limits imposed on gamblers. Currently, all riverboats go on one-hour cruises and boarding begins 1/2-hour before the scheduled departure time. You are allowed to gamble as soon as you get on the boat and upon returning you have another 1/2 hour to gamble before the next boarding begins. If, due to bad weather, the boat does not cruise, then a dockside gaming session is held and the same admission charges (if any) apply. By state law no one is allowed to enter the casino 1/2-hour after boarding begins. This means that even if the boat is not leaving the dock, you must arrive prior to the scheduled departure time or you will not be permitted to board. If a dockside gaming session is held, you are free to leave the boat at any time.

Following is information from the Indiana Gaming Commission regarding average slot payout percentages for the 1999 calendar year from January 1 through December 31:

CASINO	PAYBACK %
Argosy	94.1
Blue Chip	93.9
Grand Victoria	93.6
Trump Casino	93.5
Harrah's	93.3
Empress Casino	93.2
Caesars Indiana	93.2
Majestic Star	93.1
Casino Aztar	91.9

These figures reflect the total percentages returned by each casino for all of their electronic machines including slot machines, video poker, video keno, etc. As you can see, Argosy Casino returned the most to its electronic machine players, while Casino Aztar returned the least.

Unless otherwise noted, all casinos offer: blackjack, craps, roulette, slots, video poker, video keno and Caribbean stud poker. Optional games include: baccarat (B), mini-baccarat (MB), poker (P), pai gow poker (PGP), big 6 wheel (B6) and let it ride (LIR). The minimum gambling age is 21. For more information on Indiana tourism call (800) 289-6646.

Argosy Casino & Hotel - Lawrenceburg
777 Argosy Parkway
Lawrenceburg, Indiana 47025
(812) 539-8000
Web Site: www.argosycasinos.com
Map Location: **#3** (95 miles S.E. of Indianapolis)

Toll-Free Number: (888) ARGOSY-7
Rooms: 300 Price Range: $83-$139
Suites: 6 Price Range: $160-$310
Restaurants: 4
Buffets: B-$7.30 L-$9.40
D-$13.60/$15.70 (Fri-Sat)
Boardings: 9am, 11am, 1am, 3pm, 5pm, 7pm, 9pm, 11pm, 1am, 3am (Fri/Sat)
Prices:
$5 (Mon-Thu)/ $7 after 7pm
$9 (Fri)/$7 (5pm)
$9 (Sat)/ $7 (11pm)/$5 (9am-5pm)
$7 (Sun)/$5 (9am-11am)
Valet Parking: $3
Casino Size: 74,300 Square Feet
Other Games: MB, B6, LIR
Casino Marketing: (888) ARGOSY-7
Special Features: 4,000-passenger modern yacht that cruises the Ohio River. Closest casino to Cincinnati. 4 restaurants in land-based pavilion and one deli on boat. Hotel rates include a free breakfast buffet and casino admission. Reservations are recommended.

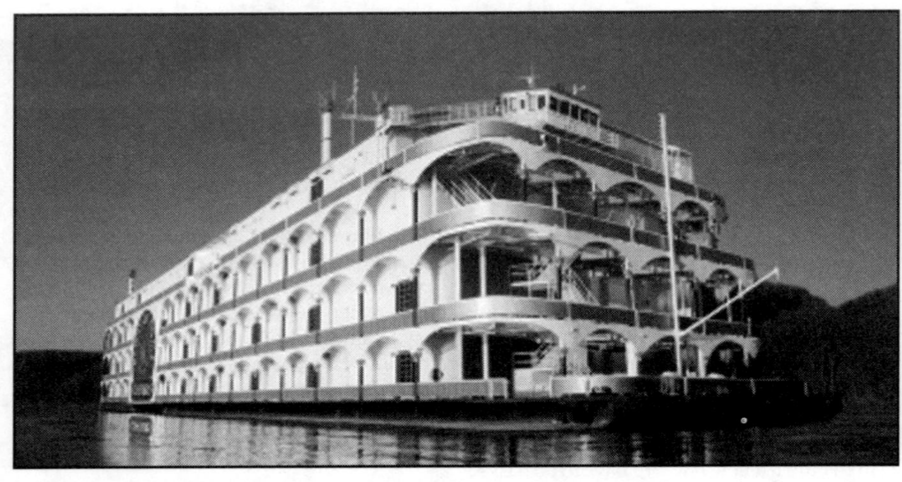

The 5,000-passenger *Glory of Rome* at Caesars Indiana is the world's largest riverboat casino.

Belterra Casino and Resort
777 Belterra Drive
Belterra, IN 47043-9402
(812) 427-4008
Web Site: www.belterraresortcasino.com
Map Location: **#10** (35 miles S.W. of Cincinnati, Ohio)

EXPECTED TO OPEN NOVEMBER 2000
Toll-Free Number: (888) BELTERRA
Rooms: 308 Price Range: $79-$149
Suites: 6 Price Range: $500
Restaurants: 6
Buffets: B-$6.95 L-$8.95 D-$12.95
Boardings: 9:30am, 11:30am, 1:30am, 3:30pm 5:30pm, 7:30pm, 9:30pm, 11:30pm, 1:30am
Prices: All cruises are free
Valet Parking: Free
Casino Size: 38,000 Square Feet
Other Games: MB, LIR
Special Features: 2,700-passenger sidewheeler that cruises on the Ohio River. Every hotel room equipped with whirlpool tub. Health club and spa. 18-hole golf course. 1,500-seat showroom.

Blue Chip Casino
2 Easy Street
Michigan City, Indiana 46360
(219) 879-7711
Web Site: www.boydgaming.com
Map Location: **#7** (40 miles E. of Chicago)

Reservation Number: (888) 879-7711
Rooms: 180 Price Range:$99-$109
Suites: Held for casino use
Restaurants: 3
Buffets: B-$6.99 (Sat-Sun) L-$7.99 D-$9.99
Boardings: 9am, 11am, 1pm, 3pm, 5pm, 7pm, 9pm, 11pm, 1am, 3am (Fri/Sat)
Prices: All cruises are free
Valet Parking: Free
Casino Size: 25,000 Square Feet
Special Features: 2,000-passenger modern yacht that cruises on a man-made body of water.

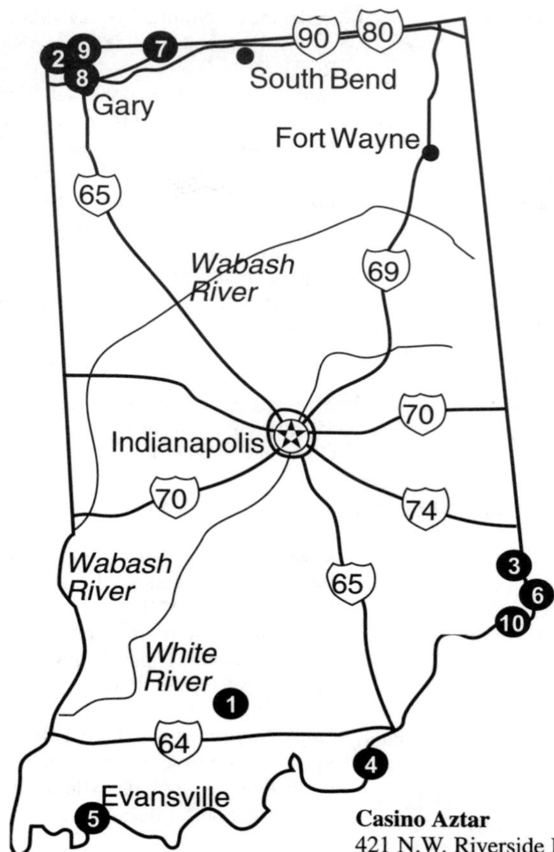

Caesars Indiana
11999 Avenue of the Emperors
Elizabeth, Indiana 47117
(812) 738-3848
Map Location: **#4** (20 miles S. of New Albany)

Toll-Free Number: (888) ROMAN-4-U
Buffets: L-$8.95 D-$13.95
Boardings: 9am, 11am, 1pm, 3pm, 5pm, 7pm, 9pm, 11pm, 1am, 3am (Fri/Sat)
Valet Parking: Free
Casino Size: 25,000 Square Feet
Other Games: B, MB, LIR, P
Senior Discount: On Wednesdays before 10:30am buy one buffet and receive a second free, if 55, or older
Special Features: 5,000-passenger side wheeler, *The Glory of Rome*, cruises on the Ohio River. New hotel expected to open by Fall 2001.

Casino Aztar
421 N.W. Riverside Drive
Evansville, Indiana 47708
(812) 433-4000
Web Site: www.casinoaztar.com
Map Location: **#5**

Toll-Free Number: (800) DIAL-FUN
Rooms: 240 Price Range: $69-$110
Suites: 10 Price Range: $159-$199
Restaurants: 5
Buffets: B-$5.95 L-$7.95 D-$12.95/$14.95 (Fri)
Boardings: 9am, 11am, 1pm, 4pm, 6pm, 8pm, 11pm, 1am, 3am
Prices: $4/$6 (Mon-Thu 7pm/9pm, Sat 9am-5pm/1am Sun 9am-9pm)/$8 (Fri-Sat 7-11pm)
Valet Parking: $5/Free for hotel guests
Casino Size: 47,863 Square Feet
Other Games: MB, LIR, B6, P
Senior Discount: Free Mon. cruise and buffet discounts, if 55, or older, and in slot club
Special Features: 2,700-passenger paddle wheeler that cruises the Ohio River. 10% discount on rooms if AAA member, or if 55, or older.

Empress Casino Hammond
One Empress Place
Hammond, Indiana 46320
(219) 473-7000
Map Location: **#2** (10 miles E. of Chicago)

Reservation Number: (888) 4-EMPRESS
Restaurants: 3
Buffets: B-$4.95/ $10.95 (Sun) L-$6.95
D-$12.95/$16.95 (Fri)
Boardings: 8am, 10am, 12pm, 2pm, 4pm, 6pm, 8pm, 10pm, 12am, 2am
Prices: All cruises are free
Valet Parking: $5/$3 with Empress Club Card.
Casino Size: 43,000 Square Feet
Other Games: B, MB, LIR, P
Senior Discount: $1.99 breakfast buffet on Mondays, if 55, or older
Special Features: 3,000-passenger modern yacht that cruises Lake Michigan. Empress Club Card members get 15% discount in restaurants and gift shop.

Grand Victoria Casino & Resort
600 Grand Victoria Drive
Rising Sun, Indiana 47040
(812) 438-1234
Map Location: **#6** (100 miles S.E. of Indianapolis)

Reservation Number: (800) GRAND-11
Rooms: 201 Price Range: $69-$119
Restaurants: 3
Buffets: B-$6.95 L-$8.95 $12.95
Boardings:9:30am, 11:30am, 1:30pm, 3:30pm, 5:30pm 7:30pm, 9:30pm, 11:30pm, 1:30am
Prices: $5/$7(7-9pm)/$9 (Fri/Sat 7-11pm)
Casino Size: 40,000 Square Feet
Other Games: LIR, P
Senior Discount: Tuesdays receive free boarding, 1/2-off buffet and a chance to win prizes. Every day receive $1 off admission and 10% off on selected amenities, if 55, or older
Special Features: 3,000-passenger paddle wheeler that cruises the Ohio River. Hotel is a Hyatt. On Fridays ladies receive free admission and 50% off lunch or breakfast buffet.

Harrah's East Chicago
One Showboat Place
East Chicago, Indiana 46312
(219) 378-3000
Web Site: www.harrahs.com
Map Location: **#9** (12 miles E. of Chicago)

Reservation Number: (877) 496-1777 or (800) HARRAHS
Restaurants: 2
Buffets: L-$9.99/$10.99 (Sat-Sun)
D-$13.99/$16.99 (Fri-Sat)
Boardings: 9am, 11am, 1pm, 3pm, 5pm, 7pm, 9pm, 11pm, 1am, 3am
Prices: Free Valet Parking: $5
Casino Size: 53,000 Square Feet
Other Games: MB, P, B6, PGP, LIR
Special Features: 3,750-passenger modern yacht that cruises Lake Michigan. Valet parking discounted for Total Rewards members

Majestic Star Casino
1 Buffington Harbor Drive
Gary, Indiana 46406
(219) 977-7777
Map Location: **#8** (15 miles E. of Chicago)

Reservation Number: (888) 2B-LUCKY
Restaurants: 3 (1 Snack Bar on boat)
Buffets: L-$9 D-$13
Boardings: 8am, 10am, 12pm, 2pm, 4pm, 6pm, 8pm, 10pm, 12am, 2am
Prices: Free Valet Parking: Free
Casino Size: 25,000 Square Feet
Other Games: MB, P, PGP, LIR, B6
Special Features: 1,300-passenger modern yacht that cruises Lake Michigan. Club card holders get buffet discounts.

Trump Hotel Casino
1 Buffington Harbor Drive
Gary, Indiana 46406
(219) 977-8980
Web Site: www.trumpindiana.com
Map Location: **#8** (15 miles E. of Chicago)

Reservation Number: (888) 218-7867
Rooms: 300 Price Range: $49-$129
Restaurants: 3 (1 Deli on boat)
Buffets: B-$4.99 L-$7.99 D-$9.99
Boardings: 9am, 11am, 1pm, 3pm, 5pm, 7pm, 9pm, 11pm, 1am, 3am
Prices: Free Valet Parking: Free
Casino Size: 37,000 Square Feet
Other Games: B, MB, PGP, B6
Special Features: 2,300-passenger modern yacht that cruises Lake Michigan. Club card members get buffet discounts.

IOWA

Iowa was the first state to legalize riverboat gambling. The boats began operating on April Fools Day in 1991 and passengers were originally limited to $5 per bet with a maximum loss of $200 per person, per cruise. Because of these restrictions several boats later moved to Mississippi which offered 24-hour, no-limit, dockside gambling.

In September 1991 the first riverboats began operating in the bordering state of Illinois and these boats didn't have Iowa's restrictive bet or loss limits. The increased competition from these boats cut deeply into the profitability of the Iowa boats and in early 1994 the Iowa legislature voted to eliminate the gambling restrictions. Additionally, a provision was added to allow slot machines (no video poker) to be placed at the state's four pari-mutuel facilities, subject to voter approval. The slot machine measure passed in referendums in three of the four affected counties.

Here's information, as supplied by the Iowa Racing and Gaming Commission, showing the electronic gaming machine payback percentages for all non-Indian locations for the 2000 fiscal year from July 1, 1999 through June 30, 2000:

LOCATION	PAYBACK %
Bluffs Run	94.73
Prairie Meadows	94.22
President	94.22
Harvey's	94.14
Ameristar	93.88
Dubuque Diamond Jo	93.88
Isle of Capri - Bettendorf	93.80
Dubuque Greyhound	93.66
Isle of Capri - Marquette	93.50
Belle of Sioux City	93.38
Mississippi Belle II	92.87
Catfish Bend	92.51

These figures reflect the total percentages returned by each riverboat casino or pari-mutuel facility for all of its electronic machines including: slots, video poker, video keno, etc. As you can see, Bluffs Run returned the most to their players, while Catfish Bend returned the least.

Admission to all Iowa riverboat casinos is free. Most boats cruise from June through October and remain dockside from November through May although there might be slight differences in those schedules among the various boats.

Iowa is also home to three Indian casinos. Unless otherwise noted, all riverboats and Indian casinos offer: blackjack, roulette, craps, slots and video poker. Some casinos also offer: mini-baccarat (MB), poker (P), pai gow poker (PGP), Caribbean stud poker (CSP), let it ride (LIR), big 6 (B6), bingo (BG), keno (K), three card poker (TCP) and Spanish 21 (S21). The minimum gambling age is 21.

For more information on visiting Iowa call the state's tourism department at (800) 345-4692.

Ameristar Casino Council Bluffs
2200 River Road
Council Bluffs, Iowa 51501
(712) 328-8888
Web Site: www.ameristars.com
Map Location: **#8**

Toll-Free Number: (877) 462-7827
Rooms: 152 Price Range: $90-$159
Suites: 8 Price Range: $225
Restaurants: 4 (1 open 24 hours)
Buffets: B-$6.99 (Sat-Sun)
L-$6.99/$10.99 (Sun)
D-$9.99/$11.99 (Fri)/$10.99 (Sat-Sun)
Casino Size: 37,000 Square Feet
Schedule: Cruises 7:30am-9:30am weekdays (Apr-Oct), then remains dockside 24 hours
Other Games: PGP, CSP, LIR, TCP.
Casino Marketing: (712) 328-8888
Senior Discount: 15% off food and hotel gift shop, if 55, or older
Special Features: 2,700-passenger sidewheeler replica that cruises the Missouri River. Sports bar with live entertainment. Kids Quest supervised children's entertainment center. Gift shop. Video arcade. Outdoor entertainment at Star Arena.

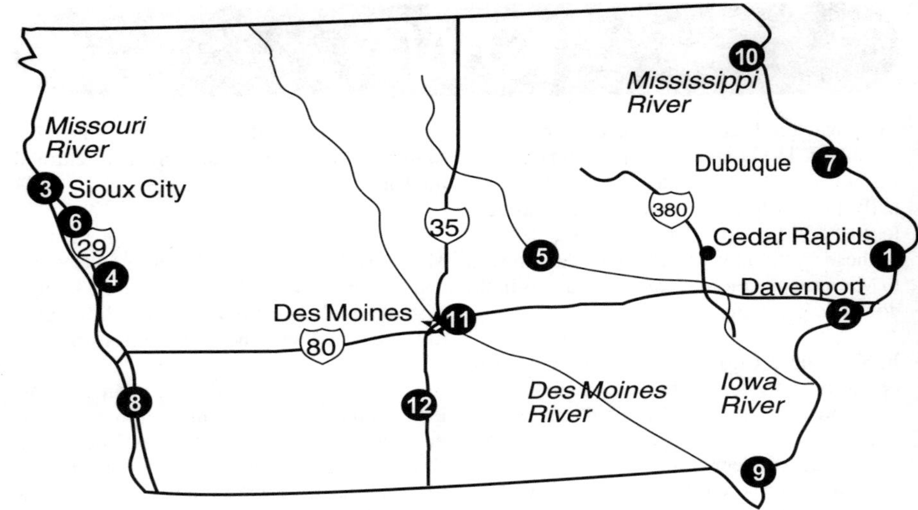

Belle of Sioux City
100 Chris Larsen Park
Sioux City, Iowa 51102
(712) 255-0080
Web Site: www.argosycasinos.com
Map Location: **#3**

Toll-Free Number: (800) 424-0080
Restaurants: 1
Buffets: B-$3.95 L-$6.95
D-$9.95/$11.95 (Fri-Sat)
Schedule: 24 hours
Other Games: P, CSP
Casino Marketing: (800) 424-0080
Special Features: 1,200-passenger old-fashioned stern wheeler that cruises the Missouri River.

Catfish Bend Casino
902 Riverview Drive
Fort Madison, Iowa 52627
(319) 372-2946
Map Location: **#9** (180 miles S.E. of Des Moines)

Toll Free Number: (800) 372-2946
Restaurants: 2
Buffets: B-$3.99 L-$6.95/$8.95 (Sun) D-$8.95/$14.95
Schedule: Opens 6:30am, cruises 7am-9am (Mon-Sat), then remains dockside and stays open until 2am/24 hours (Wed-Sun)
Other Games: P, CSP, LIR
Casino Marketing: (800) 372-2946
Senior Discount: $1 off Wednesday buffet, if 55, or older
Special Features: 1,500-passenger paddle wheeler that cruises the Mississippi River. $10 admission charge for anyone under 21 for up to two hours. Docks in Burlington, Iowa from November through April.

Dubuque Diamond Jo Casino
3rd Street Ice Harbor
Dubuque, IA 52004
(319) 583-7005
Web Site: www.diamondjo.com
Map Location: **#7**

Toll-Free Number: (800) LUCKY-JO
Restaurants: 2
Buffets: B-$4.95 (Sun) L-$7.95
D-$12.95 (Fri/Sat Only)
Schedule: Opens 7am, cruises 10am-2am (Mon-Thu) 7am- 4am (Wed-Thu), then remains dockside and is open 24 hours (Fri/Sat)
Other Games: P, CSP, LIR
Casino Marketing: (800) LUCKY-JO
Senior Discount: Players club members, 55 or older, get a 2-for-1 buffet Fridays and a 35% discount at the gift shop every day
Special Features: 1,600-passenger steamboat replica that cruises the Mississippi River. Deli on boat. Buffet in land-based pavilion. Free child-care for children 3 and older. Players club members get 20% off buffet.

Harvey's Casino Hotel - Council Bluffs
One Harvey's Boulevard
Council Bluffs, Iowa 51501
(712) 329-6000
Web Site: www.harveys.com
Map Location: **#8**

Toll-Free Number: (800) HARVEYS
Rooms: 240 Price Range: $99-$109
Suites: 11 Price Range $149
Restaurants: 3 (1 open 24 hours)
Buffets: B-$4.78/$6.90 (Sat/Sun)
L-$6.90/$10.55 (Sun)
D-$10.55/ $8.95 (Mon/Thu/Sun)
Schedule: open 24 hours
Casino Size: 26,000 Square Feet
Other Games: P, PGP, CSP, LIR, B6, S21
Fun Book: Play four hours in the casino and become eligible to receive six pack of coupons at slot club booth.
Special Features: 2,365-passenger paddle wheel-replica that cruises the Missouri River.

Isle of Capri Casino - Bettendorf
1821 State Street
Bettendorf, Iowa 52722
(319) 359-7280
Web Site: www.isleofcapricasino.com
Map Location: **#2**

Toll-Free Number: (800) 724-5825
Restaurants: 1
Buffets: B-$4.95 L-$7.95 D-$12.95
Schedule: Cruises 7am-9am (Mon-Fri), then remains dockside and stays open 24 hours
Other Games: P, PGP, CSP, LIR
Senior Discount: Club members receive room and buffet discounts, match play offers and free buffet on senior days, if 55, or older
Special Features: 2,500-passenger old-fashioned paddle wheeler that cruises the Mississippi River. Supervised video arcade on 3rd floor for minors under 21. Sports bar with 30 tv's and sports memorabilia.

Isle of Capri - Marquette
P.O. Box 460
Marquette, Iowa 52158
(319) 873-3531
Web Site: www.isleofcapricasino.com
Map Location: **#10** (60 miles N. of Dubuque)

Toll-Free Number: (800) 4-YOU-BET
Rooms: 23 Price Range: $49-$79
Suites: 1 Price Range: $150
Restaurants: 1
Buffets: B-$5.49 L-$6.49
D-$8.99/$10.99 (Fri/Sat)
Schedule: Opens 9am, cruises 10:00am to noon (Mon-Fri), then remains dockside and stays open until 3am/24 hours (Fri-Sat)
Casino Size: 30,000 Square Feet
Other Games: MB, P, CSP, LIR, B6
Fun Book: Distributed by local hotels
Senior Discount: 15% buffet discount, if 55, or older
Special Features: 1,200-passenger paddle wheeler that cruises the Mississippi River. Restaurant and showroom are located in land-based pavilion.

Lakeside Casino Resort
777 Casino Drive
Osceola, Iowa 50213
Map Location: **#12**

Toll-Free Number: (877) 477-5253
Rooms: 60 Price: $69-$85
Suites: $110-$139
Restaurants: 2
Buffets: B-$4.25/$9.25 (Sun) L-$6.25 D-$9.25
Senior Discount: Double points and buffet discount on Mondays, if 55, or older
Special Features: 1,500-passenger old-fashioned paddle wheeler that cruises on West Lake. 100-space RV park. Gift shop. Walking trails. Fishing/boating dock. 500-seat convention center. All suite hotel. $65 room rate seven days a week for AAA and AARP members

Mississippi Belle II
Showboat Landing
Clinton, Iowa 52733
(319) 243-9000
Map Location: **#1** (83 miles E. of Cedar Rapids)

Toll-Free Number: (800) 457-9975
Restaurants: 1
Buffets: B/L-$6.95D-$5.00(Mon)/$8.95(Tue)/ $9.95(Wed/Thu)/$10.95 (Fri/Sat)
Schedule: Opens 9am, cruises 1pm-3pm (Mon-Fri,May-Oct), then remains dockside and stays open until 2am/4am (Fri/Sat).
Casino Size: 10,577 Square Feet
Other Games: P, CSP, LIR , S21, TCP
Fun Book: Offered only to groups.
Special Features: 1,000-passenger old-fashioned paddle wheeler that cruises the Mississippi River. Supervised play area for children ages 3-12. Live entertainment. $10 admission charge for anyone under 21 for a 4-hour stay in the activity center.

President Riverboat Casino
130 West River Drive
Davenport, Iowa 52801
(319) 328-8000
Web Site: www.prescasino.com
Map Location: **#2** (80 miles S.E. of Cedar Rapids)

Toll-Free Number: (800) BOAT-711
Rooms: 160 Price Range: $59-$95
Suites: 29 Price Range: $125
Restaurants: 2 (1 open 24 hours)
Buffets: B-$3.95 L-$6.95 D-$10.95/$11.95 (Fri/Sat)
Schedule: Cruises 7:30-9:30am (Mon-Fri), then remains dockside and stays open 24 hours
Casino Size: 32,000 Square Feet
Other Games: P, PGP, CSP, LIR,
Casino Marketing: (800) 352-5961
Senior Discount: 99¢ breakfast buffet, 25% discount in the President Grill and gift shop, $1 off lunch/dinner buffet, if 50, or older
Special Features: 2,200-passenger paddlewheel replica that cruises the Mississippi River. Restaurants are on a barge which is docked adjacent to The President. Nearby Blackhawk Hotel (800) 553-1173 offers special gaming packages.

Indian Casinos

Casino Omaha
1 Blackbird Bend, Box 89
Onawa, Iowa 51040
(712) 423-3700
Map Location: **#4** (30 miles S. of Sioux City, 60 miles N. of Omaha, 4 miles W. of I-29 at exit 112)

Toll-Free Number: (800) 858-U-BET
Restaurants: 1 Liquor: Yes
Buffets: L-$4.50 D-$6.99
Hours: 8am-2am/24 Hours (Fri/Sat)
Other Games: P
Casino Size: 30,000 Square Feet
Casino Marketing: (800) 858-UBET, ext. 111
Senior Discount: Mon. specials if 55, or older
Fun Book: Coupons available at the slot club booth on some week days.

Meskwaki Bingo & Casino
1504 305th Street
Tama, Iowa 52339
(515) 484-2108
Map Location: **#5** (40 miles W. of Cedar Rapids)

Toll-Free Number: (800) 728-4263
Rooms: 204 Price Range: $25-$69
Suites: 4 Price Range: $175
Restaurants: 2 Liquor: No
Buffets: B-$4.95 L-$6.95 D-$7.95/$8.95 (Fri)
Hours: 24 Hours Daily
Other Games: P, CSP, LIR, MB, S21, K, BG, Simulcasting
Senior Discount: $1 off of buffet, if 55 or older.

Winnavegas
1500 330th Street
Sloan, Iowa 51055
(712) 428-9466
Map Location: **#6** (20 miles S. of Sioux City)

Toll-Free Number: (800) 468-9466
Restaurants: 1 Liquor: Yes
Buffets: L-$5.70 D-$7.50
Hours: 24 Hours Daily
Other Games: MB, P, CSP, LIR, BG
Fun Book: Only given to groups

Pari-Mutuels

Bluffs Run Casino
2701 23rd Avenue
Council Bluffs, Iowa 51501
(712) 323-2500
Web Site: www.bluffsrun.com
Map Location: **#8** (102 miles S. of Sioux City)

Toll-Free Number: (800) BET-2-WIN
Restaurants: 4 (1 open 24 hours)
Buffets: B-$3.95 L-$4.95 D-$7.95
Casino Size: 50,000 Square Feet
Hours: 24 Hours Daily
Other Games: Only slots and live Keno
Fun Book: Join Player's Club and receive newsletter with coupons 4-6 times per year
Special Features: Live dog racing (Tue-Sun). Horse and dog race simulcasting. On-property RV park.

Dubuque Greyhound Park & Casino
1855 Greyhound Park Drive
Dubuque, Iowa 52001
(319) 582-3647
Web Site: www.dgpc.com
Map Location: **#7**

Toll-Free Number: (800) 373-3647
Restaurants: 1
Buffets: L-$7.95 D-$10.95
Hours: 9am-2am/24 hours (Fri/Sat)
Other Games: Only slot machines
Senior Discount: $2 off buffet, if 55, or older
Special Features: Live dog racing (Wed-Sun) during season which runs from May through October. Dog race simulcasting all year.

Prairie Meadows Racetrack & Casino
1 Prairie Meadows Drive
Altoona, Iowa 50009
(515) 967-1000
Web Site: www.prairiemeadows.com
Map Location: **#11** (5 miles E. of Des Moines)

Toll-Free Number: (800) 325-9015
Restaurants: 2
Buffets: B-$4.50 L-$5.50
Hours: 24 Hours Daily
Other Games: Only slot machines
Special Features: Live thoroughbred and quarter-horse racing during season which runs from April through November. Simulcasting of dog and horse racing all year.

KANSAS

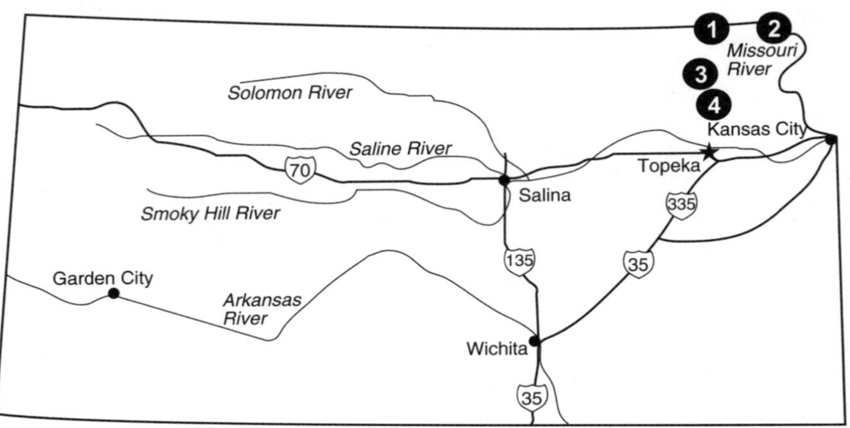

There are four Indian tribes in Kansas with casinos. According to officials at the Kansas State Gaming Agency the terms of the state's compacts with the tribes regarding the minimum payback amounts on their machines are not a matter of public record and no information can be released.

Unless otherwise noted, all Kansas casinos are open 24 hours and offer the following games: blackjack, craps, roulette, slots and video poker. Other games include: poker (P), Caribbean stud poker (CSP), let it ride (LIR), three card poker (TCP) and bingo (BG). The minimum gambling age is 21.

For more information on visiting Kansas call the state's tourism department at (800) 2-KANSAS.

Casino White Cloud
777 Jackpot Drive
White Cloud, Kansas 66094
(785) 595-3430
Map Location: **#2**

Toll-Free Number: (877) 652-6115
Restaurants: 1 Liquor: Only Beer
Buffets: L-$5.72 D-$8.00
Casino Hours: 9am-1am/3am (Fri/Sat)
Other Games: TCP, BG, No Roulette

Golden Eagle Casino
1121 Goldfinch Road
Horton, Kansas 66439
(785) 486-6601
Map Location: **#3** (45 miles N. of Topeka)
Web Site: www.goldeneaglecasino.com

Toll-Free Number: (888) 464-5825
Restaurants: 2 Liquor: No
Buffets: B-$2.95(Sat-Sun) L-$4.95
D-$8.95/$6.95(Thu)/$9.95 (Tue)
Other Games: P, LIR
Casino Marketing: (888) 464-5825, ext 251
Senior Discount: Friday "breakfast on us" program for players club members 55, or older
Special Features: 550-seat entertainment center.

Harrah's Prairie Band Casino
12305 150th Road
Mayetta, Kansas 66509
(785) 966-7777
Web Site: www.harrahs.com
Map Location: **#4** (17 miles N. of Topeka)

Toll-Free Number: (800) HARRAHS
Rooms: 100 Price Range: $70-$85
Restaurants: 1 Liquor: Yes
Buffets: B-$4.95/$5.95 (Sat-Sun)
L-$6.95/$7.95 (Sat-Sun)
D-$9.95 (Tue/Thu/Sun)
$11.95 (Mon/Wed/Sat)/$13.95 (Fri)
Casino Size: 63,000 Square Feet
Other Games: P, CSP, LIR, BG
Special Features: Alcohol is only served in the Prairie Pub and a membership card is required to enter.

Sac & Fox Casino
RR #1, Box 105-A, N. Hwy 75
Powhattan, Kansas 66527
(785)-467-8000
Map Location: **#1** (60 miles N. of Topeka)
Web site: www.sacandfoxcasino.com

Toll-Free Number: (800) 990-2946
Restaurant: 2 (1 open 24 hours) Liquor: Yes
Buffets: L-$4.95 D-$6.95/$8.95 (Wed)
Casino Size: 40,000 Square Feet
Other Games: CSP, LIR
Casino Marketing: (785)467-8000 ext 1161
Special Features: New hotel expected to open by early 2001. Membership card required to be served alcohol in the Pub.

LOUISIANA

Video poker is permitted at Louisiana truck stops, racetracks/OTB's and bars/taverns in 31 of the state's 64 parishes (counties). There is no limit to the number of machines permitted at racetracks and off-track betting locations, however, truck stops are allowed no more than 50, while bars and taverns are permitted a maximum of three.

Louisiana was the fourth state to approve riverboat casino gambling and its 1991 gambling law allows a maximum of 15 boats statewide with a limit of six in any one parish. In 1992 a provision was added for one land-based casino in New Orleans. The state also has three land-based Indian casinos.

The law requires that all boats must be paddlewheel driven and replicas of old-fashioned turn-of-the-century models. All of the boats are also required to cruise, except those located along the Red River which are exempt because those waters were deemed too dangerous to continually navigate. A section of the state's law, however, allows the captain to order any boat to remain dockside if he believes that the sailing conditions present any kind of danger to the vessel, passengers or crew. Until early 1995 many of the riverboats used this loophole to avoid cruising and almost all of them offered 24-hour dockside gaming. This eventually led to a more stringent enforcement by gaming authorities and now all riverboats (except those on the Red River) must go on 90-minute cruises. All cruises are free and boarding is scheduled 45 minutes before each cruise. Passengers can, however, actually begin boarding as soon as the boat returns from its previous cruise which is about an hour-and-a-half before the next scheduled cruise.

Casino gambling has been fairly successful everywhere in Louisiana except for New Orleans. There was a major failure in that city in June 1995 when the River City casino complex closed after only two months of operation. That complex contained two riverboats (Grand Palais and Crescent City) and couldn't generate enough business to remain open. Also, another riverboat in downtown New Orleans - the Flamingo Casino - ceased operating in 1998.

The state's only, non-Indian, land-based casino, Harrah's New Orleans, originally declared bankruptcy and closed its temporary casino in November 1995. There were lengthy negotiations between Harrah's and the state to allow the casino to re-open, however, and the casino did re-open again in 1999.

As of August 2000 there were 13 riverboat casinos in operation in 11 different locations (the two Lake Charles locations each have two boats). A 14th casino - Hollywood Casino in Shreveport - was expected to open by early 2001. Additionallly, the state's Gaming Control Board was reviewing applications from three different companies to award the 15th license and they were expected to announce their decision by early 2001.

Louisiana's gaming regulations require that gaming machines in casinos be programmed to pay back no less than 80% and no more than 99.9%. For video gaming machines at locations other than casinos the law requires a minimum return of 80% and a maximum return of 94%.

Louisiana gaming statistics are not broken down by individual properties. Rather, they are classified by region: Baton Rouge (**BR**) , Lake Charles (**LC**), New Orleans (**NO**) and Shreveport/Bossier City (**SB**).

The Baton Rouge casinos consist of the Argosy and Casino Rouge. The Lake Charles casinos include: Grand Palais, Isle of Capri, Players and Star. New Orleans area casinos are: Bally's, Boomtown, Harrah's (landbased) and Treasure Chest. The Shreveport/Bossier city casinos include: Casino Magic, Isle of Capri Harrah's and Horseshoe.

Here's information, as supplied by the Louisiana State Police - Riverboat Gaming Section, showing the average electronic machine payback percentages for each area's casinos for the five-month period from January through May, 2000:

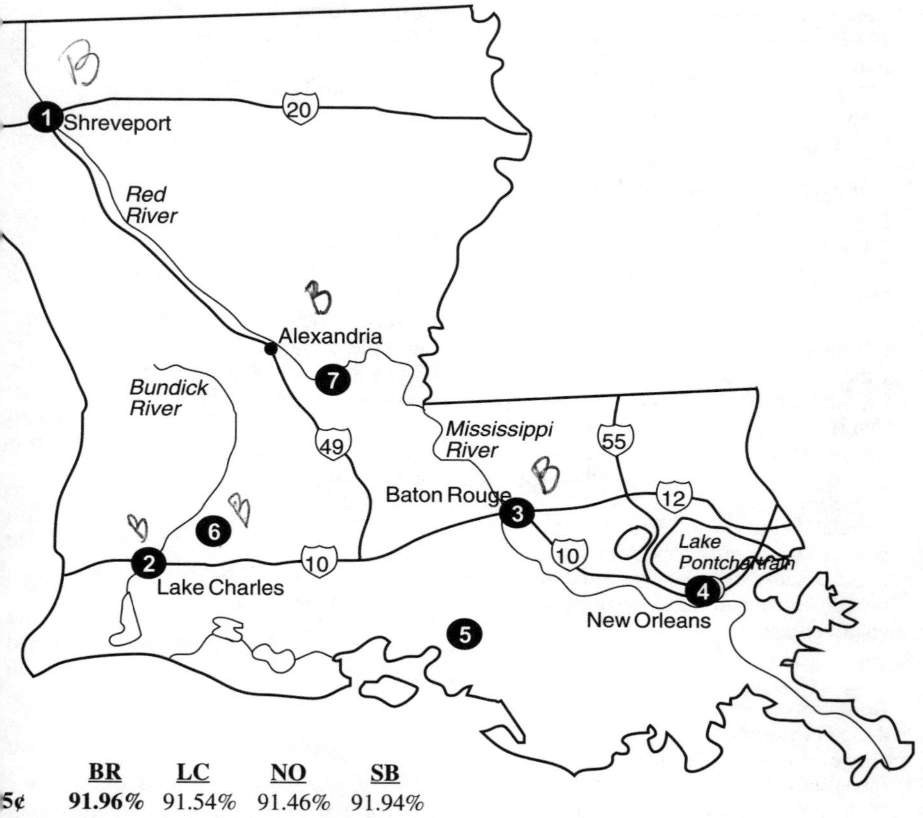

	BR	LC	NO	SB
5¢	**91.96%**	91.54%	91.46%	91.94%
25¢	**92.94%**	91.46%	92.48%	92.52%
$1	94.26%	93.44%	94.00%	**94.50%**
$5	**95.90%**	94.84%	95.34%	95.70%
All	**93.90%**	92.88%	93.14%	93.72%

These numbers reflect the percentage of money returned on each denomination of machine and encompass all electronic machines including video poker and video keno. The best returns for each category are highlighted in bold print and you can see that the Baton Rouge area casinos offered the best returns in almost every category.

All riverboat casinos are open 24 hours and the games offered are: blackjack, craps, roulette, slots and video poker. Optional games include: baccarat (B), mini-baccarat (MB), poker (P), Caribbean Stud Poker (CSP), Pai Gow Poker (PGP), let it ride (LIR), casino war (CW), big 6 wheel (B6), keno (K) and bingo (BG). The minimum gambling age is 21. For more information on visiting Louisiana call the state's tourism department at (800) 633-6970.

Bally's Casino Lakeshore Resort
1 Stars & Stripes Boulevard
New Orleans, Louisiana 70126
(504) 248-3200
Web Site: www.ballysno.com
Map Location: **#4**

Toll-Free Number: (800) 57-BALLY
Restaurants: 1 (Snack bar on boat)
Buffets: B-$5.95(Sat/Sun) L-$8.95
D-$11.95/$15.95 (Fri)
Departures: 6am/pm, 9am/pm,
12am/pm, 3am/pm
Casino Size: 30,000 Square Feet
Other Games: B, MB, P, CSP, PGP, LIR
Senior Discount: 15% discount on buffets & logo shop purchases on Mon/Thu, if 55, or older
Special Features: 1,200-passenger paddle wheeler that cruises Lake Pontchartrain. Buffets, restaurant and sports bar are located in land-based terminal.

Belle of Baton Rouge
103 France Street
Baton Rouge, Louisiana 70802
(225) 378-6000
Web Site: www.argosycasinos.com
Map Location: **#3**

Toll-Free Number: (800) 676-4847
Restaurants: 4 (1 on boat)
Buffets: L-$7.95/$9.95 (Fri)/$19.95 (Sun)
D-$12.95/$7.95 (Sat)
Departures: 6am/pm, 9am/pm,
12am/pm, 3am/pm
Casino Size: 29,000 Square Feet
Other Games: CSP, LIR
Casino Marketing: (800) 676-4VIP
Fun Book: Only given to groups
Senior Discount: If 50, or older, 15% off in restaurants. Ask to join Belles and Beaus Senior Club.
Special Features: 1,500-passenger paddle wheeler that cruises the Mississippi River. Land-based entertainment pavilion houses buffet restaurant and lounge with live entertainment.

Boomtown Casino Westbank
4132 Peters Road
Harvey, Louisiana 70058
(504) 366-7711
Web Site: www.boomtowncasinos.com
Map Location: **#4** (a suburb of New Orleans)

Toll-Free Number: (800) 366-7711
Restaurants: 2 (1 snack bar on boat)
Buffets: B-$5.95 (Sat/Sun) L-$8.65 D-$14.00
Departures: 7:45am/pm, 10:45am/pm,
1:45am/pm, 4:45am/pm
Casino Size: 30,000 Square Feet
Other Games: B, MB, PGP, CSP, LIR
Casino Marketing: (800) 366-7711
Fun Book: Need coupon from local hotels
Senior Discount: $2 off buffets, if 55, or older
Special Features: 1,600-passenger paddle wheeler that cruises on the Harvey Canal. 88,000-square-foot land-based terminal features restaurant, arcade with children's games and a lounge with live entertainment.

Casino Magic - Bossier City
300 Riverside Drive
Bossier City, Louisiana 71171
(318) 746-0711
Web Site: www.casinomagic.com
Map Location: **#1** (across the Red River From Shreveport)

Toll-Free Number: (800) 5-MAGIC-5
Rooms: 100 Price Range: $85-$125
Suites: 88 Price Range: $105-$145
Restaurants: 3
Buffets: L-$7.95 D-$9.95/$19.99 (Fri/Sat)
Schedule: 24 hours daily
Casino Size: 28,000 Square Feet
Other Games: MB, CSP, LIR
Special Features: 1,925-passenger paddle wheeler that remains dockside on the Red River. Free valet parking. Entertainment pavilion with lounge, dancing water displays and interactive illusions.

Casino Rouge
1717 River Road North
Baton Rouge, Louisiana 70802
(225) 381-7777
Web Site: www.casinorouge.com
Map Location: **#3**

Toll-Free Number: (800) 44-ROUGE
Restaurants: 2 (1 snack bar on boat)
Buffets: B-$15.95 (Sun) L-$7.95
D-$11.95/$14.95 (Fri-Sat)/$13.95 (Sun)
Departures: 6am/pm, 9am/pm,
12am/pm, 3am/pm
Casino Size: 28,146 Square Feet
Other Games: MB, P, CSP, LIR
Senior Discount: 50% off Monday lunch buffet, 10% off Tue-Thu dinner buffets, if 55, or older
Special Features: 1,500-passenger paddle wheeler that cruises on the Mississippi River. Land-based terminal features two restaurants. Cash giveaways every Tuesday.

Harrah's New Orleans
4 Canal Street
New Orleans, Louisiana 70130
(504) 533-6000
Web Site: www.harrahs.com
Map Location: **#4**

Toll-Free Number: (800) HARRAHS
Restaurants: 2 (1 open 24 hours)
Buffet: B-$6.99 L-$9.99
D-$15.99/$19.99 (Fri-Sun)
Schedule: 24 hours daily
Casino Size: 100,000 Square Feet
Other Games: B, MB, CSP, LIR, P
Casino Marketing: (318) 424-7777
Special Features: Land-based casino. Five themed gaming areas. Five-outlet food court. Gift shop. Private high-stakes rooms. Daily live jazz music and Mardi Gras parade.

Harrah's Shreveport
315 Clyde Fant Parkway
Shreveport, Louisiana 71101
(318) 424-7777
Web Site: www.harrahs.com
Map Location: **#1**

Toll-Free Number: (800) HARRAHS
Rooms: 514 Price Range: Not set at press time
Restaurants: 2 (1 open 24 hours)
Buffet: Not set at press time
Schedule: 24 hours daily
Valet Parking: $2/$4 (Fri-Sun)
Casino Size: 30,000 Square Feet
Other Games: MB, CSP, LIR
Casino Marketing: (318) 424-7777
Special Features: 1,650-passenger paddle wheeler that remains dockside on the Red River.

Hollywood Casino Shreveport
501 Clyde Fant Parkway
Shreveport, Louisiana 71101
(318) 220-0711
Web Site: www.hollywoodcasino.com
Map Location: **#1**

EXPECTED TO OPEN BY EARLY 2001
Suites: 405 Restaurants: 4
Schedule: 24 hours daily
Casino Size: 30,000 Square Feet
Special Features: 1,500-passenger paddle wheeler that remains dockside on the Red River. Land-based entertainment complex displays movie memorabilia. All-suite hotel.

Horseshoe Casino Hotel - Bossier City
711 Horseshoe Boulevard
Bossier City, Louisiana 71111
(318) 742-0711
Web Site: www.horseshoe.com
Map Location: **#1** (across the Red River from Shreveport)

Toll-Free Number: (800) 895-0711
Rooms: 200 Price Range: $79-$150
Suites: 606 Price Range: $120-$200
Restaurants: 4 (1 open 24 hours)
Buffets: B-$6.95 L-$9.95/$13.95 (Fri)
D-$10.95/$12.95 (Mon-Tue)/$16.95 (Fri)
Schedule: 24 hours daily
Other Games: MB, CSP, LIR, P
Casino Size: 29,500 Square Feet
Casino Marketing: (800) 895-0711
Special Features: Four-story, 2,930-passenger paddle wheeler that remains dockside on the Red River. Suites are at on-site hotel. Rooms are at nearby LeBossier Hotel with free shuttle service to casino.

Isle of Capri Casino & Hotel - Bossier City
711 Isle of Capri Boulevard
Bossier City, Louisiana 71111
(318) 678-7777
Web Site: www.isleofcapricasino.com
Map Location: **#1** (across the Red River from Shreveport)

Toll-Free Number: (800) THE-ISLE
Room Reservations: (800) ISLE-VIP
Suites: 312 Price Range: $110-$165
Restaurants: 3 (1 open 24 Hours)
Buffets: B-$5.99 L-$7.99 D-$15.99
Schedule: 24 hours daily
Casino Size: 30,000 Square Feet
Other Games: MB, P, PGP, CSP, LIR, K
Casino Marketing: (800) ISLE-VIP
Special Features: 1,650-passenger paddle wheeler that remains dockside on the Red River. Island Gold Card members get $20 hotel discount.

Isle of Capri Casino & Hotel - Lake Charles
100 Westlake Avenue
Westlake, Louisiana 70669
(318) 430-0711
Web Site: www.isleofcapricasino.com
Map Location: **#2** (220 miles W. of New Orleans)

Toll-Free Number: (800) THE-ISLE
Rooms: 251 Price Range: $79-$109
Restaurants: 3 (1 snack bar on boat)
Buffets: B-$4.99 L-$6.99 D-$12.99
Crown Departures: 6:30pm, 9:30am/pm, 12:30am/pm, 3:30am/pm
Grand Palais Departures: 8am/pm, 11am/pm, 2am/pm, 5am/pm
Other Games: B, MB, P, CSP, LIR
Senior Discount: If 55, or older, go to Island Gold Club booth) for special coupon book
Fun Book: Given when signing up for slot club
Special Features: Two 1,200-passenger paddle wheelers (Crown and Grand Palais) that cruise Lake Charles. With two boats there is never a wait to board because when one is out, the other is in. Land-based terminal has three restaurants.

Players Island
Hotel & Casino - Lake Charles
800 Bilbo Street
Lake Charles, Louisiana 70601
(318) 437-1500
Web Site: www.harrahs.com
Map Location: **#2** (220 miles W. of New Orleans)

Toll-Free Number: (800) 977-PLAY
Restaurants: 3 (1 open 24 Hours)
Rooms: 132 Price Range: $79-$120
Buffets: B-$7.99 (Sat/Sun) L-$7.99 D-$10.99/$14.99 (Fri/Sat)
Players Departures: 8:15am/pm, 11:15am/pm, 2:15am/pm, 5:15am/pm
Star Departures: 6:45am/pm, 9:45am/pm, 12:45am/pm, 3:45am/pm
Other Games: B, MB, P, PGP, CSP, LIR
Casino Marketing: (800) 625-BOAT
Special Features: Players Island includes two boats that cruise Lake Charles. Players Riverboat is a 1,700-passenger paddle wheeler and Star Casino is a 1,460-passenger paddle wheeler. Free hourly pirate show with special effects and life-size characters. Showroom with headliner entertainment. Rooms also available at nearby Holiday Inn (800-367-1814).

Treasure Chest Casino
5050 Williams Boulevard
Kenner, Louisiana 70065
(504) 443-8000
Web Site: www.treasurechest.com
Map Location: **#4** (a suburb of New Orleans)

Toll-Free Number: (800) 298-0711
Restaurants: 2
Buffets: B-$5.99/$15.99 (Sun) L-$9.99 D-$12.99/$19.99 (Fri/Sat)
Departures: 8am/pm, 11am/pm, 2am/pm, 5am/pm
Casino Size: 25,767 Square Feet
Other Games: MB, CSP, LIR
Casino Marketing: (800) 298-0711
Senior Discount: If 50, or older, ask to join Treasured Friends for different monthly specials
Special Features: 1,900-passenger paddle wheeler that cruises on Lake Pontchartrain. Snack bar is located on barge adjacent to riverboat. $2 discount on breakfast buffet for slot club members.

Indian Casinos

Cypress Bayou Casino
P.O. Box 519
Charenton, Louisiana 70523
(318) 923-7284
Web Site: www.cypressbayou.com
Map Location: **#5** (75 miles S. of Baton Rouge)

Toll-Free Number: (800) 284-4386
Restaurants: 3 Liquor: Yes
Casino Size: 125,000 Square Feet
Casino Hours: 10am-2am/4am (Fri/Sat)
Other Games: B6, CSP, LIR
Casino Marketing: (800) 284-4386
Special Features: Land-based casino. Free valet parking. Bocats Lounge features two 525-gallon freshwater aquariums. Gift shop.

Grand Casino Avoyelles
711 Grand Boulevard
Marksville, Louisiana 71351
(318) 253-1946
Web Site: www.grandcasinoavoyelles.com
Map Location: **#7** (30 miles S.E. of Alexandria)

Toll-Free Number: (800) WIN-1-WIN
Rooms: 200 Price Range: $59-$109
Suites: 19 Price Range: $99-$149
Restaurants: 3 (1 open 24 hours) Liquor: Yes
Buffets: B-$6.99 (Sun) L-$7.99 (Mon-Sat)
D-$10.99/$14.99 (Fri)
Casino Size: 100,000 Square Feet
Other Games: B, MB, P, PGP, CSP,
LIR, TCP, K, BG
Casino Marketing: (800) WIN-1-WIN
Fun Book: Given when you join
Grand Advantage club
Special Features: Land-based casino. RV Park. Free valet parking. Kids Quest - supervised children's activity center (6 weeks to 12 years). Video arcade. Night club. 30,000-square-foot entertainment center features concerts and sporting events. $10 room discount for AAA and AARP members.

Grand Casino Coushatta
777 Coushatta Drive
Kinder Louisiana 70648
(318) 738-7300
Web Site: www.gccoushatta.com
Map Location: **#6** (35 miles N.E. of Lake Charles)

Toll-Free Number: (800) 58-GRAND
Rooms: 223 Price Range: $69-$119
Suites: 45 Price Range: $109-$159
Restaurants: 4 (1 open 24 hours) Liquor: Yes
Buffets: L-$7.99 D-$10.99/$14.99 (Fri/Sat)
Casino Size: 71,000 Square Feet
Other Games: B, MB, P, PGP, CSP, LIR, B6
Casino Marketing: (800) 584-7263
Special Features: Land-based casino. RV park. Free valet parking. Kids Quest - supervised children's activity center (6 weeks to 12 years). Video arcade for teens. Food court.

MASSACHUSETTS

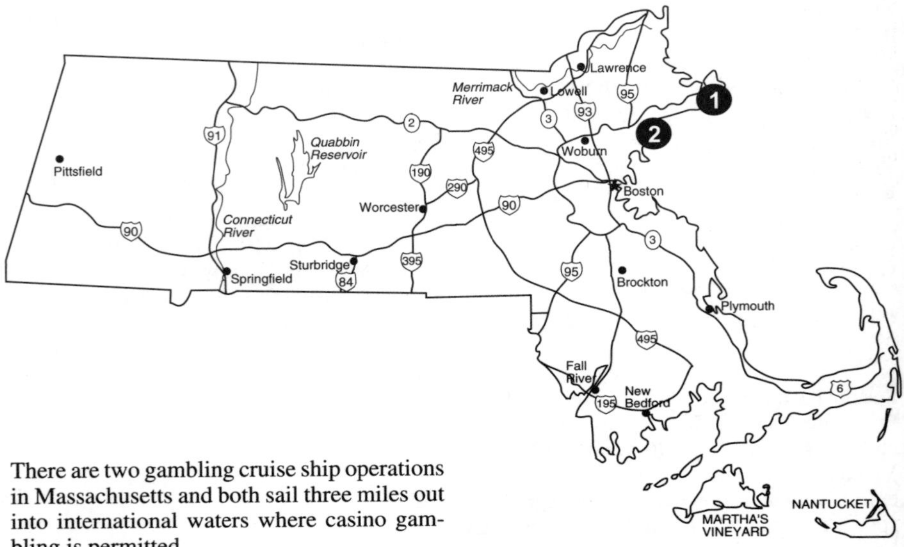

There are two gambling cruise ship operations in Massachusetts and both sail three miles out into international waters where casino gambling is permitted.

The games offered on the boats include: blackjack, craps, roulette, Caribbean stud poker, slots and video poker.

For information on visiting Massachusetts call (800) 447-MASS.

Horizon's Edge Casino Cruises
76 Marine Boulevard
Lynn, MA 01901
Map Location: **#2** (20 miles N.E. of Boston)
(781) 581-7733

Toll-Free Reservations: (877) 412-7700
Gambling Age: 21
Ship's Registry: U.S.
Buffets: Included
Schedule:
11:00am - 4:30pm
7:00pm - 11:55pm/1:00am (Fri/Sat)
Prices: $24.95 (Mon-Fri Day/Sun-Wed Eve)
$29.95 (Sat-Sun Day/Thu-Sat Eve)
Port Charges: Included
Parking: Free
Special Features: 500-passenger *Horizon's Edge* sails from Marina off of Lynnway in Lynn. No one under 21 permitted to board.

Leisure Casino Cruises
6 Rowe Square
Gloucester, Massachusetts 01930
(978) 282-3330
Map Location: **#1** (38 miles N.E. of Boston)

Toll-Free Reservations: (800) 453-1179
Gambling Age: 21
Ship's Registry: U.S.
Buffets: Included
Schedule:
1:00pm - 5:00pm (Daily)
7:00pm - 11:30pm/12:30am (Fri-Sat)
Prices: $24/$29 (Fri-Sat Eve/Sat-Sun Day)
Port Charges: Included
Parking: Included
Special Features: 450-passenger *Vegas Express* sails from Elliott's Wharf off Main Street in Gloucester. No one under 21 permitted to board.

MICHIGAN

One of Michigan's most popular casino is actually in Canada. It's Casino Windsor in Ontario which is just across the river from downtown Detroit. Casino Windsor first opened May 17, 1994 and a riverboat (Northern Belle Casino) was later added to accommodate the overflow crowds which the casino drew. The original casino and riverboat were closed in July 1998 when a new larger casino/hotel opened to replace them.

All winnings are paid in Canadian currency and the minimum gambling age is 19. The casino is open 24 hours and offers the following games: blackjack, craps, single-zero roulette, baccarat, mini-baccarat, big six wheel, pai-gow poker, Caribbean stud poker and let it ride.

Casino Windsor
377 Riverside Drive East
Windsor, Ontario N9A 7H7
(519) 258-7878
Web Site: www.casinowindsor.com
Map Location: **#12**

PRICES ARE IN CANADIAN DOLLARS
Toll-Free Number: (800) 991-7777
Room Reservations: (800) 991-8888
Rooms: 349 Price Range: $165-$225
Suites: 40 Price Range: $250-$1,450
Restaurants: 5 (1 open 24 hours)
Buffets: L-$12.50 D-$15.95/$19.95 (Fri/Sat)
Casino Size: 100,000 Square Feet
Senior Discount: AARP 10% room discount
Special Features: Nautical theme with 60-foot waterfall, babbling brook, periodic water and light show.

In November 1996 Detroit voters approved, by a 51% to 49% margin, a referendum to allow three casinos in the downtown area. Each operator has opened a temporary casino which, by law, must be replaced by a permanent casino within four years.

All three casinos are open 24 hours and offer the following games: blackjack, craps, roulette, baccarat, mini-baccarat, Caribbean stud poker, pai gow poker and let it ride. The minimum gambling age at all Detroit casinos is 21.

Greektown Casino
555 E. Lafayette Blvd.
Detroit, Michigan 48226
(313) 223-2999
Web Site: www.greektowncasino.com
Map Location: **#12**

EXPECTED TO OPEN BY EARLY 2001
Room Reservations: (800) 772-2323
Suites: 175 Price Range: $155-$700
Restaurants: 5 (1 open 24 hours)
Casino Size: 75,000 Square Feet
Special Features: Rooms are at Atheneum Hotel which is across the street from the casino. Restaurants, pastry shops and specialty boutiques are in areas adjacent to the casino property.

MGM Grand Detroit Casino
1300 John C. Lodge
Detroit Michigan 48226
(313) 393-7777
Web Site: www.detroit.mgmgrand.com
Map Location: **#12**

Toll-Free Number: (877) 888-2121
Restaurants: 2
Buffets: B-$7.95 (Sat/Sun)
L- $13.75 D-$17.95
Casino Size: 75,000 Square Feet

MotorCity Casino
2901 Grand River Avenue
Detroit, MI 48201
(313) 237-7711
Web Site: www.motorcitycasino.com
Map Location: **#12**

Toll-Free Number: (877) 777-0711
Restaurants: 5
Buffets: B-$11.95 L-$14.95 D-$18.95
Casino Size: 75,000 Square Feet
Special Features: Free valet parking. Four floors of gambling (1 nonsmoking floor). Live music daily on two separate stages.

There are 16 Indian casinos in Michigan and since the majority of the casinos are small, most of the dining facilities are more like snack bars rather than restaurants. The largest casino is Soaring Eagle which has more than 50 blackjack tables and over 4,000 slot machines.

The Indian Tribes are not required to release information on their slot machine percentage paybacks, but according to Patrick Leen at the Michigan Racing Commission, which is responsible for regulating the tribe's slots, "the machines must meet the minimum standards for machines in Nevada or New Jersey." In Nevada the minimum return is 75% and in New Jersey it's 83%. Therefore, Michigan Indian casinos must return at least 75% in order to comply with the law.

Unless otherwise noted, all Indian casinos in Michigan are open 24 hours and offer the following games: blackjack, slots and video poker. Other games offered include: craps (C), roulette (R), baccarat (B), mini-baccarat (MB), poker (P), Caribbean Stud Poker (CSP), Let It Ride (LIR), keno (K) and bingo (BG). The minimum gambling age at most Michigan casinos is 21 (at Soaring Eagle and Chip-In's Island the minimum age is 18).

For more information on visiting Michigan call the state's department of tourism at (800) 543-2937.

Bay Mills Resort & Casino
11386 Lakeshore Drive
Brimley, Michigan 49715
(906) 248-3715
Web Site: www.4baymills.com
Map Location: **#3** (12 miles S.W. of Sault Ste. Marie)

Toll-Free Number: (888) 4-BAY-MILLS
Rooms: 142 Price Range: $62-$79
Suites: 4 Price Range: $190
Restaurants: 2 (1 open 24 hrs) Liquor: Yes
Buffets: B-$5.95 L-$6.95
D-$7.95/$10.95 (Fri/Sat)
Casino Size: 15,000 Square Feet
Other Games: C, R, CSP, LIR, K
Fun Book: Given with slot club membership
Senior Discount: 10% room discount (Sun-Thu). Wednesday is Senior's Day from 8am-2pm with buffet discounts and cash drawings, if 55, or older
Special Features: Free valet parking and shuttle service to King's Club and Kewadin casinos. 18-hole golf course.

Chip-In's Island Resort & Casino
P.O. Box 351
Harris, Michigan 49845
(906) 466-2941
Web Site: www.chipincasino.com
Map Location: **#1** (13 miles W. of Escanaba on Hwy. 41)

Toll-Free Number: (800) 682-6040
Rooms: 102 Price Range: $72-$83
Suites: 11 Price Range: $117-$144
Restaurants: 1 Liquor: Yes
Buffets: B-$7.95 (Sat/Sun) L-$7.95 D-$9.95
Casino Size: 135,000 Square Feet
Other Games: C, R, P, CSP, LIR, K, BG
Fun Book: Given to all slot club members
Special Features: Free nonalcoholic beverages. Free valet parking and shuttle service. Heated pool. Fitness center. 53-space RV park.

Kewadin Casino - Christmas
N7761 Candy Cane Lane
Munising, Michigan 49862
(906) 387-5475
Web Site: www.kewadin.com
Map Location: **#9** (40 miles E. of Marquette)

Toll-Free Number: (800) KEWADIN
Restaurants: 1 Deli Liquor: Yes
Table Game Hours: 4pm-12am Daily
Slot Hours: 9am-1am Daily
Casino Size: 3,060 Square Feet
Senior Discount: $5 coin, $2 matchplay, plus other specials on Wednesdays from noon to 5pm
Special Features: Beer and wine served. Free shuttle service from local motels.

Kewadin Casino - Hessel
3 Mile Road, Box 789
Hessel, Michigan 49745
(906) 484-2903
Web Site: www.kewadin.com
Map Location: **#10** (20 miles N.E. of St. Ignace)

Toll-Free Number: (800) KEWADIN
Restaurants: 1 Deli Liquor: Yes
Table Game Hours: 5pm-1am (Mon/Thu-Sun)
Slot Hours: 9am-12am/1am (Fri/Sat)
Casino Size: 6,500 Square Feet
Senior Discount: $5 coin, $2 matchplay, plus other specials on Thursdays noon to 4pm
Special Features: Beer and wine served. Free shuttle service from local motels.

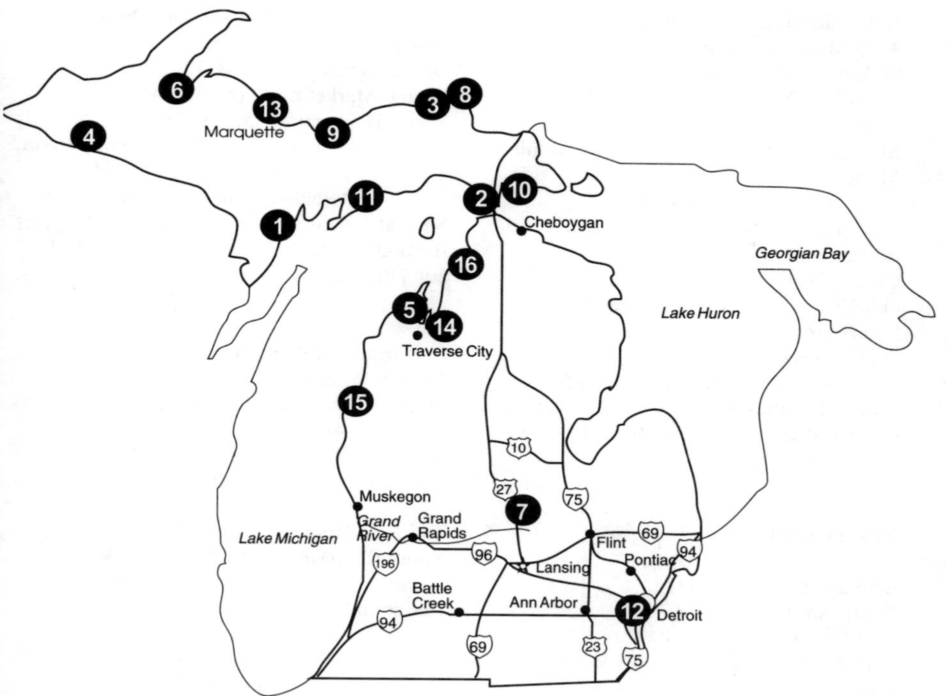

Kewadin Casino - Manistique
US 2 East, Rte 1, Box 1533D
Manistique, Michigan 49854
(906) 341-5510
Web Site: www.kewadin.com
Map Location: **#10** (95 miles S.E. of Marquette)

Toll-Free Number: (800) KEWADIN
Rooms: 40 Price Range: $55-$62
Restaurants: 1 Deli Liquor: Yes
Table Game Hours: 10am-2am Daily
Slot Hours: 24 Hours
Casino Size: 25,000 Square Feet
Other Games: C, R, CSP, LIR
Fun Book: On sale at Kewadin Inn
Senior Discount: Free slot tournament on Tuesdays at 10am. $5 coin, $2 matchplay, plus other specials on Wednesdays from noon to 5pm
Special Features: Rooms are at Kewadin Inn about one mile from casino. 10% room discount for AARP members. 20% room discount for AAA members. Sports bar. Gift shop. Free shuttle service from local motels. Coupon book distributed by local motels.

Kewadin Casino Hotel - Sault Ste. Marie
2186 Shunk Road
Sault Ste. Marie, Michigan 49783
(906) 632-0530
Web Site: www.kewadin.com
Map Location: **#8**

Toll-Free Number: (800) KEWADIN
Room Reservations: (800) KEWADIN
Rooms: 300 Price Range: $79-$89
Suites: 20 Price Range: $109-$119
Restaurants: 2 (1 open 24 hours) Liquor: Yes
Buffets: B-$5.50/$8.50 (Sun) L-$7.95
D-$10.95/$12.95 (Fri/Sat)
Casino Size: 85,123 Square Feet
Other Games: C, R, P, CSP, LIR, K, BG
Casino Marketing: (906) 635-4968
Fun Book: Given when you sign up for slot club and when you put 150 points on card in 24-hour period
Senior Discount: $5 coin, $2 matchplay, plus other specials on Thursdays 7am-11am, if 55, or older. Also, 20% off buffets.
Special Features: Free valet parking. Free shuttle service. $5 table game players can be rated. 10% off room for AARP members. 20% off room for AAA members.

Kewadin Shores Casino
3039 Mackinaw Trail
St. Ignace, Michigan 49781
(906) 643-7071
Web Site: www.kewadin.com
Map Location: **#2** (50 miles S. of Sault Ste. Marie)

Toll-Free Number: (800) KEWADIN
Restaurants: 1 Deli Liquor: Yes
Casino Size: 56,168 Square Feet
Other Games: C, R, P, PGP, CSP, LIR, K
Fun Book: Only given to bus groups
Senior Discount: Free casino packages on Thursdays from 7am to 11am, if 50, or older
Special Features: Local motels/hotels offer casino packages and free shuttle service. Sports bar with satellite tv's.

Kings Club Casino
12140 W. Lakeshore Drive
Brimley, Michigan 49715
(906) 248-3700
Web Site: www.4baymills.com
Map Location: **#3** (12 miles S.W. of Sault Ste. Marie)

Toll-Free Number: (888) 422-9645
Restaurants: 1 Deli Liquor: Yes
Casino Size: 7,400 Square Feet
Hours: 8am-2am/4am (Fri-Sat)
Other Games: Only Slots
Seniors Discount: Tuesdays are Senior's Days with double points and cash drawings from 8am to 4pm, if 50, or older
Special Features: 4 miles from Bay Mills Resort & Casino. Fridays are Canadian Days with double points and cash drawings for Canadians until 4pm.

Lac Vieux Desert Casino
N 5384 US 45 North
Watersmeet, Michigan 49969
(906) 358-4226
Map Location: **#4** (49 miles S.E. of Ironwood)

Toll-Free Number: (800) 583-3599
Room Reservations: (800) 634-3444
Rooms: 61 Price Range: $59-$129
Suites: 15 Price Range: $89-$149
Restaurants: 1 Liquor: Yes
Buffets: B-$5.95/$9.95 (Sun) L-$5.95 D-$9.95/$12.95 (Fri-Sat)
Table Game Hours: 10am-4am Daily
Slot Hours: 24 Hours Daily
Other Games: C, R, LIR, K
Casino Marketing: (906) 358-4423
Senior Discount: If 55, or older, get 2 free rolls of nickels with $10 coin buy-in on Tuesdays from 8am to Mid. 10% hotel and buffet discount.
Special Features: 9-hole golf course. Sports Bar and lounge. Live entertainment (Sat). 10% hotel discount for AAA and AARP members.

Leelanau Sands Casino
2521 N.W. Bayshore Drive
Sutton's Bay, Michigan 49682
(231) 271-4104
Web Site: www.casino2win.com
Map Location: **#5** (4 miles N. of Sutton's Bay)

Toll-Free Number: (800) 922-2946
Room Reservations: (800) 930-3008
Rooms: 51 Price Range: $85-$120
Restaurants: 1 Liquor: Yes
Casino Size: 72,000 Square Feet
Hours: 8am-3am/24 Hours (Fri/Sat)
Other Games: C, R, CSP, LIR,
Senior Discount: On Tuesdays receive $30 coin for $20, complimentary cocktail and $2 lunch or dinner discount, if 55, or older
Fun Book: Great Time Passports are offered through packages at local motels/hotels
Special Features: Rooms are at nearby GTB Motel which is within walking distance of casino. 1,000-seat showroom with headliner acts.

Little River Casino
2700 Orchard Drive
Manistee, Michigan 49660
(231) 723-1535
Map Location: **#15** (60 miles S.W of Traverse City)

Toll-Free Number: (888) 568-2244
Restaurants: 1 Liquor: Yes
Buffets: B-$6.00 L-$7.50 D-$9.95
Casino Size: 75,000 Square Feet
Other Games: C, R
Special Features: 100-room hotel expected to open by late 2001.

Ojibwa Casino Resort
Rte 1, Box 284A
Baraga, Michigan 49908
(906) 353-6333
Web Site: www.ojibwacasino.com
Map Location: **#6** (30 miles S. of Houghton)

Toll-Free Number: (800) 323-8045
Rooms: 40 Price Range: $50-$70
Suites: 4 Price Range: $85-$95
Restaurants: 1 Liquor: Yes
Buffets: B-$6.95 (Sun) L-$5.95
D-$6.95/$8.95 (Fri)
Table Game Hours: 11am-2am/4am (Fri/Sat)
Slot Hours: 24 Hours Daily
Other Games: C, R, LIR, BG (Mon-Thu)
Casino Marketing: (800) 323-8045
Fun Book: Only given to bus groups
Special Features: Each adult guest of motel receives $10 in quarters, two $5 match play coupons for casino and 10% gift shop discount. AARP discount on room. 8-lane bowling alley. Room discounts for AAA and Player's Club members.

Ojibwa Casino - Marquette
105 Acre Trail
Marquette, Michigan 49855
(906) 249-4200
Web Site: www.ojibwacasino.com
Map Location: **#13**

Toll-Free Number: (888) 560-9905
Restaurants: 1 Snack Bar Liquor: Yes
Table Hours: 12pm-4am/24 Hours (Fri/Sat)
Slot Hours: 24 Hours Daily
Other Games: C, R, CSP
Senior Discount: Free buffet, plus other discounts, on Mondays from 9am to noon, if 55, or older

Soaring Eagle Casino & Resort
6800 E Soaring Eagle Boulevard
Mount Pleasant, Michigan 48858
(517) 775-5777
Web Site: www.soaringeaglecasino.com
Map Location: **#7** (65 miles N. of Lansing)

Toll-Free Number: (888) 7-EAGLE-7
Rooms: 491 Price Range: $129-$189
Suites: 21 Price Range: $269-$309
Restaurants: 3 (2 open 24 hrs) Liquor: Yes
Buffets: B:$8.75 L/D-$12.75
Casino Size: 205,000 Square Feet
Other Games: C, R, P, BG
Fun Book: Only in hotel packages or to groups
Senior Discount: 10% off room rate, 50% buffet discount on Wednesday breakfast, if 55, or older
Special Features: Casino is housed in two separate buildings. Kid's Quest - supervised children's play center. Video arcade. Gift shop. Free valet parking. 10% room discount for AAA and AARP members.

Turtle Creek Casino
7741 M-72 East
Williamsburg, Michigan 49690
(231) 267-9574
Web Site: www.casino2win.com
Map Location: **#14** (8 miles E. of Traverse City)

Toll-Free Number: (888) 777-8946
Restaurants: 1 Deli Liquor: Yes
Casino Size: 29,000 Square Feet
Other Games: C, R, P, CSP, LIR
Fun Book: Great Time Passports are offered through packages at local motels/hotels

Victories Casino
1966 U.S. 131
Petoskey, Michigan 49770
(231) 439-9100
Map Location: **#16** (50 miles S.W of Cheboygan)

Toll-Free Number: 877-4-GAMING
Restaurants: 1 Liquor: Yes
Buffets: L-$6.50 D-$12.95
Hours: 8am-4am Daily
Other Games: R, P, CSP, LIR
Senior Discount: Every Wed. receive coupons for gaming, complimentary cocktails and dining discounts, if 55, or older.
Special Features: Sports-themed casino with many large-screen TV's. Econo Lodge across the street. Free shuttle service to/from local hotels.

MINNESOTA

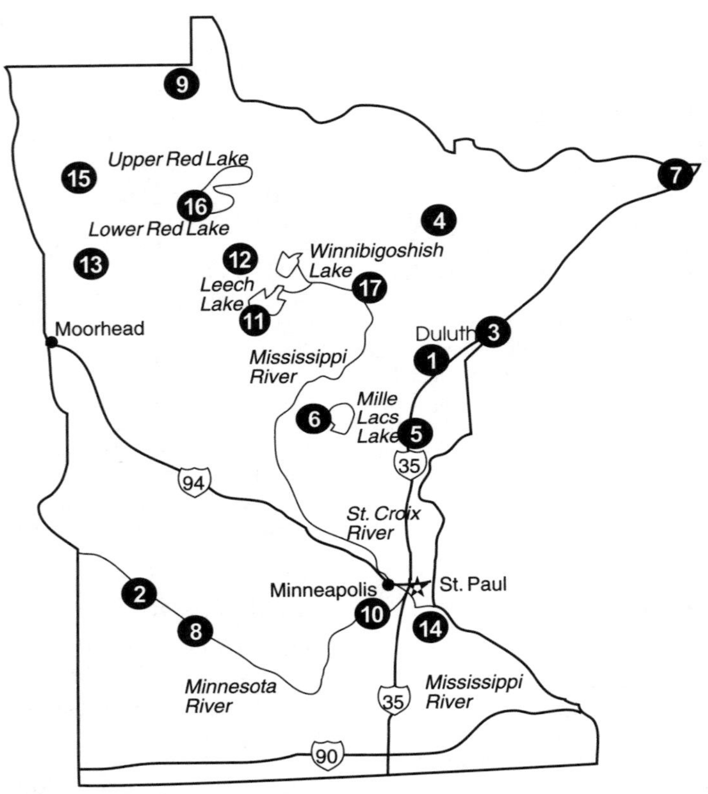

All Minnesota casinos are located on Indian reservations and under a compact reached with the state the only type of table game permitted is blackjack. Additionally, the only kind of slot machines allowed are the electronic video variety. Therefore, you will not find any mechanical slots that have traditional reels - only video screens.

Minnesota casinos vary in size starting with the intimate Lake of the Woods operation with seven blackjack tables all the way up to the massive Mystic Lake complex with its two casinos and 111 blackjack tables.

The Minnesota Indian tribes are not required to release information on their slot machine percentage paybacks. According to the terms of the compact between the state and the tribes, however, the minimum and maximum payouts are regulated as follows: video poker and video blackjack - 83% to 98%, slot machines - 80% to 95%, keno - 75% to 95%. Each tribe is free to set its machines to pay back anywhere within those limits.

The hours of operation are listed for those casinos that are not open on a 24-hour basis. Unless otherwise noted, all casinos offer: video slots, video poker, video keno and blackjack. The minimum gambling age is 18 (21 if liquor is served).

For more information on visiting Minnesota call the state's office of tourism at (800) 657-3700.

Black Bear Casino & Hotel
1785 Highway 210
Carlton, Minnesota 55718
(218) 878-2327
Web Site: www.blackbearcasinohotel.com
Map Location: **#1** (130 miles N. of Twin Cities)

Toll-Free Number: (888) 771-0777
Reservation Number: (800) 553-0022
Rooms: 158 Price Range: $49-$89
Suites: 60 Price Range: $59-$109
Restaurants: 2 (open 24 hours) Liquor: Yes
Buffets: L-$6.95 D-$8.95/$14.95 (Thurs)
Casino Size: 65,000 Square Feet
Other Games: Bingo, Video Craps
Fun Book: Only given to hotel guests
Senior Discount: 10% off rooms, if 50, or older. Mon-Wed get 10% off at gift shop, lunch buffet discount, and match play coupons

Firefly Creek Casino
Route 2, Box 96
Granite Falls, Minnesota 56241
(320) 564-2121
Web Site: www.fireflycreek.com
Map Location: **#2** (110 miles W. of Twin Cities. Five minutes S.E. of Granite Falls on Highway 67 E.)

Restaurants: 1 Liquor: Yes
Casino Size: 26,000 Square Feet
Hours: 8am-2am/24 hours (Fri/Sat)
Senior Discount: Mon. coupons, if 60, or older
Special Features: Two miles from state and city parks with RV hookups.

Fond-du-Luth Casino
129 E. Superior Street
Duluth, Minnesota 55802
(218) 722-0280
Web Site: www.fondduluthcasino.com
Map Location: **#3** (150 miles N.E. of Twin Cities)

Toll-Free Number: (800) 873-0280
Restaurants: 2 Snack Bars Liquor: Yes
Casino Size: 20,000 Square Feet
Casino Hours: 10am-2am/24 hours (Fri/Sat)
Other Games: Bingo
Senior Discount: Sunday bingo discount, if 55, or older
Special Features: One hour free parking in lot adjacent to casino (must be validated in casino).

Fortune Bay Resort/Casino
1430 Bois Forte Road
Tower, Minnesota 55790
(218) 753-6400
Web Site: www.fortunebay.com
Map Location: **#4** (150 miles N.E. of Twin Cities. 24 miles N.E. of Virginia, MN on the S. shore of Lake Vermilion)

Toll-Free Number: (800) 992-7529
Hotel Reservations: (800) 555-1714
Rooms: 85 Price Range: $59-$149
Suites: 33 Price Range: $119-$149
Restaurants: 2 Liquor: Yes
Buffets: B-$6.95 (Sat-Mon)
L-$5.95 (Tue/Wed) D-$9.95 (Sun)
$10.95 (Mon-Wed)/$12.95 (Thu)
$13.95 (Fri)/$14.95 (Sat)
Casino Size: 17,000 Square Feet
Other Games: Bingo (Wed-Sun), Keno
Casino Marketing: (800) 555-1714 ext-7507
Senior Discount: $5 casino cash Mon/Thu from 9am-5pm, if 55 or older. $5 off Sunday bingo. Buffet and room discounts.
Special Features: Located on S.E. shore of Lake Vermilion. Snowmobile and hiking trails.

Grand Casino Hinckley
777 Lady Luck Drive
Hinckley, Minnesota 55037
(320) 384-7777
Web Site: www.grandcasinosmn.com
Map Location: **#5** (76 miles N. of Twin Cities. One mile E. of I-35's Hinckley exit on Route 48)

Toll-Free Number: (800) GRAND-21
RV Reservations: (800) 995-GRAND
Hotel Reservations: (800) HOTEL-17
Rooms: 485 Price Range: $40-$85 (Hotel)
Price Range: $40-$80 (Inn)
Suites: 50 Price Range: $70-$180
Restaurants: 5 2 open 24 hours) Liquor: Yes
Buffets: L-$6.99 D-$8.99/$9.99 (Fri-Sat)
$15.99 (Tue)
Casino Size: 90,000 Square Feet
Other Games: Video Horse Racing, Video Blackjack, Video Craps, Video Roulette, Bingo(Thu-Tue)
Casino Marketing: (800) GRAND-76
Special Features: 224-space RV park with full hookup. Kid's Quest - supervised children's activity center. 2, 4 and 6-deck blackjack games. Video arcade. Free live entertainment (Tue-Sun). 18-hole golf course. Free pet kennel. AAA members get 10% room discount.

Grand Casino Mille Lacs
777 Grand Avenue
Onamia, Minnesota 56359
(320) 532-7777
Web Site: www.grandcasinosmn.com
Map Location: **#6** (90 miles N. of Twin Cities. On Highway 169 on the W. shore of Lake Mille Lacs)

Toll-Free Number: (800) 626-LUCK
Reservation Number: (800) HOTEL-17
Rooms: 284 Price Range: $45-$115
Suites: 40 Price Range: $125-$205
Restaurants: 4 (2 open 24 hours) Liquor: No
Buffets: L-$7.44 D-$9.57(Mon/Wed) $10.64 (Thu-Sun)/$17.03 (Tues)
Casino Size: 120,000 Square Feet
Other Games: Bingo (Sun-Fri), Video Horse Racing, Video Blackjack, Video Craps, Video Roulette
Casino Marketing: (800) GRAND-76
Special Features: High stakes gambling area. 2, 4 and 6-deck blackjack games. Kid's Quest - supervised children's activity center. Video arcade.

Grand Portage Lodge & Casino
P.O. Box 233
Grand Portage, Minnesota 55605
(218) 475-2401
Web Site: www.grandportagemn.com
Map Location: **#7** (N.E. tip of Minnesota. 300 miles N. of Twin Cities. On Highway 61, five miles from the Canadian border)

Reservation Number: (800) 543-1384
Rooms: 100 Price Range: $56-$66
Restaurants: 2 Liquor: Yes
Buffets: D-$8.95 (Sat)
Other Games: Bingo
Casino Marketing: (218) 475-2401
Fun Book: Only given to Lodge guests
Special Features: Located on Lake Superior with lake view rooms. Indoor pool and sauna. Hiking, skiing and snowmobile trails. Gift shop. Marina. RV hookups and campground. Free shuttle service to and from Thunder Bay, Ontario.

Jackpot Junction Casino Hotel
P.O. Box 420
Morton, Minnesota 56270
(507) 644-3000
Web Site: www.jackpotjunction.com
Map Location: **#8** (110 miles S.W. of Twin Cities)

Toll-Free Number: (800) WIN-CASH
Rooms: 156 Price Range: $55-$85
Suites: 12 Price Range: $100-$200
Restaurants: 3 (1 open 24 hours) Liquor: Yes
Buffets: B-$5.99 L-$6.99 D-$8.99
Other Games: Bingo (Thu-Tue)
Casino Marketing: (800) WIN-CASH x-7745
Special Features: Rooms are at hotel adjacent to casino. 40-unit campground with full RV hookup. Free live entertainment (Fri-Sun). On-site entertainment complex. Kids Quest.

Lake of the Woods Casino & Bingo
1012 E. Lake Street
Warroad, MN 56763
(218) 386-3381
Web Site: www.redlakegaming.com
Map Location: **#9** (400 miles N.W. of Twin Cities)

Toll-Free Number: (800) 815-8293
Restaurants: 1 Liquor: No
Casino Hours: 8am-1am/24 hours (Wed-Sun)
Casino Marketing: (800) 815-8293
Senior Discount: Thu drawings for $25 every hour, to seniors 55, or older
Fun Book: Fun Pack only for bus groups.
Special Features: Boat launches, bait shop and tour guides available.

Little Six Casino
2354 Sioux Trail N.W.
Prior Lake, Minnesota 55372
(612) 445-8982
Map Location: **#10** (25 miles S.W. of Twin Cities. On County Road 83, 3 miles S. of Canterbury Downs)

Restaurants: 1 Liquor: No
Hours: 10am-3am Daily/24 hours (Fri-Sat)
Special Features: 1/2-mile north of Mystic Lake Casino.

Mystic Lake Casino Hotel
2400 Mystic Lake Boulevard
Prior Lake, Minnesota 55372
(952) 445-9000
Web Site: www.mysticlake.com
Map Location: **#10** (25 miles S.W. of Twin Cities. On County Road 83, 3 miles S. of Canterbury Downs)

Toll-Free Number: (800) 262-7799
Reservation Number: (800) 813-7349
Rooms: 200 Price Range: $79-$99
Suites: 16 Price Range: $200-$250
Restaurants: 4 (3 open 24 hours) Liquor: No
Buffets: B-$3.99/$5.95 (11pm-3am) L-$8.25
D-$9.95 (Tue)/$10.95 (Thu-Sat)
$11.95(Fri/Sun)/$15.95(Wed)/$12.95(Mon)
Casino Size: 102,000 Square Feet
Other Games: Bingo, Video Roulette, Video Craps
Casino Marketing: (612) 496-1704
Senior Discount: Free breakfast on Tuesday, if 59, or older
Special Features: 1,200-seat bingo hall. 2, 4 and 6-deck blackjack games. Free shuttle bus service from Twin Cities area. Also has a second casino - Dakota Country with 45,000-square-feet of gaming space and an 11-store retail arcade. Health club. Child care facility. Nightly musical revue.

Northern Lights Casino
6800 Y Frontage Rd NW
Walker, Minnesota 56484
(218) 547-2744
Web Site: www.northernlightscasino.com
Map Location: **#11** (175 miles N. of the Twin Cities. Near the S. shore of Lake Leech four miles S. of Walker, MN at the junction of Highways 371 & 200)

Toll-Free Number: (800) 252-PLAY (7529)
Restaurants: 1 (Open 24 hours) Liquor: Yes
Buffets: B-$4.50 (Sun)
L/D-$7.95 (Fri-Sat) $5.50 (Sun)
Casino Marketing: (800) 252-PLAY

Palace Casino Hotel
6280 Upper Cass Frontage Rd NW
Cass Lake, Minnesota 56633
(218) 335-7000
Web Site: www.palacecasinohotel.com
Map Location: **#12** (220 miles N.W. of Twin Cities)

Toll-Free Number: (800) 228-6676
Room Reservations: (800) 442-3910
Rooms: 54 Price Range: $39-$49
Suites: 16 Price Range $59-69
Restaurants: 2 (1 open 24 hours) Liquor: No
Casino Size: 30,000 Square Feet
Other Games: Bingo
Special Features: Indoor pool. Live music. Convention Center.

Red Lake Casino & Bingo
Highway 1 East
Red Lake, MN 56671
(218) 679-2500
Web Site: www.redlakegaming.com
Map Location: **#16** (31 miles N. of Bemidji)

Toll-Free Number: (888) 679-2501
Restaurants: 1 Liquor: No
Casino Size: 19,800 Square Feet
Casino Hours: 8am-1am/24Hrs (Wed-Sun)
Other Games: Bingo (Wed-Sun)
Senior Discount: $10 in coins for $5 on Mondays from 10am-2pm, if 55, or older

River Road Casino
Rt 3, Box 168A
Thief River Falls, Minnesota 56701
(218) 681-4062
Web Site: www.redlakegaming.com
Map Location: **#15** (275 miles N.W. of Minneapolis)

Toll-Free Number: (800) 881-0712
Restaurants: 1 (open 24 hours) Liquor: No
Buffets: B-$3.95 (Sat) L/D-$6.00
Hours: 8am-1am/24 Hours (Wed-Sun)
Casino Size: 16,000 Square Feet
Other Games: Bingo (Only Mon)
Casino Marketing: (800) 568-6649
Senior Discount: $25 drawings hourly for slot club members Tuesdays, if 55, or older
Special features: New hotel and indoor water park expected to open by early 2001.

Shooting Star Casino & Hotel
777 Casino Boulevard
Mahnomen, Minnesota 56557
(218) 935-2701
Web Site: www.starcasino.com
Map Location: **#13** (250 miles N.W. of Twin Cities)

Room Reservations: (800) 453-STAR
Rooms: 281 Price Range: $47-$70
Suites: 30 Price Range: $155-$160
Restaurants: 3 (1 open 24 hours) Liquor: Yes
Buffets: B-$ 3.99 L-$6.40 D-$8.50
Other Games: Bingo, Pull tabs
Casino Marketing: (218) 935-2701 ext.-7231
Fun Book: Lodge guests receive coupons for $1.50 off breakfast and free Fun Book
Senior Discount: 5% off room, if 50, or older
Special Features: Nightly live entertainment with country/western bands. Cabaret showroom with big-name acts. Glass-enclosed pool and atrium. Kiddie arcade. RV park with full hookups.

Treasure Island Casino
5734 Sturgeon Lake Road
Red Wing, Minnesota 55066
(651) 388-6300
Web Site: www.treasureislandcasino.com
Map Location: **#14** (40 miles S.E. of Twin Cities. Halfway between Hastings and Red Wing , off Highway 61 on County Road 18)

Toll-Free Number: (800) 222-7077
Room Reservations: (888) 867-7829
Restaurants: 3 (1 open 24 hours) Liquor: Yes
Rooms: 250 Price Range: $30-$92
Suites: 28 Price Range: $115-$215
Buffets: B-$4.95 (Sat/Sun) L-$7.50 D-$8.95-$12.95
Casino Size: 110,000 Square Feet
Other Games: Bingo, Video Craps, Video Roulette
Casino Marketing: (800) 222-7077
Senior Discount: First Wednesday of each month from 10am-2pm get coupon book, if 55, or older
Special Features: Tropical island theme throughout casino. 2, 4 and 6-deck blackjack games. Weekly blackjack tournaments. RV Park. Live entertainment. Marina. 150-passenger yacht "Spirit of the Water" offers dinner and sightseeing cruises.

White Oak Casino
45830 US Hwy 2
Deer River, MN 56636
(218) 246-9600
Web Site: www.whiteoakcasino.com
Map Location: **#17** (5 miles N.W. of Grand Rapids)

Restaurants: 1 Snack Bar (1 open 24 hours)
Liquor: No
Casino Size: 11,000 Square Feet

MISSISSIPPI

Mississippi was the third state to legalize riverboat gambling when it was approved by that state's legislature in 1990. The law restricts casinos to coast waters (including the Bay of St. Louis and the Back Bay of Biloxi) along the Mississippi River and in navigable waters of counties that border the river.

Mississippi law also requires that riverboats be permanently moored at the dock and they are not permitted to cruise. This allows the riverboats to offer 24-hour dockside gambling. The Isle of Capri in Biloxi was the first casino to open on August 1, 1992 followed one month later by The President Casino.

Since the law does not require that the floating vessel actually resemble a boat, almost all of the casinos are built on barges. This gives them the appearance of a land-based building, rather than a riverboat.

The Mississippi Gaming Commission does not break down its slot statistics by individual properties. Rather, they are classified by region. The coastal region includes Biloxi, Gulfport and Bay Saint Louis. The north river region includes Tunica, Robinsonville, Greenville and Lula. The south river region includes Vicksburg and Natchez.

With that in mind here's information, as supplied by the Mississippi Gaming Commission, showing the machine payback percentages for each area's casinos for the one-year period from July 1, 1999 through June 30, 2000:

	Coastal	North	South
5¢ Slots	91.30%	91.02%	**91.91%**
5¢ Prog.	**90.71%**	86.08%	87.89%
25¢ Slots	92.47%	92.09%	**93.01%**
25¢ Prog.	88.83%	**89.08%**	88.46%
$1 Slots	94.93%	95.06%	**95.20%**
$1 Prog.	90.30%	91.00%	**91.80%**
$5 Slots	95.62%	**96.03%**	95.63%

These numbers reflect the percentage of money returned on each denomination of machine and encompass all electronic machines including video poker and video keno. The best returns for each category are highlighted in bold print and you can see that the southern and coastal casinos offered the best returns in almost every category.

Mississippi is one of the few states that breaks down its progressive machine statistics separately and you can see that the return is always much less on the machines with progressive jackpots.

Unless otherwise noted, all casinos are open 24 hours and offer: slots, video poker, blackjack, craps, roulette, poker and Caribbean Stud Poker.

Other game listings include: baccarat (B), mini-baccarat (MB), pai gow poker (PGP), let it ride (LIR), three card poker (TCP), casino war (CW), big six wheel (B6) and keno (K). The minimum gambling age is 21.

For more information on visiting Mississippi call the state's tourism department at (800) 927-6378. For Biloxi tourism information call (800) 237-9493 and for tourism information on Robinsonville call (888) 4-TUNICA.

Bay St. Louis

Map Location: **#2** (on St. Louis Bay, 40 miles E. of New Orleans)

Casino Magic - Bay St. Louis
711 Casino Magic Drive
Bay St. Louis, Mississippi 39520
(228) 467-9257
Web Site: www.casinomagic.com

Toll-Free Number: (800) 5-MAGIC-5
Rooms: 201 Price Range: $55-$85
Suites: 22 Price Range: $75-$105
Restaurants: 4 (1 open 24 hours)
Buffets: B-$6.00 L-$9.00 D-$11.50
Casino Size: 39,500 Square Feet
Other Games: MB, PGP, LIR, TCP, K
Casino Marketing: (800) 5-MAGIC-5
Special Features: 100 hook-up RV Park with picnic tables, laundromat, cable TV, showers and vending machines. 25-slip marina with boat rentals. 18-hole Arnold Palmer golf course and golf academy.

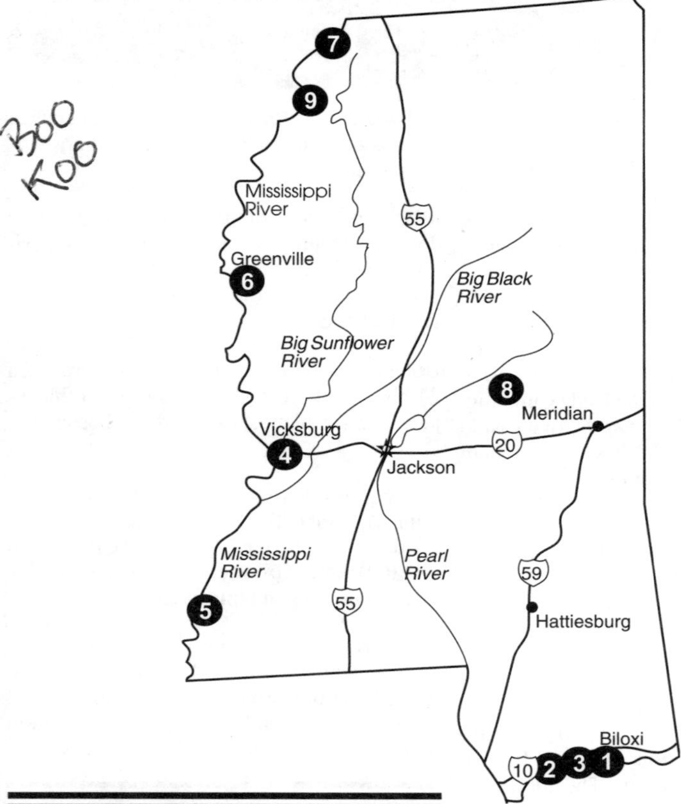

Biloxi

Map Location: **#1** (On the Gulf of Mexico, 80 miles E. of New Orleans)

Beau Rivage
875 Beach Boulevard
Biloxi, Mississippi 39530
(228) 386-7111
Web Site: www.beaurivageresort.com

Room Reservations: (888) 56-ROOMS
Rooms: 1,710 Price Range: $89-$189
Suites: 70 Price Range: $250-$325
Restaurants: 12 (1 open 24 hours)
Buffets: B-$8.99/$13.99 (Sat/Sun)
L-$9.99 D-$12.99
Casino Size: 71,500 Square Feet
Other Games: B, MB, PGP, LIR, TCP
Casino Marketing: (800) 239-2771
Special Features: Micro brewery. Health spa and salon. 30-slip marina. Retail shopping promenade. Full-service business center.

Boomtown Casino - Biloxi
676 Bayview Avenue
Biloxi, Mississippi 39530
(228) 435-7000
Web Site: www.boomtowncasinos.com

Toll-Free Number: (800) 627-0777
Restaurants: 2 (1 open 24 hours)
Buffets: B-$3.99 L-$6.95 D-$10.95
Casino Size: 33,632 Square Feet
Other Games: PGP, LIR, TCP,
No Poker, No CSP
Casino Marketing: (800) 627-0777 ext. 5011
Senior Discount: If 50, or older, join Wild Bunch Seniors Club for various discounts
Fun Book: Given when you sign up for Player's Club Card or at Welcome Center on Hwy 90
Special Features: Family entertainment center with motion dynamic theater and arcade. Live western entertainment cabaret (Thu-Sat). Gift shop with western clothing and collectibles. 24-hour bakery and coffee shop.

The Best Places To Play On The Gulf Coast

Roulette - There are no casinos on the Gulf Coast that offer single-zero roulette.

Craps -The Imperial Palace offers 20x odds, which is the highest in the area. Almost all other casinos on the Gulf Coast (including Casino Magic in Bay St. Louis) offer 10x odds. The lone exception to that is Beau Rivage which limits players to 5x odds.

Blackjack - Gulf Coast casinos offer some of the best blackjack outside of Nevada and, unlike downtown Las Vegas, there are no casinos that hit soft 17. This rule is advantageous for the player by .20%. All of the recommendations in this section apply to players using perfect basic strategy for each particular game.

Most single-deck games offer the same rules: double down on any two card total of 10 or more with splitting allowed but no doubling after splitting. The casino edge in this game is .25% and it's offered at Boomtown and the President. A slightly better single-deck game can be found at two other casinos that have the same basic rules but with slight modifications. The Copa in Gulfport allows late surrender which lowers the casino edge to .23% while Casino Magic in Bay St. Louis allows resplitting of aces which brings the casino advantage down to .22%.

Several casinos are tied for best double-deck because their games have the following rules: double down on any first two cards, re-split any pair (including aces) and doubling allowed after splitting. This works out to a casino edge of just .14% and it's offered at: Casino Magic in Biloxi and Bay St. Louis, both Grand Casinos, New Palace and Treasure Bay. The Copa in Gulfport offers a similar game except late surrender is allowed in place of re-splitting aces. The casino edge here is also .14%.

Next best are five casinos that offer the same rules as the Copa's but they don't allow late surrender: Beau Rivage, Imperial Palace, Boomtown, President and Isle of Capri. The casino edge in these games is .19%.

For six-deck shoe games the best place to play is Beau Rivage which allows doubling down on any first two cards, doubling after splitting, late surrender and re-splitting of aces. The casino advantage in this game is .26%. That same game, without re-splitting of aces, is offered at the Copa and the edge there works out to .33%. Next best are both Casino Magic casinos, both Grand Casinos, New Palace and Treasure Bay which all offer the same rules as Beau Rivage with the exception of late surrender. The edge in these games is .34%.

Boomtown, Imperial Palace, Isle of Capri and the President all offer standard six-deck shoe games that allow doubling down on any first two cards and doubling after splitting. The edge on these games is .41%.

Casino Magic (Bay St. Louis and Biloxi) and the Grand Casino (Gulfport) offer eight-deck shoe games with doubling on any 2 cards, double after split and resplitting aces allowed which works out to a .36% casino adventage. Isle of Capri offers the same eight-deck shoe game with no resplitting of aces and this works out to a .43% casino advantage.

Video Poker -Good video poker players know that three of the best varieties of machines to look for are: 9/6 Jacks or Better, 10/7 Double Bonus and full-pay Deuces Wild. By only playing these three kinds of machines, playing the maximum coin and using perfect strategy you can achieve the following payback percentages: 99.5% on 9/6 Jacks or Better, 100.1% on 10/7 Double Bonus and 100.7% on full-pay Deuces Wild. Unfortunately, the Gulf Coast's choice of machines is not nearly as good as in Nevada which still offers the country's best paying machines. As a matter of fact, only the Copa has Deuces Wild machines available with a full-pay schedule. The Copa also has full-pay Kings or Better Joker's Wild which has a payback percentage of 100.64%.

10/7 Double Bonus can be found at Casino Magic which has 25¢ machines at both of its casinos in Biloxi and Bay St. Louis. It's also available at the Copa which has 25¢ and $1 progressive machines.

The only casino to offer full-pay All American (100.72% payback) is the Isle of Capri which has them at the 25¢ level.

Quarter 9/6 Jacks or Better machines with a progressive jackpot for the royal flush can be found at Casino Magic (Biloxi), Treasure Bay, the President and the Isle of Capri. Casino Magic (Bay St. Louis), Copa and Imperial Palace also have quarter 9/6 machines but without the progressive jackpot. Casino Magic (Bay St. Louis), New Palace, Imperial Palace and Beau Rivage have $1 9/6 machines while Treasure Bay, President, Copa and Casino Magic (Biloxi) all offer $1 9/6 machines with a progressive jackpot for the royal.

Both Grand Casinos advertise "over 99% payback video poker" but this only applies to certain machines in the casino that are clearly marked. Some of these are standard 9/7 Double Bonus games but they also offer Jacks or Better machines with the following pay table (per coin with maximum coins played): Royal Flush -800; Straight Flush -50; 4-of-a-Kind (A) -80; 4-of-a-Kind (J-Q-K) -40; 4-of-a-Kind (2-10) -25; Full House -8; Flush -5; Straight -4; 3-of-a-Kind -3; 2 Pair -2; Jacks or Better -1. These same kind of machines are known in the Las Vegas market as 8/5 Bonus Poker Aces and Faces. With perfect strategy (and maximum coins played) they return 99.3%.

For slot players both Grand casinos also offer 98% paybacks on some of their $1 slot machines. The machines with these paybacks are grouped in different areas around the casino and clearly marked with signage, so be aware that not all machines are guaranteed to return that high an amount. Since statistics from the Mississippi Gaming Commission show that the average $1 slot returns around 95% it's probably worthwhile to search around for the "certified" machines if you're a $1 player.

The Treasure Bay Casino Resort in Biloxi is one of the most unique casino properties in the U.S. Its casino is housed on a dockside barge that resembles an 18th century pirate ship.

Casino Magic - Biloxi
195 E. Beach Boulevard
Biloxi, Mississippi 39530
(228) 467-9257
Web Site: www.casinomagic.com

Toll-Free Number: (800) 5-MAGIC-5
Rooms: 292 Price Range: $129-$149
Suites: 86 Price Range: $149-$199
Restaurants: 4 (1 open 24 hours)
Buffets: B-$6.49 L-$8.99 D-$12.99
Casino Size: 47,300 Square Feet
Other Games: MB, PGP, LIR, TCP, CW, No Poker
Casino Marketing: (800) 5-MAGIC-5
Senior Discount: Variety of discounts on Tuesdays, if 55, or older
Special Features: Free comedy club show on Monday nights.

Grand Casino Biloxi
265 Beach Boulevard
Biloxi, Mississippi 39530
(228) 436-2946
Web Site: www.grandbiloxi.com

Toll-Free Number: (800) WIN-2-WIN
Rooms: 591 Price Range: $79-$169
Suites: 17 Price Range: $159-$209
Restaurants: 6 (1 open 24 hours)
Buffets: L/D-$12.99
Casino Size: 134,200 Square Feet
Other Games: MB, PGP, LIR, TCP
Casino Marketing: (800) 946-2946
Fun Book: Only given to groups
Special Features: Kid's Quest - children's activity center. Video arcade. Free valet parking. Nonsmoking gaming areas. Grand Theatre features Las Vegas-style shows and special events. Hotel has pool, full-service spa and Jacuzzi. Specialty shops.

Imperial Palace Hotel & Casino
850 Bayview Avenue
Biloxi, Mississippi 39530
(228) 436-3000
Web Site: www.ipbiloxi.com

Toll-Free Number: (800) 436-3000
Room Reservations: (800) 634-6441
Rooms: 1,000 Price Range: $49-$129
Suites: 14 Price Range: $79-$189
Restaurants: 10 (1 open 24 hours)
Buffets: B-$4.99/$8.99 (Sun) L-$6.99 D-$10.99/$12.99 (Fri)
Casino Size: 70,000 Square Feet
Other Games: MB, PGP, LIR, TCP, B6
Fun Book: Only given to groups
Special Features: Six movie theaters. Legends In Concert show. Health spa. Fun Zone for children.

Isle of Capri Casino - Biloxi
151 Beach Boulevard
Biloxi, Mississippi 39530
(228) 435-5400
Web Site: www.isleofcapricasino.com

Toll-Free Number: (800) THE-ISLE
Rooms: 367 Price Range: $79-$139
Suites: 4 Price Range: $219
Restaurants: 3 (1 open 24 hours)
Buffets: B-$6.75/$11.95 (Sun) L-$8.50 D-$12.95
Casino Size: 32,500 Square Feet
Other Games: TCP, No Poker
Senior Discount: 15% room discount for AARP members
Fun Book: Coupons given through slot club.
Special Features: Tropical theme throughout casino. Hotel is Crowne Plaza Resort. Slot club members receive room discounts. 15% room discount for AAA members.

New Palace Casino
158 Howard Avenue
Biloxi, Mississippi 39530
(228) 432-8888
Web Site: www.newpalace.com

Toll-Free Number: (800) PALACE-9
Rooms: 234 Price Range: $109-$189
Suites: 2 Price Range: $500
Restaurants: 3 (1 open 24 hours)
Buffets: B-$4.95 L-$6.95 D-$9.95/$15.95 (Fri-Sun)
Casino Size: 43,500 Square Feet
Other Games: LIR, TCP, No Poker
Casino Marketing: (800) PALACE-9
Special Features: Casino is on a 3-story barge with an all-glass exterior. 500-seat theater features Las Vegas-style entertainment. Receive 50% off buffet when joining players club.

President Casino Broadwater Resort
2110 Beach Boulevard
Biloxi, Mississippi 39531
(228) 385-3500
Web Site: www.broadwater.com

Toll-Free Number: (800) THE-PRES
Rooms: 500 Price Range: $59-$125
Suites: 12 Price Range: $89-$215
Restaurants: 3 (1 open 24 hours)
Buffets: B-$4.95 L-$7.45 D-$12.95
Casino Size: 38,000 Square Feet
Casino Marketing: (800) THE-PRES
Other Games: LIR, TCP
Fun Book: Only given to hotel guests
Senior Discount: $2.95 breakfast and $4.95 lunch from 6am-2pm Mon-Fri, if 50, or older
Special Features: Covered marina. Three swimming pools. Golf packages (2 courses) also available. Tennis courts.

Treasure Bay Casino Resort
1980 Beach Boulevard
Biloxi, Mississippi 39531
(228) 385-6000
Web Site: www.treasurebay.com

Toll-Free Number: (800) PIRATE-9
Rooms: 262 Price Range: $59-$119
Suites: 8 Price Range: $189-$338
Restaurants: 3 (1 open 24 hours)
Buffets: B-$4.95 L-$7.45 D-$10.95
Size: 41,000 Square Feet
Other Games: PGP, LIR, TCP, B6
Casino Marketing: (800) 747-2839
Senior Discount: 10% room discount to AARP members. 15% discount for Silver Crew players club members (55 or older) on rooms, food and shopping.
Fun Book: Only given to hotel guests and some local non-casino hotel guests.
Special Features: Casino is a 400-foot replica of an 18th century pirate ship and fort that is built on a barge. Live free entertainment nightly at Scalawag's Show Bar. Video arcade. On-site brewery.

Greenville

Map Location: **#6** (On the Mississippi River, 121 miles N.W. of Jackson)

Bayou Caddy's Jubilee Casino
Lake Ferguson Waterfront
Greenville, Mississippi 38701
(601) 335-1111

Toll-Free Number: (800) WIN-MORE
Restaurants: 3 (1 open 24 hours)
Casino Size: 28,500 Square Feet
Casino Marketing: (800) WIN-MORE
Other Games: No Poker
Senior Discount: Join Wild Bunch Seniors Club
Special Features: Live entertainment nightly. Hotel accommodations available in the area with shuttle service to casino. Daily coin promotions and nightly cash drawings.

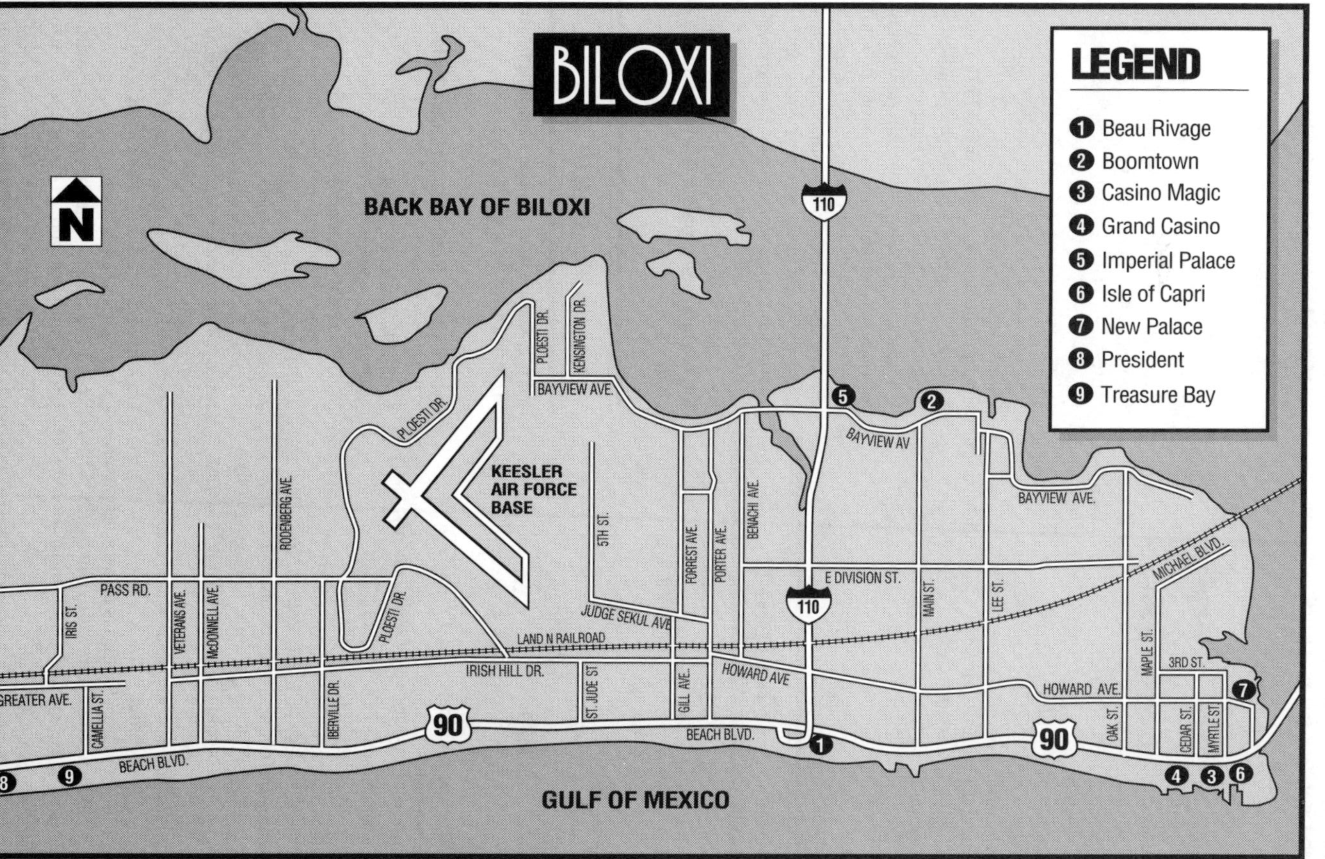
BILOXI
LEGEND
1 Beau Rivage
2 Boomtown
3 Casino Magic
4 Grand Casino
5 Imperial Palace
6 Isle of Capri
7 New Palace
8 President
9 Treasure Bay
N
BACK BAY OF BILOXI
GULF OF MEXICO
KEESLER AIR FORCE BASE
110
90
BAYVIEW AVE.
BAYVIEW AV
PLOESTI DR.
KENSINGTON DR.
5TH ST.
FORREST AVE.
PORTER AVE.
BENACHI AVE.
E DIVISION ST.
MAIN ST.
LEE ST.
MICHAEL BLVD.
MAPLE ST.
3RD ST.
HOWARD AVE.
OAK ST.
CEDAR ST.
MYRTLE ST.
JUDGE SEKUL AVE
LAND N RAILROAD
IRISH HILL DR.
ST. JUDE ST
GILL AVE.
BEACH BLVD.
RODENBERG AVE.
PASS RD.
IRIS ST.
VETERANS AVE.
McDONNELL AVE.
IBERVILLE DR.
GREATER AVE.
CAMELLIA ST.

Lighthouse Point Casino
199 N. Lakefront Road
Greenville, Mississippi 38701
(601) 334-7711

Toll-Free Number: (800) 878-1777
Rooms: 148 Price Range: $51-$79
Suites: 22 Price Range: $67-$79
Restaurants: 1
Buffets: B-$9.95 (Sun) D-$12.95 (Wed-Sat)
Casino Size: 22,000 Square Feet
Casino Marketing: (800) 878-1777
Other Games: TCP, No Poker
Fun Book: Given to hotel guests
Special Features: Hotel is Fairfield Marriottt which is across the street. Casino is on an actual paddlewheel boat. Tuesday Blackjack tournament. Thursday slot tournament.

Gulfport

Map Location: **#3** (On the Gulf of Mexico, 70 miles E. of New Orleans)

Copa Casino
P.O. Box 1600
Gulfport, Mississippi 39502
(228) 863-3330
Web Site: www.thecopacasino.com

Toll-Free Number: (800) WIN-COPA
Restaurants: 1
Buffets: L-$5.99 D-$7.99/$9.99 (Fri-Sun)
Casino Size: 27,000 Square Feet
Other Games: TCP, No Poker
Casino Marketing: (601) 867-0147
Other Games: TCP, No Poker, No CSP
Senior Discount: If 50, or older, go to Welcome Center to receive a free breakfast on Mon/Wed/Fri from 7am to 10am.
Fun Book: Present out-of-state ID at welcome center
Special Features: Casino is on a 1,500-passenger modern cruise ship with a Rio theme. $1.99 Steak & Eggs special (7am-mid). Free valet parking.

Grand Casino Gulfport
3215 W. Beach Boulevard
Gulfport, Mississippi 39501
(228) 870-7777
Web Site: www.grandgulfport.com

Toll-Free Number: (800) WIN-7777
Room Reservations: (800) 354-2450
Rooms: 1000 Price Range: $99-$149
Suites: 74 Price Range: $169-$289
Restaurants: 7 (1 open 24 hours)
Buffets: B-$7.99 L-$9.99 D-$12.99
Casino Size: 105,000 Square Feet
Other Games: MB, PGP, LIR, TCP, B6
Casino Marketing: (800) WIN-7777
Special Features: Kids Quest - children's activity center. Video arcade. Free valet parking. Nonsmoking gaming areas. Entertainment center features 4 nightclubs. 17-story beachfront hotel has indoor swimming pool, Jacuzzi, full-service spa and exercise room. Single-zero roulette. 98% payback on some slots and 99% payback on some video poker. Oasis resort and spa features a three-acre pool area and a lazy river ride. Full-service Bellisimo spa and salon for men and women. Golf packages available.

Lula

Map Location **#9** (On the Mississippi River, 70 miles S. of Memphis, TN)

Isle of Capri Resort & Casino - Lula
777 Isle of Capri Parkway
Lula, Mississippi 38644
(662) 363-4600
Web Site: www.isleofcapricasino.com

Toll-Free Number: (800) 789-LUCK
Toll-Free Number: (800) THE-ISLE
Rooms: 173 Price Range: $59-$89
Suites: 4 Price Range: $90-$129
Restaurants: 4 (1 open 24 hours)
Buffets: B-$6.37 L-$9.58 D-$12.95
Casino Size: 55,000 Square Feet
Other Games: LIR, TCP
Special Features: Hotel has outdoor swimming pool, whirlpool and workout spa. All rooms have refrigerators and Jacuzzi tubs. Land based pavilion features 1,000-seat entertainment center with headline acts, two movie theaters and a video arcade. 15% hotel discount to AAA and AARP members.

Natchez

Map Location: **#5** (on the Mississippi River, 102 miles S.W. of Jackson)

Isle of Capri Resort & Casino - Natchez
53 Silver Street
Natchez, Mississippi 39120
(601) 445-0605
Web Site: www.isleofcapricasino.com

Toll-Free Number: (800) 722-LUCK
Toll-Free Number: (800) THE-ISLE
Rooms: 147 Price Range: $40-$55
Suites: 5 Price Range: $135-$165
Restaurants: 2
Buffets: B-$8.95 L-$12.05 D-$14.05
Size: 14,300 Square Feet
Other Games: LIR, TCP
Special Features: Casino resembles an 1860's paddle wheel steamboat, but is actually built on a barge. Live entertainment in Burgundy Room on weekends.

Tunica

Map Location: **#7** (on the Mississippi River, 28 miles S. of Memphis, TN)

Bally's Saloon/Gambling Hall Hotel
1450 Bally's Boulevard
Robinsonville, Mississippi 38664
(662) 357-1500
Web Site: www.ballysms.com

Toll-Free Number: (800) 382-2559
Rooms: 235 Price Range: $19-$109
Restaurants: 2 (1 open 24 hours)
Buffets: B-$6.50 L-$7.65 D-$10.74
Casino Size: 40,000 Square Feet
Other Games: LIR, TCP, B6
Senior Discount: If 55, or older, receive 50% off buffets, if players club member
Special Features: Free breakfast with every room stay. Mini Jacuzzi's and refrigerators in every room. Free buffet with slot club enrollment.

Fitzgerald's Casino/Hotel
711 Lucky Lane
Robinsonville, Mississippi 38664
(662) 363-5825
Web Site: www.fitzgeraldstunica.com

Toll-Free Number: (800) 766-LUCK
Rooms: 507 Price Range: $29-$109
Suites: 70 Price Range: $69-$199
Buffets: B-$5.95/$8.25 (Sun) L-$7.25 D-$9.45
Restaurants: 4 (1 open 24 hours)
Casino Size: 36,000 Square Feet
Casino Marketing: (800) 766-LUCK
Other Games: LIR, TCP, No Poker
Fun Book: Only given to bus groups
Senior Discount: 10% AARP room discount
Special Features: Indoor pool and spa. Sports pub with 8 tv's. Free national act entertainment. Steak house restaurant.

Gold Strike Casino
100 Casino Center Drive
Robinsonville, Mississippi 38664
(662) 357-1111
Web Site: www.goldstrikemississippi.com

Toll-Free Number: (888) 24K-PLAY
Room Reservations: (888) 245-7829
Rooms: 1,130 Price Range: $69-$99
Suites: 70 Price Range: $169-$239
Restaurants: 3 (1 open 24 hours)
Buffets: B-$8.95 L-$10.95 D-$14.95
Casino Size: 50,486 Square Feet
Other Games: LIR, TCP
Casino Marketing: (800) 871-CLUB
Special Features: Free valet parking.

Grand Casino Tunica
13615 Old Highway 61 N.
Robinsonville, Mississippi 38664
(662) 363-2788
Web Site: www.grandtunica.com

Toll-Free Number: (800) 946-4946
Rooms: 1,356 Price Range: $49-$119
Suites: 117 Price Range: $149-$220
Restaurants: 8 (1 open 24 hours)
Buffets: B-$6.99 L-$7.49 D-$10.99/$14.99 (Tue/Fri)
Casino Size: 140,000 Square Feet
Other Games: MB, PGP, LIR, TCP, B6
Special Features: World's largest dockside ca-

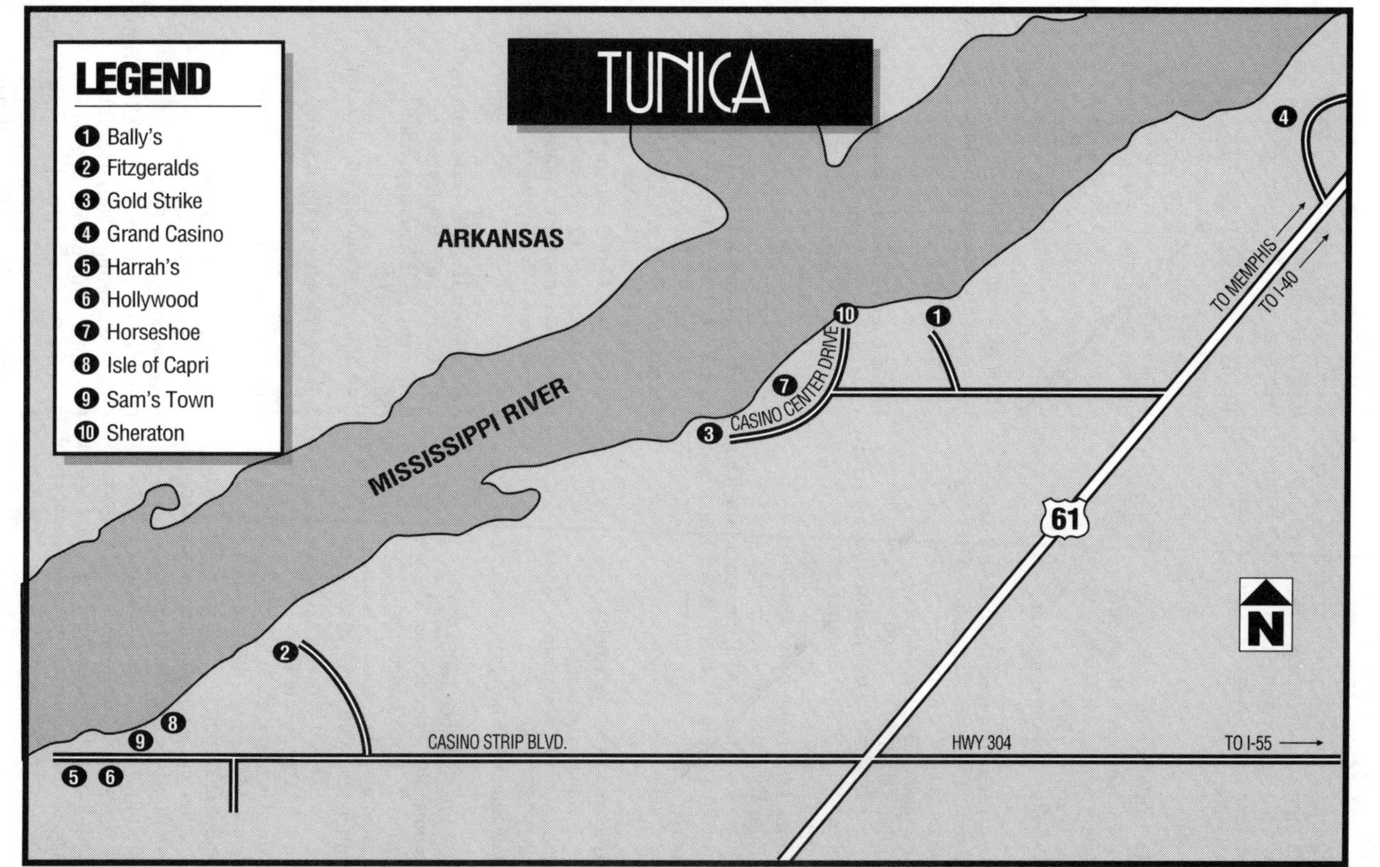
TUNICA
LEGEND
1 Bally's
2 Fitzgeralds
3 Gold Strike
4 Grand Casino
5 Harrah's
6 Hollywood
7 Horseshoe
8 Isle of Capri
9 Sam's Town
10 Sheraton
ARKANSAS
MISSISSIPPI RIVER
CASINO CENTER DRIVE
TO MEMPHIS
TO I-40
61
N
CASINO STRIP BLVD.
HWY 304
TO I-55

sino. Four themed areas: Western, New Orleans/Mardi Gras, Victorian/San Francisco and Riverpark. 18-hole golf course. Kid's Quest - children's activity center. Single-zero roulette. 98% payback on some slots and 99% payback on some video poker. 200-space RV park. Spa and salon.

Harrah's Tunica
1100 Casino Strip Boulevard
Robinsonville, Mississippi 38664
(662) 363-7777
Web Site: www.harrahs.com

Reservation Number: (800) HARRAHS
Rooms: 180 Price Range: $59-$109
Suites: 20 Price Range: $65-$114
Restaurants: 3 (open 24 hours)
Buffets: B-$5.99 L-$7.99
D-$9.99/$12.99 (Tue/Wed)/$15.99 (Fri)
Casino Size: 50,000 Square Feet
Other Games: LIR, TCP, No Poker
Casino Marketing: (888) 789-7900
Senior Discount: 10% room discount for AARP members (Sun-Thu)
Special Features: River Bend Links golf course.

Hollywood Casino Tunica
1150 Commerce Landing
Robinsonville, Mississippi 38664
(662) 357-7700
Web Site: www.hollywoodtunica.com

Toll-Free Number: (800) 871-0711
Rooms: 506 Price Range: $59-$99
Suites: 7 Price Range: $99-$250
Restaurants: 3 (1 open 24 hours)
Buffets: B-$6.99 L-$7.99
D-$10.99/$16.99 (Fri)
Size: 54,000 Square Feet
Other Games: LIR, TCP
Casino Marketing: (800) 871-0711
Senior Discount: If 55, or older, join Silver Screen club to receive various discounts
Fun Book: Only given to groups
Special Features: Casino features a collection of Hollywood memorabilia. 123-space RV park. Slot club members get 10-15% discount in hotel, restaurants and gift shop. Indoor pool and jacuzzi. 18-hole golf course.

Horseshoe Casino & Hotel
1021 Casino Center Drive
Robinsonville, Mississippi 38664
(662) 357-5500
Web Site: www.horseshoe.com

Toll-Free Number: (800) 303-7463
Rooms: 200 Price Range: $59-$89
Suites: 311 Price Range: $99-$129
Restaurants: 2 (1 open 24 hours)
Buffets: B-$5.95 L-$8.95 D-$9.95/$14.95 (Fri)
Casino Size: 45,000 Square Feet
Other Games: MB, LIR, TCP
Casino Marketing: (800) 303-7463
Special Features: Blues & Legends Hall of Fame Museum traces history of Blues music. Bluesville Showcase Nightclub features headliner artists.

Isle of Capri Casino - Tunica
1600 Isle of Capri Boulevard
Robinsonville, Mississippi 38664
(662) 357-6500
Web Site: www.isleofcapricasino.com

Toll-Free Number: (800) THE-ISLE
Rooms: 56 Price Range: $45-$85
Suites: 66 Price Range: $80-$120
Restaurants: 3 (1 open 24 hours)
Buffets: B-$5.95 L-$6.95 D-$11.50
Casino Size: 27,000 Square Feet
Other Games: TCP, No Poker
Special Features: Casino features tropical Caribbean theme. Two Wayne Newton theatres.

Sam's Town Hotel & Gambling Hall
1477 Casino Strip Boulevard
Robinsonville, Mississippi 38664
(662) 363-0711
Web Site: www.samstowntunica.com

Toll-Free Number: (800) 456-0711
Rooms: 860 Price Range: $59-$89
Suites: 44 Price Range: $119-$199
Restaurants: 5 (1 open 24 hours)
Buffets: B-$4.95 L-$6.95
D-$8.95/$14.95 (Wed/Fri)
Size: 96,000 Square Feet
Other Games: MB, PGP, LIR, TCP, K, B6, CW
Casino Marketing: (800) 946-0711
Fun Book: Only offered to groups
Special Features: Hotel has pool, sauna, Jacuzzi and exercise room. 1,600-seat indoor amphitheater with headliner-entertainment every weekend. Video arcade.

The Best Places To Play In Tunica

Roulette - Tunica's only single-zero roulette wheel can be found at the Grand Casino. The house edge in this game is cut from 5.26% down to a more reasonable 2.70%. Be aware, however, that only one table in the casino offers the single-zero game and there are five other tables with the more common double-zero wheel.

Craps - All Tunica casinos offer 20x odds. Some casinos also pay triple (rather than double) on 12 in the field which cuts the house edge on this bet in half from 5.6% to 2.8%. The six casinos offering this slightly better field bet are: Harrah's, Hollywood, Horseshoe, Gold Strike, Isle of Capri and Sam's Town.

Blackjack - The blackjack games in Tunica are most similar to those offered in downtown Las Vegas. Every casino offers both single and double-deck games, as well as six-deck shoe games. That's good. The bad part, however, is that dealers hit soft 17 at all blackjack games. This results in an extra advantage for the house of .20%. All of the following recommendations apply to players using perfect basic strategy for each particular game.

All single-deck games in Tunica allow doubling down on any first two cards. The best one-deck game can be found at the Gold Strike which allows re-splitting any pair (except aces) and doubling after splitting. The casino edge in this game is .06% but there's a $25 minimum bet.

Next best in single-deck are the Horseshoe, Grand, and Hollywood. All three of these casinos won't allow you to double down after a split but they will allow you to re-split aces. The house edge in this game is .15% and it is available at some $5 tables.

At Sam's Town and Harrah's they won't allow you to double down after a split and they also won't allow you to re-split aces which results in a slightly higher house edge of .18%. Bally's has those same single-deck rules in place, except they won't allow you to re-split *any* pair and the casino edge in their game works out to .22%.

The Grand, Bally's, Hollywood, Sheraton, Isle of Capri and Horseshoe are the best places to play double-deck because their games have the following rules: double down on any first two cards, re-split any pair (including aces), and double down after split. This works out to a casino edge of .35%.

Tunica's remaining four casinos: Sam's Town, Harrah's, Fitzgeralds and Gold Strike, all offer the next best game. The only rule change from the previous casinos is that you aren't allowed to re-split aces and the casino edge in this game is .40%.

Six-deck shoe games in Tunica are pretty much the same at all of the casinos. The rules are identical to those offered in the better two-deck games and the casino advantage in this game is .56%.

The only exception on the six-deck games are those offered at Fitzgeralds, Gold Strike and Sam's Town. All three of them offer a game with a slightly higher casino edge of .63% because none of them will allow you to re-split aces.

Video Poker -Good video poker players know that three of the best machines to look for are: 9/6 Jacks or Better, 10/7 Double Bonus and full-pay Deuces Wild. By only playing these three kinds of machines, playing the maximum coin and using perfect strategy you can achieve the following payback percentages: 99.5% on 9/6 Jacks or Better, 100.17% on 10/7 Double Bonus and 100.76% on full-pay Deuces Wild. Unfortunately, Tunica's choice of machines is not nearly as good as in Nevada which still offers the country's best paying machines. As a matter of fact, there are no full-pay Deuces Wild machines in Tunica, nor are there any 10/7 Double Bonus machines available. 9/6 machines are available but they're difficult to find, especially for the 25¢ player.

The most 25¢ 9/6 Jacks or Better games can be found at the Hollywood which has a bank of six located across from the change booth by the Box Office bar. The only other casinos offering quarter games are Fitzgeralds, Harrah's and the Isle of Capri.

For 50¢ players, 9/6 Jacks or Better games can be found at Harrah's, Hollywood and Sheraton. All three of these casinos also offer 9/6 games at the $1 level . The Gold Strike and Sheraton have the area's only $5 9/6 games.

Quarter 9/7 Double Bonus machines (99.11% payback) can be found at the Grand Casino. The Gold Strike also has them in their Odyssey Four-Draw machines as well as in their bar tops at the Bullion Bar. 9/7 Double Bonus machines at the $1 level are available at Fitzgeralds and Horseshoe. The Sheraton also has a $1 9/6 Double Bonus machine with a progressive jackpot. Fitzgeralds has some 5¢ multi-game machines with 9/7 Double Bonus pay tables.

Most of the other Tunica casinos have 9/6 Double Bonus games in both quarter and dollar machines, but with an expected return of just 97.81% you would definitely be better off seeking out the higher paying 9/7 machines.

The Grand Casino has some standard 9/7 Double Bonus games but they also offer Jacks or Better machines with the following pay table (per coin with maximum coins played): Royal Flush -800; Straight Flush -50; 4-of-a-Kind (A) -80; 4-of-a-Kind (J-Q-K) -40; 4-of-a-Kind (2-10) -25; Full House -8; Flush -5; Straight -4; 3-of-a-Kind -3; 2 Pair -2; Jacks or Better -1. These same kind of machines are known in the Las Vegas market as 8/5 Bonus Poker Aces and Faces. With perfect strategy (and maximum coins played) they return 99.3%.

Most of the Tunica casinos offer 7/5 Bonus games (98.02% return) but a few do offer the better-paying 8/5 versions (99.2% payback): Bally's has quarter machines, Gold Strike has them on their 25¢ Odyssey Four-Draw machines, and Fitzgeralds offers them on their $5 machines.

For slot players the Grand casino also offers 98% paybacks on some of its $1 slot machines. The machines with these paybacks are grouped in different areas around the casino and clearly marked with signage, so be aware that not all machines are guaranteed to return that high an amount. Since statistics from the Mississippi Gaming Commission show that the average $1 slot in Tunica returns around 95% it's probably worthwhile to search around for the "certified" machines if you're a $1 player.

Sheraton Casino & Hotel
1107 Casino Center Drive
Robinsonville, Mississippi 38664
(662) 363-4900

Toll-Free Number: (800) 391-3777
Suites: 140 Price Range: $89-$169
Restaurants: 4 (1 open 24 hours)
Buffets: B-$5.96 L-$6.95
D-$11.00/$13.00 (Fri)
Casino Size: 32,800 Square Feet
Other Games: MB, LIR, TCP, B6, No Poker
Casino Marketing: (800) 391-3777
Senior Discount: If 55, or older, receive $2 buffet on Mon/Fri from 11am to 4pm
Special Features: Three-story barge casino has an English Tudor-style appearance. Free live entertainment nightly in RiverStage lounge. Nonsmoking gaming areas. Health spa with private massages, Jacuzzis, saunas and tanning. Free valet parking.

Vicksburg

Map Location: **#4** (on the Mississippi River, 44 miles W. of Jackson)

Ameristar Casino - Vicksburg
4146 Washington Street
Vicksburg, Mississippi 39180
(601) 638-1000
Web Site: www.ameristars.com

Reservation Number: (800) 700-7770
Rooms: 146 Price Range: $49-$119
Suites: 4 Price Range: $189
Restaurants: 2 (1 open 24 hours)
Buffets: L-$6.95 D-$8.95
Casino Size: 38,500 Square Feet
Other Games: LIR, TCP
Fun Book: Provided to tour and bus groups
Casino Marketing: (601) 638-1000
Senior Discount: 15% discount on food or gift shop purchase if 50, or older. AARP members receive a 10% hotel discount.
Special Features: Free cabaret entertainment. Free valet parking. Free shuttle bus service.

Harrah's Vicksburg Casino Hotel
1310 Mulberry Street
Vicksburg, Mississippi 39180
(601) 636-DICE
Web Site: www.harrahs.com

Reservation Number: (800) HARRAHS
Rooms: 101 Price Range: $69-$119
Suites: 16 Price Range: $99-$169
Restaurants: 3 (1 open 24 hours)
Buffets: B-$4.95 L-$6.95
D-$7.95/$9.95 (Fri/Sat)
Casino Size: 20,879 Square Feet
Other Games: LIR, TCP, No Poker, No CSP
Casino Marketing: (601) 630-2003
Special Features: Casino is on *Star of Vicksburg* a 1,200-passenger old-fashioned paddlewheel riverboat. Nonsmoking gaming area. Planet 4 Kidz child care facility.

Isle of Capri Casino - Vicksburg
3990 Washington Street
Vicksburg, Mississippi 39180
(601) 636-5700
Web Site: www.casinoamerica.com

Toll-Free Number: (800) THE-ISLE
Rooms: 61 Price Range: $30-$80
Suites: 61 Price Range: $50-$120
Restaurants: 2 (1 open 24 hours)
Buffets: B-$6.95 L-$7.51 D-$11.34
Casino Size: 24,000 Square Feet
Other Games: LIR, TCP, No Poker
Casino Marketing: (800) WIN-ISLE
Senior Discount: Get Paradise 50+ coupons, if 50, or older, ask for details at booth
Special Features: Casino features tropical Caribbean theme. 67-space RV park.

Rainbow Casino
1380 Warrenton Road
Vicksburg, Mississippi 39182
(601) 636-7575
Web Site: www.rainbowcasino.com

Toll-Free Number: (800) 503-3777
Rooms: 89 Price Range: $40-$65
Restaurants: 1
Buffets: B-$3.99 L-$5.75/$6.25 (Fri/Sat)
D-$8.50/$10.99 (Fri/Sat)
Casino Size: 25,000 Square Feet
Other Games: TCP, No Poker
Senior Discount: Players Club members, 50 and older, receive various discounts

Indian Casino

Silver Star Resort & Casino
Highway 16 West
Philadelphia, Mississippi 39350
(601) 650-1234
Web Site: www.silverstarresort.com
Map Location:
(81 miles N.E. of Jackson)

Toll-Free Number: (800) 557-0711
Rooms: 450 Price Range: $69-$129
Suites: 50 Price Range: $150-$325
Restaurants: 6 (1 open 24 hours)
Buffets: L-$7.95 D-$9.95
Casino Size: 90,000 Square Feet
Other Games: B, MB, LIR, TCP
Casino Marketing: (800) 557-0711 ext-1317
Senior Discount: If 55, or older, join Sunrise Senior Club for free gift, free breakfast and double point specials. 10% room discount for AARP members (Sun-Thu)
Special Features: Health spa, outdoor pool and hot tubs. Beauty salon. Gift shop.

MISSOURI

In November, 1992 Missouri voters approved a state-wide referendum to allow riverboat gambling. That made Missouri the fifth state to approve this form of gambling. There is no limit to the number of licenses that may be issued by the state's gaming commission and all boats remain dockside.

All Missouri riverboats initially conducted two-hour gaming sessions with a $500 loss-limit on each session. In August 1999, however, the state's gaming commission began a pilot program allowing some casinos to offer continuous boardings. The program was successful and all Missouri casino now offer continuous boardings.

The state's loss limit provision is still in force, however, and you are not allowed to lose more than $500 within a two-hour period. All casinos base that two-hour period beginning on even hour times: 12-2, 2-4, 4-6, 6-8, 8-10 and 10-12.

When you first enter a casino you must present an ID and you will be issued an electronic card which will track your chip and/or slot token purchases. (Some casinos may do this with your regular player's card). Once you have purchased $500 worth of chips or tokens you will not be able to buy anymore until the beginning of the next even hour. There is no limit on winnings.

Here's information from the Missouri Gaming Commission regarding the payback percentages for each casino's electronic machines for the six-month period from January 1, 2000 through June 30, 2000:

CASINO	PAYBACK %
Argosy	94.78
Isle of Capri	94.68
Harrah's M.H.	94.36
Harrah's K.C.	94.21
Station-St. Charles	93.90
Station-Kansas City	93.88
President	93.70
St. Jo Frontier	93.55
Aztar	90.49

These figures reflect the total percentages returned by each casino for all of their electronic machines including slot machines, video poker, video keno, etc. As you can see, Argosy Casino returned the most to its slot machine players, while Casino Aztar returned the least. Although these numbers are only for a one-year period they pretty much remain constant with the same casinos at the top and bottom of the list.

Unless otherwise noted, all casinos offer: slots, video poker, craps, blackjack, roulette, poker and Caribbean stud poker. Optional games include: baccarat (B), mini-baccarat (MB), poker (P), pai gow poker (PGP), let it ride (LIR), Spanish 21 (S21) and 3-Card Poker (TCP). The minimum gambling age is 21.

For more information on visiting Missouri call the state's Travel Center at (800) 877-1234.

Argosy Casino
777 N.W. Argosy Parkway
Riverside, Missouri 64150
(816) 746-3100
Web Site: www.argosycasinos.com
Map Location: **#1** (3 miles W. of Kansas City)

Toll-Free Number: (800) 900-3423
Restaurants: 4 (Deli on boat)
Buffets: B-$5.95 L-$6.95
D-$10.95/$17.95 (Fri-Sat)
Hours: 8am-5am/24 hours (Fri/Sat)
Admission: Free
Valet Parking: $4
Casino Size: 30,000 Square Feet
Other Games: PGP, LIR, S21, TCP
Casino Marketing: (816) 746-3151
Senior Discount: SVP club members receive discounts on select days, if 55, or older
Special Features: 1,800-passenger old-fashioned paddle wheeler that remains dockside on the Missouri River. Buffet and fine-dining restaurant are in land-based pavilion. Banquet and meeting facilities. Slot club members receive dining discounts.

Casino Aztar
777 East Third
Caruthersville, Missouri 63830
(573) 333-6000
Map Location: **#4** (200 miles S. of St. Louis)

Toll-Free Number (800) 679-4945
Restaurants: 1
Buffets: B-$9.95 (Sun) L-$5.95
D-$9.95/$12.95 (Sat)
Hours: 10am-2am/4am (Fri/Sat)
Admission: $3
Valet Parking: $2
Senior Discount: Free Wed cruises and 1/2 off any other cruise for club members, if 55, or older
Casino Size: 12,000 Square Feet
Other Games: LIR, TCP
Special Features: 875-passenger sternwheeler that cruises the Mississippi River. Restaurant and sports bar are located in land-based pavilion. Snack bar and gift shop on boat.

Harrah's St. Louis
777 Casino Center Drive
Maryland Heights, Missouri 63043
(314) 770-8100
Web Site: www.harrahs.com
Map Location: **#2**

Toll-Free Number: (800) HARRAHS
Rooms: 277 Price Range: $71-$139
Suites: 14 Price Range: $169-$206
Restaurants: 6
Buffets: B-$5.95 L-$7.95
D-$12.99/$16.95 (Mon/Wed/Fri/Sat)
Hours:
Easy Street: 8am-5am/24 hours (Fri-Sat)
Mardi Gras: 9am-5am/24 hours (Fri-Sat)
Catamaran: 12pm-4am
Grand Cayman: 11am-5am
Admission: Free
Valet Parking: $5
Senior Discount: $1.50 off breakfast and lunch buffets
Casino Size: 60,000 Square Feet
Other Games: MB, LIR, TCP
.Special Features: Four 1,800-passenger barges that remain dockside on the Missouri River. Catamaran casino is slots only. Land-based pavilion contains a lounge with live entertainment nightly except Monday, plus Planet 4 Kidz - a supervised children's play center.

Harrah's North Kansas City
One Riverboat Drive
Kansas City, Missouri 64116
(816) 472-7777
Web Site: www.harrahs.com
Map Location: **#1**

Toll-Free Number: (800) HARRAHS
Rooms: 200 Price Range: $89-$150
Suites: 15 Price Range: $139-$190
Restaurants: 6 (Deli on both boats)
Buffets: B-$5.99/$10.99 (Sat/Sun) L-$7.99
D-$11.99/$16.99 (Mon/Wed/Fri/Sat)
Hours: 8am-5am/24 Hrs (Fri/Sat)
Admission: Free
Casino Size: 33,000 Square Feet (North Star)
Casino Size: 44,000 Square Feet (Mardi Gras)
Valet Parking: $5
Other Games: MB, LIR, PGP, TCP
Senior Discount: $2.99 breakfast buffet with Players Club Card, if 55, or older
Special Features: Two riverboats that remain dockside on the Missouri River. North Star is 1,800-passenger sternwheeler and Mardi Gras is 1,700-passenger paddlewheeler. Hotel, buffet, car wash and retail shop discounts when you show Harrah's Card. Restaurants, sports bar and video arcade are located in land-based pavilion. Room discount offered to slot club members.

Isle of Capri Casino - Kansas City
1800 E. Front Street
Kansas City, Missouri 64120
(816) 855-7777
Web Site: www.isleofcapricasino.com
Map Location: **#1**

Toll-Free Number: (800) 946-8711
Restaurants: 2
Buffets: B-$6.48 L-$9.74 D-$19.54
Hours: 8am-5am/24 hours (Fri/Sat)
Admission: Free
Valet Parking: Free
Casino Size: 30,000 Square Feet
Other Games: LIR, PGP, TCP, P
Senior Discount: $4 off breakfast buffet, $2 off lunch or dinner buffet, if 55, or older with Player's Club Card
Special Features: 2,000-passenger Caribbean-themed barge that remains dockside in a man-made lake fed by the Missouri River. Players club members receive a $2 buffet discount.

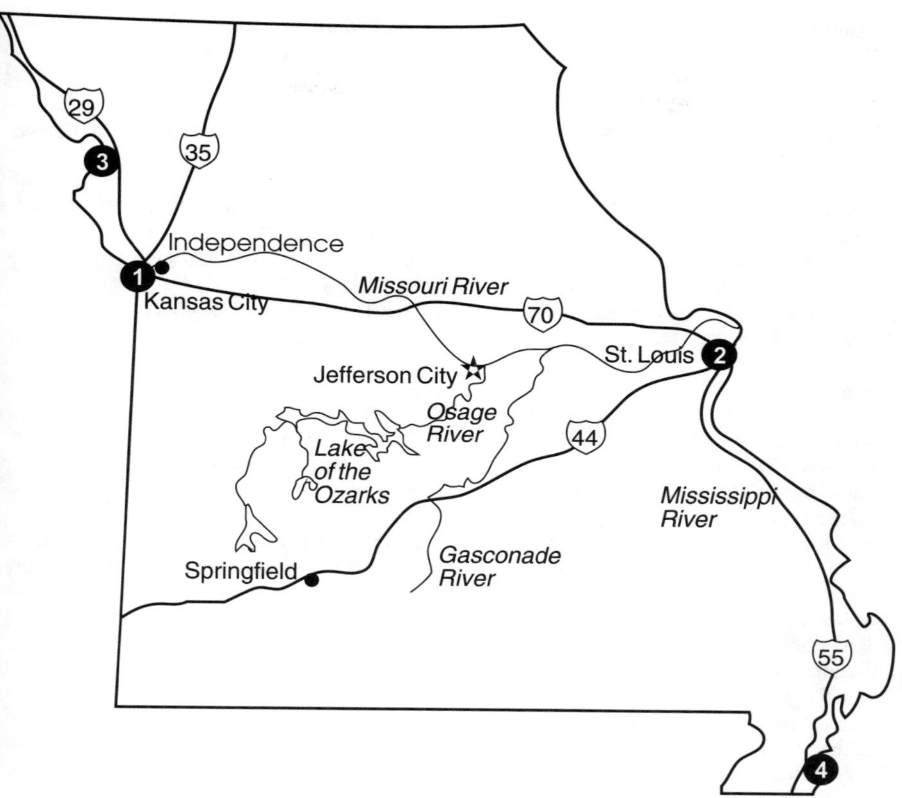

President Casino by the Arch
800 North First Street
St. Louis, Missouri 63102
(314) 622-1111
Web Site: www.presidentcasino.com
Map Location: **#2**

Toll-Free Number: (800) 772-3647
Restaurants: 2 on boat
Buffets: L-$6.95 D-$11.95
Hours: 8am-4am/24hrs (Fri/Sat)
Admission: $2
Parking: Free with casino validation
Valet Parking: $5
Other Games: P, B6
Senior Discount: 2-for-1 lunch buffet and other discounts on Thursdays, if 55, or older
Special Features: 1940's vintage, 2,500-passenger, art deco riverboat that remains dockside on the Mississippi River at the foot of the Gateway Arch. Free shuttle service to and from all downtown hotels. One block from Laclede's Landing Metro Link Light Rail Station. Special group packages for 20 or more.

Station Casino Kansas City
3200 North Stanton Drive
Kansas City, Missouri 64161
(816) 414-7000
Web Site: www.kansascitystation.com
Map Location: **#1**

Toll-Free Number: (800) 499-4961
Rooms: 176 Price Range: $89-$169
Suites: 12 Price Range: $349
Restaurants: 4
Buffets: B-$6.49 L-$8.49
D-$12.99/$15.99 (Fri/Sat)/$17.99 (Tue)
Hours: 8am-5am/24hrs (Fri/Sat)
Admission: Free
Valet Parking: $5
Other Games: MB, P, PGP, LIR
Special Features: Two 3,000-passenger barges that remain dockside on the Missouri River. Seven fast food outlets. Bavarian brew pub. 18 theater movie complex.

Station Casino St. Charles
P.O. Box 720
St. Charles, Missouri 63302
(314) 949-4300
Web Site: www.stcharlesstation.com
Map Location: **#2** (5 miles W. of St. Louis)

Toll-Free Number: (800) 325-7777
Restaurants: 4 (Snack bar on boat)
Buffets: B-$6.99 L-$8.99
D-$11.99/$13.99 (Sat)/$15.99 (Fri)
Hours: 8am-5am/ 24hrs (Fri/Sat/Holidays)
Admission: Free
Valet Parking: $5
Casino Size: 55,000 Square Feet
Other Games: MB, LIR, TCP, PGP, P
Casino Marketing: (800) 325-7777
Fun Book: Only given to groups
Senior Discount: Mon-Thu from 8am-6pm receive double points, gift shop discounts, $1 lunch and free valet parking, by joining *Golden Opportunities*, if 55, or older
Special Features: 2,000-passenger paddlewheeler that remains dockside on the Missouri River and another casino on a barge. Live entertainment on weekends. Burger King and TCBY Yogurt on barge. Attached 4,000-space covered parking garage. Free hotel shuttle on weekends. Slot club members receive $2 buffet discount.

St. Jo Frontier Casino
77 Francis Street
St. Joseph, Missouri 64501
(816) 279-7577
Map Location: **#3** (55 miles N. of Kansas City)

Toll-Free Number: (800) 888-2WIN
Restaurants: 2 (1 Deli on boat)
Buffets: B-$4.49 (Wed/Sat/Sun) L-$5.99
D-$7.77
Hours: 8am-2am/4am (Fri/Sat)
Admission: Free
Valet Parking: Not Offered
Casino Size: 9,260 Square Feet
Other Games: LIR, TCP
Casino Marketing: (800) WIN-STJO
Fun Book: Only offered to groups
Senior Discount: 2-for-1 buffet on Wed, if 55, or older.
Special Features: 600-passenger paddlewheeler that remains dockside on the Missouri River. Entertainment barge next to the casino has a bar and gift shop.

MONTANA

Montana law permits bars and taverns to have up to 20 video gaming devices that play video poker, video keno, or video bingo. These machines are operated in partnership with the state and are not permitted to pay out in cash; instead, they print out a receipt which must be taken to a cashier. The maximum bet is $2 and the maximum payout is limited to $800. Montana gaming regulations require these machines to return a minimum of 80%.

There are five Indian Tribes with video gaming machines that also print out a receipt. The maximum bet is $2 and the maximum payout is capped at $1,000. According to Wilbur Raymond of Montana's Gambling Control Division, there are no minimum payback amounts required for gaming machines on Indian reservations. The minimum gambling age in Montana is 18. For Montana tourism information call (800) VISIT-MT.

Charging Horse Casino
P.O. Box 128
Lame Deer, Montana 59043
(406) 477-6677
Map Location: **#3** (90 miles S.E. of Billings on Hwy. 212)

Restaurants: 1 Snack Bar Liquor: No
Hours: 10am-2am Daily

4 C's Cafe & Casino
Rocky Boy Route, Box 544
Box Elder, Montana 59521
(406) 395-4850
Map Location: **#1** (75 miles N.E. of Great Falls)

Restaurants: 1 Liquor: No
Hours: 8am-2am Daily

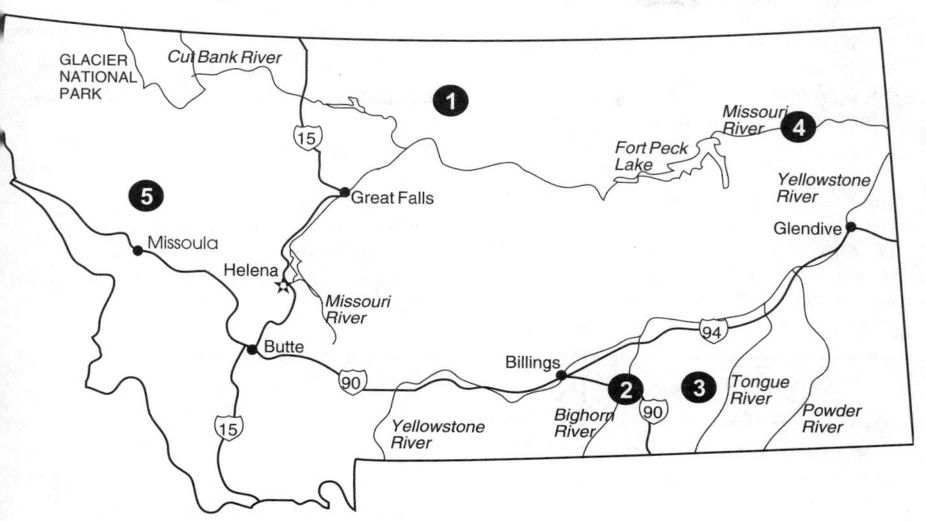

KwaTaqNuk Casino Resort
303 Highway 93
E. Polson, Montana 59860
(406) 883-3636
Map Location: **#5** (65 miles N. Of Missoula)

Room Reservations: (800) 882-6363
Restaurants: 1 Liquor: Yes
Rooms: 112 Price Range: $99-$129
Hours: 24 Hours Daily
Special Features: Hotel is affiliated with Best Western. Indoor pool and hot tub.

Little Big Horn Casino
P.O. Box 580
Crow Agency, Montana 59022
(406) 638-4444
Map Location: **#2** (65 miles S.E. of Billings)

Restaurants: 1 Liquor: No
Hours: 9am-2am/4am (Fri/Sat)
Other Games: Bingo (Thu-Sat)

Silverwolf Casino
P.O. Box 726
Wolf Point, Montana 59201
(406) 653-3476
Map Location: **#4** (180 miles N.E of Billings on Hwy. 2)

Restaurants: 1 Snack Bar Liquor: No
Hours: 11am-Mid Daily
Other Games: Bingo (Tue-Sun)

NEVADA

All Nevada casinos are open 24 hours and, unless otherwise noted, offer: slots, video poker, craps, blackjack, and roulette. The minimum gambling age is 21.

Other games in the casino listings include: sports book (SB), race book (RB), baccarat (B), mini-baccarat (MB), pai gow (PG), poker (P), pai gow poker (PGP), Caribbean stud poker (CSP), let it ride (LIR), red dog (RD), double down stud (DDS), Spanish 21 (S21), casino war (CW), keno (K) and bingo (BG).

Amargosa Valley

Map Location: **#8** (91 miles N.W. of Las Vegas on Hwy. 95)

Longstreet Inn and Casino
Route 373, HCR 70, Box 559
Amargosa Valley, Nevada 89020
(775) 372-1777

Toll-Free Number: (800) 508-9493
Rooms: 60 Price Range: $59-$89
Restaurants: 1
Other Games: No Craps or Roulette
Special Features: 50-space RV Park.

Stateline Saloon
Route 15, Box 566R
Amargosa Valley, Nevada 89020
(775) 372-5238

Restaurants: 1
Other Games: No Craps or Roulette

Battle Mountain

Map Location: **#9** (215 mile N.E. of Reno)

Nevada Hotel & Casino
8 E. Front Street
Battle Mountain, Nevada 89820
(775) 635-2453

Rooms: 13 Price Range: $17-$50
Restaurants: 1
Casino Size: 840 Square Feet
Other Games: No Craps or Roulette

Beatty

Map Location: **#10** (120 miles N.W. of Las Vegas on Hwy. 95)

Burro Inn Motel & Casino
Highway 95 South
Beatty, Nevada 89003
(775) 553-2225

Reservation Number: (800) 843-2078
Rooms: 61 Price Range: $35-$45
Suites: 1 Price Range: $65
Restaurants: 1 (open 24 hours)
Other Games: No Craps or Roulette
Fun Book: Given to hotel guests.
Special Features: 43-space RV park.

Exchange Club Casino & Motel
P.O. Box 97
Beatty, Nevada 89003
(775) 553-2368

Rooms: 43 Price Range: $38-$45
Suites: 1 Price Range: $68
Casino Size: 7,620 Square Feet
Other Games: No Craps or Roulette
Fun Book: Ask at motel office

Stagecoach Hotel & Casino
P.O. Box 836
Beatty, Nevada 89003
(775) 553-2419
Web Site: www.stagecoachhotel.com

Reservation Number: (800) 4-BIG-WIN
Rooms: 50 Price Range: $35-$40
Restaurants: 2
Casino Size: 7,900 Square Feet
Fun Book: Ask at front desk or cashier cage
Special Features: Swimming pool and Jacuzzi. 7 miles from Rhyolite ghost town. 90-space RV Park next door (775) 553-2238.

Boulder City

Map Location: **#11** (22 miles S.E. of Las Vegas on Hwy. 93)

Hacienda Hotel & Casino
U.S. Highway 93
Boulder City, Nevada 89005
(702) 293-5000

Reservation Number: (800) 245-6380
Rooms: 378 Price Range: $29-$59
Restaurants: 3 (1 open 24 hours)
Buffets: L/D-$4.99
Casino Size: 27,440 Square Feet
Other Games: SB, RB, P, K
Casino Marketing: (800) 245-6380

Carson City

Map Location: **#7** (32 miles S. of Reno on Hwy. 395)

Carson Nugget
507 N. Carson Street
Carson City, Nevada 89701
(775) 882-1626
Web Site: www.ccnugget.com

Toll-Free Number: (800) 426-5239
Reservation Number: (800) 338-7760
Rooms: 82 Price Range: $38-$61
Restaurants: 5 (1 open 24 hours)
Buffets: L-$5.50/$7.50 (Sat/Sun)
D-$7.50/$12.95 (Fri)
Casino Size: 24,320 Square Feet
Other Games: SB, RB, LIR, K, BG
Fun Book: Available at local motels
Senior Discount: 10% discount on room and food, if 50, or older
Special Features: Free supervised children's lounge. Free valet parking. Rare gold display.

Carson Station Hotel/Casino
900 S. Carson Street
Carson City, Nevada 89702
(775) 883-0900

Reservation Number: (800) 528-1234
Rooms: 92 Price Range: $55-$85
Suites: 3 Price Range: $80-$105
Restaurants: 2 (1 open 24 hours)
Casino Size: 6,750 Square Feet
Other Games: SB, RB, K
Fun Book: Only given to hotel guests
Special Features: Affiliated with Best Western.

Ormsby House Hotel Casino
600 S. Carson Street
Carson City, Nevada 89701
(775) 882-1890

Reservation Number: (800) 662-1890
Rooms: 190 Price Range: $39-$60
Suites: 10 Price Range: $75-$200
Restaurants: 3 (1 open 24 hours)
Buffets: B-$9.99 (Sun)
Casino Size: 8,790 Square Feet
Other Games: SB, RB

Piñon Plaza Casino Resort
2171 Highway 50 East
Carson City, Nevada 89701
(775) 885-9000
Web Site: www.pinonplaza.com

Toll-Free Number: (877) 519-5567
Rooms: 148 Price Range: $40-$90
Suites: 22 Price Range: $100-$150
Restaurants: 2
Casino Size: 15,926 Square Feet
Other Games: SB, RB
Fun Book: Given to resort/RV guests or at local motels
Senior Discount: 10% off at restaurant, if 55, or older
Special Features: Hotel is affiliated with Best Western. 30-space RV park. 32-lane bowling center. Free children's playroom. Video arcade. 10% room discount to AAA and AARP members.

Elko

Map Location: **#3** (289 miles N.E. of Reno on I-80)

Commercial Casino
345 4th Street
Elko, Nevada 89801
(775) 738-3181
Web Site: www.fh-inc.com

Toll-Free Number: (800) 648-2345
Restaurants: 2 (1 open 24 hours)
Casino Size: 6,440 Square Feet
Other Games: No Craps or Roulette
Fun Book: Show out-of-Elko ID at cashier cage
Special Features: Oldest continually operating casino in Nevada. 10-foot-tall stuffed polar bear in casino. Large gunfighter art collection.

Gold Country Motor Inn
2050 Idaho Street
Elko, Nevada 89801
(775) 738-8421

Room Reservations: (800) 621-1332
Rooms: 151 Price Range: $89-$109
Restaurants: 1 (1 open 24 hours)
Casino Size: 2,359 Square Feet
Other Games: No Craps or Roulette
Special Features: Motor Inn is affiliated with Best Western.

Red Lion Inn & Casino
2065 Idaho Street
Elko, Nevada 89801
(775) 738-2111
Web Site: www.redlioncasino.com

Reservation Number: (800) 545-0044
Rooms: 223 Price Range: $79-$119
Suites: 2 Price Range: $259
Restaurants: 2 (1 open 24 hours)
Buffets: B-$5.25 L-$6.50
D-$8.50/$11.50 (Fri)
Casino Size: 14,700 Square Feet
Other Games: P, LIR, K, BG
Casino Marketing: (800) 545-0044
Fun Book: Show out-of-state ID at front desk
Special Features: Air junkets offered from 90 cities in the U.S. - call (800) 258-8800. Video arcade. Sports bar with 14 large screen tv's.

Stockmen's Hotel & Casino
340 Commercial Street
Elko, Nevada 89801
(775) 738-5141
Web Site: www.fh-inc.com

Reservation Number: (800) 648-2345
Rooms: 141 Price Range: $39-$60
Suites: 1 Price Range: $84-$110
Restaurants: 2 (1 open 24 hours)
Buffets: D-$7.95/$11.95 (Fri)
Casino Size: 7,030 Square Feet
Other Games: SB
Casino Marketing: (800) 648-2345
Fun Book: Show out-of-Elko ID at cashier cage
Special Features: Western-themed hotel. 24-hour shuttle service.

Ely

Map Location: **#12** (317 miles E. of Reno on Hwy. 50)

Hotel Nevada & Gambling Hall
501 Aultman Street
Ely, Nevada 89301
(775) 289-6665
Web Site: www.hotelnevada.com

Reservation Number: (888) 406-3055
Rooms: 45 Price Range: $20-$48
Suites: 1 Price Range: $50-$85
Restaurants: 1 (open 24 hours)
Casino Size: 2,980 Square Feet
Other Games: P, No Craps or Roulette
Fun Book: Ask at front desk
Special Features: Built in 1929. Historical display of mining, ranching and railroad artifacts. 10% room discount to AARP members

Fallon

Map Location: **#13** (61 miles E. of Reno on Hwy. 50)

Bird Farm
128 E. Williams Avenue
Fallon, Nevada 89406
(775) 423-7877

Other Games: P, No Roulette
Special Features: Blackjack and craps played after 7pm.

Bonanza Inn & Casino
855 W. Williams Avenue
Fallon, Nevada 89406
(775) 423-6031

Reservation Number: (702) 423-6031
Rooms: 75 Price Range: $35-$50
Suites: 2 Price Range: $50-$65
Restaurants: 1 (Open 24 hours)
Casino Size: 5,830 Square Feet
Other Games: K, No Craps or Roulette
Casino Marketing: (702) 423-3111 ext.-228
Fun Book: Only given to hotel guests
Senior Discount: $5 room discount, if 55, or older

Depot Casino & Restaurant
875 W. Williams Avenue
Fallon, Nevada 89406
(775) 423-2411

Restaurants: 1
Casino Size: 4,655 Square Feet
Other Games: BG, No Craps or Roulette
Special Features: Blackjack played Wed-Sat after 6pm.

Fallon Nugget
70 S. Maine Street
Fallon, Nevada 89406
(775) 423-3111

Restaurants: 1
Casino Size: 3,500 Square Feet
Other Games: P, No Craps or Roulette
Special Features: Blackjack played daily (except Mon) after 4pm.

Stockman's Casino
1560 W. Williams Avenue
Fallon, Nevada 89406
(775) 423-2117

Toll-Free Number: (800) HOLIDAY
Rooms: 60 Price Range: $49-$89
Suites: 8 Price Range: $89-$169
Restaurants: 2 (1 open 24 hours)
Casino Size: 7,587 Square Feet
Other Games: SB, RB, K, No Roulette
Senior Discount: Various, if 60, or older
Special Features: Hotel is affiliated with Holiday Inn Express. 10% AAA discount offered.

Gardnerville

Map Location: **#15** (45 miles S. of Reno on Hwy. 395)

Ed's Topaz Nugget
1929 Highway 395 South
Gardnerville, Nevada 89410
(775) 266-4890

Rooms: 32 Price Range: $50-$60
Restaurants: 1
Other Games: SB, RB, No Craps or Roulette
Fun Book: Ask at cashier cage
Special Features: Hotel is the Best Western Inn at Topaz Lake.

Sharkey's Nugget
P.O. Box 625
Gardnerville, Nevada 89410
(775) 782-3133

Restaurants: 1 (open 24 hours)
Casino Size: 694 Square Feet
Other Games: No Craps or Roulette. BJ opens at 4pm/12pm (Fri-Sat)

Topaz Lodge & Casino
1979 Highway 395 South
Gardnerville, Nevada 89410
(775) 266-3338
Web Site: www.enterit.com/topaz3338

Reservation Number: (800) 962-0732
Rooms: 59 Price Range: $39-$58
Restaurants: 1 (open 24 hours)
Buffets: B-$6.95 (Sun)
D-$13.95(Fri)/$7.95(Sat)
Casino Size: 12,800 Square Feet

Gerlach

Map Location: **#31** (107 miles N.E. of Reno)

Bruno's Country Club
445 Main Street
Gerlach, Nevada
(775) 557-2220

Rooms: 40 Price Range: $40-$45
Restaurants: 1
Other Games: No Craps or Roulette.

Hawthorne

Map Location: **#16** (138 miles S.E. of Reno on Hwy. 95)

El Capitan Resort Casino
540 F Street
Hawthorne, Nevada 89415
(775) 945-3321

Reservation Number: (775) 945-3321
Rooms: 103 Price Range: $36-$54
Restaurants: 1 (open 24 hours)
Casino Size: 10,000 Square Feet
Other Games: No Craps or Roulette
Fun Book: Ask at front desk

Henderson

Map Location: **#17** (15 miles S.E. of Las Vegas on Hwy. 93)

Barley's Casino & Brewing Co.
4500 E. Sunset Road #30
Henderson, Nevada 89014
(702) 458-2739

Restaurants: 2 (1 open 24 hours)
Casino Size: 10,000 Square Feet
Other Games: SB
Special Features: Located in a strip mall. Four varieties of beer micro-brewed on the premises.

Eldorado Casino
140 Water Street
Henderson, Nevada 89015
(702) 564-1811
Web Site: www.boydgaming.com

Restaurants: 2 (1 open 24 hours)
Casino Size: 17,756 Square Feet
Other Games: SB, PGP, K, BG

Hyatt Regency Lake Las Vegas Resort
101 Montelago Boulevard
Las Vegas, Nevada 89011
(702) 567-1234
Web site: www.lakelasvegas.hyatt.com

Reservation Number: (800) 55-HYATT
Rooms: Price Range: $115-$450
Restaurants: 4
Casino Size: 8,000 Square Feet
Special Features: Located on 25 acres of waterfront property on Nevada's largest privately owned lake. 18-hole Jack Nicklaus designed golf course.

Jokers Wild
920 N. Boulder Highway
Henderson, Nevada 89015
(702) 564-8100
Web Site: www.boydgaming.com

Restaurants: 1 (open 24 hours)
Buffets: B-$8.95 (Sun) L-$4.25
D-$5.49/$8.49 (Fri)/$7.49 (Sat)
Casino Size: 23,698 Square Feet
Other Games: SB, K
Senior Discount: $1 off dinner buffet, if 55, or older
Special Features: Live entertainment Wed-Sun.

Klondike Sunset Casino
444 West Sunset
Henderson, Nevada 89015
(702) 568-7575

Restaurants: 1
Buffets: B-$1.99 L-$2.99 D-$3.99
Other Games: No craps.

Railroad Pass Hotel & Casino
2800 S. Boulder Highway
Henderson, Nevada 89015
(702) 294-5000
Web Site: www.railroadpass.com

Toll-Free Number: (800) 654-0877
Rooms: 100 Price Range: $29-$59
Suites: 20 Price Range: $34-$79
Restaurants: 3 (1 open 24 hours)
Buffets: B-$5.89 (Sat/Sun) L-$4.49
D-$5.49/$8.99 (Fri)
Casino Size: 23,584 Square Feet
Other Games: SB, RB, K
Fun Book: Show out-of-state ID at front desk
Senior Discount: Buffet is $2.67 after 3pm on Mondays, if 55, or older
Special Features: Swimming pool. Video arcade. Gift shop.

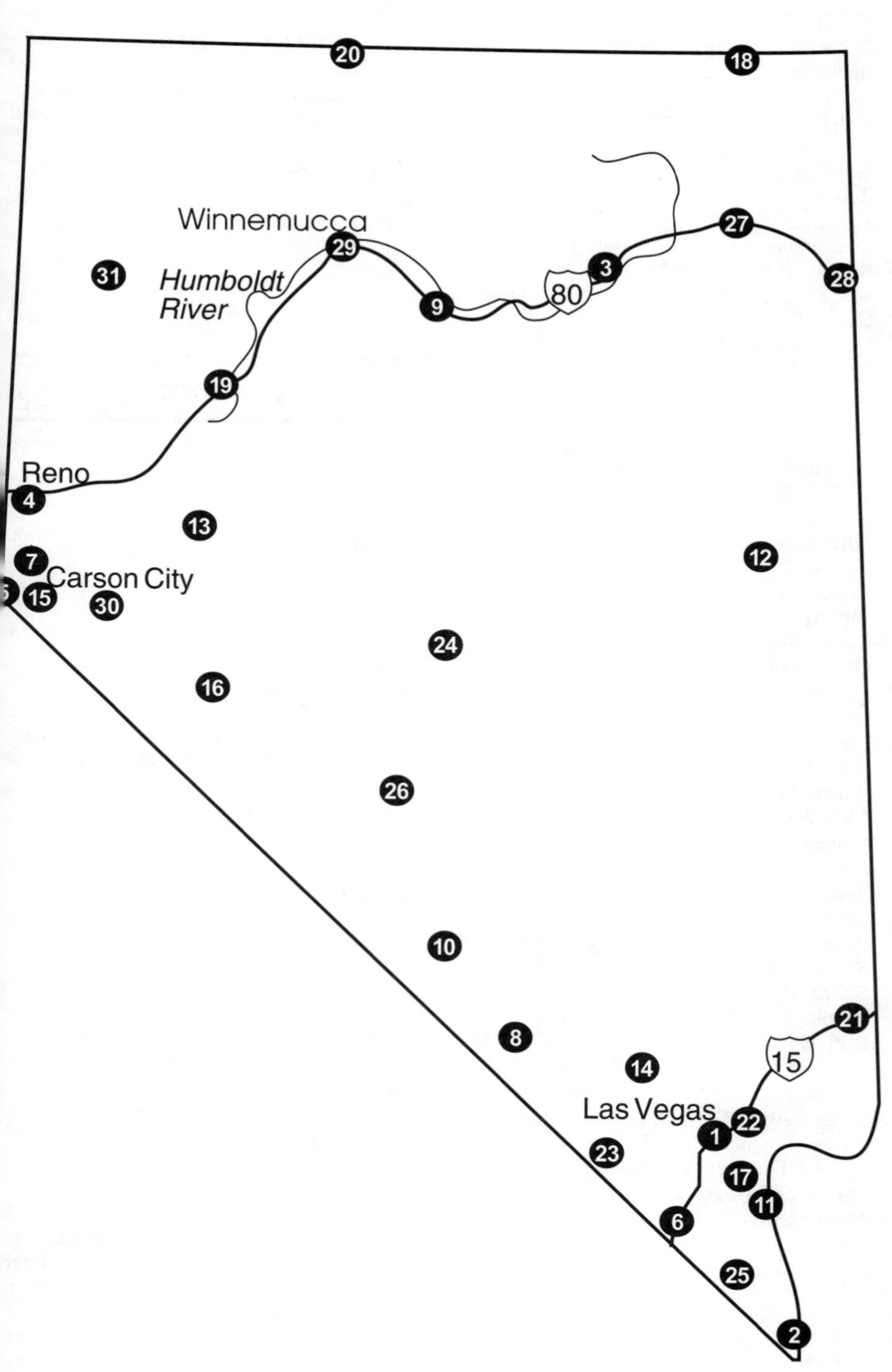
Winnemucca
Humboldt River
Reno
Carson City
Las Vegas
80
15
20
18
27
28
29
3
9
31
19
4
13
7
15
30
12
24
16
26
10
8
14
21
22
1
23
17
11
6
25
2

The Reserve Hotel & Casino
777 West Lake Mead Drive
Henderson, Nevada 89015
(702) 558-7000
Web Site: www.ameristars.com

Toll-Free Number: (888) 899-7770
Rooms: 200 Price Range: $39-$59
Suites: 24 Price Range: $89-$129
Restaurants: 3 (1 open 24 hours)
Buffets: B-$9.99 (Sat/Sun) L-$5.99
D-$8.99/$11.99 (Fri)/$9.99 (Sat/Sun)
Casino Size: 40,862 Square Feet
Other Games: SB, PGP, LIR, K, BG
Special Features: African safari-themed casino. Single-zero roulette.

Skyline Restaurant & Casino
1741 N. Boulder Highway
Henderson, Nevada 89015
(702) 565-9116

Restaurants: 1 (open 24 hours)
Buffets: L-$3.95
Casino Size: 8,500 Square Feet
Other Games: SB, RB, P, No Craps or Roulette
Fun Book: Available through local hotels/motels

Sunset Station
1301 W. Sunset Road
Henderson, Nevada 89014
(702) 547-77777
Web Site: www.sunsetstation.com

Reservation Number: (888) 786-7389
Rooms: 448 Price Range: $49-$149
Suites: 18 Price Range: $89-$275
Restaurants: 12 (2 open 24 hours)
Buffets: B-$4.99/$8.99 (Sat/Sun) L-$6.99
D-$9.99/$10.99 (Thu/Sat)/$12.99 (Fri)
Casino Size: 131,082 Square Feet
Other Games: SB, RB, B, MB, P, PGP,
LIR, K, BG
Special Features: 13 movie theaters. Kid's Quest child-care facility. Video arcade. Microbrewery.

Indian Springs

Map Location: **#14** (35 miles N.W. of Las Vegas on Hwy. 95)

Indian Springs Casino
372 Tonopah Highway
Indian Springs, Nevada 89018
(702) 879-3456

Restaurants: 1
Other Games: P, No Craps or Roulette

Jackpot

Map Location: **#18** (Just S. of the Idaho border on Hwy. 93)

Barton's Club 93
Highway 93
Jackpot, Nevada 89825
(775) 755-2341

Toll-Free Number: (800) 258-2937
Rooms: 98 Price Range: $35-$75
Suites: 4 Price Range: $90-$135
Restaurants: 2 (1 open 24 hours)
Buffets: B-$4.93 (Sat/Sun) D-$4.93 (Wed)/
$5.93 (Thu/Sun)/$9.93 (Fri/Sat)
Casino Size: 9,550 Square Feet
Other Games: K, LIR
Fun Book: Ask at registration desk

Cactus Pete's Resort Casino
1385 Highway 93
Jackpot, Nevada 89825
(775) 755-2321
Web Site: www.ameristars.com

Reservation Number: (800) 821-1103
Rooms: 272 Price Range: $70-$95
Suites: 28 Price Range: $125-$185
Restaurants: 5 (1 open 24 hours)
Buffets: B-$5.99 (Sat)/$8.99 (Sun) L-$5.99
D-$7.99/$9.99 (Fri/Sat)
Casino Size: 25,351 Square Feet
Other Games: SB, P, LIR, K
Senior Discount: 15% off room and restaurant, 20% off gift shop if 60, or older. Free dinner on birthday and anniversary.
Special Features: Four-diamond rated by AAA. Every Wednesday from 5pm-11pm all restaurants are half-price. Pool and spa. 18-hole golf course.

Horseshu Hotel & Casino
Highway 93
Jackpot, Nevada 89825
(702) 755-7777
Web Site: www.ameristars.com

Reservation Number: (800) 432-0051
Rooms: 110 Price Range: $45-$85
Suites: 10 Price Range: $65-$95
Restaurants: 1 (open 24 hours)
Casino Size: 3,520 Square Feet
Other Games: K, No Roulette

Jean

Map Location: **#6** (22 miles S.W. of Las Vegas on I-15; 12 miles from California border)

Gold Strike Hotel & Gambling Hall
1 Main Street/P.O. Box 19278
Jean, Nevada 89019
(702) 477-5000
Web Site: www.goldstrike-jean.com

Reservation Number: (800) 634-1359
Rooms: 800 Price Range: $20-$50
Suites: 13 Price Range: $24-$110
Restaurants: 5 (2 open 24 hours)
Buffets: B-$6.96 (Sat/Sun) L-$6.42 D-$7.50
Casino Size: 37,006 Square Feet
Other Games: CSP, K
Casino Marketing: (800) 634-1359
Fun Book: Ask at hotel registration desk
Special Features: Children's video arcade. Free shuttle to Nevada Landing Hotel & Casino. 99¢ breakfast special.

Nevada Landing Hotel & Casino
2 Goodsprings Road/P.O. Box 19278
Jean, Nevada 89019
(702) 387-5000
Web Site: www.nevadalanding.com

Reservation Number: (800) 628-6682
Rooms: 287 Price Range: $20-$89
Suites: 16 Price Range: $70-$125
Restaurants: 4 (1 open 24 hours)
Buffets: B-$6.96 (Sat/Sun) L-$6.42 D-$7.50
Casino Size: 35,700 Square Feet
Other Games: SB, PGP, CSP, K
Fun Book: Ask at hotel registration desk
Special Features: Children's video arcade. Free shuttle to Gold Strike. 99¢ breakfast special. Live music six nights per week.

Lake Tahoe

Map Location: **#5** (directly on the Nevada/California border; 98 miles northeast of Sacramento and 58 miles southwest of Reno).

The area is best known for its many recreational activities with skiing in the winter and water sports in the summer. Lake Tahoe Airport is located at the south end of the basin. The next closest airport is in Reno with regularly scheduled shuttle service by bus. Incline Village and Crystal Bay are on the north shore of Lake Tahoe, while Stateline is located on the south shore.

For South Lake Tahoe information call the Lake Tahoe Visitors Authority at (800) AT-TAHOE and for North Lake Tahoe information call the Incline Village/Crystal Bay Convention & Visitors Authority at (800) GO-TAHOE.

Here's information, as supplied by Nevada's State Gaming Control Board, showing the slot machine payback percentages for all of the south shore casinos for the fiscal year beginning July 1, 1999 and ending June 30, 2000:

Denomination	Payback %
5¢ Slots	91.94
25¢ Slots	93.72
$1 Slots	95.81
$1 Megabucks	85.16
$5 Slots	97.14
All Slots	95.01

And here's that same information for the north shore casinos:

Denomination	Payback %
5¢ Slots	93.58
25¢ Slots	94.22
$1 Slots	95.08
$1 Megabucks	90.99
$5 Slots	95.74
All Slots	94.50

These numbers reflect the percentage of money returned to the players on each denomination of machine. All electronic machines including slots, video poker and video keno are included in these numbers.

Optional games in the Lake Tahoe casino listings include: sports book (SB), race book (RB), baccarat (B), mini-baccarat (MB), poker (P), pai gow poker (PGP), Caribbean stud poker (CSP), let it ride (LIR), keno (K) and bingo (BG).

Bill's Casino
U.S. Highway 50/P.O. Box 8
Stateline, Nevada 89449
(775) 588-2455
Web Site: www.harrahstahoe.com

Restaurants: 1 (open 24 hours)
Casino Size: 18,000 Square Feet
Fun Book: Need flyer from local motels
Special Features: Separate casino that is owned by Harrah's Lake Tahoe.

Caesars Tahoe
55 Highway 50
Stateline, Nevada 89449
(775) 588-3515
Web Site: www.caesars.com

Reservation Number: (800) 648-3353
Rooms: 403 Price Range: $89-$215
Suites: 37 Price Range: $375-$650
Restaurants: 5 (1 open 24 hours)
Buffets: Brunch-$6.99/$9.99 (Sun)
D-$10.99/$14.99 (Fri)/$16.99 (Sat)
Casino Size: 40,500 Square Feet
Other Games: SB, RB, B, MB, PG,
PGP, CSP, LIR, K
Casino Marketing: (800) 648-3353
Fun Book: Show out-of-state ID at
Emperors Club Booth
Special Features: Located on south shore of Lake Tahoe. Health spa offers massages. Planet Hollywood restaurant. Beauty shop offers facials and body wraps. Indoor pool with waterfalls.

Cal-Neva Lodge Resort
Hotel, Spa & Casino
P.O. Box 368
Crystal Bay, Nevada 89402
(775) 832-4000
Web Site: www.calnevaresort.com

Reservation Number: (800) CAL-NEVA
Rooms: 180 Price Range: $89-$169
Suites: 27 Price Range: $149-$309
Restaurants: 1
Casino Size: 9,700 Square Feet
Other games: P
Casino Marketing: (800) CAL-NEVA
Fun Book: Only given to hotel guests
Special Features: Located on north shore of Lake Tahoe. Lakeview rooms. Euro-Spa offers a variety of massages, aromatherapy, hydrotherapy, sauna and body wraps. Outdoor pool and tennis courts. 3 wedding chapels. Honeymoon packages. Florist. Photography studio. Bridal boutique. Gift shop. Airport shuttle. Nevada's oldest operating casino. Internet cafe. Straddles California and Nevada state lines.

Crystal Bay Club Casino
14 Highway 28
Crystal Bay, Nevada 89402
(775) 831-0512
Web Site: www.crystalbayclub.com

Restaurants: 2 (1 open 24 hours)
Casino Size: 10,300 Square Feet
Other Games: SB, RB, K
Fun Book: Look for rack card at local hotels
and welcome centers
Special Features: Children's arcade. Live music and dancing nightly from 9pm.

Harrah's Lake Tahoe
Highway 50/P.O. Box 8
Stateline, Nevada 89449
(775) 588-6611
Web Site: www.harrahstahoe.com

Reservation Number: (800) HARRAHS
Rooms: 451 Price Range: $129-$279
Suites: 62 Price Range: $199-$800
Restaurants: 7 (1 open 24 hours)
Buffets: B-$8.99/$15.99 (Sun) L-$10.99
D-$14.99/$19.99 (Fri)/$18.99 (Sat)
Casino Size: 68,388 Square Feet
Casino Marketing: (800) 346-6569
Other Games: SB, RB, B, MB, PG,
PGP, CSP, LIR, K
Fun Book: Only given to hotel guests and groups
Special Features: Located on south shore of Lake Tahoe. Free shuttle service to several ski areas including Heavenly Valley and Squaw Valley. Family Fun Center. Indoor pool. Health club. Pet kennel. Warner Brothers specialty store. Harley Davidson store. 800-seat showroom.

Harveys Resort Hotel/Casino - Lake Tahoe
P.O. Box 128 - Highway 50
Stateline, Nevada 89449
(775) 588-2411
Web Site: www.harveys.com

Toll-Free Number: (800) 553-1022
Reservation Number: (800) HARVEYS
Rooms: 740 Price Range: $99-$239
Suites: 36 Price Range: $300-$500
Restaurants: 8 (1 open 24 hours)
Buffets: B-$5.95/$12.50 (Sun) L-$7.25
D-$10.95/$17.95 (Fri)
Casino Size: 81,731 Square Feet
Other Games: SB, RB, B, MB, P,
PGP, LIR, B6, K
Casino Marketing: (800) 654-3284
Special Features: Located on south shore of Lake Tahoe. Rated 4-Diamonds by AAA and 4-Stars by Mobil. Largest hotel and casino in Lake Tahoe. 10% to 20% room discount for AAA members. Health Club offers massages, aromatherapy. Outdoor pool and spa.

Hyatt Regency Lake Tahoe Resort & Casino
P.O. Box 3239
Incline Village, Nevada 89450
(775) 832-1234
Web Site: www.hyatt.com

Reservation Number: (800) 233-1234
Rooms: 412 Price Range: $99-$280
Suites: 48 Price Range: $225-$850
Restaurants: 2 (1 open 24 hours)
Buffets: B-$9.50 L-$7.25 D-$15.99/$10.99
(5-6pm)/$19.50 (Fri)/$15.50 (Fri 5-6pm)
Casino Size: 18,900 Square Feet
Other Games: SB, CSP, LIR
Casino Marketing: (702) 832-1234
Fun Book: Given for package bookings and
groups, also distributed by local motels
Special Features: Located on north shore of Lake Tahoe. Two Robert Trent Jones golf courses.

Lake Tahoe Horizon
50 Highway 50/P.O. Box C
Lake Tahoe, Nevada 89449
(775) 588-6211
Web Site: www.horizoncasino.com

Toll-Free Number: (800) 322-7723
Reservation Number: (800) 648-3322
Rooms: 519 Price Range: $59-$150
Suites: 20 Price Range: $125-$500
Restaurants: 5 (1 open 24 hours)
Buffets: Brunch-$7.95 (Sat)/$9.95 (Sun)
D-$10.95/$12.95 (Fri/Sat)
Casino Size: 30,999 Square Feet
Other Games: SB, RB, PG, B6, K
Casino Marketing: (800) 322-7723 ext.-3062
Fun Book: Only given to hotel guests
Senior Discount: 10% to 25% off hotel rate,
if 50, or older
Special Features: Located on south shore of Lake Tahoe. Outdoor heated pool with 3 hot tubs. Wedding chapel. Shopping promenade. Video arcade. Nightly entertainment. Baskin-Robbins ice cream store. Enterprise Rent a Car location.

Lakeside Inn & Casino
Highway 50 & Kingsbury Grade
Stateline, Nevada 89449
(775) 588-7777
Web Site: www.lakesideinn.com

Toll-Free Number: (800) 523-1291
Room Reservations: (800) 624-7980
Rooms: 123 Price Range: $79-$99
Suites: 2 Price Range: $110-$280
Restaurants: 1 (open 24 hours)
Casino Size: 14,975 Square Feet
Other Games: SB, K
Casino Marketing: (800) 523-1291
Special Features: Located on south shore of Lake Tahoe. Gift shop. Video arcade. $7.95 prime rib special in restaurant (4pm-10pm). $1 drinks at all times. Some rooms with scenic mountain views.

Tahoe Biltmore Lodge & Casino
#5 Highway 28/P.O. Box 115
Crystal Bay, Nevada 89402
(775) 831-0660
Web Site: www.tahoebiltmore.com

Reservation Number: (800) BILTMOR
Rooms: 92 Price Range: $69-$109
Suites: 7 Price Range: $89-$139
Restaurants: 2 (1 open 24 hours)
Casino Size: 10,480 Square Feet
Other Games: SB, RB, K
Casino Marketing: (800) 245-8667
Fun Book: Show out-of-state ID at casino cage
Special Features: Located on north shore of Lake Tahoe. Some lake view rooms. All rooms include free breakfast. 3-egg breakfast for $1.99. Pub & Grille with 30 beers on tap. Video arcade. Weekly video keno and blackjack tournaments.

Las Vegas

Map Location: **#1**

Las Vegas is truly the casino capital of the world! While many years ago the city may have had a reputation as an "adult playground" run by "shady characters," today's Las Vegas features many family-oriented facilities run by some of America's most familiar corporate names.

Las Vegas has more hotel rooms - 120,000 - than any other city in the U.S. and it attracts more than 34 million visitors each year. The abundance of casinos in Las Vegas forces them to compete for customers in a variety of ways and thus, there are always great bargains to be had, but only if you know where to look.

Las Vegas Advisor newsletter publisher, Anthony Curtis is the city's resident expert on where to find the best deals. His monthly 12-page publication is always chock full of powerful, money-saving, profit-making and vacation enhancing tips for the Las Vegas visitor and here are some of his thoughts on the Best of Las Vegas:

Best Las Vegas Bargain
Shrimp Cocktail, 99¢, Golden Gate

The Golden Gate's 99¢ shrimp cocktail is not only the current best bargain in town, it's been one of the best for more than 40 years. The six-ounce sundae glass full of shrimp was introduced back in 1957 for 50¢ and remained at that price until it was raised to 99¢ in 1991. All shrimp. No filler. Served 24 hours a day.

Best Room Rate
Free, Las Vegas Hotel-Casinos

The only other vacation scenario that includes this possibility involves a tent, sleeping bag, and a lot of wilderness. Why would casinos give rooms away? Competition. Hotels with 3,000, 4,000, and 5,000 rooms open, and the owners of hotels with only 1,000 or 2,000 rooms get nervous. Lulls, city-wide occupancy levels sometimes plummet below 90%, especially in December. Gasp! But mostly, it's the gambling. Gambling winnings subsidize the room department (and the food department, and the alcohol department, and the entertainment department, and ...). The best way to get in on the free-room bonanza is to join slot clubs.

Best Loss Leader
Free Spin to Win Airfare, Vacation Village

Win reimbursement of up to half the price of your airline ticket in Vacation Village's unique, risk-free, spin-for-airfare promotion. Present your valid airline ticket at the casino (located at the far south end of the Strip) within 12 hours of arrival and you'll get one free spin on a big wheel. Every spin pays a cash prize ranging from $1 to half the round-trip ticket price (up to $400). You have a 1-in-54 chance of hitting the top prize, and the average return per spin is $8.69. Spins are conducted on the even hours; if you get there when the promotion booth is closed, you'll be issued a raincheck.

Best Breakfast
Old Guard- Steak & Eggs, $2.49,
Arizona Charlie's (East and West)
New Guard-Any breakfast buffet, about $5

The Arizona Charlie's deal has been around for several years now, with its four- to six-ounce sirloin steak and eggs served 24 hours in the coffee shop. The compact steak is thick enough to cook perfectly to order, and because they serve so many of them, the preparation is expert. Service is good, too. With last year's opening of a new Arizona Charlie's on Boulder Highway, the deal is now available on both the east and west sides of town.

While prices climb for lunch and dinner buffets, breakfast buffets continue to remain bargain priced. Eggs cooked to order, breakfast meats, fresh fruit, pastries and rolls, plus all the beverages you desire, usually go in the $5-to-$6 range. The best to emerge lately is the gourmet spread at the Regent Las Vegas (see next).

Best Buffet
Upstairs Market Buffet at the Regent Las Vegas, $5.95-$13.95

The emergence of the "superbuffets" over the past half decade has spawned a food fight so ferocious, the casinos are on the verge of running out of improvements. The Regent Las Vegas' (formerly Resort at Summerlin) Upstairs Market Buffet, featuring a distinctly high-end food selection, occupies the top spot in the Las Vegas buffet hierarchy. Dinner ($13.95) and lunch ($9.95) both feature excellent appetizers and entrees, plus an especially creative assortment of desserts. The best deal, though, is breakfast, which includes bagels and lox, eggs Benedict, and the best omelet station in Las Vegas for just $5.95.

The best alternatives (all similarly priced) are the buffets at Fiesta, Main Street Station, Texas Station, Sunset Station, the Reserve, and the Rio.

Best Sunday Brunch
Bally's, $55

A vacation-topping Sunday brunch is the perfect Las Vegas splurge, and the epic Sterling Brunch at Bally's is as good as it gets. Despite being the highest-priced spread in town, the Sterling Brunch still qualifies as a bargain, offering sushi, oysters and clams, lobster tails, prime meats, and fantastic desserts, including goblets of fresh berries. The brand of champagne changes, but it's always a step or two above that served at the other brunches in town.

Best Meal
T-Bone Steak Dinner, $7.95, Gold Coast

If you eat only one meal in Las Vegas, this should be it. The colossal 16-ounce T-bone harkens back to Las Vegas' bargain steak heyday of a half-decade ago. Charcoal-grilled and cooked perfectly to your specifications, the meat comes with potatoes, onion rings, baked beans, garlic bread, big dinner salad and a glass of draft beer. It's served 24 hours a day, seven days a week in the Gold Coast's Monterey coffee shop. Perhaps, best of all, it's barely advertised, so this steak appears destined to be around for a good long time.

Best Snack Bar
Binion's Horseshoe

The two 24-hour snack bars at Binion's Horseshoe are tops in town, both for quality and price. The soup of the day is $1.75, the greasy-but-tasty chili is $3, and the turkey sandwiches—still made from real turkey—are $3.75. The best deal remains the daily chef's special of ham and beans (a different bean every day), served with cornbread, for $2.

Best Prime Rib
$7.95-$21, Jerry's Nugget

Some 60 Las Vegas casinos serve prime rib specials. The best in terms of quality and choice is Jerry's Nugget (N. Las Vegas Blvd. a couple miles north of downtown), which has three cuts to choose from. The $7.95 cut is a standard 8-10 ounces, leaning toward the higher. It's good, but for an extra $2.55 you can step up to an enormous 28-ouncer that's two-plus inches thick. Then there's the $21 "spectacle" prime rib, the one that elicits "ooohs" and "ahhhs" from everyone in the restaurant when it's served. It's listed on the menu as the "double cut," but a more apt description is the "Fred Flintstone cut" (remember the dinosaur bones that tipped Fred's car in the old TV series?). Not many people will finish this big three and a half pounder, so get it for the spectacle ... or the leftovers.

Best Freebie
Pirate Show, Treasure Island

This swashbuckling, cannon-firing, powder-keg-exploding free show is a definite must-see, and more than once. It plays six times a night, weather cooperating, every 90 minutes starting at 4:30 p.m. The best viewing area, at the north end of the veranda at the Battle Bar, should be staked out as early as 45 minutes prior to show times. Another good viewing locale is the plank bridge between the ships, as close to the frigate-side rope railing as possible. It is necessary to arrive at least 30 minutes prior to show time to secure a good spot. It's a good show for young children, unless they are bothered by crowds, in which case you should watch from the sidewalk across the street.

Best Funbook
New Frontier, Free

Easy to get and valuable, the best funbook in Las Vegas is distributed daily at the New Frontier. The book contains 10-5 matchplay coupons for blackjack, craps, and roulette, plus a discount keno ticket worth playing. The coupons are worth about $7 in expected winnings, and there's also a coupon for a 50¢ beer.

Unlike New Jersey, the Nevada Gaming Control Board does not break down its slot statistics by individual properties. Rather, they are classified by area.

The annual gaming revenue report breaks the Las Vegas market down into four different areas: Strip, Downtown, Boulder Strip and North Las Vegas. There is a very big locals market in Las Vegas and those casinos are shown in the gaming revenue report for the North Las Vegas and Boulder Strip area casinos.

When choosing where to do your slot gambling, you may to keep in mind the following slot payback percentages for Nevada's fiscal year beginning July 1, 1999 and ending June 30, 2000:

5¢ Slot Machines
The Strip - 90.94%
Downtown - 91.99%
Boulder Strip - 93.34%
N. Las Vegas - 93.70%

25¢ Slot Machines
The Strip - 92.85%
Downtown - 95.01%
Boulder Strip - 96.24%
N. Las Vegas - 96.73%

$1 Slot Machines
The Strip - 94.90%
Downtown - 95.40%
Boulder Strip - 96.69%
N. Las Vegas - 97.39%

$1 Megabucks Machines
The Strip - 88.77%
Downtown - 90.19%
Boulder Strip - 90.64%
N. Las Vegas - 90.86%

$5 Slot Machines
The Strip - 95.91%
Downtown - 96.03%
Boulder Strip - 97.10%
N. Las Vegas - N/A

All Slot Machines
The Strip - 93.98%
Downtown - 94.69%
Boulder Strip - 95.58%
N. Las Vegas - 96.05%

These numbers reflect the percentage of money returned to the players on each denomination of machine. All electronic machines including slots, video poker and video keno are included in these numbers.

As you can see, the machines in downtown Las Vegas pay out 1% to 2% more than those located on the Las Vegas Strip for the lower denomination 5¢ and 25¢ machines. When you get to the $1 and $5 machines the difference is less noticeable but you can clearly see that the downtown casinos always return more than the Strip area casinos. This information is pretty well known by the locals and that's why many of them do their slot gambling away from the Strip unless they are drawn by a special slot club benefit or promotion.

Returns even better than the downtown casinos can be found at some of the other locals casinos along Boulder Highway such as Boulder Station and Sam's Town.

The best returns of all, however, can be found at the locals casinos in the North Las Vegas area which would include the Fiesta, Santa Fe, Jerry's Nugget and Texas Station casinos. Not only are those numbers the best returns in the Las Vegas area, they are also the best payback percentage returns for anywhere in the United States.

One area where the Strip casinos do offer an advantage over the locals casinos is in the game of blackjack. You will find that all downtown and North Las Vegas casinos will "hit" a soft 17 (a total of 17 with an ace counted as 11 rather than one). This is a slight disadvantage (-0.2%) for the player and the Strip casinos do not hit a soft 17.

Flying to Las Vegas? Make This Your First Stop!

A great "guaranteed winner" promotion being run by one of the smaller Las Vegas casino hotels is at Vacation Village which will give you the chance to win the cost of your airfare to Las Vegas. To participate you must go to the Promotions Booth and present your airline ticket within 12 hours of your arrival in Las Vegas. The booth is open from 9 a.m. until 10 p.m. Monday through Friday and from 10 a.m. until 10 p.m. on Saturday and Sunday.

The personnel at the promotion booth allow you to spin the prize wheel on even hours only. Therefore, you should try to time your arrival to coincide with the even hour spin time or else you might have to wait around. If you get there during the hours when the booth is closed you should go to the table games area and ask one of the floor supervisors for a raincheck for a 12-hour extension. This will allow you to come back anytime within the next 12 hours for your free spin.

The wheel itself is a converted big-6 wheel with the vast majority of the prizes being $1. If your spin lands on the one spot marked "airfare" they will give you one-half the cost of your airline ticket, which represents payment of your airfare *to* Las Vegas. The maximum amount they will give you is $400 and there is a 1-in-54 chance of winning the big prize. If you use your frequent flyer miles and didn't pay for your ticket, or if there is no price shown on your ticket, they will give you a flat $100 if your spin lands on the airfare prize.

On a trip to Vegas in 1996 I won $1, my wife won $2 and the lady behind us won $400. Actually, the best I've ever done through the years was to win $10 but I have landed right next to that big prize on several occasions (breaks your heart doesn't it?). Okay, so I didn't win a fortune, but it was fun and it was free! Just make believe you're on *The Price Is Right* and you're spinning the big wheel trying to make it into the final showcase showdown. Who knows, maybe you'll win the airfare prize and actually, the odds aren't all that bad. According to *Las Vegas Advisor* publisher Anthony Curtis the average spin is worth $8.69.

Keep in mind that the property isn't exactly in the class of the glitzier Strip casinos, but for a few minutes of your time it's definitely worth the trip and if you like to play video poker you'll especially enjoy the visit because both casinos offer a variety of good machines. In some past "Best of Las Vegas" poll sconducted by the *Las Vegas Review-Journal*, Vacation Village has won the award for best video poker because of its generous pay tables and bonus award promotions. The casino also conducts daily drawings for cash prizes and while you're there you can go to the front bar and get a free hot dog & beer with a $10 change buy-in (nickels or quarters). The promotions booth will also give you a Fun Sheet with several matchplay coupons and a free 50-cent play on a Quartermania slot machine.

Vacation Village is about three miles south of the airport at 6711 Las Vegas Boulevard South. From McCarran Airport take the I-215 Airport Beltway to exit 9. For more information call (702) 897-1700 or (800) 658-5000.

As mentioned before, one of the best sources for finding out about the best "deals" on a current basis in the Las Vegas area is the *Las Vegas Advisor*. It is a 12-page monthly newsletter published by gaming expert Anthony Curtis. *Las Vegas Advisor* accepts no advertising and each issue objectively analyzes the best values in lodging, dining, entertainment and gambling to help you get the most for your money when visiting Las Vegas.

The *Las Vegas Advisor* newsletter is especially well known for its "Top Ten Values" column which is often quoted by major travel publications. Each subscription also comes with a benefit package valued at more than $600. Ordering information for *Las Vegas Advisor* can be found later in this section.

There are many free tourist magazines that run coupon offers for casino fun books or special deals. Some sample titles are: *Tour Guide, Showbiz, What's On In Las Vegas, Best Read Guide* and *Today in Las Vegas.* All of these magazines are usually available in the hotel/motel lobbies or in the rooms themselves. If a fun book listing in this section says to look for an ad in a magazine, then it can probably be found in one of these publications.

For Nevada tourism information call (800) NEVADA-8. For Las Vegas information call the city's Convention & Visitors Authority at (702) 892-0711, or visit their web site at: www.lasvegas24hours.com.

Other games in the casino listings include: sports book (SB), race book (RB), baccarat (B), mini-baccarat (MB), pai gow (PG), poker (P), pai gow poker (PGP), Caribbean stud poker (CSP), let it ride (LIR), red dog (RD), big 6 wheel (B6), sic bo (SIC), keno (K) and bingo (BG).

Aladdin Hotel & Casino
3667 Las Vegas Boulevard S.
Las Vegas, Nevada 89109
(702) 785-5555
Web Site: www.aladdincasino.com

Reservation Number: (877) 333-9474
Rooms: 1,878 Price Range: $99-$299
Parlor Rooms: 466 Price Range: $279-$349
Suites: 223 Price Range: $399-$469
Restaurants: 21
Buffets: B-$10.99 L-$12.99 D-$18.99
Casino Size: 100,000 Square Feet
Other Games: SB, RB, B, MB, PGP, CSP, LIR B6, K
Special Features: Separate high-limit casino. 130-store "Desert Passage" retail mall. 7,000-seat Theater of the Performing Arts. Health spa and salon.

Arizona Charlie's - East
4575 Boulder Highway
Las Vegas, Nevada 89121
(702) 951-9000
Web Site: www.azcharlies.com

Reservation Number: (800) 362-4040
Rooms: 300 Price Range: $29-$44
Restaurants: 3 (1 open 24 hours)
Buffets: B-$3.75/$5.95 (Sat/Sun) L-$4.75 D-6.75/$8.95 (Wed)
Casino Size: 40,000 Square Feet
Other Games: SB, P, PGP, BG
Senior Discount: $5 off weekend room rate, if 65, or older, 10% off buffet, if 55, or older
Special Features: 239-space RV park.

Arizona Charlie's - West
740 S. Decatur Boulevard
Las Vegas, Nevada 89107
(702) 258-5200
Web Site: www.azcharlies.com

Reservation Number: (800) 342-2695
Rooms: 245 Price Range: $35-$109
Suites: 10 Price Range: $75-$350
Restaurants: 5 (1 open 24 hours)
Buffets: B-$3.50 L-$4.50 D-$6.50
Casino Size: 56,316 Square Feet
Other Games: SB, RB, P, PGP, K, BG
Casino Marketing: (800) 882-5445
Senior Discount: $5 off weekend room rate, if 65, or older/10% off buffet, if 55, or older
Special Features: 50 championship bowling lanes (open 24 hours). 400-seat bingo parlor. Free shuttle to airport and Strip for guests.

Bally's Las Vegas
3645 Las Vegas Blvd. South
Las Vegas, Nevada 89109
(702) 739-4111
Web Site: www.ballyslv.com

Toll-Free Number: (800) 7-BALLYS
Reservation Number: (888) 215-1078
Rooms: 2,814 Price Range: $39-$175
Suites: 222 Price Range: $329-$499
Restaurants: 11 (1 open 24 hours)
Buffets: B-$9.99 L-$11.99 D-$15.99
Casino Size: 68,278 Square Feet
Other Games: SB, RB, B, MB, PG, PGP, CSP, LIR, B6, K
Casino Marketing: (800) 7-BALLYS ext. 4561
Special Features: Two main showrooms. Men's and women's health spas. Shopping mall with more than 40 stores. 8 tennis courts. Free monorail service to MGM Grand.
Show: "Jubilee" $49.50-$66.00, 7:30/10:30 Wed-Mon, dark Tuesday. Must be 18 or older.

Barbary Coast Hotel & Casino
3595 Las Vegas Blvd. South
Las Vegas, Nevada 89109
(702) 737-7111
Web Site: www.barbarycoastcasino.com

Reservation Number: (888) 227-2279
Rooms: 200 Price Range: $44-$144
Suites: 12 Price Range: $200-$450
Restaurants: 3 (1 open 24 hours)
Casino Size: 31,000 Square Feet
Other Games: SB, RB, MB, LIR, PGP
Casino Marketing: Call and ask for Fun Club
Fun Book: Only given to hotel guests or when joining slot club

Barcelona Hotel & Casino
5011 E. Craig Road
Las Vegas, Nevada 89115
(702) 644-6300

Toll-Free Number: (800) 223-6330
Rooms: 178 Price Range: $45-$60
Restaurants: 1 (open 24 hours)
Casino Size: 2,220 Square Feet
Other Games: SB, RB, No Craps
Senior Discount: $5 off room, if 62, or older,
Special Features: Weekly room rate of $158. $5 room discount for AAA members.

Bellagio
3600 Las Vegas Blvd. South
Las Vegas, Nevada 89109
(702) 693-7111
Web Site: www.bellagioresort.com

Reservation Number: (888) 987-6667
Rooms: 2,688 Price Range: $179-$299
Suites: 308 Price Range: $250-$1,400
Restaurants: 12 (2 open 24 hours)
Buffets: B-$10.95/$18.50 (Sat-Sun) L-$13.95 D-$19.95
Casino Size: 156,257 Square Feet
Other Games: SB, RB, B, MB, P, PG, PGP, CSP, LIR, B6, K
Special Features: 8.5-acre lake with nightly light and water show. Shopping esplanade. Two wedding chapels. Beauty salon and spa. Five outdoor pools.
Show: Cirque du Soleil's "O" $110 on main floor, $99 in balcony, 7:30/10:30 Fri-Tue, dark Wed/Thu.

Binion's Horseshoe Casino and Hotel
128 E. Fremont Street
Las Vegas, Nevada 89101
(702) 382-1600
Web Site: www.binions.com

Reservation Number: (800) 937-6537
Rooms: 300 Price Range: $35-$189
Suites: 34 Price Range: $55-$500
Restaurants: 3 (1 open 24 hours)
Buffets: B-$4.95 L-$6.95 D-$9.95/$14.95 (Fri)
Casino Size: 56,929 Square Feet
Other Games: SB, RB, MB, P, B6, K, BG
Casino Marketing: (800) 237-6537
Special Features: Home of the World Series of Poker. Steak House on 23rd floor offers panoramic view of Las Vegas. 4% commission on mini-baccarat.

Boardwalk Casino - Holiday Inn
3750 Las Vegas Blvd. South
Las Vegas, Nevada 89109
(702) 735-2400
Web Site: www.hiboardwalk.com

Reservation Number: (800) 635-4581
Rooms: 644 Price Range: $59-$129
Suites: 9 Price Range: $125-$750
Restaurants: 4 (3 open 24 hours)

Buffets: B-$5.99 L-$6.99 D-$8.49
Casino Size: 23,000 Square Feet
Other Games: SB, RB, LIR
Casino Marketing: (800) 635-4581
Special Features: 24-hour surf buffet. Steak and eggs buffet for $4.99 from 11pm to 6 am. **Show:** "The Dream King" 8:30 nightly, dark Sun/Mon.

Boulder Station Hotel & Casino
4111 Boulder Highway
Las Vegas, Nevada 89121
(702) 432-7777
Web Site: www.stationcasinos.com

Toll-Free Number: (800) 981-5577
Reservation Number: (800) 683-7777
Rooms: 300 Price Range: $42-$109
Restaurants: 13 (1 open 24 hours)
Buffets: B-$4.99/$8.99 (Sun) L-$6.99
D-$9.99/$10.99 (Thu-Sat)
Casino Size: 89,433 Square Feet
Other Games: SB, RB, MB, P, PGP,
LIR, K, BG
Casino Marketing: (800) 915-3322
Special Features: 99¢ Margaritas and $1.25 beer-steamed hot dogs available at all bars. Free shuttle service to Palace Station with connecting service to the Strip. Live entertainment nightly. 11-screen movie theater complex. Kid Quest - supervised child care center.

Bourbon Street Hotel & Casino
120 East Flamingo Road
Las Vegas, Nevada 89109
(702) 737-7200

Reservation Number: (800) 634-6956
Rooms: 150 Price Range: $39-$59
Suites: 16 Price Range: $89-$250
Restaurants: 1 (open 24 hours)
Other Games: SB, RB
Special Features: Casino only offers slots.

Caesars Palace
3570 Las Vegas Blvd. South
Las Vegas, Nevada 89109
(702) 731-7110
Web Site: www.caesars.com

Toll-Free Number: (800) 634-6001
Reservation Number: (800) 634-6661
Rooms: 2,469 Price Range: $89-$299
Suites: 250 Price Range: $450-$5,000
Restaurants: 9 (1 open 24 hours)
Buffets: B-$7.99/$14.99 (Sat/Sun) L-$9.99
D-$14.99/$24.99 (Fri/Sat)
Casino Size: 125,000 Square Feet
Other Games: SB, RB, B, MB, PG,
PGP, CSP, LIR, B6, K
Casino Marketing: Slots - (800) 262-2502
Tables - (800) 888-1710
Special Features: Health spa. Beauty salon. The Forum Shops at Caesars shopping mall features Planet Hollywood Restaurant and Warner Brothers Store.

California Hotel & Casino
12 Ogden Avenue
Las Vegas, Nevada 89101
(702) 385-1222
Web Site: www.thecal.com

Reservation Number: (800) 634-6505
Rooms: 781 Price Range: $35-$110
Suites: 74 Price Range: Private Use
Restaurants: 4 (1 open 24 hours)
Casino Size: 35,848 Square Feet
Other Games: SB, PGP, CSP, LIR, K
Casino Marketing: (800) 634-6505
Special Features: 93-space RV park with full hookup service. Suite upgrades are $50-$60 additional, when available.

Casino Royale & Hotel
3411 Las Vegas Blvd. South
Las Vegas, Nevada 89109
(702) 737-3500
Web Site: www.casinoroyalehotel.com

Toll-Free Number: (800) 854-7666
Rooms: 151 Price Range: $39-$69
Restaurants: 3 (1 open 24 hours)
Casino Size: 15,000 Square Feet
Other Games: CSP
Casino Marketing: (702) 737-0084
Special Features: Offers 100x odds on craps. Free in-room coffee. On-property Denny's and Subway.

The Five Best Slot Clubs in Las Vegas

By John Kelley

FREMONT - One of the best for both food comps and room offers. Only 100 points ($1,000 action) in that day will get you a choice between a buffet, the Lanai Cafe, or Tony Roma's.

Room offers are frequent, outstanding and almost automatic with any play at all, and usually include some free food. Some include free slot tournaments, the most recent of which offered $10,000 in cash prizes (and only about 100 entrants), an excellent awards dinner, two free weekend nights, and a nice gift (manicure set) worth about $20. Their recently refurbished casino is now one of the more pleasant places to play downtown, and their rooms, while tiny, have recently been redone as well

NEVADA LANDING/GOLD STRIKE - Technically two separate casinos, but not really. Location in Jean, 22 miles on I-15 southwest of the strip, these two are both owned by Mandalay Bay (Circus-Circus).

The player's clubs are nearly identical, and points earned at one casino can be used for comps at the other. Like Sam's, the cashback is weak (0.1%), but the comps are the easiest on the planet and each casino has a limited but adequate inventory of full-pay video poker. It only takes $75 of play to get a breakfast, $200 of play (about 20 minutes of quarters!) gets you a (admittedly so-so) buffet, $300 earns a (unlimited) comp to the snack bar, $700 gets you a great meal at their (pretty good) coffee shop, $1,200 gets a comp to their Chinese restaurant (the Jade Room), the gourmet steakhouse is $3,000 and $1,200 gets you a comped room, seven nights a week.

All of this will be cheerfully and patiently explained to you when you sign up for your slot club card, complete with a pamphlet spelling it all out. No mysteries, no hassle. Signing up for a slot club card seems to automatically generate a mailed free-room night offer, but with room comps as easy as these, it hardly matters. The only drawback is the location (middle of nowhere), but it's only about 20 minutes to the strip on I-15.

GOLDEN NUGGET - A very strong .67% cashback (matching the highest offered anywhere in town) and .67% comps, and great room offers, and enough 9/6 jacks-or-better to keep video poker players busy.

The bad news: only $1 and up machines yield slot club benefits, and you have to be an "active member," which takes $2,250 play (which will get you $15 cashback and a free buffet for two). However, achieving this status is worthwhile - Golden Nugget's room offers are among the strongest: 2 to 3 night offers (which really are free: no points are deducted from your comp account for using them), sometimes including free food, are issued three or four times a year.

Another feature that I like: while it takes 76 points ($5,700 play) to get a free night, this is the case 365 days a year, which makes the Nugget an excellent choice for those hard-to-get dates.

NEW YORK NEW YORK - .67% cashback, .67% in comps, and yet another .67% in "stuff" (hats, T-shirts, etc.), and a decent inventory of quarter 9/6 jacks-or-better and quarter and dollar Pick'em.

Hosts are exceptional with extra comps for guests: as little as $4,000 play has gotten a free weeknight comp, which is extraordinary for a premium Strip hotel. Not terribly good with free room offers, but calling a host and describing your typical play often yields a free night or two.

LAS VEGAS CLUB - When is no slot club better than any other slot club? When you are a visitor at the LVC!

Great goodies, but only for visitors, as the director of slots is: 1) Convinced that locals are cunning sharks that bankrupt them in no time. 2) Convinced that visitors are dweebs with all but holes in their pockets through which the money falls out. 3) Stuck with 409 aging rooms to fill.

The result of all this is while locals get bupkis, low-rolling visitors are in nirvana, thanks to their "Season's Pass" program. Winning any sort of jackpot $200 (on ANY machine, regardless of denomination) or greater gets you a "Season's Pass": three free nights in any three-month season, four times in the coming year (12 nights a year!) - just make sure to talk to slot manager before you play off your winning hand.

Additionally, when you show up for your free stays, awaiting you is dinner for two in their "Great Moments" restaurant, a Zagat Award Winner (Worth over $60). Any Royal Flush gets you a "Great Moments" comp, too, with dinner and two drinks per person. The casino has recently been remodeled and is looking great, and the north tower rooms are pretty nice (a lot nicer than the south tower, anyway!)

John Kelly is the webmaster of "Lodestones's Las Vegas." His site contains information for the Las Vegas visitor and can be found at http://www.flash.net/~mchino. John is also the editor of "Video Poker Player" newsletter. Ordering information for his newsletter can be found on page 94.

16 "Tips" Mostly Unknown By Tourists Going To Las Vegas

By Billhere

The following list is not in order of importance. That is determined by each person's expertise.

1. All Las Vegas Hotels have toll free 800 telephone numbers. You can get the 800 telephone number for free by looking them up in this guide or calling the 800 information operator at 1-800-555-1212. If your telephone company does not connect you to the 800 telephone information operator for free, you can receive an e-mail of all the toll free Las Vegas Hotel telephone numbers by submitting your e-mail address on the internet at:http://www.aglitter.com/TollFree.asp

Most of your questions can be answered by a simple, toll free telephone call. Pose your question to the Hotel telephone operator who answers and she will connect you to the right department. If you are not satisfied, call them back; it's their dime!

2. Room rates change often, even the same day. Keep calling the Hotels (see item 1 above). Also call room consolidators often. Their rates also change. See the weekly specials in the Las Vegas Hotel and room consolidators ads in the Sunday edition of the Los Angeles Times, Calendar Section. The Los Angeles Times is available in your local Barnes & Noble and Borders Book Shops. You can also find these LA Times hotel specials in the "Casino Travel" section of the American Casino Guide web site. You do NOT have to live in Los Angeles to avail yourself of these specials. Just tell the telephone operator that you want the specials as advertised in the LA Times.

3. Buffet - Line Passes. All buffets have a VIP line, which is always much shorter than the regular line. You will get a buffet line pass much easier than a comp because the pit boss will not be charged for it, as it has no monetary value. The buffet line pass will only make you eligible to go into the VIP line. You still have to pay the regular price for the buffet. So remember; if the line to get into the buffet is a mile long (it usually is), the answer is the "Buffet Line Pass."

4. Tip in places where you have never tipped before when in Las Vegas. When "Valet Parking is Full" then $5 will make Valet Parking "Unfull" quickly. Place $20 on the registration desk counter, when checking in, and ask for a room, with a view of The Strip or even an upgrade. Place $10 on the registration desk counter, when renting a car, and ask for a free upgrade.

5. There are three secrets for getting comps (free food, shows etc.) in Las Vegas:- ask, Ask and ASK. Millions of dollars are given away by the casinos every year. Make sure you get your share. +++ASK+++

6. Get to know casino hosts and slot hosts. They love giving out their business card. They can fulfill impossible demands. Their comps usually do not entail any loss of slot club points. Start a conversation with them by asking for their business card when you are gambling or call the Hotels 800 telephone number (see item 1 above) before you arrive and ask the telephone operator to speak to a Casino or slot host.

7. Money Management for travelers is really very simple. Divide your money, which is allocated to gambling, by the number of days you are staying and put it in envelopes. Here is an example. You are staying four days and have $500 put aside for gambling. Put $125 in each of four envelopes and mark the day that each envelope is for. You cannot gamble, on any day, more than the money inside the envelope that is allocated for that day. If you win for the day, the envelope is sealed and not to be opened until you get back home.

8. Use package deals, internet travel planners, the American Casino Guide web site, travel agents and casino internet specials to plan your trip economically. Keep calling (it's their dime) and you will save hundreds of dollars. Ask the reservation clerk for any specials and ask your casino/slot host for casino rates on Hotel rooms. A casino rate which is lower than the standard rate is usually automatically given just by asking a casino host.

9. Make a list of the things you want to do day-by-day. Don't go home saying "I ran out of time." Las Vegas is open 24 hours per day. You do not sleep in Las Vegas, you sleep at home!

10. Learn to gamble at home where it does not cost you anything. Then start in the casinos with small minimum tables ($1) or 5-cent slot or video poker machines. Play more downtown on Fremont Street and definitely more at casinos where the "locals" play.

11. Respect is a beautiful thing in casinos. You get respect from a casino by going up the comp ladder: ONE, TWO and THREE.

ONE - Join ALL the slot clubs, even if you do not play in that casino. Most of you are doing this.

TWO - If you are coming with a minimum of $500 as a gambling budget, deposit the money in the Casino Cashiers Cage. You can withdraw, in any multiples of $100 you want, at the table games by just asking for a marker from the dealer. For video poker or slot machines you ask any change girl to get you a slot supervisor. The slot supervisor will have you sign a withdrawal slip (marker) and will go to the Cage and get your money for you. You do not even have to leave your machine. Most people are not doing this. That is a mistake, because you will get more promotions mailed to your home than by just joining a slot club.

THREE - Request a line of credit by filling in an application which is similar to a credit card application. The Application for Credit Forms are available at all Casino Cashier Cages. Call the Hotel's 800 telephone number and ask for the "Casino Cashier Cage" and they will fax the "Application for Credit" form to you! The minimum amount of credit to apply for is $2,500. All credit applications go to "Central Credit" for approval, which is the major credit reporting agency for casinos.

A line of credit at a casino will get you promotions in the mail like you have never received before. However, if you cannot be responsible in your gambling, then don't get a line of credit and don't use the ATM machines! Each casino has their own minimums, forms, policies etc. ASK.

12. Do not play: keno, the big six wheel, bingo, any slots, proposition sports bets, the center bets in craps, on a double-zero roulette wheel, or in a live poker game. The odds against you are huge!

Do play: blackjack, craps (pass line and odds), sports wagering and video poker. You do have a chance.

For video poker, start to play at a simple game like a full pay 9/6 Jacks or Better. That is a video poker machine that has the following payout schedule, for one coin put in: Flush has a 6-coin payout AND Full house has a 9-coin payout AND Will pay out on any Jacks or better hand.

13. Note: There never is an unlucky number 13 in Las Vegas. No hotel has a 13th floor.

14. A shameless plug for my "Viva Las Vegas" newsletter, the "Viva Las Vegas Information List" and the "coupons+lists" index. All are free. Just go on the internet to: http://www.billhere.com to include your e-mail address.

15. The free, weekly visitors magazines are great for information and free coupons. They available at: Palace Station, next to the Bell Captains Desk and others are on the ticket reservation counter, Plaza downtown, at the entrance to the arcade in the back ACROSS from the food court (if you can't find the Plaza magazine location, just ask any employee where the food court or arcade are). *Showbiz Magazine* is only available on the Bell Captains Desks in Caesars Palace and Lady Luck. All four hotels are open 24 hours a day, 7 days a week.

16. The “Standby Line” is to get tickets to a show, at the last minute, when you cannot get reservations and don’t have tickets. You hope that other people will cancel their reservations or the casino will release tickets that they ALWAYS block for possible comps for high rollers. If you get lucky, you can snag some last minute tickets. If you are successful, you will pay the standard price. This is not a ticket scalping operation and is legally set up by management. The Standby Line is usually a special cordoned off line near the box office.

The following is for the "O" show at Bellagio: 1. You stand in line in the designated "Standby Line". 2. The line starts to form exactly two hours before show time. 3. One hour before show time they announce how far down the Standby Line, people in line will get tickets. It's first-come, first-served.

There is no guarantee of getting in but I do see a lot of people getting lucky and seeing the show.

The above details are only for the "O" show at the Bellagio. Most first rate shows have "Standby Lines." You must call the Box Office of the show you want to see for the details, which are not the same for all shows. So, if you just have to see that show, that night, remember the “STANDBY LINE”.

Billhere lives in Las Vegas and publishes an electronic newsletter with information on current events and happenings in that city. To subscribe to his newsletter just visit his web page at - http://www.billhere.com

The Best Places To Play In Las Vegas

Roulette - The best roulette game in Las Vegas can be found in the London Club at the Aladdin which has single-zero wheel with a surrender rule in effect. Single-zero roulette has only a 2.70% edge as compared to the usual 5.26% edge on a double-zero roulette wheel. Additionally, the surrender rule means that if you make an even-money bet (odd-even, red-black, or high-low) and zero comes in, then you only lose half of your bet. This lowers the house edge to just 1.35% on those particular bets. The minimum bet is $25.

Single-zero wheels, without a surrender rule, can be found at Monte Carlo, Reserve, Stratosphere, MGM Grand, Caesars Palace, Bellagio, Mandalay Bay, Paris and Venetian. The house edge in this game is 2.70%. Be aware, however, that only the Reserve has single-zero roulette exclusively. All of the other casinos offer it at just some of their roulette games and not all of them. Only the first three casinos offer $5 minimum bets, the minimum is $25 at MGM, Paris and Caesars (sometimes $10 during the day), while Bellagio, Venetian and Mandalay Bay require $100 minimums.

Craps - Two casinos allow up to 100x odds on their craps tables: Casino Royale and Sam's Town. The minimum bet at Casino Royale is $2 and at Sam's Town it's $5.

Mini-Baccarat - The normal 5% commission charged on winning bank bets in this game is reduced to only 4% at Binion's Horseshoe. This lowered commission reduces the house edge on bank bets from the standard 1.17% to just .067%.

Blackjack - All recommendations in this section apply to basic strategy players. For single-deck players the best game is at Slots A Fun (located next to Circus Circus on the north end of the Strip) which has these rules: dealer stands on soft 17, double down on any first two cards, re-split any pair (except aces) and double after split. The edge in this game is actually in favor of the basic strategy player by .13%.

Next best are Fiesta and Binion's Horseshoe which both have the same rules as Slots A Fun except: the dealer hits soft 17, you're allowed to re-split aces and you're not allowed to double after a split. The casino edge in this game is .15%.

Next best are 10 casinos that offer single-deck with the same rules as the last two, except they don't allow the re-splitting of aces: El Cortez, Golden Gate, Westward Ho, Gold Spike, Lady Luck, Reserve, Sam's Town, Joker's Wild, Plaza, Santa Fe and the Western. The casino edge here is .18%.

The Las Vegas Hilton is the best place to play double-deck blackjack. Their two-deck game has the following rules: dealer stands on soft 17, double down on any first two cards, re-split any pair (except aces), double down after split and late surrender. This works out to a casino edge of just .14% but there is a minimum bet requirement of $25 and it is sometimes raised to $100.

Next best are 16 casinos that offer those same basic rules, except for late surrender: Bally's, Barbary Coast, Venetian, Frontier, Bellagio, Flamingo Hilton, Mirage, Monte Carlo, Riviera, Paris, San Remo, Slots A Fun, Stardust, Treasure Island, Aladdin and Tropicana. The casino edge in these games is .19%. Keep in mind that these games aren't offered at every table, just some of them, so you'll have to look around each casino to find out where these better games are located. Also, some of these casinos may require higher minimum bets on these games, but if you go in the morning to mid-afternoon you can usually find these tables available with $5 minimums.

For six-deck shoe games the best place to play is the Las Vegas Club which offers a liberal variety of rules: dealer hits soft 17, double down on any first two, three or four cards, re-split any pair (including aces), double down after split, late surrender offered and any six-card hand totaling 21 or under is an automatic winner (even against a dealer's 10 up with an ace in the hole). The casino edge in this game is .12% but it is only offered at a few of the casino's tables.

After the Las Vegas Club there are 12 casinos with identical rules in their six-deck games: dealer stands on soft 17, double after split allowed, late surrender offered and resplitting of aces allowed. The casino edge in this game works out to .26% and you can find it at most of the major casino properties: Bellagio, Caesars Palace, Golden Nugget, Luxor, Aladdin, Mandalay Bay, MGM Grand, Mirage, Rio, New York New York, Treasure Island and the Venetian.

Video Poker - Las Vegas is the best place in the world for video poker. The three best varieties to look for are: 9/6 Jacks or Better, 10/7 Double Bonus and full-pay Deuces Wild. By only playing these three kinds of machines, playing the maximum coin and using perfect strategy you can achieve, theoretically, the following payback percentages: 99.54% on 9/6 Jacks or Better, 100.17% on 10/7 Double Bonus and 100.76% on full-pay Deuces Wild. All three kinds can be found in 25-cent (and some $1) denominations in the following casinos: Arizona Charlie's (East and West), Barbary Coast, El Cortez, Fiesta, New Frontier, Gold Coast, Hard Rock, Plaza, Orleans, Reserve, Sam's Town, San Remo, Santa Fe, Showboat, Silverton, and the Stardust. By restricting your play to just these machines and taking advantage of the slot club benefits offered at these casinos you should be able to play at a 100%+ level.

Sometimes 10/7 Double Bonus games can be found with a payoff of 80-for-1 on straight flushes. That higher payoff on straight flushes raises the overall return to 100.51%. These better-paying quarter games can be found at the Four Queens, Gold Coast, Main Street Station, Riviera, Arizona Charlie'sWest, and Texas Station. Additionally, some full pay Deuces Wild machines can occasionally be found that pay 4,700 coins for the royal flush whih raises the return to 101.07% on those games. The Plaza in downtown has some of these quarter machines at the bar.

9/6 and 10/7 can be found at the $1 level (there are rare full pay Deuces Wild machines which occasionally pop up - the Las Vegas Club has a slow coin-dropping version) and triple and 10 play at the quarter levels. above the $1 level you can find 9/6 jacks or brtter at some casinos and a few 10/7 double bonus machines (Fiesta, Arizona Charlie's, Santa Fe). There are rarer machines that return over 100% including joker's wild kings or better and All-American which can occassionally be found.

On the Strip generally the best machines you will find are 9/6 Jacks or Better. The only Strip locations to offer 10/7 Double Bonus are Bally's, O'Shea's, Circus Circus, Barbary Coast, New Frontier, Imperial Palace, Riviera, San Remo, Stardust and Stratosphere (which offers some unique games). Only the Barbary Coast, Boardwalk, Frontier, San Remo, Stardust and Stratosphere offer full pay Deuces Wild on the Strip.

Slots - For slot players it pays to play where the machines are set to return the most. According to the Nevada Gaming Control Board, for the fiscal year ending June 30, 2000 the average Las Vegas Strip slot machine returned 93.98% while the average downtown casino's slots returned 94.69%. Among Boulder Highway casinos such as Sam's Town and Boulder Station the average return was 95.58%. The highest returns of all, however, were found in north Las Vegas which is home to the "locals" casinos: Fiesta, Jerry's Nugget, Texas Station and Santa Fe. The average return on these machines was 96.05%.

Circus Circus Hotel & Casino
2880 Las Vegas Blvd. South
Las Vegas, Nevada 89109
(702) 734-0410
Web Site: www.circuscircus-lasvegas.com

Reservation Number: (800) 634-3450
Rooms: 3,770 Price Range: $39-$139
Suites: 122 Price Range: $99-$278
Restaurants: 9 (2 open 24 hours)
Buffets: B-$5.49/$6.99 (Sat/Sun) L-$6.49
D-$7.99/$8.99 (Fri/Sat)
Casino Size: 110,979 Square Feet
Other Games: SB, RB, MB, P, PGP,
CSP, LIR, B6, K
Fun Book: Given to hotel guests at check-in
Special Features: Free circus acts 11 a.m. to midnight. 370-space RV park. Wedding chapel. Midway and arcade games. Five-acre indoor water theme park.

El Cortez Hotel & Casino
600 E. Fremont Street
Las Vegas, Nevada 89101
(702) 385-5200
Web Site: www.elcortez.net

Reservation Number: (800) 634-6703
Rooms: 302 Price Range: $23-$40
Restaurants: 2 (1 open 24 hours)
Casino Size: 45,300 Square Feet
Other Games: SB, RB, MB, P, K
Special Features: Children's video arcade. Gift shop and ice cream parlor.

Ellis Island Casino
4178 Koval Lane
Las Vegas, Nevada 89109
(702) 734-8638

Restaurants: 1 Deli
Casino Size: 11,256 Square Feet
Other Games: SB, No Craps or Roulette

Excalibur Hotel/Casino
3850 Las Vegas Blvd. South
Las Vegas, Nevada 89109
(702) 597-7777
Web Site: www.excalibur-casino.com

Reservation Number: (800) 937-7777
Rooms: 4,008 Price Range: $49-$109
Suites: 46 Price Range: $275-$375
Restaurants: 6 (1 open 24 hours)
Buffets: B-$6.99 L-$7.99 D-$9.99
Casino Size: 121,544 Square Feet
Other Games: SB, RB, MB, P, PGP,
CSP, LIR, B6, K
Special Features: Two Magic Motion machines. Canterbury Wedding Chapel. Strolling Renaissance entertainment. Video arcade and Fantasy Faire Games for kids.
Show: "Tournament of Kings" $36.95 dinner show, 6:00/8:30 nightly.

Fiesta Casino Hotel
See North Las Vegas section

Fitzgeralds Casino & Holiday Inn
301 Fremont Street
Las Vegas, Nevada 89101
(702) 388-2400
Web Site: www.fitzgeraldslasvegas.com

Reservation Number: (800) 274-5825
Rooms: 634 Price Range: $30-$100
Suites: 14 Price Range: $100-$250
Restaurants: 5 (1 open 24 hours)
Buffets: B-$5.99/$8.99 (Sat/Sun) L-$5.99
D-$8.99
Casino Size: 42,301 Square Feet
Casino Marketing: (800) 274-5825
Other Games: SB, PGP, LIR, K
Fun Book: Ask at Card Center
Senior Discount: 10% off room, if 55, or older
Special Features: Hotel affiliated with Holiday Inn.

FREE Food in Las Vegas!

You may have heard the phrase "there's no such thing as a free lunch" but it certainly doesn't apply to Las Vegas where there really are some FREE "eats."

Slots-A-Fun - Stop by here in the morning and help yourself to free donuts. Other times of the day you're welcome to come in and have some free popcorn.

Westward Ho - Just go to the main lounge in the casino any day between noon and 4 p.m. and get a free sundae. They'll give you a dish of soft-serve, plus a chocolate chip cookie and then you can help yourself to your own selection of toppings: chocolate or butterscotch syrup, nuts and sprinkles. You must be 21 for this freebie so don't plan on bringing the kids.

Wild Wild West - Make a buy-in at the bar for $20 to put through the video poker machines and lunch is on the house. Choose your meal from a special menu that includes hamburgers, sandwiches and finger food such as chicken tenders. Since you're already at the bar you can also enjoy a free beverage. You are, however, required to run the entire $20 through the video poker machines. This one's not exactly free but, mathematically speaking, your expected loss is only about 60 cents.

Vacation Village - Another buy-in program at the bar. Here it's only $10 and you get a free beer-steamed hot dog, plus a free beer. With this one though you don't have to bet the ten bucks. You could just walk on over to the cashier cage and cash it back in.

Flamingo Las Vegas
3555 Las Vegas Blvd. South
Las Vegas, Nevada 89109
(702) 733-3111
Web Site: www.hilton.com

Toll-Free Number (800) 329-3232
Reservation Number: (800) 732-2111
Rooms: 3,642 Price Range: $89-$199
Suites: 209 Price Range: $250-$699
Restaurants: 8 (1 open 24 hours)
Buffets: B-$8.75 L-$9.95 D-$13.99
Casino Size: 81,309 Square Feet
Other Games: SB, RB, MB, P, PGP, CSP, LIR, SIC, B6, K
Casino Marketing: (800) 225-4882
Fun Book: Given to hotel guests, or look for ad in magazines
Special Features: Health Spa. Five outdoor swimming pools. Shopping arcade. Tennis Club and Pro Shop. Six floors of rooms for nonsmokers.
Show: "Forever Plaid" $24.95, 7:30/10:00 nightly, dark Mon.

Four Queens Hotel/Casino
202 Fremont Street
Las Vegas, Nevada 89101
(702) 385-4011
Web Site: www.fourqueens.com

Reservation Number: (800) 634-6045
Rooms: 700 Price Range: $29-$89
Suites: 40 Price Range: $99-$240
Restaurants: 4 (1 open 24 hours)
Casino Size: 27,389 Square Feet
Casino Marketing: (800) 634-6045
Other Games: SB, RB, PGP, CSP, LIR, K
Special Features: 99¢ shrimp cocktail.

Fremont Hotel & Casino
200 E. Fremont Street
Las Vegas, Nevada 89101
(702) 385-3232
Web Site: www.fremontcasino.com

Reservation Number: (800) 634-6460
Rooms: 428 Price Range: $40-$85
Suites: 24 Price Range: Private Use
Restaurants: 4 (1 open 24 hours)
Buffets: B-$4.99/$8.99 (Sat/Sun) L-$6.49
D-$9.99/$14.99 (Sun/Tue/Fri)
Casino Size: 28,408 Square Feet
Other Games: SB, RB, PGP, CSP, LIR, K
Casino Marketing: (800) 874-0711
Special Features: 99¢ shrimp cocktail at the snack bar next to the Lanai Cafe.

Gold Coast Hotel & Casino
4000 W. Flamingo Road
Las Vegas, Nevada 89103
(702) 367-7111
Web Site: www.goldcoastcasino.com

Toll-Free Number: (800) 331-5334
Room Reservations: (888) 402-6278
Rooms: 750 Price Range: $29-$109
Suites: 26 Price Range: $150-$250
Restaurants: 5 (1 open 24 hours)
Buffets: B-$3.95/$7.95 (Sun) L-$5.95
D-$8.45
Casino Size: 71,000 Square Feet
Other Games: SB, RB, MB, PGP, LIR, K, BG
Casino Marketing: (800) 331-5334 and ask for Slot Club Booth
Senior Discount: Flat $40, or best available room rate (Sun-Thu), if 62, or older
Special Features: 72-lane bowling center. 2 movie theaters. 700-seat bingo parlor. 2 entertainment lounges with no cover/no minimum. Dance hall. Free child-care.

Gold Spike Hotel & Casino
400 E. Ogden Avenue
Las Vegas, Nevada 89101
(702) 384-8444

Reservation Number: (800) 634-6703
Rooms: 102 Price Range: $24.20
Suites: 7 Price Range: $36.30
Restaurants: 1 (open 24 hours)
Casino Size: 5,820 Square Feet
Other Games: P, K, No Craps or Roulette

Golden Gate Hotel & Casino
One Fremont Street
Las Vegas, Nevada 89101
(702) 385-1906

Reservation Number: (800) 426-1906
Rooms: 106 Price Range: $29-$53
Restaurants: 2 (2 open 24 hours)
Casino Size: 9,090 Square Feet
Other Games: SB, RB, CSP, LIR
Special Features: Shrimp cocktail for 99¢ (24 hours) at the San Francisco Shrimp Bar & Deli. Las Vegas' oldest hotel - established 1906.

The Golden Nugget
129 E. Fremont Street
Las Vegas, Nevada 89101
(702) 385-7111
Web Site: www.goldennugget.com

Toll-Free Number: (800) 634-3403
Reservation Number: (800) 634-3454
Rooms: 1,805 Price Range: $59-$139
Suites: 102 Price Range: $175-$3750
Restaurants: 5 (1 open 24 hours)
Buffets: B-$5.50/$10.50 (Sun)
L-$7.25 D-$9.95
Casino Size: 34,680 Square Feet
Other Games: SB, RB, MB, PGP, CSP, LIR, B6, K
Casino Marketing: (800) 289-4269
Special Features: Mobil "Four Star" and AAA "Four Diamond" rating. Spa, beauty salon, fitness center and his and hers spas. World's largest gold nugget (61 pounds) on display.

Hard Rock Hotel & Casino
4455 Paradise Road
Las Vegas, Nevada 89109
(702) 693-5000
Web Site: www.hardrockhotel.com

Toll-Free Number: (800) HRD-ROCK
Rooms: 340 Price Range: $69-$250
Suites: 28 Price Range: $350-$500
Restaurants: 2 (1 open 24 hours)
Casino Size: 28,000 Square Feet
Other Games: SB, RB, B, MB, PGP, CSP, LIR
Casino Marketing: (800) 693-ROCK
Special Features: Rock and Roll memorabilia located throughout hotel and casino. Piano-shaped roulette tables. Slot machines with guitar handles. *The Joint* - 1,400-seat showroom. Beach Club with whirlpools, spas, cabanas and sandy beaches. Lagoon with underwater music. Athletic club. Hard Rock retail store.

Free Things To See In Las Vegas!

Masquerade Village

The Masquerade Show in the Sky is a $25-million extravaganza in the sky and on the stage at the Rio Hotel & Casino. Five floats travel on an overhead track above the casino, while 36 dancers, musicians, aerialists and stiltwalkers perform on stage, or from eight attractions that drop from the ceiling or from two circular lifts that rise from the floor.

There are three differently themed shows: Disco, Beach Party and Street Party. Showtimes are at 4 p.m., 6 p.m., 8 p.m. and 10 p.m. every day, except Tuesday and Wednesday.

Harrah's Las Vegas
3475 Las Vegas Blvd. South
Las Vegas, Nevada 89109
(702) 369-5000
Web Site: www.harrahsvegas.com

Toll-Free Number: (800) 392-9002
Reservation Number: (800) HARRAHS
Rooms: 2,672 Price Range: $95-$195
Suites: 94 Price Range: $250-$350
Restaurants: 8 (1 open 24 hours)
Buffets: B-$8.99 L-$9.99 D-$14.99
Casino Size: 86,664 Square Feet
Other Games: SB, RB, B, MB, P, PGP, LIR, B6, K
Casino Marketing: (800) 392-9002
Special Features: Mardi Gras and Carnaval themed casino. Health club.
Show: "Clint Holmes - Takin' It Uptown" $44.95, 7:30 (Thu-Tue)/10:00 (Thu/Sat), dark Wed.

Hotel San Remo Casino & Resort
115 East Tropicana Avenue
Las Vegas, Nevada 89109
(702) 739-9000
Web Site: www.sanremolasvegas.com

Reservation Number: (800) 522-REMO
Rooms: 694 Price Range: $39-$109
Suites: 17 Price Range: $109-$169
Restaurants: 5 (1 open 24 hours)
Buffets: B-$7.95 L-$7.95 D-$9.95
Other Games: SB, PGP, CSP, LIR, B6, K
Casino Size: 27,000 Square Feet
Casino Marketing: (800) 235-5987
Special Features: Free live entertainment in the Bonne Chance Lounge.
Show: "Les Trix" $25.99, 8:00 (covered)/10:30 (topless) nightly, dark Mon.

Imperial Palace Hotel & Casino
3535 Las Vegas Blvd. South
Las Vegas, Nevada 89109
(702) 731-3311
Web Site: www.imperialpalace.com

Reservation Number: (800) 634-6441
Rooms: 2,700 Price Range: $49-$109
Suites: 225 Price Range: $89-$279
Restaurants: 9 (1 open 24 hours)
Buffets: B-$6.25 L-$7.50 D-$8.50
Casino Size: 47,625 Square Feet
Other Games: SB, RB, MB, PGP, CSP, LIR, B6, K
Casino Marketing: (800) 351-7400 ext.-1
Special Features: Oriental theme throughout hotel and casino. Rare and antique Auto Collection on display (admission charge). Mini shopping mall. Video arcade for children. 24-hour wedding chapel. Independent 24-hour medical facility with no appointment necessary and most travel insurance accepted.
Show: "Legends In Concert" $34.50/$19.50 children under 12, 7:30/10:30 nightly, dark Sun. Price includes two drinks, tax and tip.

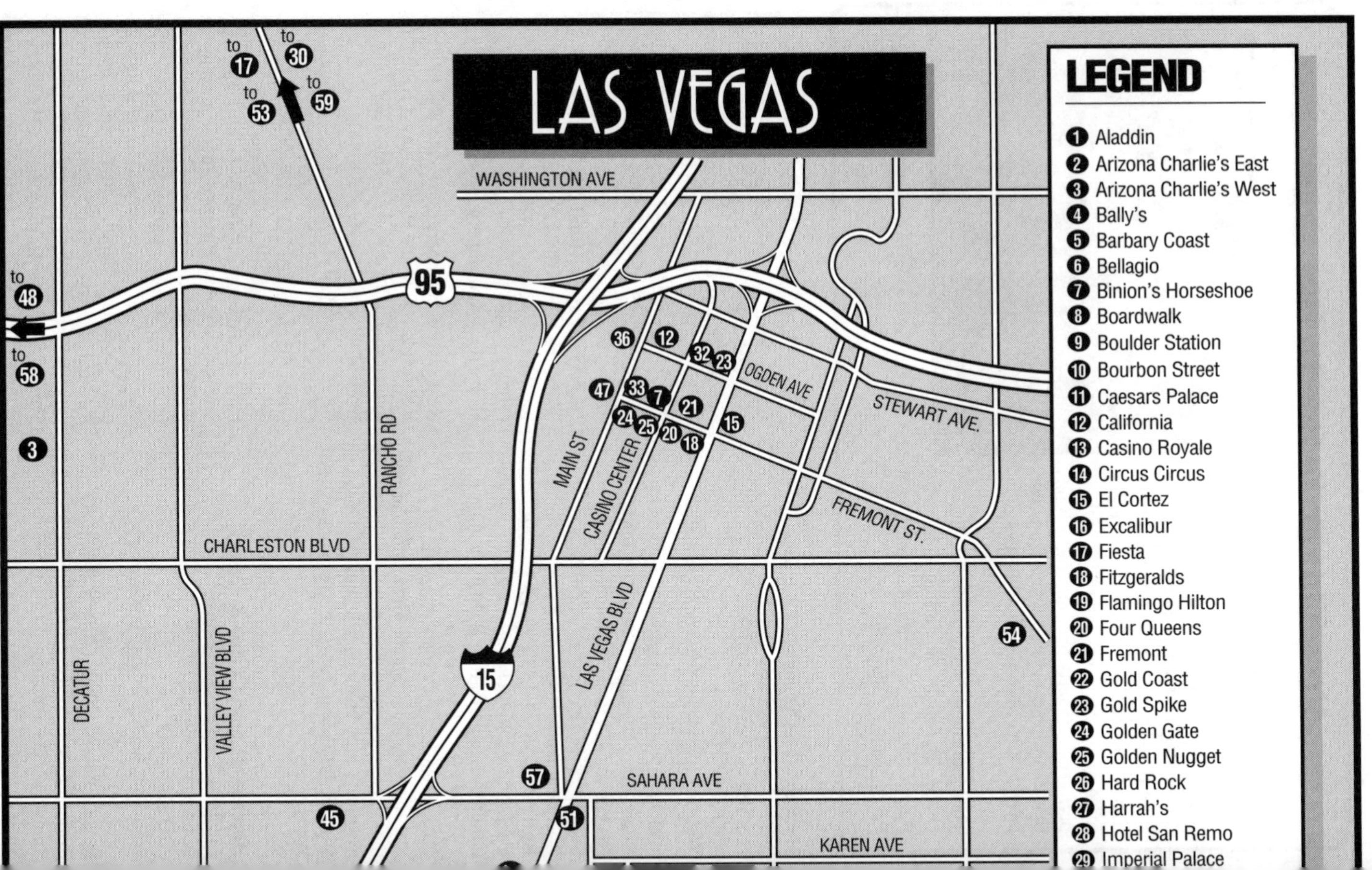
LAS VEGAS
LEGEND
1 Aladdin
2 Arizona Charlie's East
3 Arizona Charlie's West
4 Bally's
5 Barbary Coast
6 Bellagio
7 Binion's Horseshoe
8 Boardwalk
9 Boulder Station
10 Bourbon Street
11 Caesars Palace
12 California
13 Casino Royale
14 Circus Circus
15 El Cortez
16 Excalibur
17 Fiesta
18 Fitzgeralds
19 Flamingo Hilton
20 Four Queens
21 Fremont
22 Gold Coast
23 Gold Spike
24 Golden Gate
25 Golden Nugget
26 Hard Rock
27 Harrah's
28 Hotel San Remo
29 Imperial Palace
WASHINGTON AVE
CHARLESTON BLVD
SAHARA AVE
KAREN AVE
DECATUR
VALLEY VIEW BLVD
RANCHO RD
MAIN ST
CASINO CENTER
LAS VEGAS BLVD
OGDEN AVE
STEWART AVE.
FREMONT ST.
95
15
to 17
to 30
to 53
to 59
to 48
to 58

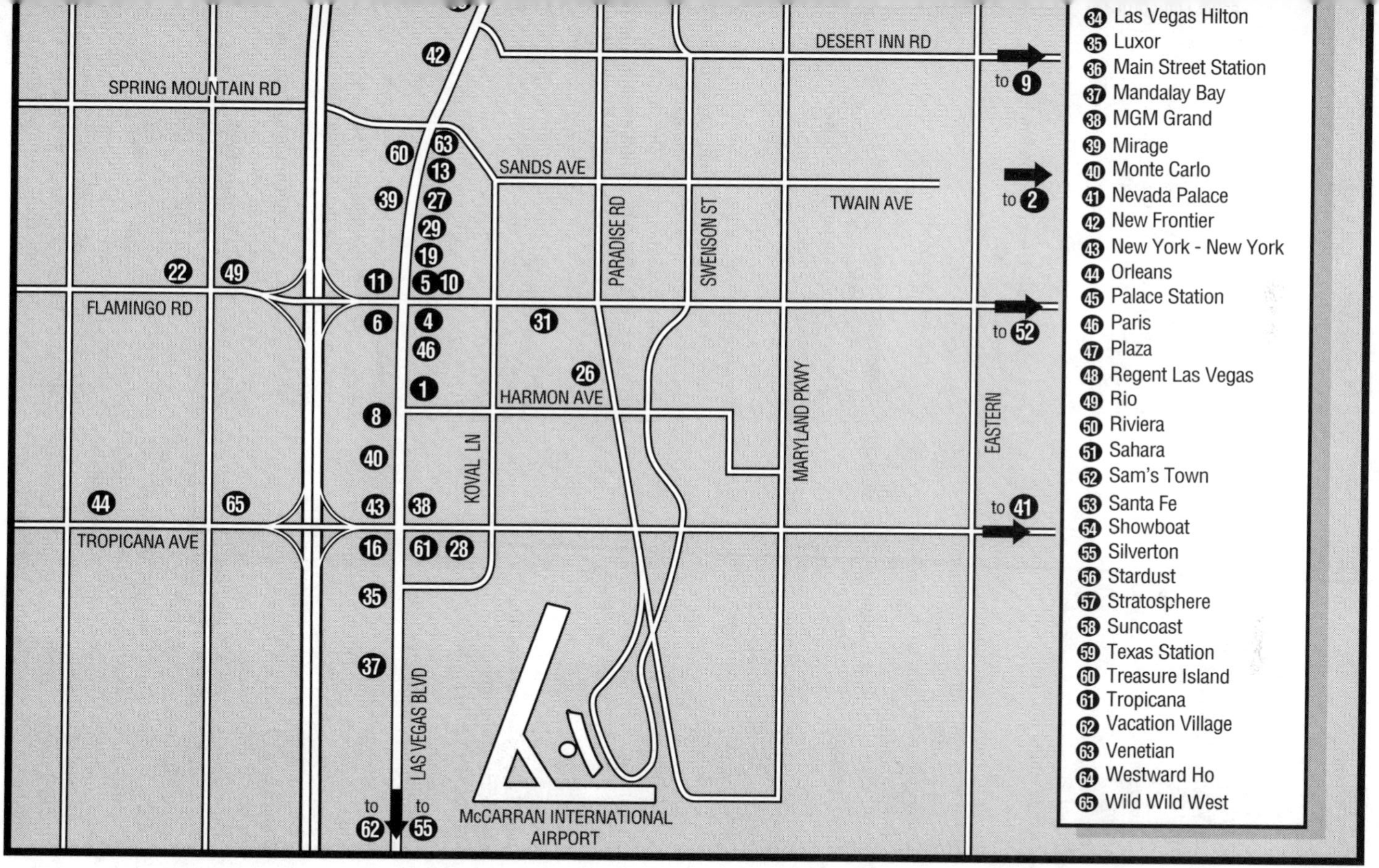

34 Las Vegas Hilton
35 Luxor
36 Main Street Station
37 Mandalay Bay
38 MGM Grand
39 Mirage
40 Monte Carlo
41 Nevada Palace
42 New Frontier
43 New York - New York
44 Orleans
45 Palace Station
46 Paris
47 Plaza
48 Regent Las Vegas
49 Rio
50 Riviera
51 Sahara
52 Sam's Town
53 Santa Fe
54 Showboat
55 Silverton
56 Stardust
57 Stratosphere
58 Suncoast
59 Texas Station
60 Treasure Island
61 Tropicana
62 Vacation Village
63 Venetian
64 Westward Ho
65 Wild Wild West

DESERT INN RD
SPRING MOUNTAIN RD
SANDS AVE
TWAIN AVE
PARADISE RD
SWENSON ST
FLAMINGO RD
HARMON AVE
KOVAL LN
MARYLAND PKWY
EASTERN
TROPICANA AVE
LAS VEGAS BLVD
McCARRAN INTERNATIONAL AIRPORT
to 9
to 2
to 52
to 41
to 62
to 55
42 60 63 13 39 27 29 19 22 49 11 5 10 6 4 31 46 26 1 8 40 44 65 43 38 16 61 28 35 37

Jerry's Nugget
See North Las Vegas section

Key Largo Casino & Quality Inn
377 East Flamingo Road
Las Vegas, Nevada 89109
(702) 733-7777

Reservation Number: (800) 634-6617
Rooms: 314 Price Range: $40-$129
Restaurants: 1
Casino Size: 8,572 Square Feet
Other Games: SB, RB
Casino Marketing: (702) 733-7777 ext. 2031
Fun Book: Given upon check-in
Senior Discount: 10% off room, if 50, or older
Special Features: All rooms are mini-suites with wet bars/refrigerators. Swimming pool with whirlpool spa. Coin-operated laundry facilities. Gift shop. Complimentary airport and Strip shuttle 8am-11:30pm daily.

Klondike Hotel & Casino
5191 Las Vegas Boulevard S.
Las Vegas, Nevada 89119
(702) 739-9351

Rooms: 150 Price Range: $39-$99
Restaurants: 1
Casino Size: 7,700 Square Feet
Other Games: No Craps

Lady Luck Casino Hotel
206 N. Third Street
Las Vegas, Nevada 89101
(702) 477-3000
Web Site: www.ladyluck.com

Toll-Free Number: (800) 634-6580
Room Reservations: (800) LADY-LUCK
Rooms: 792 Price Range: $44-$79
Suites: 134 Price Range: $60-$95
Restaurants: 4 (1 open 24 hours)
Buffets: B-$4.95 L-$5.95 D-$7.95
Casino Size: 18,350 Square Feet
Other Games: SB, RB, PGP, CSP, LIR, K
Casino Marketing: (800) 634-6580
Fun Book: Given to all hotel guests. Also given to non-Nevada residents with valid photo ID, or with flyer/coupon from magazines. Go to Mad Money booth to redeem.
Special Features: Daily and weekly gaming tournaments. $2.99 steak and eggs from 11pm-6am.

Las Vegas Auto/Truck Plaza
8050 S. Industrial Road
Las Vegas, Nevada 89118
(702) 361-1176

Restaurants: 1 (Open 24 hours)
Casino Size: 1,700 Square Feet
Other Games: LIR, No Craps or Roulette
Special Features: Players Club gives table players comps and discounts in stores and restaurants.

Las Vegas Club Hotel & Casino
18 E. Fremont Street
Las Vegas, Nevada 89101
(702) 385-1664
Web Site: www.playatlvc.com

Reservation Number: (800) 634-6532
Rooms: 415 Price Range: $18-$65
Suites: 8 Price Range: $125-$500
Restaurants: 4 (1 open 24 hours)
Casino Size: 48,500 Square Feet
Other Games: SB, RB, LIR, K
Casino Marketing: (800) 634-6532
Special Features: Sports theme throughout all areas with large private collection of sports memorabilia from the past to the present. Casino offers very liberal blackjack rules at some of its six-deck games. Sports bar.

Las Vegas Hilton
3000 Paradise Road
Las Vegas, Nevada 89109
(702) 732-5111
Web Site: www.lv-hilton.com

Reservation Number: (800) 732-7117
Rooms: 2,900 Price Range: $49-$199
Suites: 305 Price Range: $359-$995
Restaurants: 12 (1 open 24 hours)
Buffets: B-$8.99/$12.99 (Sat/Sun)
L-$9.99 D-$13.99
Casino Size: 84,335 Square Feet
Other Games: SB, RB, B, MB, PG, PGP, CSP, LIR, B6, K
Casino Marketing: (800) 547-2600
Special Features: *Star Trek: The Experience* - an interactive adventure. Largest race and sports book in Las Vegas. State-of-the-art health club. Outdoor heated Olympic pool and 24-seat spa. Putting green. 6 tennis courts.

Free Gambling In Las Vegas!

Stratosphere's Guaranteed Winner Program

In June 2000 the Stratosphere Casino Hotel and Tower introduced a new slot club program where you are guaranteed to win money.

The program only applies to new slot club members, it's not valid for greater Las Vegas area residents, and you can only use it one time.

You need to go and sign up for a slot club card and use it every time you play any slot or video poker machine. The casino then guarantees to return any loss you may incur (up to $125) during the first 30 minutes of play on that card, plus they ill give you an extra 10% of those losses. This mean that if you lose the maximum of $125 in the first 30 minutes the casino would return to you $125, plus an extra $12.50, for a total of $137.50. That's the good news.

The Stratosphere Tower is the most visible landmark in Las Vegas.

The bads news, however, is that the money is mailed to you in the form of a voucher at your home address and you have to bring it back to the casino in order to get your cash. The length of time you have to return with the voucher, according to the staff at the booth, is one year. You will also receive some sort of discounted room offer along with your voucher.

If you know you're going to return to Las Vegas then this is a great program because you know you can walk away a winner. If you're not going to go back to Las Vegas then the program may be worthless to you.

I signed up for the program in July 2000 and I was fortunate enough to have won money on a $1 9/6 Jacks or Better machine, so I didn't get a voucher. I did, however, receive a room offer for two nights at $29.50 per night weekdays, or $57.50 per night on weekends. My friend tried out the program the following month and he lost $30. He received a voucher for $33 along with an offer for a free room for three nights on weekdays, or $19.50 for two nights on weekends, plus free admsision for two to the Stratosphere Tower. His offer was better than mine but, according to some casino discussion groups out on the Internet, the Stratosphere doesn't necessarily send the better offer to losing players. Some players have won money and also received the free room offer which makes this a truly great deal for them.

If you're going to sign up for the Stratosphere program the best strategy seems to be to start on $1 machines and if you get close to losing the maximum $125 then move down to quarter machines until you've fulfilled the minimum 30-minute requirement. This way, if you get lucky and win early, you'll be hitting on a $1 machine which could produce a good-sized win for you. If you're unlucky you'll just end up losing the maximum $125 and still walk away $12.50 ahead.

Free Rooms in Las Vegas?

Bally's *Celebration* Package

One of the best "package" values in Las Vegas can be found at Bally's Hotel and Casino. Their *Celebration* package includes: deluxe room for two nights, two tickets to their big production show *Jubilee*, two breakfast buffets per person and a $9 discount off spa admission

Paris and Bally's are sister properties on the Las Vegas Strip. They are connected by a walkway mall.

The total cost is $178 but it's truly a great bargain because it includes all taxes and tips and when you add up your savings it's almost like getting the room for free.

The regular cost for *Jubilee* tickets alone is $49.50 per person. The brunch buffet runs $9.99, but since they also include the tax and tip, the four buffets would normally cost about $50. The bellman's tip for handling your bags is also included and this probably saves you another $4. Finally, the room tax rate in Las Vegas is 9% and, depending on when you stay, the lowest rate you'll probably find on a room at Bally's is $69. This means the taxes would run you a minimum of about $13 for the two nights. Add it all together and it totals a minimum value of $166. This means you're paying just $12 for your hotel room for two nights in one of Las Vegas' nicer hotels. Even better, if you're a spa kind of person and will actually use the two discount tickets for $9 savings off the regular $20 admission to the spa it would be like getting the room for free!

Of course, if you don't want to see a show this package won't have much value for you. If, however, you want to see a truly lavish production show you won't find anything better than *Jubilee*. It originally opened in 1981 and it has a huge cast of nearly 100 dancers, singers and specialty acts. The costumes are beautiful and the sets are spectacular. More than $3 million has been spent on the show and it includes some great special effects (especially good are "The Sinking of the Titanic" and "The Destruction of the Temple by Samson"). Of course, no Las Vegas production show would be complete without topless showgirls and this show has plenty. Not only do they appear on stage but they also swing down from the ceiling, appear on stages on both sides of the audience and also walk across a bridge that's temporarily suspended over the audience. *Jubilee* is the kind of show that Las Vegas is famous for and if you're looking for something in that genre you won't be disappointed.

Besides the fact that Bally's is a first-class property with nicely appointed rooms and good service there is another good reason to stay at the hotel: the free monorail shuttle to the MGM Grand. It operates daily from 9 a.m. to 1 a.m. and it's just a short walk from your hotel room. For room reservations, or more information on the Celebration Package call Bally's direct at (800) 634-3434.

Free Things To See In Las Vegas!

Buccaneer Bay

Cannons fire, pyrotechnics explode and stuntmen are thrown into the waters of Buccaneer Bay as the British Royal Navy challenges the pirates in a battle to the finish at the front entrance of Treasure Island.

Live actions show daily at 4, 5:30, 7, 8:30, 10 and 11:30p.m. Lines start forming in front about 45 minutes before showtime. To avoid the huge crowds get there early and then go into the resort and head to the Battle Bar. Grab a table near the railing, buy a soda for $2.00, or a domestic beer for $3.25 and you'll have a front row seat for the show!

Longhorn Casino
5288 Boulder Highway
Las Vegas, Nevada 89122
(702) 435-9170
Web Site: www.longhorncasino.com

Restaurants: 1 (open 24 hours)
Casino Size: 1,675 Square Feet
Other Games: No Craps or Roulette
Special Features: $1 blackjack games.

Luxor Las Vegas
3900 Las Vegas Blvd. South
Las Vegas, Nevada 89119
(702) 262-4000
Web Site: www.luxor.com

Reservation Number (800) 288-1000
Rooms: 3,962 Price Range: $69-$299
Suites 464 Price Range: $169-$500
Restaurants: 9 (1 open 24 hours)
Buffets: B-$8.49 L-$8.99 D-$12.99
Casino Size: 100,000 Square Feet
Other Games: SB, RB, B, MB, PG, P, PGP, CSP, B6, K
Casino Marketing: (800) 956-0289
Special Features: 30-story pyramid-shaped hotel with elevators that move at a 39-degree angle. Adventure rides. Full-size replica of King Tut's tomb.
Show: "Blue Man Group" $55/$65, 7:00 (Wed-Mon)/10pm (Wed-Sat), dark Tue.
Show: "Lasting Impressions" $39.95, 8:00 (Sat-Thu)/10:00 (Mon), dark Fri.

Main Street Station Hotel & Casino
200 N. Main Street
Las Vegas, Nevada 89101
(702) 387-1896
Web Site: www.mainstreetcasino.com

Toll-Free Number: (800) 713-8933
Reservation Number: (800) 465-0711
Rooms: 406 Price Range: $40-$125
Suites: 14 Price Range: Private Use
Restaurants: 4 (1 open 24 hours)
Buffets: B-$4.99/$7.99 (Sat/Sun) L-$6.99 D-$9.99/$13.99 (Fri)/$10.99 (Tue/Thu)
Casino Size: 27,398 Square Feet
Other Games: PGP, LIR, K

Mandalay Bay
3950 Las Vegas Blvd. South
Las Vegas, Nevada 89109
(702) 632-7777
Web Sit: www.mandalaybay.com

Reservation Number: (877) 632-7000
Rooms: 3,220 Price Range: $99-$399
Suites: 436 Price Range: $149-$899
Restaurants: 11 (1 open 24 hours)
Buffets: B-$9.95 L-$10.50 D-$17.95
Casino Size: 137,540 Square Feet
Other Games: SB, RB, B, MB, P, PG, PGP, CSP, LIR, B6
Special Features: 424-room Four Seasons Hotel on 35th-39th floors. *House of Blues* restaurant. 11-acre water park with sand and surf beach, swim-up shark tank and lazy river ride. Shark Reef (admission charge). Spa.

MGM Grand Hotel Casino
3799 Las Vegas Blvd. South
Las Vegas, Nevada 89109
(702) 891-1111
Web-Site: www.mgmgrand.com

Toll-Free Number: (800) 929-1111
Reservation Number: (800) 646-7787
Rooms: 4,254 Price Range: $69-$399
Suites: 751 Price Range: $129-$650
Restaurants: 8 (1 open 24 hours)
Buffets: B/L-$9.50 D-$13.95
Casino Size: 175,000 Square Feet
Other Games: SB, RB, B, MB, PG, P, PGP, CSP, LIR, B6, K
Casino Marketing: (702) 891-3651
Special Features: The world's largest hotel. 2 showrooms. 5 lounges/bars. Comedy Club. Rainforest Cafe. "Youth hotel" with supervised activities for children of hotel guests. Midway arcade. Swimming complex with beach-entry pool and cabanas. "MGM Grand Adventures" theme park. Lion habitat. Hotel check-in offered at McCarran Airport.
Show: "EFX" $51.50 ($72 preferred)/$37 (children), 7:30/10:30 nightly, dark Sun/Mon.

The Mirage
3400 Las Vegas Blvd. South
Las Vegas, Nevada 89109
(702) 791-7111
Web Site: www.themirage.com

Reservation Number: (800) 627-6667
Rooms: 3,044 Price Range: $79-$399
Suites: 279 Price Range: $300-$750
Restaurants: 11 (1 open 24 hours)
Buffets: B-$8.95/$14.95 (Sun) L-$9.95 D-$14.95
Casino Size: 94,000 Square Feet
Other Games: SB, RB, B, MB, PG, P, PGP, CSP, LIR, B6, K
Casino Marketing: (800) 627-6667
Special Features: The Secret Garden of Siegfried and Roy features six rare animals ($10 charge includes admission to Dolphin Habitat with 1.5 million-gallon pool; children under 10 are free). 20,000-gallon saltwater aquarium at reception area. 24-hour royal white tiger habitat viewing area. "Live" volcano at entrance that erupts periodically.
Show: "Siegfried & Roy" $95 (includes two drinks, tax, tip, program), 7:30/11:00 nightly, dark Wed/Thu.
Show: "Danny Gans" $67.50/$90 (preferred), 8:00 nightly, dark Mon/Fri.

Monte Carlo Resort & Casino
3770 Las Vegas Blvd. South
Las Vegas, Nevada 89109
(702) 730-7777
Web Site: www.monte-carlo.com

Reservation Number: (800) 311-8999
Rooms: 3,002 Price Range: $89-$149
Suites: 259 Price Range: $180-$400
Restaurants: 7 (1 open 24 hours)
Buffets: B-$8.49/$12.99 (Sun) L-$8.25 D-$11.49
Casino Size: 102,197 Square Feet
Other Games: SB, RB, B, MB, PG, P, PGP, CSP, B6, K
Casino Marketing: (800) 822-8656
Special Features: Single-zero roulette. Food court with McDonald's, Nathan's, Sbarro's, Haagen Daz and bagel Shop. On premises brewery serves six varieties of beer. 3 swimming pools and "easy river" ride. Health spa. Tennis courts. 12 retail shops.
Show: "Lance Burton, Master Magician" $44.95/$49.95, 7/10 nightly, dark Sun/Mon.

Nevada Palace Hotel & Casino
5255 Boulder Highway
Las Vegas, Nevada 89122
(702) 458-8810
Web Site: www.nevadapalace.com

Reservation Number: (800) 634-6283
Rooms: 210 Price Range: $40-$100
Restaurants: 2 (1 open 24 hours)
Buffets: B-$4.99 D-$5.99 (Mon-Thu)/ $6.99 (Sat/Sun)/$9.99 (Fri)
Casino Size: 13,625 Square Feet
Other Games: SB, P, K
Fun Book: Only given to hotel guests

New Frontier Hotel & Casino
3120 Las Vegas Blvd. South
Las Vegas, Nevada 89109
(702) 794-8200
Web Site: www.frontierlv.com

Toll-Free Number: (800) 421-7806
Reservation Number: (800) 634-6966
Rooms: 550 Price Range: $49-$109
Suites: 434 Price Range: $59-$199
Restaurants: 3 (1 open 24 hours)
Buffets B-$6.95 L-$7.95 D-$9.95
Casino Size: 41,325 Square Feet
Other Games: SB, RB, MB, PGP, CSP, LIR, B6, K, BG
Fun Book: Ask at desk at front of casino

Free Things To See In Las Vegas!

Fremont Street Experience

This $70 million computer-generated sound and light show takes place 90 feet in the sky over a pedestrian mall stretching four city blocks in downtown Las Vegas. It has more than 2.1 million lights, 208 speakers and needs 121 computers to make it all run like clockwork.

There are eight differently themed shows: Country Western, Odyssey, Dancing in the Street, Heartbeat of a Planet, Las Vegas Legends, the Rescue and Viva Las Vegas. Showtimes are daily at 7:30pm and every hour on the hour from 8pm to midnight. During the winter months the 7:30 pm show is moved to 7pm.

New York-New York Hotel & Casino
3790 Las Vegas Blvd. South
Las Vegas, Nevada 89109
(702) 740-6969
Web Site: www.nynyhotelcasino.com

Reservation Number: (800) 693-6763
Rooms: 2,024 Price Range: $89-$189
Suites: 12 Price Range: Only casino guests
Restaurants: 6 (1 open 24 hours)
Casino Size: 87,254 Square Feet
Other Games: SB, RB, MB, PGP, CSP, LIR, B6, K
Fun Book: Given to guests at check-in
Special Features: Design recreates the New York skyline and includes a replica of the Statue of Liberty and the Empire State Building. *Manhattan Express* - a Coney Island-style roller coaster.
Show: "Michael Flatley's Lord of the Dance" $59 (Tue-Wed)/$68 (Fri-Sat), 7:30/10:30 nightly, dark Sun/Mon.

Orleans Hotel & Casino
4500 W. Tropicana Avenue
Las Vegas, Nevada 89103
(702) 365-7111
Web Site: www.orleanscasino.com

Reservation Number: (800) ORLEANS
Rooms: 825 Price Range: $39-$139
Suites: 15 Price Range: $175-$275
Restaurants: 5 (1 open 24 hours)
Buffets: B-$4.95/$9.95 (Sun) L-$6.95
D-$9.95/$13.95 (Mon)
Casino Size: 94,380 Square Feet
Other Games: SB, RB, MB, P, PG, LIR, K
Casino Marketing: (702) 365-6095
Fun Book: Given to hotel guests
Senior Discount: $5 room discount on rate of $54 or higher Sun-Thu, if 62, or older
Special Features: New Orleans theme throughout hotel and casino. All rooms are "petite suites" with separate sitting areas. Wedding chapel. 70-lane bowling center. 12 movie theaters. Free shuttle service to Strip and other Coast properties.

O'Shea's Casino
3555 Las Vegas Blvd. South
Las Vegas, Nevada 89109
(702) 697-2767

Toll-Free Number: Call Flamingo Hilton at (800) 329-3232 ask for O'Shea's
Other Games: LIR
Fun Book: Ask at cashier cage
Special Features: Part of the Flamingo Hilton but run as a separate casino. Burger King.
Show: "Hip-Nosis" $24.95, includes one drink 7:00/10:00 (Adults Only) nightly, dark Sun/Mon

Palace Station Hotel & Casino
2411 West Sahara Avenue
Las Vegas, Nevada 89102
(702) 367-2411
Web Site: www.stationcasinos.com

Reservation Number: (800) 634-3101
Rooms: 948 Price Range: $39-$129
Suites: 82 Price Range: $69-$750
Restaurants: 5 (1 open 24 hours)
Buffets: B-$4.99/$8.99 (Sat/Sun) L-$6.99 D-$8.99/$9.99 (Thu/Fri/Sat)
Casino Size: 84,000 Square Feet
Other Games: SB, RB, MB, P, PGP, CSP, LIR, K, BG
Casino Marketing: (800) 367-2717
Fun Book: Boarding pass members can receive a fun book every 30 days.
Special Features: 99¢ Margaritas at the Guadalajara bar (24 hours). Nonsmoking slot area and hotel floors. Free shuttle to Strip, airport and other Station properties.

Paris Casino Resort
3645 Las Vegas Blvd. South
Las Vegas, Nevada 89109
Web Site: www.paris-lv.com

Reservation Number: (888) BON-JOUR
Rooms: 2,914 Price Range: $99-$179
Suites: 300 Price Range: $500-$1,250
Restaurants: 8 (1 open 24 hours)
Buffets: B-$10.95 L-$14.95 D-$21.95
Casino Size: 68,278 Square Feet
Other Games: SB, RB, MB, PGP, CSP, LIR
Special Features: Recreates the city of Paris with replicas of the Arc de Triomphe, the Opera House, Parc Monceau, the River Seine, and a 50-story Eiffel Tower topped with a restaurant and observation deck. Bakery.

Plaza Hotel & Casino
1 Main Street
Las Vegas, Nevada 89101
(702) 386-2110

Reservation Number: (800) 634-6575
Rooms: 1,037 Price Range: $30-$75
Suites: 60 Price Range: $60-$180
Restaurants: 3 (1 open 24 hours)
Casino Size: 57,120 Square Feet
Other Games: SB, RB, MB, P, PGP, LIR, K
Casino Marketing: (800) 634-6575
Special Features: High-rise restaurant has full view of Fremont Street Experience.

The Reserve Hotel & Casino
See Henderson section

The Regent Las Vegas
see North Las Vegas section

Rio Suite Hotel & Casino
3700 W. Flamingo Road
Las Vegas, Nevada 89103
(702) 252-7777
Web Site: www.playrio.com

Reservation Number: (800) PLAY RIO
Suites: 2,563 Price Range: $89-$425
Restaurants: 16 (1 open 24 hours)
Buffets: B-$8.00 L-$11.00 D-$14.00
Seafood Buffets: D-$27.00 (opens 4pm)
Casino Size: 99,500 Square Feet
Other Games: SB, RB, B, MB, PG, PGP, CSP, LIR, B6, K
Casino Marketing: (800) 777-1711
Special Features: All rooms are suites. Masquerade Village area offers free "Masquerade Show in the Sky" on select days and hours. Seafood buffet served in separate restaurant. Two-level shopping mall with more than 25 shops. Three wedding chapels. Four pools with waterfalls and sand beach.
Show: "David Cassidy at the Copa" $58 (includes one drink, tax, tip), 7:00 (Wed/Sat)/7:30 (Tue/Thu/Fri/Sun)/9:00 (Wed/Sat), dark Mon.

Free Things To See In Las Vegas!

MGM Grand Lion Habitat

MGM Grand's $9 million Lion Habitat is located inside the property near the entertainment dome and it showcases up to five lions daily.

The Habitat is open from 11 a.m. to 11 p.m. daily and features four separate waterfalls, overhangs, a pond and Acacia trees. There are numerous viewing areas that will allow you to get an upclose view of the lions, including overhead and beneath you as you follow the walkway.

The Habitat has a retail souvenir shop and, for a $20 fee, you can have your photo taken with a lion club. For more information on the Lion Habitat you can call the MGM Grand at (800) 929-1111, or visit their web site at www.mgmgrand.com

Riviera Hotel & Casino
2901 Las Vegas Blvd. South
Las Vegas, Nevada 89109
(702) 734-5110
Web Site: www.theriviera.com

Toll-Free Number: (800) 634-3420
Reservation Number: (800) 634-6753
Rooms: 2,100 Price Range: $79-$149
Suites: 154 Price Range: $195-$500
Restaurants: 6 (1 open 24 hours)
Buffets: B-$6.99 L-$7.99 D-$9.99
Casino Size: 109,800 Square Feet
Other Games: SB, RB, B, MB, P, PGP, LIR, SIC, B6, K, BG
Casino Marketing: Slots (800) 637-5687
Casino Marketing: Tables (800) 437-7951
Fun Book: Look for ad in magazines
Special Features: Four showrooms. Men's and women's health facilities. Many specialty shops. 2 lighted tennis courts. On-site nondenominational worship services with Strip's only on-site chaplain. Food court has Burger King, Pizza Hut, Panda Express, Chick-A-Dee and several other fast food outlets.
Show: "Splash" $39.50/$49.50 (VIP seating), 7:30/10:30 (adults only) nightly.
Show: "An Evening at La Cage" $22.25/ $32.25 (VIP seating) , 7:30/9:30 nightly, dark Tue. Price includes one drink.
Show: "Crazy Girls" $19.25/$29.25 (VIP seating), 8:30 and 10:30 nightly/12:00am (Sat), dark Mon.
Show: "Riviera Comedy Club" $15.25, 8:00 and 10:00 nightly/11:45 (Fri/Sat). Price includes one drink.

Sahara Hotel & Casino
2535 Las Vegas Blvd. South
Las Vegas, Nevada 89109
(702) 737-2111
Web Site: www.saharahotelandcasino.com

Toll-Free Number: (800) 634-6645
Reservation Number: (800) 634-6666
Rooms: 1,949 Price Range: $39-$109
Suites: 100 Price Range: $200
Restaurants: 5 (1 open 24 hours)
Buffets: B/L-$5.49/$8.49 (Sat/Sun) D-$6.49
Casino Size: 125,850 Square Feet
Other Games: SB, RB, P, PGP, CSP, LIR, B6, K
Casino Marketing: (800) 634-6645
Fun Book: Ask at cashier cage
Show: "The Rat Pack is Back" $34.95, 7:30 and 10:00(Tue/Sat)/8:00 (Wed-Fri/Sun), dark Mon.

Sam's Town Hotel & Gambling Hall
5111 Boulder Highway
Las Vegas, Nevada 89122
(702) 456-7777
Web Site: www.samstown.com

Toll-Free Number: (800) 897-8696
Reservation Number: (800) 634-6371
Rooms: 620 Price Range: $40-$70
Suites: 30 Price Range: $165-$270
Restaurants: 10 (1 open 24 hours)
Buffets: B-$3.99/$8.99 (Sun) L-$6.99
D-$8.99/$15.99 (Fri/Sat)
Casino Size: 118,000 Square Feet
Other Games: SB, RB, P, PGP, CSP,
LIR, K, BG
Casino Marketing: (702) 454-8126
Special Features: An indoor promenade with a free laser-light show called "sunset stampede" which is shown four times daily. 56-lane bowling center (open 24 hours). Two RV parks with 500 spaces and full hookups. Western wear retail store. Sports bar. 1,100-seat entertainment center. 18-theater movie complex. Child-care center. Video arcade.

Santa Fe Hotel & Casino
See North Las Vegas section

Showboat Hotel & Casino
2800 Fremont Street
Las Vegas, Nevada 89104
(702) 385-9123
Web Site: www.showboat-lv.com

Reservation Number: (800) 826-2800
Rooms: 480 Price Range: $39-$89
Suites: 5 Price Range: $149-$199
Restaurants: 5 (1 open 24 hours)
Buffets: B-$4.95/$6.95 (Sat/Sun) L-$5.95
D-$6.95/$7.95 (Sun)/$8.95 (Sat)
$11.95 (Wed/Thu/Fri)
Casino Size: 74,300 Square Feet
Other Games: SB, RB, PGP, LIR, K, BG
Casino Marketing: (800) 826-2800
Special Features: Casino has single-deck blackjack. 106-lane bowling center. 1,100-seat bingo hall is largest in Las Vegas. Mardi Gras Room has live entertainment daily.

Silver Saddle Saloon
2501 E.Charleston Boulevard
Las Vegas, Nevada 89104
(702) 474-2900

Restaurants: 1
Other Games: No Craps or roulette. Blackjack only played 4pm-4am (Fri)/9pm-4am (Sat)

Silverton Hotel Casino & RV Resort
3333 Blue Diamond Road
Las Vegas, Nevada 89139
(702) 263-7777
Web Site: www.silvertoncasino.com

Toll-Free Number: (800) 588-7711
Rooms: 292 Price Range: $29-$89
Suites: 8 Price Range: $150-$195
Restaurants: 5 (1 open 24 hours)
Buffets: B-$3.99 L-$6.49 D-$7.99/$9.99
(Wed/Thu/Sun)/$10.99 (Sat)/$13.49 (Fri)
Casino Size: 32,134 Square Feet
Other Games: PGP, LIR, K
Casino Marketing: (800) 588-7711
Fun Book: Given to slot club members
Senior Discount: If 55, or older, join Silver Seekers Club for 10% off room/$1off buffet
Special Features: 460-space RV park. Country/western lounge with free entertainment (Wed-Sun). 3 pools with water slides. 24-hour grocery store. Free shuttle to Strip.
Show: "Always...Patsy Cline" $27.50, 8:00 (Wed-Fri/Sun)/6:00 and 9:00 (Sat), dark Mon/Tue.

Slots-A-Fun
2890 Las Vegas Blvd. South
Las Vegas, Nevada 89109
(702) 794-3814

Restaurants: 1 Snack Bar
Casino Size: 16,733 Square Feet
Other Games: CSP, LIR
Casino Marketing: (702) 794-3842
Special Features: $1.25 for imported brands of bottled beer.

Sports World Casino
3049 Las Vegas Blvd. South
Las Vegas, Nevada 89109
(702) 796-1111

Restaurants: 1 Deli
Casino Size: 6,000 Square Feet
Other Games: No Craps

Free Things To See In Las Vegas!

The Fountains at Bellagio

The Fountains at Bellagio is one of the most ambitious water features ever conceived in terms of choreography, complexity and scale.

More than one thousand fountains dance in front of the hotel, creating a marvelous union of water, music and light. The display spans more than 1,000 feet, with water soaring as high as 240 feet in the air. The fountains are choreographed to music ranging from classical and operatic pieces to songs from Broadway shows.

Showtimes are approximately every 20 minutes from 3 p.m. to midnight on weekdays and from noon to midnight on weekends.

Stardust Resort & Casino
3000 Las Vegas Blvd. South
Las Vegas, Nevada 89109
(702) 732-6111
Web Site: www.stardustlv.com

Toll-Free Number: (800) 824-6033
Reservation Number: (800) 634-6757
Rooms: 2,340 Price Range: $45-$125
Suites: 161 Price Range: $150
Restaurants: 6 (1 open 24 hours)
Buffets: B-$6.95 L-$7.95 D-$10.95
Casino Size: 65,538 Square Feet
Other Games: SB, RB, B, MB, P, PGP, CSP, LIR, B6, K
Casino Marketing: (800) 824-6033
Fun Book: Ask at Logo shop
Show: "Wayne Newton" $49.95, 8:00 and 11:00 (Sat)/9:00 (Sun-Thu), dark Fri. Price includes one drink and tip.

Stratosphere Hotel & Casino
2000 Las Vegas Blvd. South
Las Vegas, Nevada 89117
(702) 380-7777
Web Site: www.stratlv.com

Reservation Number: (800) 99-TOWER
Rooms: 1,350 Price Range: $35-$129
Suites: 150 Price Range: $65-$219
Restaurants: 5 (1 open 24 hours)
Buffets: B-$5.49 L-$6.49 D-$8.99/$11.25 (Fri/Sun)
Casino Size: 51,800 Square Feet
Other Games: SB, RB, MB, P, PGP, CSP, LIR, B6, K
Casino Marketing: (800) 946-7771
Senior Discount: $1 off tower admission, 10% off room rate, if 55, or older
Special Features: America's tallest free standing observation tower at 1,149 feet (135 stories high). Indoor and outdoor observation decks. 2 thrill rides. 4 wedding chapels. 360-seat revolving restaurant. Retail shopping mall with 20 stores. Kid's Quest child care center. Children's video arcade.
Show: "American Superstars" $29.65/$24.15 children (5-12), 7:00 (Sun-Wed/Fri/Sat)/10:00 (Wed/Fri/Sat), dark Thur.
Show: "Viva Las Vegas" $11.00, 2:00 and 4:00 daily, dark Sun.

Sunset Station
See Henderson section

Texas Station
See North Las Vegas section

Treasure Island
3300 Las Vegas Blvd. South
Las Vegas, Nevada 89109
(702) 894-7111
Web Site: www.treasureislandlasvegas.com

Reservation Number: (800) 944-7444
Rooms: 2,688 Price Range: $49-$200
Suites: 212 Price Range: $130-$300
Restaurants: 8 (1 open 24 hours)
Buffets: B-$6.99/$11.50 (Sat/Sun)
L-$7.50 D-$11.50
Casino Size: 69,629 Square Feet
Other Games: SB, RB, B, MB, PG, PGP, CSP, LIR, B6, K
Casino Marketing: (800) 944-7444
Special Features: Front of hotel has lagoon with live-action sea battle between pirates and British sailors that take place every 90 minutes from 4pm until 10pm/11:30pm in summer. 18,000-square-foot arcade. Health spa and salon. Two wedding chapels.
Show: Cirque du Soleil's "Mystere" $75, 7:30/ 10:30 nightly, dark Mon/Tue.

Tropicana Resort & Casino
3801 Las Vegas Blvd. South
Las Vegas, Nevada 89109
(702) 739-2222
Web Site: www.tropicana.lv.com

Reservation Number: (800) 634-4000
Rooms: 1,877 Price Range: $39-$169
Suites: 115 Price Range: $250-$500
Restaurants: 7 (1 open 24 hours)
Buffets: B-$7.95/$10.95 (Sat/Sun) L-$7.95
D-$11.95/$14.95 (Wed)
Casino Size: 62,327 Square Feet
Other Games: SB, RB, MB, PG, PGP, CSP, LIR
Fun Book: Get coupons through player's club
Casino Marketing: (800) 521-8767
Senior Discount: Various, if 65, or older
Special Features: Five-acre tropical gardens and pool. Wedding chapel. Swim-up blackjack table (seasonal). Free wildlife nature walk.
Show: "The Best of the Folies Bergere" $44.95 (table)/$54.95 (booth), 7:30/10:00 nightly, dark Thurs. Must be 16 or older.
Show: "The Illusionary Magic of Rick Thomas" $16.95 (table)/$21.95 (booth), 2:00/4:00 daily, dark Fri.
Show: "Comedy Stop" comedy club $16.00, 8:00/10:30 nightly. Price includes two drinks, tax and tip.

Vacation Village Hotel/Casino
6711 Las Vegas Blvd. South
Las Vegas, Nevada 89119
(702) 897-1700

Reservation Number: (800) 658-5000
Rooms: 313 Price Range: $35-$65
Suites: 8 Price Range: $125-$225
Restaurants: 2 (2 open 24 hours)
Casino Size: 15,750 Square Feet
Other Games: SB, RB
Fun Book: Ask at promotions booth
Casino Marketing: (702) 897-1700
Special Features: Closest hotel to airport. Room-front parking. 2 pools. Frequent casino promotions.

The Venetian Resort Hotel Casino
3355 Las Vegas Blvd. South
Las Vegas, Nevada 89109
(702) 414-1000
Web Site: www.venetian.com

Reservation Number: (888) 283-6423
Suites: 3,036 Price Range: $129-$10,000
Restaurants: 15
Casino Size: 105,344 Square Feet
Other Games: SB, RB, B, MB, P, PG, PGP, CSP, LIR, B6, K
Special Features: Recreates the city of Venice, Italy with canals, gondoliers and famous landmarks including: Campanile Tower, St. Mark's Square, Doge's Palace and the Rialto Bridge. Retail shopping arcade with 90 stores and boutiques. Madame Tussaud's House of Wax museum.
Show: "Andre Philippe Gagnon" $45/$75/$92, 7:00 (Tue-Sun), dark Mon.

Western Hotel & Casino
899 East Fremont Street
Las Vegas, Nevada 89101
(702) 384-4620

Reservation Number: (800) 634-6703
Rooms: 116 Price Range: $21.88
Restaurants: 1 (open 24 hours)
Casino Size: 15,225
Other Games: K, BG, P, No Craps

Westward Ho Hotel & Casino
2900 Las Vegas Blvd. South
Las Vegas, Nevada 89109
(702) 731-2900
Web Site: www.westwardho.com

Reservation Number: (800) 634-6803
Rooms: 777 Price Range: $40-$75
Suites: 60 Price Range: $71-$111
Restaurants: 2 (both open 24 hours)
Buffets: B/L-$6.95 D-$8.95
Casino Size: 34,457 Square Feet
Other Games: CSP
Special Features: Free airport shuttle. Room-front parking. 7 pools and Jacuzzi.

Wild Wild West Casino
3330 West Tropicana Avenue
Las Vegas, Nevada 89103
(702) 736-8988

Reservation Number: (800) 634-3488
Rooms: 305 Price Range: $39-$59
Restaurants: 1 (open 24 hours)
Casino Size: 6,314 Square Feet
Other Games: SB
Casino Marketing: (800) 634-3488
Special Features: Affiliated with Station Casinos.

Laughlin

Map location: **#2** (on the Colorado River, 100 miles south of Las Vegas and directly across the river from Bullhead City, Arizona)

Laughlin is named after Don Laughlin, who owns the Riverside Hotel & Casino and originally settled there in 1966. The area offers many water sport activities on the Colorado River as well as at nearby Lake Mojave. If you are planning an overnight visit it is strongly recommended that you make advance reservations because if the casino hotels are fully booked there are no other rooms in the city. For Laughlin tourism information call: (800) 4-LAUGHLIN. You can also visit their web site at: http://www.visitlaughlin.com.

Here's information, as supplied by Nevada's State Gaming Control Board, showing the slot machine payback percentages for all of Laughlin's casinos for the fiscal year beginning July 1, 1999 and ending June 30, 2000:

Denomination	Payback %
5¢ Slots	90.53
10¢ Slots	89.69
25¢ Slots	94.43
$1 Slots	95.43
$1 Megabucks	88.77
$5 Slots	96.36
All Slots	94.29

These numbers reflect the percentage of money returned to the players on each denomination of machine. All electronic machines including slots, video poker and video keno are included in these numbers.

Optional games in the casino listings include: sports book (SB), race book (RB), baccarat (B), mini-baccarat (MB), poker (P), pai gow poker (PGP), Caribbean stud poker (CSP), let it ride (LIR), keno (K), big 6 wheel (B6) and bingo (BG).

Colorado Belle Hotel & Casino
2100 S. Casino Drive
Laughlin, Nevada 89029
(702) 298-4000
Web Site: www.coloradobelle.com

Reservation Number: (800) 458-9500
Rooms: 1,216 Price Range: $19-$51
Suites: 10 Price Range: $125-$175
Restaurants: 6 (1 open 24 hours)
Buffets: B-$4.49/$6.99 (Sun) L-$4.99
D-$6.49/$12.99 (Fri)
Casino Size: 40,258 Square Feet
Other Games: SB, P, PGP, CSP, LIR, K
Special Features: River view rooms. 2 swimming pools and spa.

Don Laughlin's
Riverside Resort Hotel & Casino
1650 S. Casino Drive
Laughlin, Nevada 89029
(702) 298-2535
Web Site: www.riversideresort.com

Reservation Number: (800) 227-3849
Rooms: 1,404 Price Range: $19-$79
Executive Rooms: 93 Price Range: $35-$109
Restaurants: 6 (2 open 24 hours)
Buffets: B-$3.99 L-$4.49
D-$5.99/$11.95 (Fri)
Casino Size: 80,763 Square Feet
Other Games: SB, RB, P, CSP, K, BG

Casino Marketing; (702) 298-2535 ext-5040
Senior Discount: 10% AARP room discount
Fun Book: Only given to hotel guests or groups and seniors, 55 or older.
Special Features: Executive rooms are slightly larger than standard rooms. 840-space RV park with full hookups. Six-plex cinema. Classic car exhibition hall. Boating and river cruises.

Edgewater Hotel Casino
2020 S. Casino Drive
Laughlin, Nevada 89029
(702) 298-2453
Web Site: www.edgewater-casino.com

Reservation Number: (800) 677-4837
Rooms: 1,420 Price Range: $19-$70
Suites: 23 Price Range: $75-$220
Restaurants: 4 (1 open 24 hours)
Buffets: B-$3.99 L-$5.49 D-$6.99/$8.99 (Fri/Sat)
Casino Size: 53,139 Square Feet
Other Games: SB, RB, P, PGP, CSP, LIR, K
Casino Marketing: (800) 289-8777
Senior Discount: Room discount, if 55, or older
Fun Book: Look in brochure racks at tourist information centers for coupon to redeem at cashier's cage.
Special Features: River view rooms. Pool and spa. Children's video arcade. Cruises aboard Edgewater Belle paddlewheel riverboat. Free airport shuttle. Nonsmoking and handicapped rooms. Lounge with free nightly entertainment.

Flamingo Hilton Laughlin
1900 S. Casino Drive
Laughlin, Nevada 89029
(702) 298-5111
Web Site: www.flamingo-laughlin.com

Reservation Number: (800) 292-3711
Rooms: 1,900 Price Range: $19-$99
Suites: 90 Price Range: $75-$350
Restaurants: 6 (1 open 24 hours)
Buffets: B-$3.99 L-$4.49 D-$6.99
Casino Size: 57,680 Square Feet
Other Games: SB, RB, MB, P, PGP, CSP, LIR, SIC, B6, K
Casino Marketing: (800) 662-6050
Fun Book: Inquire at Magic Club
Special Features: Most rooms have a river view. 3,100-seat outdoor amphitheater. Laughlin's only Burger King and Dairy Queen. Colorado River tour boat Celebration offers daily cruises. Banquet facilities.

Golden Nugget Laughlin
2300 S. Casino Drive
Laughlin, Nevada 89029
(702) 298-7111
Web Site: www.gnlaughlin.com

Reservation Number: (800) 237-1739
Rooms: 300 Price Range: $25-$65
Suites: 4 Price Range: $150
Restaurants: 4 (1 open 24 hours)
Buffets: B-$3.99 L-$4.99 D-$6.99
Casino Size: 32,600 Square Feet
Other Games: SB, RB, CSP, K
Casino Marketing: (800) 955-SLOT
Fun Book: Only offered to groups
Special Features: Atrium entrance with 2 water falls. Tarzan's lounge with nightly entertainment. Gift shop. 10% room discount for AAA and AARP members. Suites must be booked through the casino.

Harrah's Laughlin Casino & Hotel
2900 S. Casino Drive
Laughlin, Nevada 89029
(702) 298-4600
Web Site: www.harrahs.com

Reservation Number: (800) HARRAHS
Rooms: 1,656 Price Range: $24-$85
Suites: 39 Price Range: $140-$200
Restaurants: 5 (1 open 24 hours)
Buffets: B-$5.99 L-$7.99 D-$11.99
Casino Size: 47,000 Square Feet
Other Games: SB, RB, MB, PGP, LIR, K
Casino Marketing: (702) 298-4600
Fun Book: Only given to groups
Special Features: Separate nonsmoking casino. Only beach and health club in Laughlin. Covered parking. R/V plaza and convenience store.

Pioneer Hotel & Gambling Hall
2200 S. Casino Drive
Laughlin, Nevada 89029
(702) 298-2442
Web Site: www.santafecasino.com

Reservation Number: (800) 634-3469
Rooms: 395 Price Range: $23-$70
Suites: 20 Price Range: $80-$90
Restaurants: 2 (1 open 24 hours)
Buffets: B-$4.95 D-$6.95/$11.95 (Fri)
Casino Size: 19,500 Square Feet
Other Games: LIR, K
Casino Marketing: (800) 634-3469 ext. 4135

Ramada Express Hotel & Casino
2121 S. Casino Drive
Laughlin, Nevada 89029
(702) 298-4200
Web Site: www.ramadaexpress.com

Toll-Free Number: (800) 243-6846
Rooms: 1,501 Price Range: $21-$149
Suites: 55 Price Range: $69-$200
Restaurants: 5 (1 open 24 hours)
Buffets: B-$5.99 D-$7.99/$11.99
Casino Size: 52,000 Square Feet
Other Games: SB, RB, CSP, LIR, K
Casino Marketing: (800) 343-4533 and ask for slot club host
Fun Book: Given at slot club booth
Special Features: Victorian railroad station themed-hotel/casino with more than $1 million worth of railroad antiques and memorabilia. Free train rides on a replica 19th century steam train. Train-shaped swimming pool. Free airport shuttle. Nonsmoking rooms. 3 gift shops. Video arcade. Daily multimedia show "On the Wings of Eagles," a salute to American heroes (free). American Heroes museum.

Regency Casino
1950 Casino Way
Laughlin, Nevada 89029
(702) 298-2439

Restaurants: 1 (open 24 hours)
Casino Size: 5,000 Square Feet
Other Games: No Craps or Roulette

River Palms Resort Casino
2700 S. Casino Drive
Laughlin, Nevada 89029
(702) 298-2242
Web Site: www.rvrpalm.com

Reservation Number: (800) 835-7903
Rooms: 995 Price Range: $20-$55
Suites: 8 Price Range: $100-$300
Restaurants: 4 (1 open 24 hours)
Buffets: B-$3.00 L-$4.00 D-$6.90
Casino Size: 71,300 Square Feet
Other Games: SB, RB, P, PGP, CSP, LIR, B6, K, BG
Casino Marketing: (800) 835-7904 ext.-2206
Fun Book: Only given to hotel guests
Senior Discount: Get $1 buffet discount , if 55, or older.

Lovelock

Map Location: **#19** (92 miles N.E. of Reno on I-80)

Sturgeon's Casino
1420 Cornell Avenue
Lovelock, Nevada 89419
(775) 273-2971
Web Site: www.ramadainn.com

Toll-Free Number: (888) 234-6835
Rooms: 74 Price Range: $40-$69
Spa Rooms: 2 Price Range: $75-$100
Restaurants: 1 (open 24 hours)
Casino Size: 5,625 Square Feet
Other Games: No Craps or Roulette
Fun Book: Only given to hotel guests
Special Features: Hotel is affiliated with Ramada Inn. Room discount for AAA and AARP members.

McDermitt

Map Location: **#20** (Just S. of the Oregon border on Hwy. 95)

Say When
P.O. Box 375
McDermitt, Nevada 89421
(775) 532-8515

Restaurants: 1 (open 24 hours)
Casino Size: 5,940 Square Feet
Other Games: No Craps or Roulette

Mesquite

Map Location: **#21** (77 miles N.E. of Las Vegas on I-15 at the Arizona border)

Here's information, as supplied by Nevada's State Gaming Control Board, showing the slot machine payback percentages for all of the Mesquite area casinos for the fiscal year beginning July 1, 1999 and ending June 30, 2000:

Denomination	Payback %
5¢ Slots	92.78
10¢ Slots	92.13
25¢ Slots	95.05
$1 Slots	95.65
$1 Megabucks	91.79
$5 Slots	95.21
All Slots	94.67

These numbers reflect the percentage of money returned on each denomination of machine and encompass all electronic machines including slots, video poker and video keno.

Casablanca Resort & Casino
950 W. Mesquite Boulevard
Mesquite, Nevada 89027
(702) 346-7259
Web Site: www.casablancaresort.com

Reservation Number: (800) 459-7529
Rooms: 500 Price Range: $39-$99
Suites: 18 Price Range: $99-$249
Restaurants: 3 (1 open 24 hours)
Buffets: B-$5.25 L-$6.25
D-$8.99/$11.99 (Fri/Sat)
Casino Size: 27,775 Square Feet
Other Games: SB, RB, P, PGP, LIR, K
Fun Book: Given to hotel guests
Senior Discount: Various discounts and age requirements.
Special Features: 18-hole golf course. 3 lighted tennis courts. Lagoon swimming pool with waterfall and slide. Full-service health spa offering massages, body care, facials and mud treatments. 500-seat showroom.

Eureka Casino & Hotel
275 Mesa Boulevard
Mesquite, Nevada 89027
(702) 346-4600

Reservation Number: (800) 346-4611
Rooms: 182 Price Range: $30-$49
Suites: 18 Price Range: $70-$100
Restaurants: 3 (1 open 24 hours)
Buffets: B-$4.95 L-$6.95 D-$7.95
Casino Size: 31,100 Square Feet
Other Games: SB, RB, P, BG
Fun book: Given to hotel guests and new slot club members.

Si Redd's Oasis Resort Hotel & Casino
P.O. Box 360
Mesquite, Nevada 89024
(702) 346-5232
Web Site: www.siredd.com/oasis

Reservation Number: (800) 621-0187
Rooms: 1,000 Price Range: $29-$69
Suites: 100 Price Range: $119-$139
Restaurants: 4 (1 open 24 hours)
Buffets: B-$4.99/$7.99 (Sun) L-$5.99
D-$7.99
Casino Size: 33,557 Square Feet
Other Games: SB, RB, P, PGP, LIR, K
Fun Book: Only given to hotel guests
Special Features: Three 18-hole golf courses. 5 swimming pools. Wagon trail rides. Video arcade. Shotgun sports club. RV park. Health club and spa. Weekly blackjack and slot tournaments.

Stateline Casino
490 W. Mesquite Boulevard
Mesquite, Nevada 89027
(702) 346-5752

Room Reservation: (775) 346-5752
Rooms: 11 Price Range: $27.25-$38.15
Restaurants: 1 (open 24 hours)
Casino Size: 4,500 Square Feet
Other Games: No Craps or Roulette
Special features: No room reservations taken. Rooms are available on a first come, first served basis beginning at 11am.

Virgin River Hotel & Casino
100 Pioneer Boulevard
Mesquite, Nevada 89027
(702) 346-7777
Web Site: www.virginriver.com

Reservation Number: (800) 346-7721
Rooms: 720 Price Range: $22-$100
Suites: 3 Price Range: $150-$250
Restaurants: 2 (1 open 24 hours)
Buffets: B-$4.49 L-$5.49
D-$7.99/$9.99 (Tue/Fri)
Casino Size: 36,000 Square Feet
Other Games: SB, RB, P, K, BG
Fun Book: Given to hotel guests.
Special Features: 24-lane bowling center. 4 movie theaters. Lagoon pool with a waterfall and slide. Arcade.

Minden

Map Location: **#15** (42 miles S. of Reno on Hwy. 395)

Carson Valley Inn
1627 Highway 395 N.
Minden, Nevada 89423
(775) 782-9711
Web Site: www.cvinn.com

Reservation Number: (800) 321-6983
Rooms: 220 Price Range: $39-$99
Suites: 9 Price Range: $119-$169
Restaurants: 3 (1 open 24 hours)
Casino Size: 11,500 Square Feet
Other Games: SB, RB, K
Casino Marketing: (775) 783-7711
Senior Discount: If 50, or older, ask for Senior Inn Club card to get room, shop and restaurant discounts
Fun Book: Given to all motor lodge, hotel and RV park guests
Special Features: 60-space RV park with full hookups and laundry. 24-hour convenience store. Live entertainment. Wedding chapel. Golf, hunting and ski packages offered. Supervised children's recreation center.

N. Las Vegas

Map Location: **#22** (5 miles N.E. of the Las Vegas Strip on Las Vegas Blvd. N.)

Bighorn Casino
3016 E. Lake Mead Boulevard
N. Las Vegas, Nevada 89030
(702) 642-1940

Restaurants: 1 (open 24 hours)
Casino Size: 3,300 Square Feet
Other Games: No Craps or Roulette

Fiesta Casino Hotel
2400 N. Rancho Drive
Las Vegas, Nevada 89130
(702) 631-7000
Web Site: www.fiestacasinohotel.com

Reservation Number: (800) 731-7333
Rooms: 100 Price Range: $29-$150
Suites: 2 Price Range: $59-$300
Restaurants: 7 (1 open 24 hours)
Buffets: B-$4.99/$8.99 (Sun) L-$6.49
D-$8.99/$11.99 (Mon)/$13.99 (Wed)/
$10.99 (Fri)
Casino Size: 47,086 Square Feet
Casino Marketing: (800) 731-7333
Other Games: SB, RB, PGP, LIR, K, BG
Special Features: Weekly blackjack and video poker tournaments. Buffet offers 12 separate eating stations. Drive-through sports/race book. Coffee bar.

Jerry's Nugget
1821 Las Vegas Blvd. North
N. Las Vegas, Nevada 89030
(702) 399-3000
Web Site: www.jerrysnugget.com

Restaurants: 2 (1 open 24 hours)
Casino Size: 33,101 Square Feet
Other Games: SB, RB, K, BG
Special Features: European Bakery. Live entertainment. Live entertainment and dancing at Royals Street Theater.

Mahoney's Silver Nugget
2140 Las Vegas Blvd. North
N. Las Vegas, Nevada 89030
(702) 399-1111
Web Site: www.mahoneyscasino.com

Restaurants: 1 (open 24 hours)
Casino Size: 18,100 Square Feet
Other Games: SB, K, BG, No Craps or Roulette
Special Features: 24-lane bowling center.

Opera House Saloon & Casino
2542 Las Vegas Blvd. North
N. Las Vegas, Nevada 89030
(702) 649-8801

Restaurants: 1 (open 24 hours)
Casino Size: 4,420 Square Feet
Other Games: K, No Craps or Roulette

Ramada Inn Speedway Casino
3227 Civic Center Drive
N. Las Vegas, Nevada 89030
(702) 399-3297
Web Site: www.ramada.com

Reservation Number: (877) 333-9291
Rooms: 115 Price Range: $49-$89
Suites: 3 Price Range: $109-$159
Restaurants: 1 (open 24 hours)
Casino Size: 4,420 Square Feet
Other Games: RB, SB, No Craps
Special Features: Closest hotel/casino to Las Vegas Motor Speedway.

The Regent Las Vegas
221 N. Rampart Boulevard
Las Vegas, Nevada 89128
(702) 869-7777
Web Site: www.regentlasvegas.com

Toll-Free Number: (877) 869-8777
Rooms: 216 Price Range: $109-$400
Suites: 70 Price Range: $600-$2,100
Restaurants: 11 (1 open 24 hours)
Buffets: B-$5.95/$19.95 (Sun) L-$9.95
D-$13.95
Casino Size: 50,000 Square Feet
Other Games: SB, RB, B, MB, PGP, LIR, BG
Senior Discount: 25% off dinner buffet, if 55, or older and member of slot club
Special Features: Golf course. Spa.

The Poker Palace
2757 Las Vegas Blvd. North
N. Las Vegas, Nevada 89030
(702) 649-3799

Restaurants: 1 (open 24 hours)
Casino Size: 14,350 Square Feet
Other Games: SB, RB, P, BG, No Craps or Roulette

Suncoast Hotel and Casino
9090 Alta Drive
Las Vegas, Nevada 89145
(702) 636-7111
Web Site: www.suncoastcasino.com

Toll-Free Number: (877) 677-7111
Rooms: 352 Price Range: $49-$99
Suites: 40 Price Range: Not set at press time
Restaurants: 6 (1 open 24 hours)
Buffets: Prices not set at press time
Casino Size: 50,000 Square Feet
Other Games: SB, RB, B, PGP, BG
Special Features: Child care center. Video arcade. 64-lane bowling center. Affiliated with Gold Coast, Barbary Coast and Orleans Casinos and expected to provide shuttle service to the Strip in Las Vegas.

Santa Fe Hotel & Casino
4949 North Rancho Drive
N. Las Vegas, Nevada 89130
(702) 658-4900
Web Site: www.santafecasino.com

Reservation Number: (800) 872-6823
Rooms: 200 Price Range: $49-$89
Restaurants: 5 (1 open 24 hours)
Buffets: B-$4.49/$7.50 (Sun) L-$5.49
D-$8.49/$12.50 (Thu)
Casino Size: 77,882 Square Feet
Other Games: SB, RB, P, PGP, LIR, K, BG
Casino Marketing: (702) 658-4950
Fun Book: Only given to hotel guests
Special Features: 17,000-square-foot ice arena. 60-lane bowling center open 24 hours. 2 lounges with live entertainment. On-property nursery for children 6 months to 8 years open 9am-11pm. Affiliated with Station Casinos.

Texas Station
2101 Texas Star Lane
N. Las Vegas, Nevada 89102
(702) 631-1000
Web Site: www.texasstation.com

Reservation Number: (800) 654-8888
Rooms: 200 Price Range: $49-$129
Suites: 2 Price Range: $259-$329
Restaurants: 7 (1 open 24 hours)
Buffets: B-$3.99/$7.99 (Sat/Sun)
L-$6.49 D-$8.99/$10.99 (Fri/Sat)
Casino Size: 109,000 Square Feet
Other Games: SB, RB, MB, P,
PGP, LIR, K, BG
Casino Marketing: (800) 654-8804
Special Features: 18 movie theaters. Western dance hall and lounge. Kids quest. Live entertainment in Armadillo Lounge.

Pahrump

Map Location: **#23** (59 miles W. of Las Vegas on Hwy. 160)

Mountain View Recreation Center
1750 S. Pahrump Valley Boulevard
Pahrump, Nevada 89048
(775) 727-7777

Restaurants: 1 (1 open 24 hours)
Buffets: B-$2.95 L-$3.95/$4.95 (Sat/Sun)
D-$5.95/$7.95 (Fri)
Casino Size: 25,800 Square Feet
Other Games: No Craps or Roulette
Senior Discount: 10% off Sat-Thu dinner buffets, if 55, or older

Saddle West Hotel/Casino & RV Park
1220 S. Highway 160
Pahrump, Nevada 89048
(775) 727-5953
Web Site: www.saddlewest.com

Reservation Number: (800) GEDDY-UP
Rooms: 110 Price Range: $37-$55
Suites: 9 Price Range: $60-$109
Restaurants: 1 (1 open 24 hours)
Buffets: B-$2.99/$5.99 (Sat/Sun) L-$3.99
D-$4.99/$6.99 (Fri)
Casino Size: 18,757 Square Feet
Other Games: SB, RB, P, K, BG
Senior Discount: Room discount for AARP and AAA members.

Terrible's Lakeside Casino & RV Park
5870 S. Homestead Road
Pahrump, Nevada 89048
(775) 751-7770
Web Site: terriblespahrump.com

Toll Free Number: (888) 558-LAKE
Restaurants: 1
Buffets: B-$3.95 L-$4.95 D-$5.95
Casino Size: 8,300 Square Feet
Other Games: SB, BG, No Roulette
Special Features: 160-space RV park. General store and Chevron gas station.

Terrible's Town
771 Frontage Road
Pahrump, Nevada 89048
(775) 751-7777
Web Site: www.terriblespahrump.com

Toll Free Number: (888) 837-7425
Restaurants: 1
Casino Size: 10,100 Square Feet
Other Games: SB, RB, BG
Special Features: Blimpie's, Pizza Hut and Baskin-Robbins. General store and gas station.

Primm

Map Location: **#6** (25 miles S.W. of Las Vegas on I-15; 9 miles from the California border)

Buffalo Bill's Resort & Casino
I-15 South
Primm, Nevada 89019
(702) 382-1212
Web Site: www.primadonna.com

Toll-Free Number: (800) FUN-STOP
Rooms: 1,242 Price Range: $20-$55
Suites: 15 Price Range: $195
Restaurants: 5 (1 open 24 hours)
Buffets: B-$5.63 L-$6.70 D-$7.45
Casino Size: 62,130 Square Feet
Other Games: SB, RB, MB, P, PGP,
CSP, LIR, B6, K, BG
Fun Book: Look for brochure in rack at
tourist welcome centers
Special Features: Ghost town attraction. Roller coaster. Two motion-simulator theaters. Flume Ride. 3,000-foot rainbow arch. Buffalo-shaped swimming pool. 2 water slides. Movie theater. Video arcade. Western-style train shuttle connects to Whiskey Pete's and Primm Valley.

Primm Valley Resort & Casino
I-15 South
Primm, Nevada 89019
(702) 382-1212
Web Site: www.primadonna.com

Reservation Number: (800) FUN-STOP
Rooms: 661 Price Range: $25-$65
Suites: 4 Price Range: $195
Restaurants: 3 (1 open 24 hours)
Buffets: B-$5.63 L-$6.70 D-$7.45
Casino Size: 38,049 Square Feet
Other Games: SB, RB, MB, PGP, CSP, LIR, K
Fun Book: Look for brochure in rack at tourist welcome centers that can be redeemed at cashier cage
Special Features: RV park with 199 spaces and full hookups. Free rides on 100-foot-tall ferris wheel and indoor merry-go-round. 8-lane bowling alley. Video arcade. Free monorail service to Whiskey Pete's Casino Hotel.

Whiskey Pete's Hotel & Casino
I-15 South
Primm, Nevada 89019
(702) 382-1212
Web Site: www.primadonna.com

Reservation Number: (800) FUN-STOP
Rooms: 777 Price Range: $18-$49
Suites: 4 Price Range: $195
Restaurants: 4 (1 open 24 hours)
Buffets: B-$5.31 L-$6.38 D-$6.97
Casino Size: 36,400 Square Feet
Other Games: SB, RB, PGP, CSP, LIR, K
Fun Book: Look for brochure in rack at tourist welcome centers that can be redeemed at cashier cage
Special Features: Children's entertainment center. Pool with water slide. Fully restored Dutch Schultz gangster car, plus Bonnie and Clyde's "Death Car" are on display. Free monorail service to Primm Valley Resort & Casino.

Reno

Map Location: **#4** (near the California border, 58 miles N.E. of Lake Tahoe and 32 miles N. of Carson City).

Reno may be best known for its neon arch on Virginia Street which welcomes visitors to "The Biggest Little City in the World." The current arch is actually the fourth one since the original arch was built in 1927. The area also houses the nation's largest car collection at the National Automobile Museum. For Reno information call the Reno/Sparks Convention & Visitors Authority at (800) FOR-RENO.

Here's information, as supplied by Nevada's State Gaming Control Board, showing the slot machine payback percentages for all of the Reno area casinos for the fiscal year beginning July 1, 1999 and ending June 30, 2000:

Denomination	Payback %
5¢ Slots	93.27
10¢ Slots	94.89
25¢ Slots	94.25
$1 Slots	95.95
$1 Megabucks	90.92
$5 Slots	96.79
All Slots	95.04

These numbers reflect the percentage of money returned on each denomination of machine and encompass all electronic machines including slots, video poker and video keno. For the 5¢ slot player Reno's casinos offer slightly better returns than the Las Vegas Strip casinos and are among the highest in the state in that denomination.

Optional games in the casino listings include: sports book (SB), race book (RB), baccarat (B), mini-baccarat (MB), pai gow (PG), poker (P), pai gow poker (PGP), Caribbean stud poker (CSP), let it ride (LIR), red dog (RD), big 6 wheel (B6), keno (K) and bingo (BG).

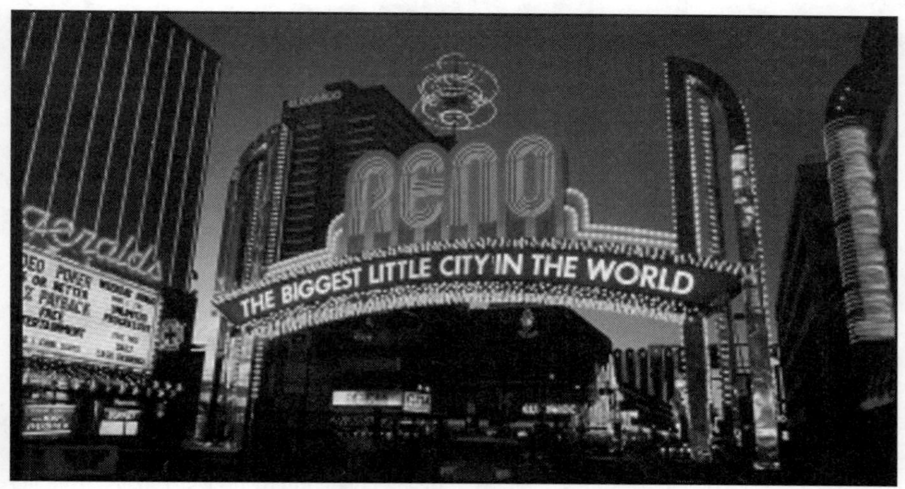

The arch in downtown Reno that welcomes visitors to "The Biggest Little City in the World" is the city's most famous landmark.

Atlantis Casino Resort
3800 S. Virginia Street
Reno, Nevada 89502
(775) 825-4700
Web Site: www.atlantiscasino.com

Reservation Number: (800) 723-6500
Rooms: 590 Price Range: $59-$169
Suites: 26 Price Range: $125-$350
Restaurants: 7 (1 open 24 hours)
Buffets: B-$6.99/$8.99 (Sat)/$13.99 (Sun) L-$7.99/$8.99 (Sat) D-$10.99/$19.99 (Fri/Sat)
Casino Size: 32,000 Square Feet
Other Games: SB, RB, MB, PGP, LIR, K
Casino Marketing: (800) 994-5900
Senior Discount: 10% off buffet, plus various discounts, if 55, or older
Special Features: Exotic island theme casino with waterfalls, thatched huts and tropical gardens. Indoor and outdoor heated pool and spa.

Bonanza Casino
4720 N. Virginia Street
Reno, Nevada 89503
(775) 323-2724
Web Site: www.bonanzacasino.com

Restaurants: 2 (1 open 24 hours)
Buffets: B-$6.95 L-$5.95 D-$8.95
Casino Size: 12,583 Square Feet
Other Games: SB, K, No Roulette
Senior Discount: 10% off at restaurant if 60, or older
Fun Book: Show out-of-town ID

Bordertown
19575 Highway 395
N. Reno, Nevada 89506
(775) 972-1309

Toll-Free Number: (800) 443-4383
Restaurants: 1
Casino Size: 4,650 Square Feet
Other Games: No Craps or Roulette
Fun Book: Ask at cashier's cage

Circus Circus Hotel Casino/Reno
500 N. Sierra Street
Reno, Nevada 89503
(775) 329-0711
Web Site: www.circusreno.com

Reservation Number: (800) 648-5010
Rooms: 1,464 Price Range: $39-$119
Suites: 108 Price Range: $99-$450
Restaurants: 6 (1 open 24 hours)
Buffets: B-$5.49 L-$6.49 D-$8.99/$12.99 (Fri-Sat)
Casino Size: 60,180 Square Feet
Other Games: SB, RB, MB, P, PGP, CSP, LIR, K
Casino Marketing: (800) 262-8705
Fun Book: Only given to hotel guests
Senior Discount: AARP members get $5 off room rates Sun-Thu during non-holiday and non-promotional days.
Special Features: Free live circus acts. Midway with carnival games. Video arcade. 24-hour gift shop/liquor store.

Club Cal-Neva/Virginian Hotel and Casino
38 E. Second Street
Reno, Nevada 89505
(775) 323-1046
Web Site: www.clubcalneva.com

Toll-Free Number (877) 777-7303
Rooms: 420 Price Range: $39-$119
Suites: 9 Price Range: $99-$450
Restaurants: 5 (1 open 24 hours)
Buffets: B-$3.95/$4.95 (Sat/Sun)
L-$4.95/$5.95 (Sat/Sun)
Casino Size: 43,250 Square Feet
Other Games: SB, RB, P, PGP, CSP, LIR, K
Casino Marketing: (775) 323-1046 ext.-3266
Fun Book: Ask at cashier's cage
Senior Discount: Show ID at cage to obtain discount coupons.

Comstock Hotel Casino
200 W. Second Street
Reno, Nevada 89501
(775) 329-1880
Web Site: www.thecomstock.com

Reservation Number: (800) COM-STOC
Rooms: 304 Price Range: $36-$100
Suites: 6 Price Range: $160-$275
Restaurants: 3 (1 open 24 hours)
Casino Size: 15,900 Square Feet
Casino Marketing: (800) COM-STOC
Fun Book: Only given to hotel guests
Other Games: SB, K
Special Features: 1800's atmosphere with rooms in Victorian decor. Pool, Jacuzzi, sauna and exercise facilities. Video arcade. Gift shop.

Diamond's Casino at Holiday Inn
1010 E. 6th Street
Reno, Nevada 89512
(775) 323-4183

Reservation Number: (800) 648-4877
Rooms: 280 Price Range: $69-$109
Suites: 6 Price Range: $125-$175
Restaurants: 2 (1 open 24 hours)
Casino Size: 10,000 Square Feet
Other Games: SB, RB, No Roulette
Fun Book: Only given to hotel guests
Special Features: Located in the Holiday Inn. Free airport and downtown shuttle.

Eldorado Hotel/Casino
345 N. Virginia Street
Reno, Nevada 89501
(775) 786-5700
Web Site: www.eldoradoreno.com

Reservation Number: (800) 648-5966
Rooms: 817 Price Range: $49-$119
Suites: 127 Price Range: $110-$750
Restaurants: 9 (1 open 24 hours)
Buffets: B-$5.89/$7.99 (Sat)/$8.99 (Sun)
L-$6.96 D-$9.99/$18.99 (Fri)/$13.99 (Sat)
Casino Size: 81,500 Square Feet
Other Games: SB, RB, MB, PG, P, PGP, CSP, LIR, B6, K
Casino Marketing: (800) 648-4597
Special Features: In-house coffee roasting. Pasta shop. Micro brewery featuring 7 made-on-premises micro brews. Bakery. Butcher shop. Gelato factory. Video arcade. Pool and Jacuzzi. 580-seat headliner showroom.

Fitzgeralds Casino/Hotel - Reno
255 N. Virginia Street
Reno, Nevada 89504
(775) 785-3300
Web Site: www.fitzgeralds.com

Toll-Free Number: (800) 535-LUCK
Room Reservations: (800) 648-5022
Rooms: 351 Price Range: $38-$150
Suites: 8 Price Range: $78-$240
Restaurants: 3 (1 open 24 hours)
Buffets: B-$4.99/$5.99 (Sat/Sun)
L-$5.99/$6.99 (Sat/Sun)
D-$7.77/$8.77 (Sat/Sun)
Casino Size: 26,380 Square Feet
Other Games: SB, RB, LIR, RD, K
Casino Marketing: (775) 785-3421
Special Features: Irish-themed casino. Room discount for AAA members.

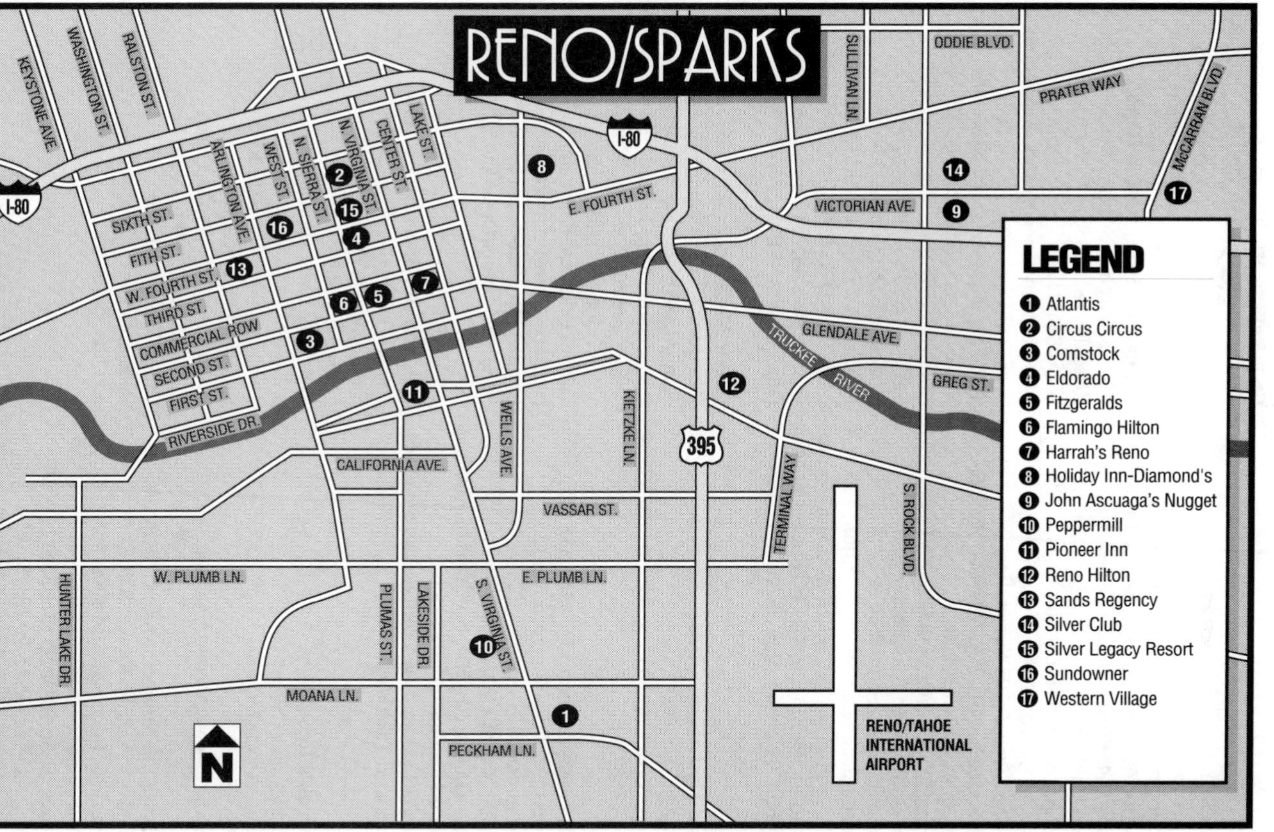
RENO/SPARKS
LEGEND
1 Atlantis
2 Circus Circus
3 Comstock
4 Eldorado
5 Fitzgeralds
6 Flamingo Hilton
7 Harrah's Reno
8 Holiday Inn-Diamond's
9 John Ascuaga's Nugget
10 Peppermill
11 Pioneer Inn
12 Reno Hilton
13 Sands Regency
14 Silver Club
15 Silver Legacy Resort
16 Sundowner
17 Western Village
KEYSTONE AVE.
WASHINGTON ST.
RALSTON ST.
I-80
SIXTH ST.
FITH ST.
W. FOURTH ST.
THIRD ST.
COMMERCIAL ROW
SECOND ST.
FIRST ST.
RIVERSIDE DR.
ARLINGTON AVE.
WEST ST.
N. SIERRA ST.
N. VIRGINIA ST.
CENTER ST.
LAKE ST.
E. FOURTH ST.
CALIFORNIA AVE.
WELLS AVE.
KIETZKE LN.
395
VASSAR ST.
W. PLUMB LN.
E. PLUMB LN.
HUNTER LAKE DR.
PLUMAS ST.
LAKESIDE DR.
S. VIRGINIA ST.
MOANA LN.
PECKHAM LN.
N
SULLIVAN LN.
ODDIE BLVD.
PRATER WAY
McCARRAN BLVD.
VICTORIAN AVE.
GLENDALE AVE.
TRUCKEE RIVER
GREG ST.
TERMINAL WAY
S. ROCK BLVD.
RENO/TAHOE INTERNATIONAL AIRPORT

Flamingo Hilton Reno
255 N. Sierra Street
Reno, Nevada 89501
(775) 322-1111
Web Site: www.flamingoreno.com

Reservation Number: (800) 648-4882
Rooms: 604 Price Range: $45-$219
Suites: 64 Price Range: $150-$245
Restaurants: 6
Buffets: B-S6.99/$16.95 (Sun) L-$7.99 D-$10.99
Casino Size: 50,794 Square Feet
Other Games: SB, RB, MB, PG, P, PGP, CSP, LIR, K
Casino Marketing: (800) 950-2WIN
Fun Book: Go to Club Flamingo
Senior Discount: Join "Silver Edition" Club
Special Features: Top of the Hilton - Reno's only rooftop restaurant. Nonsmoking rooms in hotel. Benihana Steak House. Baskin Robbins ice cream shop. Pizza Hut Express.

Gold Dust West
444 Vine Street
Reno, Nevada 89503
(775) 323-2211

Toll-Free Number: (800) 438-9378
Rooms: 31 Price Range: $30-$125
Restaurants: 1
Casino Size: 12,000 Square Feet
Other Games: SB, RB, No Craps or Roulette
Senior Discount: Join 50+ Club
Special Features: Two-for-one entrees in restaurant on Tuesdays.

Harrah's Reno
219 N. Center Street
Reno, Nevada 89501
(775) 786-3232
Web Site: www.harrahsreno.com

Reservation Number: (800) HARRAHS
Rooms: 456 Price Range: $39-$139
Suites: 60 Price Range: $69-$185
Restaurants: 7 (1 open 24 hours)
Buffets: B-$6.50/$8.99 (Sat/Sun) L-$6.99 D-$8.99/$15.99 (Fri/Sat)
Casino Size: 54,500 Square Feet
Other Games: SB, RB, B, MB, PG, PGP, LIR, K
Casino Marketing: (800) 423-1121
Special Features: Fully equipped health club. Complimentary airport shuttle and cable TV movies. Planet Hollywood restaurant. Some rooms are at world's largest Hampton Inn which is connected to Harrah's. Free airport shuttle.

Peppermill Hotel Casino Reno
2707 S. Virginia Street
Reno, Nevada 89502
(775) 826-2121
Web Site: www.peppermillcasinos.com

Toll-Free Number: (800) 648-6992
Reservation Number: (800) 282-2444
Rooms: 1,070 Price Range: $59-$130
Suites: 185 Price Range: $99-$400
Restaurants: 6 (1 open 24 hours)
Buffets: B-$7.99/$12.99 (Sat)/$15.95 (Sun) L-$9.99 D-$14.99/$24.99 (Fri)/$22.99 (Sat)
Casino Size: 44,751 Square Feet
Other Games: SB, B, PG, P, PGP, CSP, LIR, K
Casino Marketing: (800) 648-5555
Fun Book: Only given to hotel guests
Senior Discount: 25% discount on breakfast buffet Mon-Fri and 10% on other meals and some shows, if 55, or older, with slot card and 55 sticker.
Special Features: Free valet parking. Complimentary airport shuttle. 24-hour gift shop. Health club. Year-round heated pool with waterfall and computer-driven wildlife show.

Ramada Inn Speakeasy Casino
200 E 6th Street
Reno, Nevada 89501
(775) 329-7406
Web Site: www.ramada.com

Toll-Free Number: (888) RENO-777
Rooms: 224 Price Range: $29-$179
Restaurants: 1 (open 24 hours)
Casino Size: 12,000 Square Feet
Other Games: SB, RB
Special Features: Free shuttle to airport, train and bus stations.

The Best Places To Play in Reno/Tahoe

Roulette - The best roulette game in the Reno/Tahoe area can be found at Club Cal-Neva in downtown Reno which offers a single-zero roulette wheel. Single-zero roulette has only a 2.70% edge as compared to the usual 5.26% edge on a double-zero roulette wheel. Club Cal-Neva has three roulette wheels in the casino but only one of them is single-zero. The minimum bet is $2.

Craps - Almost all Reno-Tahoe area casino offer double odds on their craps games. The casinos offering the highest odds are the Sands Regency in Reno and the Lakeside Inn in Lake Tahoe which both offer 10 times odds. Next best is Club Cal-Neva in downtown Reno which allows triple odds. For lower limit players quarter craps games are offered at the Bonanza in Reno and Pinon Plaza (only on Friday and Saturday nights) in Carson City.

Blackjack - There's good news and bad news for blackjack players in Northern Nevada. The good news is that there is an abundance of single-deck and double-deck games available. The bad news though is that unlike Las Vegas, where most Strip-area casinos stand on soft 17 in their blackjack games, all casinos in the Reno/Tahoe area hit soft 17 on their games. This results in a slightly higher advantage (.20%) for the casinos. Some casinos may also restrict your double-downs to two-card totals of 9, 10 or 11 only. The following recommendations apply to basic strategy players.

For single-deck players the best game is at the Lakeside Inn on the south shore of Lake Tahoe which has these rules: double down on any first two cards, split any pair, resplit any pair (including aces) and double after splitting. The casino edge in this game is .03%.

Next best is the Alamo Travel Center in Sparks which has similar rules to the Lakeside Inn, except they won't allow you resplit aces, but they do allow late surrender and they will also count a Six-Card Charlie as an automatic winner. The casino edge in this game is .10%.

Following those two is the game at the Sundowner where they will only allow you to double down on first-two-card-totals of 9, 10 or 11 but they will give you a "push" if your cards total 21 and the dealer has a blackjack with an ace in the hole. The casino edge in this game is .15%.

Next best are nine casinos that offer single-deck with the basic Northern Nevada rules: double down on any first two cards, split any pair and resplit any pair (except aces): Crystal Bay Club, Baldini's, Peppermill, Atlantis, Ascuaga's Nugget, Western Village, Boomtown and the Silver Club. The casino edge here is .18%.

The Reno Hilton is the best place to play double-deck blackjack. Their two-deck game has the following rules: double down on any first two cards, split any pair, resplit any pair (except aces) and double down after split. This works out to a casino edge of .40%

Next best are four casinos in Reno that offer those same basic rules, except for doubling after splitting: Silver Legacy, Bonanza, Eldorado and Club Cal-Neva. John Ascuaga's Nugget in Sparks also offers the same game. The casino advantage in this game is .53%.

For six-deck shoe games the best place to play is the Silver Legacy which offers the following rules (which are similar to the Las Vegas Club in downtown Vegas): double down on any number of cards, split any pair, resplit any pair (except aces) and double down after splitting on any number of cards. The casino edge in this game is .39%.

The next best game, with an edge of .46%, can be found at Caesars Tahoe which has these rules: double down on any two cards, split any pair, resplit any pair (including aces), double allowed after split and late surrender. A similar game, with the exception of surrender, is offered at Ascuaga's Nugget in Sparks and the Lakeside Inn in south Lake Tahoe. The casino edge in this game is .56%.

If you take away resplitting of aces from the above Nugget game you have a game with a casino edge of .63% that's offered in Reno at the Flamingo Hilton, Reno Hilton and Circus Circus. It's also offered in Lake Tahoe at Harrah's, Horizon, Bill's and Harvey's.

Video Poker - Smart video poker players know that the three best varieties of machines to look for are: 9/6 Jacks or Better, 10/7 Double Bonus and full-pay Deuces Wild. By only playing these three kinds of machines, playing the maximum coin and using perfect strategy you can achieve, theoretically, the following payback percentages: 99.54% on 9/6 Jacks or Better, 100.17% on 10/7 Double Bonus and 100.76% on full-pay Deuces Wild.

Fortunately, excellent video poker opportunities are available in Northern Nevada with quarter 9/6 Jacks or Better games available in various denominations at almost every casino. A few of those casinos even offer a progressive jackpot for the royal.

10/7 Double Bonus (some with progressives) in various denominations is offered in both single and multi-play forms at: Atlantis, Club Cal-Neva, Eldorado, Fitzgeralds and Western Village in Reno and Harrah's and Harvey's in Lake Tahoe.

Full-pay Deuces Wild is offered in quarter denominations at Circus-Circus, Peppermill, Reno Hilton, and the Silver Legacy in Reno, as well as at Harrah's in Lake Tahoe.

Slots - For slot players it pays to play where the machines are set to return the most. According to the Nevada Gaming Control Board, for the fiscal year ending June 30, 2000 the average north Lake Tahoe slot machine returned 94.50% while the average south Lake Tahoe machine returned 95.01%. In Reno the average return was 95.04% and the highest return of all was 95.42% in Sparks. Additionally, Sparks seems to be an especially good spot for low limit players because the city's nickel and dime machines had the had the highest returns in the state. It was 94.98% for nickels and 95.81% for dimes.

Reno Hilton
2500 E. Second Street
Reno, Nevada 89595
(775) 789-2000
Web Site: www.renohilton.com

Reservation Number: (800) 648-5080
Rooms: 1,847 Price Range: $50-$200
Suites: 154 Price Range: $275-$875
Restaurants: 10 (1 open 24 hours)
Buffets: B-$6.49 L-$6.99 D-$10.99
Casino Size: 114,600 Square Feet
Other Games: SB, RB, B, PG, P, PGP, LIR, B6, K
Casino Marketing: (775) 789-2362
Fun Book: Only given to hotel guests
Special Features: Largest hotel in Reno. Free valet parking. 2 movie theaters. 265-space RV park. 50-lane bowling center. Health club. Shopping mall. 5 indoor and 3 outdoor tennis courts. Family amusement center. Aqua golf driving range. Nightclub.

The Sands Regency Hotel Casino
345 North Arlington Avenue
Reno, Nevada 89501
(775) 348-2200
Web Site: www.sandsregency.com

Reservation Number: (800) 648-3553
Rooms: 911 Price Range: $39-$89
Suites: 27 Price Range: $89-$375
Restaurants: 9 (1 open 24 hours)
Buffets: B-$4.99
Casino Size: 27,000 Square Feet
Other Games: SB, PGP, LIR, K, BG
Casino Marketing: (775) 348-2200
Fun Book: Show out-of-town ID at Redemption Center
Special Features: Health club and spa with outdoor pool. Arby's, Tony Roma's, Pizza Hut Express, Orange Julius and Blimpie's Subs on premise. Discount liquor store. Video arcade.

Silver Legacy Resort Casino
407 N. Virginia Street
Reno, Nevada 89501
(775) 329-4777
Web Site: www.silverlegacy.com

Toll-Free Number: (800) 687-7733
Reservation Number: (800) 687-8733
Rooms: 1,720 Price Range: $42-$109
Suites: 150 Price Range: $100-$210
Restaurants: 5 (1 open 24 hours)
Buffets: B-$5.89 L-$6.96 D-$8.99
Casino Size: 88,400 Square Feet
Other Games: SB, RB, B, PG, PGP, CSP, LIR, B6, K
Casino Marketing: (800) 215-7721
Special Features: Victorian themed hotel. Connected by skyways to both Circus Circus and Eldorado Hotels. Tallest hotel in Nevada - 37 stories. Automated mining machine 120 feet above casino floor. Health spa and beauty salon. Shopping mall with 8 stores. Catch a rising Star Comedy club. World's largest composite dome featuring laser, light and sound shows.

Sundowner Hotel Casino
450 N. Arlington Avenue
Reno, Nevada 89503
(775) 786-7050

Reservation Number: (800) 648-5490
Rooms: 583 Price Range: $30-$69
Suites: 10 Price Range: $109-$200
Restaurants: 3 (1 open 24 hours)
Buffets: B-$5.95 (Sat/Sun) D-$6.95/$9.95 (Fri)
Casino Size: 19,040 Square Feet
Other Games: SB, RB, K
Casino Marketing: (800) 648-5490
Fun Book: Only given to hotel guests

Searchlight

Map Location: **#25** (58 miles S. of Las Vegas on Hwy. 95)

Searchlight Nugget Casino
100 N. Highway 95
Searchlight, Nevada 89046
(702) 297-1201

Room Reservations: (702) 297-1144
Rooms: 20 Price Range: $35-$50
Casino Size: 3,260 Square Feet
Other Games: P, No Craps or Roulette

Sparks

Map Location: **#4** (Sparks is a suburb of Reno and is located one mile east of Reno on I-80)

Here's information, as supplied by Nevada's State Gaming Control Board, showing the slot machine payback percentages for all of the Sparks area casinos for the fiscal year beginning July 1, 1999 and ending June 30, 2000:

Denomination	Payback %
5¢ Slots	94.98
10¢ Sots	95.81
25¢ Slots	95.20
$1 Slots	96.19
$1 Megabucks	90.38
$5 Slots	96.37
All Slots	95.42

These numbers reflect the percentage of money returned on each denomination of machine and encompass all electronic machines including slots, video poker and video keno. For nickel slot players Sparks' casinos offer the highest returns in the state.

Alamo Travel Center
1959 East Greg Street
Sparks, Nevada 89431
(775) 355-8888
Web Site: www.thealamo.com

Restaurants: 1
Casino Size: 7,150 Square Feet
Other Games: K, No Craps or Roulette
Special Features: Truck stop, arcade, post office and service station.

Baldini's Sports Casino
865 South Rock Boulevard
Sparks, Nevada 89431
(775) 358-0116
Web Site: www.baldinissportscasino.com

Restaurants: 4 (1 open 24 hours)
Buffets: B-$3.99/$6.99 (Sat/Sun)
L-$5.99 D-$6.99
Casino Size: 17,340 Square Feet
Other Games: SB, RB, K, No Roulette
Casino Marketing: (775) 358-0116
Senior Discount: 20% off in restaurant, if 55, or older
Special Features: Periodic autograph signings by celebrity athletes. Convenience store with propane and RV dump. Gas station. Free six-pack of Pepsi awarded with natural 4-of-a-kind, or better, in video poker with maximum coins bet.

John Ascuaga's Nugget
1100 Nugget Avenue
Sparks, Nevada 89431
(775) 356-3300
Web Site: www.janugget.com

Toll-Free Number: (800) 468-4388
Reservation Number: (800) 648-1177
Rooms: 1,600 Price Range: $45-$195
Suites: 150 Price Range: $99-$295
Restaurants: 8 (1 open 24 hours)
Buffets: B-$9.50 (Sat)/$11.50 (Sun) L-$7.99
D-$11.50 (Wed/Sun)/$13.50 (Tue/Thu)/
$17.95 (Fri/Sat)/$14.95 (Mon)
Casino Size: 82,600 Square Feet
Other Games: SB, RB, MB, P, PGP, LIR, K, BG
Casino Marketing: (800) 648-1177
Special Features: Wedding chapel. Video game arcade. Year-round pool and health club.

Rail City Casino
2121 Victorian Avenue
Sparks, Nevada 89431
(775) 359-9440

Restaurants: 1 (open 24 hours)
Buffets: L-$5.95 D-$6.95
Casino Size: 16,620 Square Feet
Other Games: SB, RB, K, No Roulette
Senior Discount: 20% off buffet, if 50, or older
Special Features: Live entertainment Thu-Sat.

Silver Club Hotel/Casino
1040 Victorian Avenue
Sparks, Nevada 89432
(775) 358-4771
Web Site: www.silverclub.com

Reservation Number: (800) 905-7774
Rooms: 207 Price Range: $45-$69
Suites: 8 Price Range: $85-$165
Restaurants: 4 (1 open 24 hours)
Buffets: D-$6.99
Casino Size: 17,502 Square Feet
Other Games: SB, RB, LIR, K
Casino Marketing: (800) 648-1137

Western Village Inn & Casino
815 Nichols Boulevard
Sparks, Nevada 89432
(775) 331-1069

Reservation Number: (800) 648-1170
Rooms: 280 Price Range: $25-$70
Suites: 5 Price Range: $179-$229
Restaurants: 3 (1 open 24 hours)
Casino Size: 27,000 Square Feet
Other Games: SB
Casino Marketing: (800) 648-1170
Fun Book: Only given to hotel guests, or at cage after cashing a check
Senior Discount: Room discount, if 55, or older
Special Features: Free shuttle to/from airport.

Tonopah

Map Location: **#26** (200 miles N.W. of Las Vegas on Hwy. 95 where it meets Hwy. 6)

The Station House
P.O. Box 1351
Tonopah, Nevada 89049
(775) 482-9777

Rooms: 75 Price Range: $35-$80
Suites: 3 Price Range: $60-$82
Restaurants: 1 (open 24 hours)
Casino Size: 4,800 Square Feet
Other Games: No Roulette
Special Features: 20-space RV camp with full hookups.

Verdi

Map Location: **#4** (4 miles W. of Reno on I-80 at the California border)

Boomtown Hotel & Casino
P.O. Box 399
Verdi, Nevada 89439
(775) 345-6000
Web Site: www.boomtowncasinos.com

Reservation Number: (800) 648-3790
Rooms: 318 Price Range: $49-$150
Suites: 20 Price Range: $99-$279
Restaurants: 4 (2 open 24 hours)
Buffets: B-$9.99 (Sat/Sun) L-$6.99
D-$8.99/$19.99 (Fri/Sat)
Casino Size: 39,668 Square Feet
Other Games: SB, RB, P, PGP, LIR, K
Casino Marketing: (775) 345-8640
Fun Book: Ask at hotel registration desk
Special Features: 203-space RV park. 24-hour mini-mart. Two pools. Family fun center with indoor ferris wheel, 9-hole miniature golf course, dynamic motion theater, antique carousel and more than 150 video and arcade games. Free nightly cabaret entertainment. 2 spas.

Gold Ranch Casino
P.O. Box 160
Verdi, Nevada 89439
(775) 345-6789

Restaurants: 1 (open 24 hours)
Casino Size: 3,100 Square Feet
Other Games: No Craps or Roulette

Wells

Map Location: **#27** (338 miles N.E. of Reno on I-80)

Four Way Bar/Cafe & Casino
U.S. 93 & Interstate 80
Wells, Nevada 89835
(775) 752-3344

Restaurants: 1 (open 24 hours)
Casino Size: 4,500 Square Feet
Other Games: No Craps or Roulette
Fun Book: Ask at cage

Lucky J's Casino
PO Box 515/U.S. 93 & Interstate 80
Wells, Nevada 89835
(775) 752-2252

Restaurants: 1 (open 24 hours)
Casino Size: 900 Square Feet
Other Games: No Craps or Roulette
Special Features: Located in Flying J Truck Stop. Blackjack is open from 7:30am to 11:30 pm.

W. Wendover

Map Location: **#28** (Just W. of the Utah border on I-80)

Peppermill Inn & Casino
680 Wendover Boulevard
W. Wendover, Nevada 89883
(775) 664-2255
Web Site: www.peppermillcasinos.com

Reservation Number: (800) 648-9660
Rooms: 198 Price Range: $39-$110
Suites: 26 Price Range: $120-$200
Restaurants: 1 (open 24 hours)
Buffets: B-$4.95/$8.95 (Sun) L-$6.95
D-$9.95/$15.95 (Fri)
Casino Size: 24,880 Square Feet
Other Games: SB, K
Fun Book: Only given to hotel guests
Senior Discount: $2 off buffet, if 65, or older
Special Features: Single-zero roulette offered.

Rainbow Hotel & Casino
1045 Wendover Boulevard
W. Wendover, Nevada 89883
(775) 664-4000

Toll-Free Number: (800) 217-0049
Rooms: 94 Price Range: $39-$65
Suites: 20 Price Range: $55-$200
Restaurants: 2 (1 open 24 hours)
Buffets: L-$8.50/$8.95 (Sat/Sun)
D-$10.95/$13.95 (Fri/Sat)
Casino Size: 34,133 Square Feet
Casino Marketing: (800) 217-0049
Other Games: SB, PGP, P, LIR
Fun Book: Only given to hotel guests
Senior Discount: $2 off buffet, if 65, or older

Red Garter Hotel & Casino
P.O. Box 2399
W. Wendover, Nevada 89883
(775) 664-3315
Web Site: www.fh-inc.com

Toll-Free Number: (800) 982-2111
Rooms: 46 Price Range: $22-$65
Restaurants: 1 (open 24 hours)
Casino Size: 13,600 Square Feet
Casino Marketing: (800) 982-2111
Other Games: SB
Fun Book: Ask at welcome center
Special Features: Show out-of-state ID for $1 in cash and $9 in bonus coupons. $1.99 ham & eggs special offered 24-hours.

State Line/Silver Smith Hotel Casinos
100 Wendover Boulevard
W. Wendover, Nevada 89883
(775) 664-2221 (State Line)
(775) 664-2231 (Silver Smith)
Web Site: www.statelinenv.com

Reservation Number: (800) 848-7300
Rooms: 498 Price Range: $25-$69
Suites: 50 Price Range: $70-$175
Restaurants: 8 (2 open 24 hours)
Buffets: B-$9.95 (Sat/Sun)
D-$11.95/$13.95 (Fri/Sat)
Casino Size: 25,538 Square Feet (Silver Smith)
Casino Size: 47,358 Square Feet (State Line)
Other Games: SB, MB, P, PGP, LIR, K
Casino Marketing: (800) 848-7300
Fun Book: Only for hotel guests or groups
Special Features: 2 casinos connected by sky bridge. Nonsmoking rooms. 2 pools. Tennis courts and gym. Gift shop. Live entertainment nightly. Golf packages available. On weekends suites can only be booked through the casino.

Winnemucca

Map Location: **#29** (164 miles N.E. of Reno on I-80)

Model T Hotel/Casino/RV Park
1130 W. Winnemucca Blvd.
Winnemucca, Nevada 89446
(775) 623-2588
Web Site: www.modelt.com

Reservation Number: (800) 645-5658
Rooms: 75 Price Range: $50-$70

Restaurants: 3 (1 open 24 hours)
Casino Size: 9,535 Square Feet
Other Games: SB, LIR, K, No Craps or Roulette
Casino Marketing: (702) 625-1111
Fun Book: Only given to hotel/RV guests, or groups
Senior Discount: AARP room discount
Special Features: 58-space RV park. Food court with Baskin-Robbins, KFC Express, Taco Bell Express and gourmet coffee shop. Live entertainment. Country candy store. Video arcade. Seasonal pool facilities.

Red Lion Inn & Casino
741 W. Winnemucca Boulevard
Winnemucca, Nevada 89445
(775) 623-2565

Reservation Number: (800) 633-6435
Rooms: 100 Price Range: $79-$89
Suites: 7 Price Range: $105-$165
Restaurants: 1 (open 24 hours)
Casino Size: 3,050 Square Feet
Other Games: SB, RB, No Craps or Roulette
Fun Book: Given to all hotel guests and also distributed by local motels

Winners Hotel/Casino
185 W. Winnemucca Boulevard
Winnemucca, Nevada 89445
(775) 623-2511
Web Site: www.winnerscasino.com

Reservation Number: (800) 648-4770
Rooms: 125 Price Range: $35-$56
Suites: 2 Price Range: $70-$80
Restaurants: 2 (1 open 24 hours)
Buffets: B-$5.49 (Sat/Sun)
D-$8.99 (Fri/Sat)
Casino Size: 11,340 Square Feet
Other Games: LIR, BG
Casino Marketing: (800) 648-4770
Fun Book: Given to all hotel guests and tour groups. Also available to guests of local motels and RV parks.
Senior Discount: $1 off buffet, if 55, or older
Special Features: Courtesy car service to other motels, local businesses and airport/transportation facilities. Lounge with live entertainment. Gift shop. Children's video arcade.

Yerington

Map Location: **#30** (60 miles S.E. of Reno on Hwy. Alt. 95)

Casino West
11 N. Main Street
Yerington, Nevada 89447
(775) 463-2481

Reservation Number: (800) 227-4661
Rooms: 79 Price Range: $38-$56
Restaurants: 1
Buffets: B-$3.95 (Sun) D-$4.95 (Sun/Tue-Thu)/$5.95 (Sat)/$12.95 (Fri)
Casino Size: 4,550 Square Feet
Other Games: K, No Craps or Roulette
Senior Discount: Room discounts, which vary with day and room type, if 55, or older
Special Features: Movie theater. 12-lane bowling alley. Slot club members receive $1 off buffet.

Indian Casino

Avi Hotel & Casino
10000 Aha Macav Parkway
Laughlin, Nevada 89029
(702) 535-5555
Web Site: www.aviresort.com
Map Location: **#2**

Toll-Free Number: (800) AVI-2-WIN
Rooms: 300 Price Range: $20-$65
Suites: 29 Price Range: $50-$99
Restaurants: 3 (1 open 24 hours)
Buffets: B-$4.49 L-$5.49
D-$6.99/$7.99 (Sat)/$9.99 (Fri)
Casino Size: 25,000 Square Feet
Other Games: SB, P, CSP, LIR, K, BG
Fun Book: Ask at Advantage Club
Special Features: 300-space RV park with full hook ups. Located on Colorado River with boat dock, launch and area's largest private beach. Video arcade. Baskin-Robbins and Subway shops. Gas station. Smoke shop. Kid's Quest.

NEW JERSEY

Map Location: **#1** (on the Atlantic Ocean in southeast New Jersey, 130 miles south of New York City and 60 miles southeast of Philadelphia)

Once a major tourist destination that was world-famous for its steel pier and boardwalk attractions, Atlantic City gradually fell into decline and casino gambling was seen as its salvation when voters approved it there in 1976.

The first casino (Resorts International) opened to "standing-room-only crowds" in 1978. Since then 11 more casinos have opened and all but two are located along the boardwalk. The other two (Harrah's and Trump Marina) are located in the Marina section.

In mid-1997 Bally's Wild Wild West casino (Atlantic City's first themed casino) opened and it is the 13th casino in the city. Due to a quirk in the licensing law, however, this casino is considered as part of Bally's Park Place.

Las Vegas-based MGM-Mirage Resorts is planning to build to build a $2 billion, 4,000-room resort called Le Jardin on a 125-acre site known as the H-tract in Atlantic City's Marina district. That company is also developing a joint project with Boyd Gaming Corp. in another $1 billion, 40-story, 2,010-room resort on an adjacent 25-acre site that will be connected to Le Jardin. Groundbreaking for the new Borgata began in mid-2000 and the resort is expected to open in mid-2003.

In early 1993 the New Jersey Casino Control Commission authorized simulcasting of pari-mutuel events, plus the addition of poker. On May 30, 1993 the Showboat became the first Atlantic City casino to offer betting on races that were simulcast to its facility. Poker made its Atlantic City debut the next month. Later that year the commission gave the okay for keno and the first casinos began offering it on June 15, 1994.

Following is information from the New Jersey Casino Control Commission regarding average slot payout percentages for the 12-month period from January through December 1999:

CASINO	PAYBACK %
Harrah's	92.4
Tropicana	92.1
Trump Plaza	92.0
Trump's Marina	91.9
Sands	91.9
A.C. Hilton	91.8
Caesars	91.8
Bally's Park Place	91.8
Trump Taj Mahal	91.7
Claridge	91.1
Showboat	91.0
Resorts	90.6

These figures reflect the total percentages returned by each casino for all of their electronic machines which includes slot machines, video poker, etc.

All Atlantic City casinos are open 24 hours and, unless otherwise noted, the games offered at every casino are: slots, video poker, big six, craps, blackjack, roulette, baccarat, mini-baccarat, Caribbean stud poker, let it ride, pai gow poker and keno. Additional games offered include: simulcasting (S), poker (P), pai gow (PG), sic bo (SB), double exposure blackjack (DE) and casino war (W). The minimum gambling age is 21.

For more information on visiting New Jersey you can contact the state's Travel & Tourism Department at (800) 537-7397. For information only on Atlantic City call (800) 262-7395.

Trip Report - Atlantic City

April, 2000 - I flew on Spirit Airlines (800-772-7117) nonstop from Fort Lauderdale to Atlantic City Airport. Spirit is a regional carrier that offers direct service on 120-passenger DC-9 jets to Atlantic City from nine different cities throughout the eastern U.S. They also offer more flights to the A.C. airport than any other carrier. The airport itself is rather small (only 10 gates) but it underwent a major renovation about four years ago and it is a nice modern facility.

It's about a 10-mile drive from the airport to Atlantic City and the Super Shuttle (888-640-2222) offers service directly to any of the casinos for $16 per person. That price is reduced, however, to just $10 per person if two or more ride in the van. Rental cars are expensive; I had a compact that normally cost $57 a day but I was able to get a 15% discount. All of the rental car companies will also add a 10% airport fee, plus 6% sales tax on top of the daily rental rate. My total bill for three days was $169.44 (including the discount) which, in Las Vegas, would have gotten me a much nicer car for a full week. The only three rental car companies at the airport are Hertz, Avis and Budget. You can also take a taxi directly from the airport for $27, plus $1 for each additional passenger.

There is a $2 charge per 24 hours (6 a.m. to 6 a.m.) for parking in a garage at any casino hotel in Atlantic City. Whenever you pay the $2 you are issued a receipt which you can then use to park for free at *one* other casino. When you leave the second garage you must give them the receipt from the first garage.

For transportation among the casinos there are two options, besides taxis. A jitney service makes stops along Pacific Avenue and will drop you off by any casino including Harrah's and Trump Marina. The cost for the jitney is $1.50 per person. On the Boardwalk itself, there are the *Famous Rolling Chairs*. These are covered two-seater wicker chairs on wheels that are pushed by an attendant as he walks to your destination. They are all owned by the same company so the rates are the same: $5 for up to five blocks, $10 for six to 13 blocks, $15 for 14 to 21 blocks, and $20 for 22 to 32 blocks.

Most A.C. casinos have cash back slot club programs where they mail you a check at home which must be brought back to the casino within 90 days to be cashed. These are fine for locals, but if you're not planning to return anytime soon they are virtually worthless. You need to be aware of the rules when you sign up for theses programs because if they mail you a check and you're not planning to go back you'll have wasted your time.

The casinos in A.C. do seem to be somewhat liberal with their rooms comps. On all of my previous trips I took advantage of my membership in Harrah's slot club for two free nights. Unfortunately, on this trip they were completely booked up and I was on my own. I arranged for a two-night stay at the Claridge (the most 9/6 video poker games in town!) at the casino rate of $25 per night but on Friday night the cheapest rate I could find was $125 ($142 with taxes) at Resorts. You might think the room would be nice at a rate like that but the quality of the room was barely comparable to a Holiday Inn. Evidently, they spent a lot of money on upgrading the casino to make it beautiful but they didn't spend a dime to upgrade the rooms.

Of course, no visit to A.C. would be complete without a visit to the White House Sub Shop at the corner of Mississippi and Arctic Avenues (609-345-8599) for lunch. They've been in that same location since 1946 and are known for having the best cheesesteak subs. It's a dumpy old place but everybody goes there (the walls are filled with autographed photos of celebrity visitors) and the subs are excellent!

The blackjack games offered at A.C. casinos are pretty much all the same: eight-deck shoe games with double down on any first two cards, dealers stands on soft 17, a pair can be split up to three time and doubling after splitting is allowed. This works out to a casino edge of .44% against a player using basic strategy. The best game was at the Claridge which offered late surrender, but wouldn't allow resplitting of pairs. That brought the casino edge in this game down to .40% against a basic strategy player.

If you're willing to make higher minimum bets you can find slightly better games. Most casinos offer six-deck games with minimum bets of $25 per hand. This six-deck game, with the standard rules in place, lowers the casino edge from .44% to .41% The best I found for a higher limit game was at the Claridge where they had a four-deck shoe game with double on any first two cards, re-split pairs (including aces) up to two times, dealer stands on soft 17 and late surrender. The good news here is that the casino edge on this game is only .22%. The bad news though is that you have to bet a minimum of $100 a hand. And speaking of minimum bets, you'll find that the minimums are much higher in Atlantic City than Las Vegas. You'll never find a blackjack table with less than a $5 minimum and in the evening most are raised to $10. The one casino that seemd to offer the most $5 games, even at night, was Wild Wild West.

As a recreational video poker player I usually play 25¢ 9/6 jacks or better machines (99.5% return with maximum coin and perfect play) which are very prevalent in Las Vegas. Finding them in Atlantic City was much harder. Actually, I only found them at two casinos. The Claridge had about 30 of them on the mezzanine and Trump Plaza had about five.

Most Atlantic City casinos offer 7/5 pay tables (97.3% return) on their 25¢ jacks or better machines and at one casino I found a $1 machine with a 6/5 pay table that only returned 15-for-1 (rather than 25) on four-of-a-kind. This was truly a terrible machine! One thing I discovered is that many of the casinos that had 7/5 or 6/5 pay tables on their regular machines also had 8/5 pay tables on their Game Maker machines. If you're not familiar with a Game Maker machine it refers to a video touch-screen machine made by Bally that offers multiple games in one unit: slots, video poker, keno, Let It Ride, etc. This means it paid to go to those machines, hit the menu button and take a look at the pay tables they offered.

The best 5¢ machine I found was at Trump Plaza. This jacks or better machine had an 8/5 pay table which was much better than the usual 6/5 pay tables at most of the nickel games. For $1 players there were 9/6 machines at: Caesars (also 50¢), Harrah's, Trump Marina (also one 50¢ machine), Resorts, Trump Taj Mahal, Sands, Tropicana (also 50¢) and Trump Plaza.

If you've read the video poker story in the front of this book you'll know that 9/6 jacks or better is just one of the better machines to play. There are also full pay deuces wild (100.76%) and 10/7 double bonus (100.17%) machines which are two of the best games available. Although both of these machines can be found in many Las Vegas casinos there were none in A.C., with one exception: Trump Plaza had one $1 10/7 double bonus machine (#P-036) in its high limit game area.

Actually, one of the best video poker games available in Atlantic City was a double joker machine with a 99.97% payback. The paytable to look for was one that offered 9-for-1 on 4-of-a-kind (rather than 8-for-1 which lowered the payback to 98.10%). There were 25¢ games at the Claridge (three machines on the mezzanine) and the Showboat (13 machines at the west end). The Tropicana had just one 25¢ machine (#R-115). However, the best double joker games, with a 100.41% payback, were found at two casinos which offered a three-coin maximum version which paid 1,000-for-1 on a royal flush, rather than the usual 800. Taj Mahal had three $5 machines and Bally's Park Place offered one $1 machine.

Another good video poker game was Pick'em Poker (99.99% with maximum coin). This game was widely available in 1999 but it pretty much disappeared the following year. Only three casinos had them: Resorts (25¢), Bally's (25¢ and $1) and Wild Wild West (25¢).

For craps players some casinos offered double odds on their $5 games and five times odds on their higher limit tables. The best odds I found was at Trump Marina and Trump Taj Mahal which both offered 10x odds on their $25 game. A few of the casinos, however, offered a straight five times odds on all of their games: Caesars, Claridge, Tropicana and Resorts.

For roulette players Atlantic City does offer a slight advantage over Las Vegas and that's because of the "surrender" rule. All Atlantic City casinos feature double-zero wheels that have both 0 and 00 - there are no single-zero wheels. If you bet red or black, odd or even, 1 to 18 or 19 to 36, and the ball stops on 0 or 00, you only lose one-half of your bet. This is known as the "surrender" rule and it cuts the casino edge on these bets in half from 5.26% to only 2.63%. Keep in mind that it only applies to the even-money bets and for all other bets the casino edge remains at 5.26%. This "surrender" rule is a state law and is in force at all casinos. Single-zero roulette wheels can be found at the Tropicana, Sands, Harrah's and Bally's Park Place. The casino edge on these wheels is 2.70% but with even-money bets it is reduced to only 1.35% because of the surrender rule. Now for the bad news: these wheels are only open on weekends and the minimum bet is either $25 or $50. Still, they're the best roulette games you'll find in the U.S.!

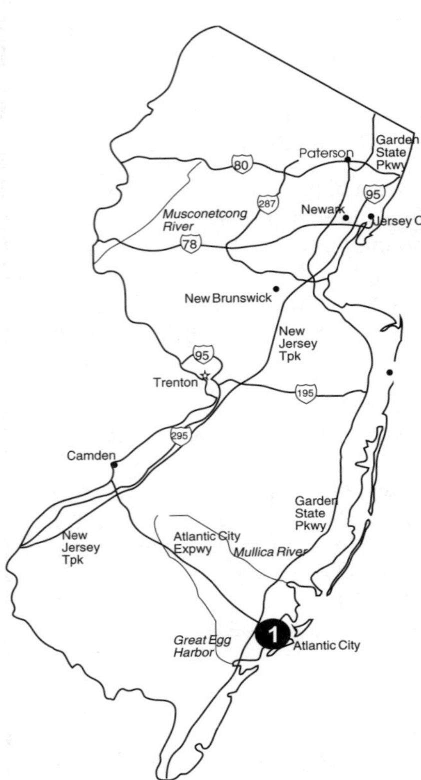

Atlantic City Hilton Casino Resort
Boston & The Boardwalk
Atlantic City, New Jersey 08401
(609) 347-7111
Web Site: www.hiltonac.com

Reservation Number: (800) 257-8677
Rooms: 675 Price Range: $175-$275
Suites: 54 Price Range: $220-$600
Restaurants: 6 (1 open 24 hours)
Buffets: L/D-$14.99 (Mon-Fri)/$15.99 (Sat-Sun)
Casino Size: 59,440 Square Feet
Other Games: S, PG, SB, DE
Casino Marketing: (800) THE-GRAND
Senior Discount: $99 AARP midweek room rate (when available)
Special Features: Beachside resort with water sports and beachfront bar. Spa facilities with indoor pool. 2,000-seat entertainment theater. Unisex salon.

Bally's Park Place
Park Place and the Boardwalk
Atlantic City, New Jersey 08401
(609) 340-2000
Web Site: www.ballysac.com

Reservation Number: (800) 225-5977
Rooms: 1,162 Price Range: $125-$400
Suites: 92 Price Range: $315-$620
Restaurants: 9 (1 open 24 hours)
Buffet (Park Place): B-$12.00 L-$15.00 D-$20.00
Buffet (Wild Wild West): L/D $20.00
Casino Size (Park Place): 80,809 Square Feet
Casino Size: (W.W. West) 73,935 Square Feet
Other Games: S, PG, SB
Casino Marketing: (800) 772-7777 ext. 2700
Special Features: Walkway connects to Wild Wild West themed casino.

Caesars Atlantic City
2100 Pacific Avenue
Atlantic City, New Jersey 08401
(609) 348-4411
Web Site: www.caesars.com/atlantic_city

Toll-Free Number: (800) 443-0104
Reservation Number: (800) CAESARS
Rooms: 1,479 Price Range: $120-$375
Suites: 198 Price Range: $175-$1,000
Restaurants: 12 (1 open 24 hours)
Buffets: B-$10.95 L-$12.95 D-$13.95/ $17.95 (Wed-Fri)/$16.95 (Sat-Sun)
Casino Size: 120,231 Square Feet
Casino Marketing: (800) 367-3767
Other Games: S, P, PG, SB
Special Features: Planet Hollywood restaurant. Health spa. Shopping arcade. Outdoor pool. Rooftop tennis. Unisex beauty salon.

Claridge Casino Hotel
Boardwalk & Park Place
Atlantic City, New Jersey 08401
(609) 340-3400

Reservation Number: (800) 257-8585
Rooms: 449 Price Range: $130-$180
Suites: 53 Price Range: $390-$495
Restaurants: 5 (1 open 24 hours)
Buffet: L/D-$12.50
Casino Size: 58,565 Square Feet
Other Games: SB, DE
Casino Marketing: (800) 847-LUCK
Special Features: Blackjack games offer surrender. Indoor pool and health spa.

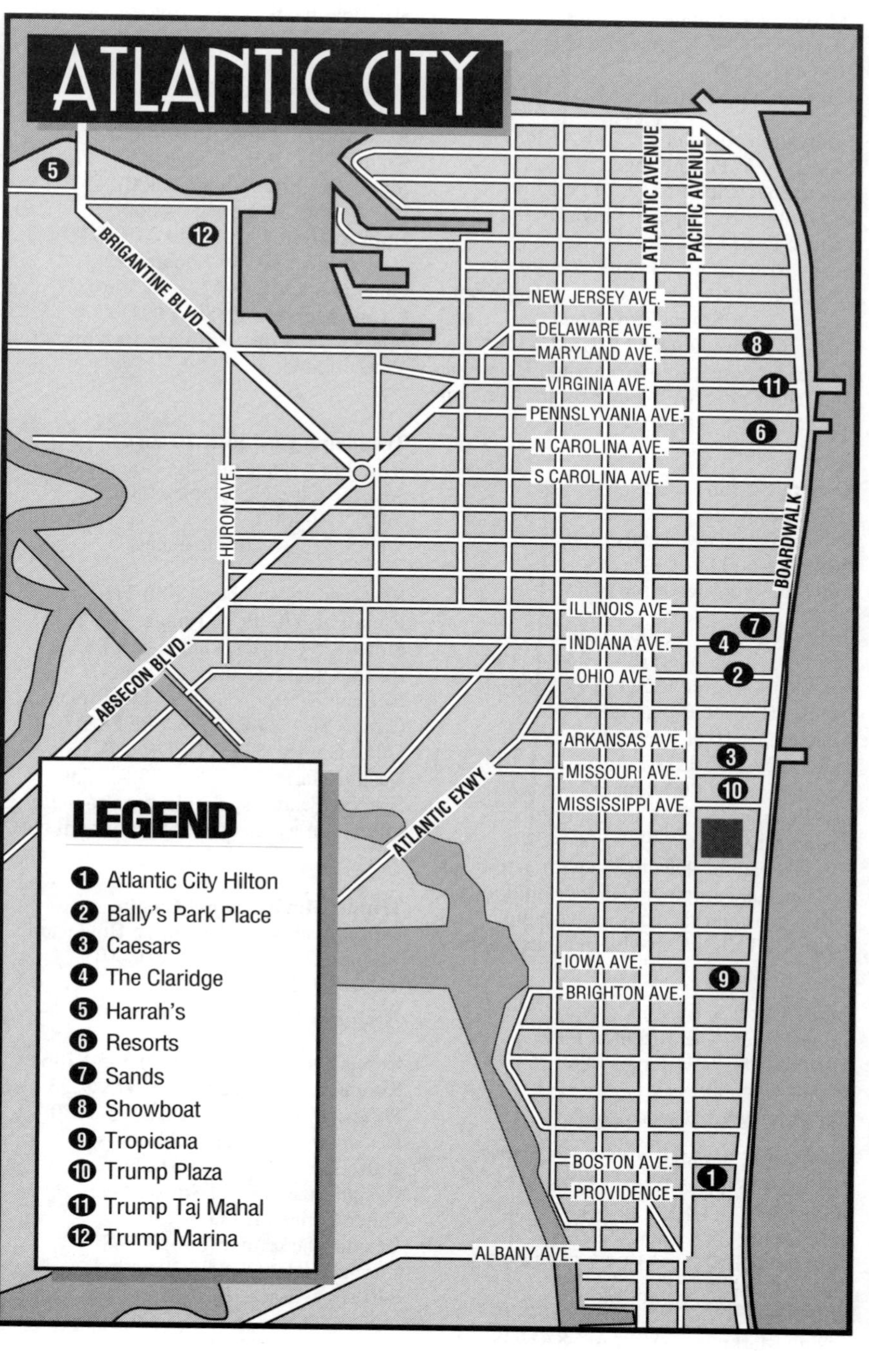
ATLANTIC CITY
ATLANTIC AVENUE
PACIFIC AVENUE
BRIGANTINE BLVD
NEW JERSEY AVE.
DELAWARE AVE.
MARYLAND AVE.
VIRGINIA AVE.
PENNSLYVANIA AVE.
N CAROLINA AVE.
S CAROLINA AVE.
HURON AVE.
BOARDWALK
ILLINOIS AVE.
INDIANA AVE.
OHIO AVE.
ABSECON BLVD.
ARKANSAS AVE.
MISSOURI AVE.
MISSISSIPPI AVE.
ATLANTIC EXWY.
IOWA AVE.
BRIGHTON AVE.
BOSTON AVE.
PROVIDENCE
ALBANY AVE.
LEGEND
1 Atlantic City Hilton
2 Bally's Park Place
3 Caesars
4 The Claridge
5 Harrah's
6 Resorts
7 Sands
8 Showboat
9 Tropicana
10 Trump Plaza
11 Trump Taj Mahal
12 Trump Marina

Harrah's Casino Hotel
777 Harrah's Boulevard
Atlantic City, New Jersey 08401
(609) 441-5000
Web Site: www.harrahs.com

Reservation Number: (800) HARRAHS
Rooms: 907 Price Range: $99-$269
Suites: 267 Price Range: $119-$299
Restaurants: 8 (1 open 24 hours)
Buffets: D-$17.99
Casino Size: 89,617 Square Feet
Other Games: P, W , Fast Action Hold'Em, Single-Zero Roulette
Casino Marketing: (800) 2-HARRAH
Special Features: 65-slip marina. Beauty salon. Teen center with game room. Miniature golf course (in season).

Resorts Casino Hotel
1133 Boardwalk
Atlantic City, New Jersey 08401
(609) 344-6000
Web Site: www.resortsac.com

Toll-Free Number: (800) 336-6378
Reservation Number: (800) 334-6378
Rooms: 644 Price Range: $99-$250
Suites: 30 Price Range: $159-$500
Restaurants: 10 (1 open 24 hours)
Buffets: B-$9.95 L/D-$14.95/$17.95 (Fri-Sun)
Casino Size: 77,000 Square Feet
Other Games: S, P, PG, 3-Card Poker
Casino Marketing: (800) 438-7424
Special Features: Health Spa with state-of-the-art Nautilus equipment. Indoor/outdoor pool with saunas and Jacuzzis. Squash club. Game room. 1133 Nightclub with free entertainment.

Sands Hotel & Casino
Indiana Avenue & Brighton Park
Atlantic City, New Jersey 08401
(609) 441-4000
Web Site: www.acsands.com

Reservation Number: (800) 257-8580
Rooms: 476 Price Range: $125-$275
Suites: 58 Price Range: $300-$475
Restaurants: 5 (1 open 24 hours)
Buffets: B-$7.95 L-$12.95 D-$14.95
Casino Size: 57,296 Square Feet
Other Games: S, P, PG, SB
Casino Marketing: (800) AC-SANDS
Special Features: Food court with six restaurants and fast food outlets.

Showboat Casino-Hotel
801 Boardwalk
Atlantic City, New Jersey 08401
(609) 343-4000
Web Site: www.harrahs.com

Reservation Number: (800) 621-0200
Rooms: 731 Price Range: $130-$180
Suites: 69 Price Range: $200-$472
Restaurants: 8 (1 open 24 hours)
Buffets: B-$6.49 L-$7.49 D-$10.99
Casino Size: 80,707 Square Feet
Other Games: S, P, PG
Casino Marketing: (800) 621-0200
Special Features: 60-lane Bowling Center. Video arcade.

Tropicana Casino & Resort
Brighton Avenue and the Boardwalk
Atlantic City, New Jersey 08401
(609) 340-4000
Web Site: www.tropicana.net

Reservation Number: (800) THE-TROP
Rooms: 1,370 Price Range: $98-$275
Suites: 254 Price Range: $148-$355
Restaurants: 8 (1 open 24 hours)
Buffets: B-$9.95 L-$9.95 D-$14.95
Casino Size: 114,320 Square Feet
Other Games: S, P, PG, DE
Casino Marketing: (800) 338-5553
Special Features: Single-zero roulette game offered on weekends ($50 minimum bet).

Trump Marina Hotel Casino
Huron Avenue & Brigantine Boulevard
Atlantic City, New Jersey 08401
(609) 441-2000
Web Site: www.trumpmarina.com

Reservation Number: (800) 365-8786
Rooms: 568 Price Range: $75-$225
Suites: 160 Price Range: $175-$450
Restaurants: 7 (1 open 24 hours)
Buffets: B-$7.50 L/D-$12.50
Casino Size: 73,734 Square Feet
Other Games: P, PG, SB
Casino Marketing: (800) 777-8477
Special Features: Adjacent to state marina with 640 slips. 3-acre recreation deck with pools, jogging track, tennis courts, miniature golf course and health club.

Trump Plaza Hotel and Casino
The Boardwalk at Mississippi Avenue
Atlantic City, New Jersey 08401
(609) 441-6000
Web Site: www.trumpplaza.com

Reservation Number: (800) 677-7378
Rooms: 1,331 Price Range: $105-$225
Suites: 73 Price Range: $325-$400
Restaurants: 11 (1 open 24 hours)
Buffets: L-$12.95 D-$12.95/$16.95 (Fri-Sun)
Casino Size: 138,295 Square Feet
Other Games: PG, SB
Casino Marketing: (800) 677-0711
Special Features: Health spa with massage, herbal wraps and salt-glo loofah cleansing. Indoor pool. East Side Lounge offers live entertainment nightly with no cover and one drink minimum.

Trump Taj Mahal Casino Resort
1000 Boardwalk at Virginia Avenue
Atlantic City, New Jersey 08401
(609) 449-1000
Web Site: www.trumptaj.com

Reservation Number: (800) 825-8888
Rooms: 1,013 Price Range: $145-$250
Suites: 237 Price Range: $375
Restaurants: 9 (1 open 24 hours)
Buffets: B-$6.95 L-$9.95 D-$14.95
Casino Size: 116,199 Square Feet
Casino Marketing: (800) 234-5678
Other Games: S, P, PG, SB
Senior Discount: Room discount if 50, or older, with Trump Card
Special Features: Health spa and indoor Olympic-size pool. Warner Brothers studio store. All-Star Cafe.

NEW MEXICO

New Mexico has 11 Indian casinos that offer an assortment of table games and electronic gaming machines. Additionally, slot machines are allowed at four of the state's race tracks as well as at about 30 various fraternal and veterans clubs.

New Mexico gaming regulations require that electronic machines at racetracks and fraternal/veterans organizations be set to return a minimum of 80% and a maximum of 96%.

New Mexico's Indian tribes do not make their slot machine payback percentages a matter of public record but the terms of the compact between the state and the tribes require all electronic gaming machines to return a minimum of 80%.

Unless otherwise noted, all New Mexico Indian casinos are open 24 hours and offer: blackjack, craps, roulette, video slots and video poker. Some casinos also offer: mini-baccarat (MB), poker (P), pai gow poker (PGP), Caribbean stud poker (CSP), let it ride (LIR), big 6 wheel (B6), keno (K), bingo (BG) and Simulcasting (S). The minimum gambling age is 18 (21 if liquor is served).

For information on visiting New Mexico call the state's tourism department at (800) 733-6396.

Camel Rock Casino
Route 11, Box 3A
Santa Fe, New Mexico 87501
(505) 984-8414
Web Site: www.camelrockcasino.com
Map Location: **#2**

Toll-Free Number: (800) GO-CAMEL
Restaurants: 4 (2 open 24 hours) Liquor: No
Buffets: B-$3.95 L-$5.95 D-$6.95
Casino Size: 60,000 Square feet
Other Games: P, CSP, BG

Casino Apache
P.O Box 205
Mescalero, New Mexico 88340
(505) 630-4100
Map Location: **#4** (90 miles N.E. of Las Cruces)

Toll-Free Number: (877) 277-5677
Room Reservations: (800) 545-9011
Rooms: 250 Price Range: $90-$139
Restaurants: 3 Liquor: Yes
Buffets: B-$5.95 L-$7.95 D-$9.95
Hours: 7am-3am/24 hours (Fri-Sat)
Casino Size: 45,000 Square Feet
Other Games: P, CSP, K
Casino Marketing: (505) 630-1400
Senior Discount: 20% buffet discount, if 60, or older
Special Features: Hotel offers golf, swimming, horseback riding, tennis, and video arcade.

Cities of Gold Casino/Hotel
10-B Cities of Gold Road
Santa Fe, New Mexico 87501
(505) 455-3313
Web Site: www.citiesofgold.com
Map Location: **#2**

Toll-Free Number: (800) 455-3313
Room Reservations: (877) 455-0515
Rooms: 124 Price Range: $65-$95
Suites: 2 Price Range: $136
Restaurants: 2 Liquor: Yes
Buffets: B-$3.95 L-$5.95 D-$6.95/$9.95 (Sun)
Hours: 8am-4am/24 hours (Fri-Sat)
Casino Size: 40,000 Square Feet
Other Games: P, LIR, BG, S
Fun Book: "Bonus Book" given when you sign up for slot club
Senior Discount: AARP room discount of 30%
Special Features: They also operate the Pojoaque Sports Bar which is one block away from main casino. Liquor is served there but they only have slots - no table games. AAA room discounts available.

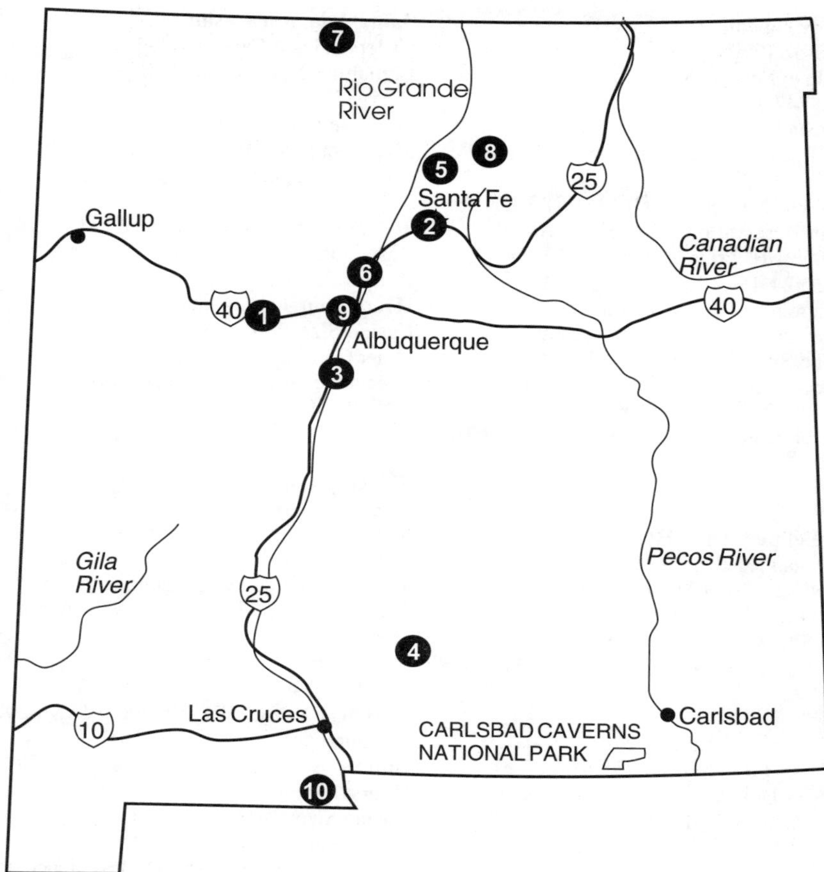

Dancing Eagle Casino
P.O. Box 520
Casa Blanca, New Mexico 87007
(505) 552-0942
Web Site: www.dancingeaglecasino.com
Map Location: **#1** (40 miles W. of Albuquerque)

Toll-Free Number: (877) 440-9969
Restaurants: 1 Liquor: No
Buffets: B-$4.50 L-$6.95 D-$7.95
Hours: 8am-4am/24 hours (Fri-Sun)
Casino Size: 21,266 Square Feet

Isleta Gaming Palace
11000 Broadway S.E.
Albuquerque, New Mexico 87022
(505) 869-2614
Web Site: www.isletagamingpalace.com
Map Location: **#3**

Toll-Free Number: (800) 460-5686
Restaurants: 1 Liquor: No
Buffets: L/D $6.95
Hours: 7am-3am/24 hours (Fri-Sun)
Casino Size: 30,000 Square Feet
Other Games: P, BG
Special Features: Convenience store. Gas station. Golf course located across the street.

Ohkay Casino
P.O. Box 1270
San Juan Pueblo, New Mexico 87566
(505) 747-1668
Web Site: www.ohkay.com
Map Location: **#5** (24 miles N. of Santa Fe)

Toll-Free Number: (800) PLAY-AT-OK
Room Reservation (877) STAY-AT-OK
Rooms: 101 Price Range: $55-$105
Suites: 24 Price Range: $85-$125
Restaurants: 2 (1 open 24 hours) Liquor: Yes
Buffets: B-$4.95 L-$6.95 D-$7.95
Casino Size: 35,000 Square Feet
Senior Discount: 10% room discount, if 60, or older
Special Features: Lounge entertainment Tue-Sun.

San Felipe Casino Hollywood
25 Hagan Road
Algodones, New Mexico 87001
(505) 867-6700
Web Site:www.sanfelipecasino.com
Map Location: **#6** (17 miles N. of Albuquerque)

Restaurants: 1 Liquor: No
Buffets: B-$3.75 L-$4.75/$6.00 (Tue) D-$5.75
Other Games: PGP, LIR

Sandia Casino
P.O. Box 10188
Albuquerque, New Mexico 87184
(505) 897-2173
Web Site: www.sandiacasino.com
Map Location: **#3**

Toll-Free Number: (800) 526-9366
Restaurants: 2 (1 open 24 hours) Liquor: No
Buffets: B-$2.50 L-$4.00 D-$5.00/$6.95 (Thu)/$11.95 (Fri)/$8.95 (Sat)
Casino Size: 65,000 Square feet
Other Games: P, CSP, LIR, K, BG
Special Features: Largest casino in New Mexico. Subway sandwich shop.

Santa Ana Star Casino
54 Jemez Dam Canyon Road
Bernalillo, New Mexico 87004
(505) 867-0000
Web Site:www.santaanastar.com
Map Location: **#6** (17 miles N. of Albuquerque)

Toll-Free Number: (877) 288 STAR
Restaurants: 2 Liquor: No
Buffets: B-$4.50 L-$6.95 D-$7.95
Hours: 8am-4am/24 hours (Fri-Sat)
Casino Size: 19,000 Square Feet
Other Games: P, CSP, LIR
Special Features: New hotel expected to open by Fall 2001.

Sky City Casino
P.O. Box 519
San Fidel, New Mexico 87049
(505) 552-6017
Web Site: www.skycitycasino.com
Map Location: **#1** (50 miles W. of Albuquerque)

Toll-Free Number: (888) SKY-CITY
HOTEL EXPECTED TO OPEN JAN. 2001
Restaurants: 1 Liquor: No
Buffets: B-$5.95 (Sat/Sun) L-$6.95 D-$8.95
Hours: 8am-4am/24 hours (Fri-Sat)
Casino Size: 30,000 Square Feet
Other Games: P, B6, S
Special Features: Gift shop. Convenience store and gas station across the street.

Taos Mountain Casino
P.O. Box 1477
Taos, New Mexico 87571
(505) 758-4460
Web Site:www.taosmountaincasino.com
Map Location: **#8** (50 miles N.E. of Santa Fe)

Toll-Free Number: (888) WIN-TAOS
Restaurants: 1 Deli Liquor: No
Hours: 7am-2am/3am (Fri/Sat)
Other Games: No Craps

Pari-Mutuels

Downs at Albuquerque
P.O. Box 8510
Albuquerque, NM 87198
(505) 266-5555
Web Site: www.nmracing.com
Map Location: **#9**

Restaurants: 1
Buffets: L/D-$6.00
Hours: 10am-10pm
Other Games: Only machines
Special Features: Live horse racing March through June. Horse race simulcasting all year.

Ruidoso Downs & Billy The Kid Casino
P.O. Box 449
Ruidoso Downs, NM 88346
(505) 378-4431
Web Site: www.btkcasino.com
Map Location: **#4** (90 miles N.E. of Las Cruces)

Restaurants: 1
Hours: 11am-11pm
Other Games: Only machines
Senior Discount: 15% buffet discount, if 55, or older
Special Features: Live horse racing (Thu-Sun) during season which runs from Memorial Day through Labor Day. Horse race simulcasting all year.

Sunland Park
1200 Futurity Drive
Sunland Park, NM 88063
(505) 589-1131
Web Site: www.nmracing.com
Map Location: **#10** (5 miles W. of El Paso, TX)

Restaurants: 1
Hours: Noon-Midnight
Other Games: Only machines
Special Features: Live thoroughbred and quarter-horse racing during season which runs from November through May. Simulcasting of horse racing all year.

NEW YORK

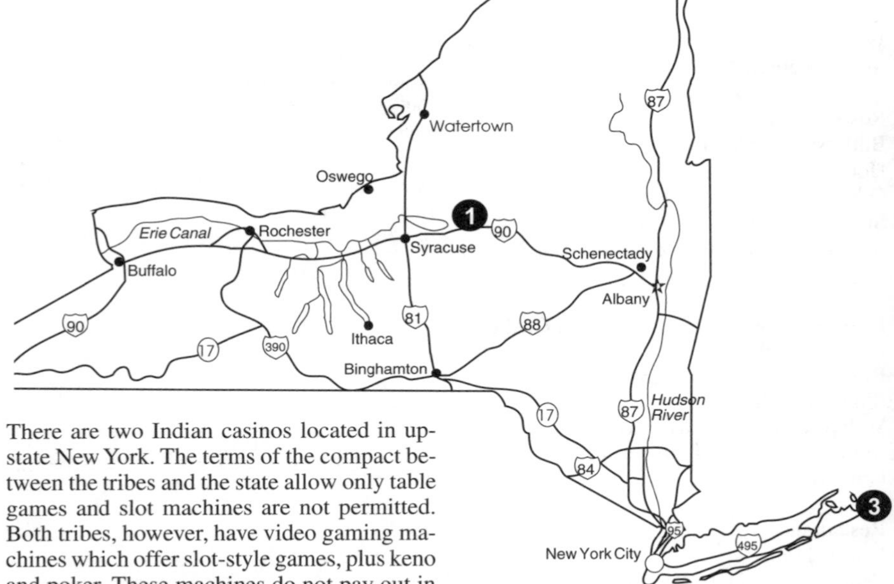

There are two Indian casinos located in upstate New York. The terms of the compact between the tribes and the state allow only table games and slot machines are not permitted. Both tribes, however, have video gaming machines which offer slot-style games, plus keno and poker. These machines do not pay out in cash. Instead, they print out a receipt which must be exchanged for cash.

Both casinos are open 24 hours and offer the following games: blackjack, craps, roulette, Pai Gow poker, mini-baccarat, Caribbean stud, poker, let it ride, money (big six) wheel and poker. The minimum gambling age at both casinos is 18.

For more information on visiting New York call the state's travel information center at (800) 225-5697.

Akwesasne Mohawk Casino
Route 37, Box 670
Hogansburg, New York 13655
(518) 358-2222
Web Site: www.mohawkcasino.com
Map Location: **#2** (65 miles W. of Champlain)

Toll-Free Number: (888) 622-1155
Restaurants: 2 (1 open 24 hours)
Buffets: B-$3.95 L-$7.95 D-$11.95
Liquor: Yes
Casino Size: 40,000 Square Feet
Special Features: Gift shop.

Turning Stone Casino Resort
Patrick Road
Verona, New York 13478
(315) 361-7711
Web Site: www.turning-stone.com
Map Location: **#1** (adjacent to NY State Thruway exit 33 at Verona, off Route 365, 35 miles E. of Syracuse)

Toll-Free Number: (800) 771-7711
Rooms: 277 Price Range: $96-$159
Suites: 30 Price Range: $149-$299
Restaurants: 6 (1 open 24 hours)
Buffets: B-$7.95 D-$8.75/$12.75 (Fri/Sat)
Liquor: No
Casino Size: 90,000 Square Feet
Other Games: Baccarat, Sic Bo, Bingo, Keno
Casino Marketing: (800) 771-7711
Fun Book: Only given to groups
Special Features: Juice/soda/coffee bar in casino. Gift shop. Discount smoke shop.

New York also has two casino boats on Long Island which both travel three miles out into international waters where gambling is permitted. Both boats offer: blackjack, craps, roulette, slots and video poker.

Freeport Casino Cruises
361 Woodcleft Avenue
Freeport, New York 11520
(516) 377-7400
Map Location **#3**

Reservation Number: (516) 377-7400
Gambling Age: 21
Ship's Registry: U.S.A.
Buffet: Included
Schedule:
11:30am - 5:00pm
7:00pm - 11:30pm/12:30am (Fri-Sat)
Price: Free
Port Charges: Included
Parking: Free
Special Features: 500-passenger, *Midnight Gambler II* departs from Freeport's Nautical Mile. Normal $15 admission charge was temporarily suspended at press time but may be reinstated at a later date.

Majesty Casino Cruises
395 Woodcleft Avenue
Freeport, New York 11520
(516) 777-5825
Web Site: www.majestycasino.com
Map Location **#3**

Reservation Number: (516) 777-5825
Gambling Age: 21
Ship's Registry: U.S.A.
Buffet: Included
Schedule:
Noon - 5:30pm
7:30pm - 12:30am/1am (Fri-Sat)
Price: $20/$25 (Eves)
Port Charges: Included
Parking: Free
Other Games: Poker, Bingo, Mini-Baccarat
Special Features: 450-passenger, *Majesty* departs from Freeport's Nautical Mile. First-time visitors can show any slot club card and sail for $5.

NORTH CAROLINA

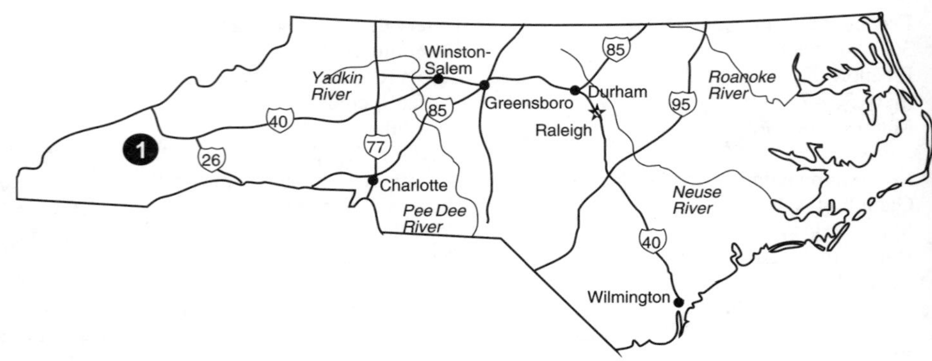

North Carolina has one Indian casino. In August, 1994 the state's Eastern Band of Cherokee Indians signed a compact with the governor to allow some form of video gambling with jackpots of up to $25,000. According to the terms of the compact the video machines must be games of skill and they are also required to return a minimum of 83% and a maximum of 98%.

No table games are offered at the Cherokee Casino, only video slots, video poker, and video versions of craps and blackjack. The slots are different than slots you will find in other casinos because of the required "skill" factor. With these "skill" slots you have two opportunities to spin the reels. The "skill" factor comes into play because after the seeing the results of the first spin you then have to decide whether to keep one, two, or all three of the symbols on each reel before you spin them again.

The casino is open 24 hours and the minimum gambling age is 18. For more information on visiting North Carolina call the state's division of travel & tourism at (800) 847-4862.

Harrah's Cherokee Casino
P.O. Box 1959
Cherokee, North Carolina 28719
(828) 497-7777
Web Site: www.harrahs.com
Map Location: **#1** (55 miles S.W. of Asheville)

Toll-Free Number: (800) HARRAHS
Restaurants: 4 Liquor: No
Buffets: L-$8.95 D-$12.95
Special Features: No on-site hotel but casino patrons can get $77 "Play and Stay" package at one of five nearby hotels. Planet-4-Kidz child-care center.

NORTH DAKOTA

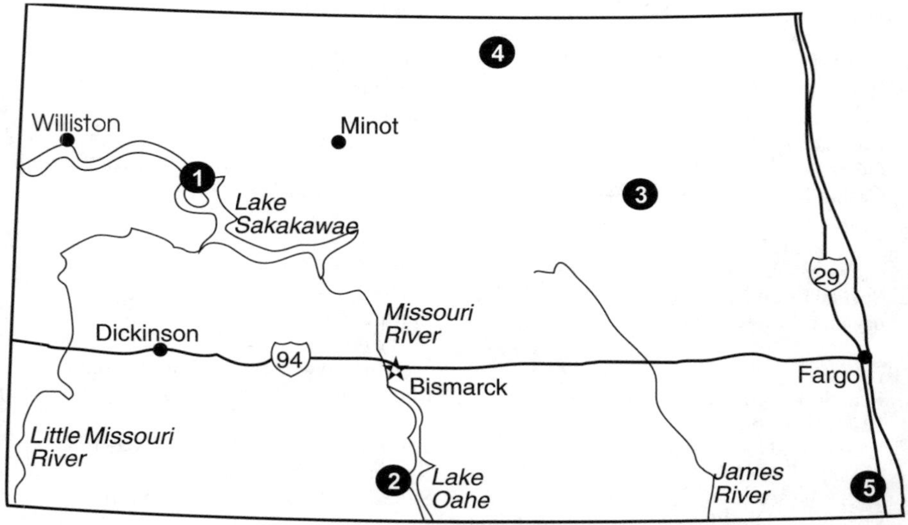

North Dakota has more than 800 sites throughout the state that offer blackjack, with a $5 maximum bet, for the benefit of charities.

There are also six Indian casinos which, although not restricted to that same $5 amount, are limited by law to the following maximum bets: blackjack-$50, craps-$25, slots-$5, video poker-$5 and poker-$10 per bet, per round with a maximum of three rounds.

The terms of the state's compact with the tribes require the electronic machines to return a minimum of 80% and a maximum of 100%. However, if a machine is affected by skill, such as video poker or video blackjack, the machines must return a minimum of 83%.

All casinos are open 24 hours and offer: blackjack, craps, poker, slots, video poker, video keno and video blackjack. Optional games include: Caribbean stud poker (CSP), let it ride (LIR), keno (K), bingo (BG), big-6 wheel (B6) and simulcasting (S). Roulette is not allowed in North Dakota. The minimum gambling age is 18 (21 if liquor is served).

For information on visiting North Dakota call the state's tourism office at (800) 437-2077

Dakota Magic Casino
16849 102nd Street SE
Hankinson, North Dakota 58041
(701) 634-3000
Web Site: www.dakotamagiccasino.com
Map Location: **#5** (50 miles S. of Fargo)

Toll-Free Number: (800) 325-6825
Restaurants: 1 Liquor: Yes
Buffets: B-$4.95 L-$6.25 D-$8.35
Hours: 8am-2am(Sun-Thu)/ 24Hrs (Sat/Sun)
Casino Size: 24,000 Square Feet
Other Games: LIR, S (Wed-Mon), K

Four Bears Casino & Lodge
HC 3, Box 2-A
New Town, North Dakota 58763
(701) 627-4018
Web Site: 4bearscasino.com
Map Location: **#1** (150 miles N.W. of Bismarck)

Toll-Free Number: (800) 294-5454
Rooms: 40 Price Range: $55
Restaurants: 2 (1 open 24 hours) Liquor: Yes
Buffets: B-$4.95 L-$6.95 D-$8.95
Other Games: BG, B6
Casino Marketing: (800) 294-5454 ext 303
Senior Discount: $49.50 room rate, if 55, or older. Also, receive $5 in players cash on designated days until 5pm
Special Features: 80-space RV park with laundry and shower facilities.

Prairie Knights Casino & Lodge
HC 1, Box 26-A
Fort Yates, North Dakota 58538
(701) 854-7777
Web Site: www.prairieknights.com
Map Location: **#2** (60 miles S. of Bismarck)

Toll-Free Number: (800) 425-8277
Rooms: 67 Price Range: $45-$75
Suites: 2 Price Range: $85-$130
Restaurants: 2 Liquor: Yes
Buffets: B-$5.00 L-$8.95
D-$8.95/$9.95 (Fri/Sat)
Casino Size: 42,000 Square Feet
Casino Marketing: (701) 854-7777
Senior Discount: $5.25 buffet 11am-3pm (Mon-Thu), if 55, or older
Fun Book: Only given to bus or limo groups
Special Features: Live entertainment on weekends. Two bars. RV parking. Marina with boat slips and 32 RV sites, tent camping, picnic area, beach area. Mountain bike and walking trails.

Sky Dancer Hotel & Casino
P.O. Box 900, Highway 5 West
Belcourt, North Dakota 58316
(701) 244-2400
Map Location: **#4** (120 miles N.E. of Minot)

Toll-Free Number: (800) 477-3497
Room Reservations: (877) 475-9367
Rooms: 97 Price Range: $50-$70
Restaurants: 2 Liquor: Yes
Casino Size: 25,000 Square Feet
Other Games: LIR, BG, S, No Craps
Special Features: Gift shop. Live entertainment. 12 Free RV hookups.

Spirit Lake Casino & Resort
Highway 57
Spirit Lake, North Dakota 58370
(701) 766-4747
Web Site: www.spiritlakecasino.com
Map Location: **#3** (6 miles S. of Devil's Lake)

Toll-Free Number: (800) WIN-U-BET
Rooms: 64 Price Range: $65
Suites: 16 Price Range: $80-$125
Restaurants: 2 Liquor: No
Buffets: B-$4.50/$7.95 (Sun) L-$5.95
D-$9.95/$14.95 (Wed)
Casino Size: 45,000 Square Feet
Other Games: CSP, LIR, K, BG
Fun Book: Given to hotel gusts
Senior Discount: 10% off room, if 55, or older
Special Features: Free continental breakfast for hotel guests. Free shuttle service from Devil's Lake. Gift shop. Discount smoke shop. Free RV parking. 10% room discount for AAA members.

Turtle Mountain Chippewa Mini-Casino
P.O. Box 1449, Highway 5 West
Belcourt, North Dakota 58316
(701) 477-6438
Map Location: **#4** (120 miles N.E. of Minot)

Restaurants: 1 Liquor: Yes
Other Games: Only Machines - No Table Games
Special Features: Located 4 miles east of main Turtle Mountain Casino.

OREGON

Oregon law permits bars and taverns to have up to five video lottery terminals that offer various versions of video poker. The maximum bet is $2 and the maximum payout on any machine is $600. These machines are the same as regular video gaming devices but are called lottery terminals because they are regulated by the state's lottery commission which receives some of the revenue. The machines accept cash but do not pay out in cash; instead, they print out a receipt which must be taken to a cashier.

During the Oregon Lottery's fiscal year from July 1, 1999 through June 30, 2000, the VLT's had an actual return of 93.3%.

There are eight Indian casinos in operation in Oregon. According to Chip Lazenby, legal counsel in the governor's office which regulates the Tribe's compacts, "there is no minimum payback percentage required on the Tribe's machines. Each Tribe is free to set their own limits on their machines."

All casinos offer blackjack, poker, video slots, video poker, video keno, video blackjack and pull tabs. Some casinos also offer: craps (C), roulette (R), poker (P), Pai Gow Poker (PGP), let it ride (LIR), big 6 wheel (B6), bingo (BG), keno (K) and simulcasting. Unless otherwise noted, all casinos are open 24 hours and the minimum gambling age is 18 (21 if liquor is served). For Oregon tourism information call (800) 547-7842.

Chinook Winds Gaming Center
1777 N.W. 44th Street
Lincoln City, Oregon 97367
(541) 996-5700
Web Site: www.chinookwindscasino.com
Map Location: **#4** (45 miles W. of Salem)

Toll-Free Number: (888) CHINOOK
Restaurants: 3 Liquor: Yes
Buffets: B-$5.99 L-$6.99
D-$10.99/$12.99 (Fri/Sat)
Other Games: P, B, K
Fun Book: Given with slot club membership.
Senior Discount: Buffet discount, if 55, or older
Special Features: Smoke-free VLT area. Child-care center. Video arcade. Gift shop.

Indian Head Casino
P.O. Box 1240
Warm Springs, Oregon 97761
(541) 553-6123
Web Site: www.kah-nee-taresort.com
Map Location: **#5** (100 miles E. of Portland)

Toll-Free Number: (800) 238-6946
Reservation Number: (800) 554-4786
Rooms: 169 Price Range: $129-$260
Suites: 6 Price Range: $189-$210
Restaurants: 2 Liquor: Yes
Buffets: B-$12.99
Hours of Operation:
8:30am-2am (Spring and Summer)
10am-2am (Mon-Fri in Fall and Winter)
8:30am-2am(Sat/Sun in Fall and Winter)
Other Games: P
Fun Book: Given to lodge guests and bus groups, seniors on Monday, and ladies on Wednesdays 6pm-9pm.
Senior Discount: Free fun book on Mondays
Special Features: Casino is located inside the Kahneeta Resort which contains a restaurant and bar. Resort features 18-hole golf course, tennis, horseback riding, hot springs spa and water slide. Campground.

Kla-Mo-Ya Casino
34333 Hwy 97 North
Chiloquin, Oregon 97624
(541) 783-7529
Map Location: **#7** (20 miles N. of Klamath Falls)

Toll-Free Number: (888) 552-6692
Restaurants: 2 Liquor: No
Buffets: L-$5.99 (Sat-Sun) D-$7.99
Hours: 9am-1am/24 Hours (Fri/Sat)
Other Games: P, B
Senior Discount: $1 buffet discount. Various promotions on Mondays including $25 for a $20 buy-in at blackjack.

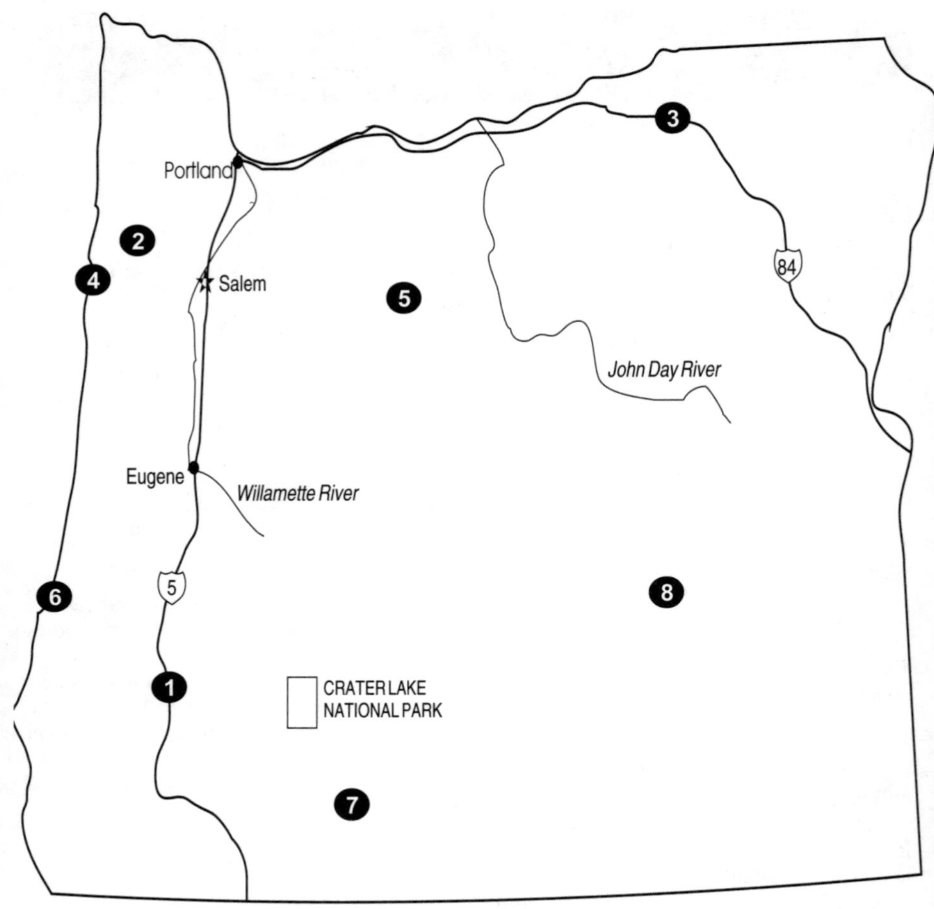

The Mill Resort & Casino
3201 Tremont Avenue
North Bend, Oregon 97459
(541) 756-8800
Web Site: www.themillcasino.com
Map Location: **#6** (75 miles S.W. of Eugene)

Toll-Free Number: (800) 953-4800
Rooms: 112 Price Range:$69-$99
Suites: $150-$175
Restaurants: 2 (1 open 24 hours) Liquor: Yes
Buffets: B-$6.95 L-$5.95 D-$7.95
Other Games: P, B
Senior Discount: 10% off in restaurant, if 55, or older
Special Features: $1 blackjack tables. Free valet parking. Free shuttle bus from local motels. Children's video arcade.

The Old Camp Casino
2205 W. Monroe Street
Burns, Oregon 97720
(541) 573-1500
Map Location: **#8** (250 miles S. of Pendleton)

Restaurants: 1 Deli Liquor: Yes
Hours: 11am-2pm (Sun-Wed)/ 11am -3pm(Thu)/2am Thu-Sat)
Other Games: P, B, B6
Special Features: Liquor sold in lounge and Restaurant only. RV park.

Seven Feathers Hotel & Casino Resort
146 Chief Miwaleta Lane
Canyonville, Oregon 97417
(541) 839-1111
Web Site: www.sevenfeathers.com
Map Location: **#1** (80 miles S. of Eugene)

Toll-Free Number: (800) 548-8461
Rooms: 156 Price Range: $99-$109
Suites: 2 Price Range: $175
Restaurants: 3 Liquor: Yes
Buffets: D-$10.95/$14.50 (Sun)
Casino Size: 30,000 Square Feet
Other Games: C, R, LIR, P, K, B
Fun Book: Birthday coupon book offered to customers anytime during birthday month
Senior Discount: Room discount, if 55, or older
Special Features: RV park. Convention center. Room discount for AAA members.

Spirit Mountain Casino
P.O. Box 39
Grand Ronde, Oregon 97347
(503) 879-2350
Web Site: www.spirit-mountain.com
Map Location: **#2** (85 miles S.W. of Portland)

Toll-Free Number: (800) 760-7977
Restaurants: 4 (2 open 24 hours) Liquor: Yes
Buffets: B-$5.75 L-$6.75 D-$9.75
Fun Book: Given free at Player Services Desk on Tuesdays and to bus groups.
Other Games: C, R, P, PGP, LIR, B6, K, B, S
Special Features: Separate nonsmoking casino and bingo area. Liquor sold in lounge only. Children's day care center. Video arcade. Headliner entertainment.

Wild Horse Gaming Resort
72777 Highway 331
Pendleton, Oregon 97801
(541) 278-2274
Web Site: www.wildhorseresort.com
Map Location: **#3** (211 miles E. of Portland)

Toll-Free Number: (800) 654-9453
Rooms: 100 Price Range: $45-$69
Suites: 4 Price Range: $69-$119
Restaurants: 2 (1 open 24 hours) Liquor: No
Buffets: B-$6.99
Casino Size: 40,000 Square Feet
Other Games: P, K, B, S
Fun Book: Only for hotel or RV park guests
Senior Discount: 10% off buffet and hotel discount, if 55, or older
Special Features: RV park. Indoor and outdoor pools. Live entertainment. 18-hole championship golf course. Spa. Tamastslikt Cultural Institute. 10% hotel discount for AAA members.

RHODE ISLAND

Rhode Island has two pari-mutuel facilities which both feature video lottery terminals (VLT's). These machines are the same as regular video gaming devices but are called lottery terminals because they are regulated by the state's lottery commission which receives a share of each machine's revenue. The machines accept cash but don't pay out in cash; instead, they print out a receipt which must be taken to a cashier.

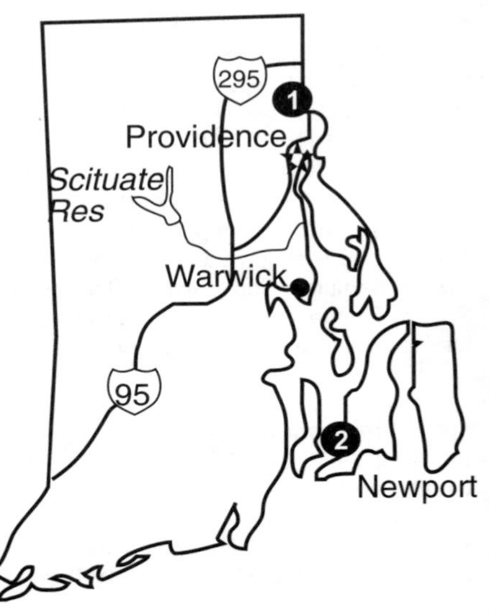

All VLT's are programmed to play at least six different games: blackjack, keno, slots and three versions of poker (jacks or better, joker poker and deuces wild). The Rhode Island Lottery does not provide figures to determine the actual paybacks on its VLT's, however, according to William DiMuccio, gaming manager for the Rhode Island Lottery, the VLT's are programmed to pay back the following amounts over time: Blackjack - 99.1%, Video Poker - 95%, 25¢ Keno - 92%, 50¢ Keno - 94%, and $1 Keno - 96%.

The minimum gambling age in Rhode Island is 18. For information on visiting Rhode Island call the state's tourism division at (800) 556-2484.

Lincoln Park
1600 Louisquisset Pike
Lincoln, Rhode Island 02865
(401) 723-3200
Web Site: www.lincolparkri.com
Map Location: **#1** (10 miles N. of Providence)

Toll-Free Number: (800) 720-7275
Restaurants: 3
Hours: 10am-Mid/1am (Fri-Sat)
Special Features: Live dog racing (Mon/Wed/Fri/Sat) throughout the year. Daily simulcasting of horse and dog racing. Free admission and free valet parking.

Newport Grand Jai-Alai
150 Admiral Kalbfus Road
Newport, Rhode Island 02840
(401) 849-5000
Web Site: www.newportgrand.com
Map Location: **#2**

Toll-Free Number: (800) 451-2500
Restaurants: 1
Hours: 10am-1am Daily
Special Features: Live jai-alai games (Thu-Mon) during the season which runs from early March through Labor Day weekend. Daily (except Tuesday) simulcasting of horse and dog racing.

SOUTH CAROLINA

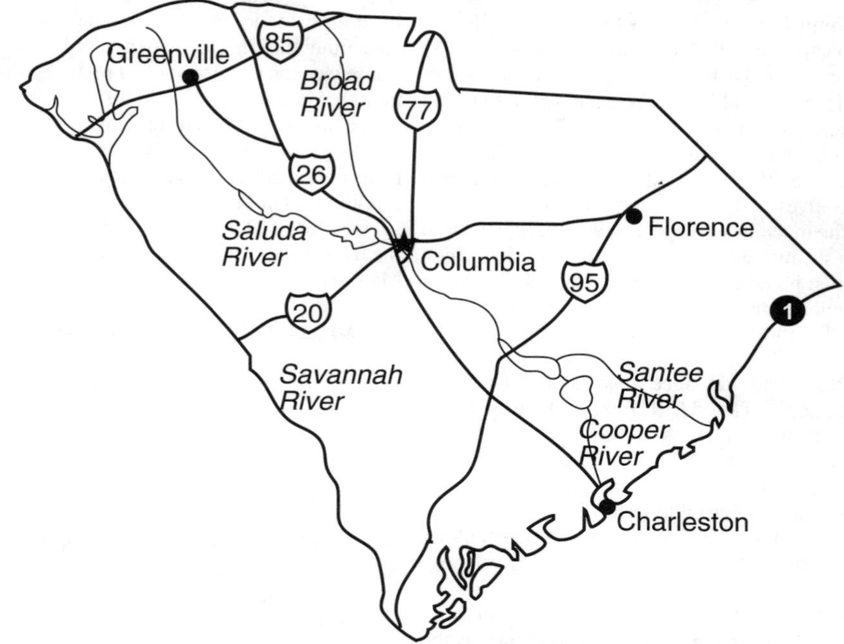

South Carolina has two gambling cruise ships which sail three miles out into international waters where casino gambling is permitted. Both boats offer: blackjack, craps, roulette, oasis stud poker, slots and video poker.

For more information on visiting South Carolina call the state's tourism department at (800) 872-3505.

Stardancer Casino Cruises
1180 Hwy 17 North
Little River, South Carolina 29566
(843) 280-7731
Map Location: **#1** (35 miles N. of Myrtle Beach)

Reservation Number: (800) 2345-WIN
Gambling Age: 21
Meal Service: $6 Day/$12 Eve
Schedule: 11:30am - 5:00pm (Daily)
7:00pm - 12:30am (Daily)
Prices: Free Port Charges: None
Parking: Free
Special Features: 506-passenger *Stardancer* sails from N. Myrtle Beach Marina. Must be 21, or older, to board.

SunCruz Casino - Myrtle Beach
4491 Waterfront Drive
Little River, South Carolina 29566
(843) 280-8322
Web Site: www.suncruzcasino.com
Map Location: **#1** (35 miles N. of Myrtle Beach)

Reservation Number: (877) 250-5825
Gambling Age: 18
Buffets: $5 Day/$7 Eve
Schedule:
11:00am - 4:00pm (Mon-Thu)
Noon - 5:00pm (Sat-Sun)
7:00pm - 12:00am (Daily)
Prices: $10 (Free with advance reservations)
Port Charges: Included
Parking: Free
Other Games: Poker
Special Features: 600-passenger *SunCruz VII* sails from Little River Waterfront. Must be 18, or older, to board. Free hors d'oeuvres, soft drinks and coffee.

SOUTH DAKOTA

South Dakota's bars and taverns are allowed to have up to 10 video lottery terminals (VLT's) that offer the following games: poker, keno, blackjack and bingo. These machines are the same as regular video gaming devices but are called lottery terminals because they are regulated by the state's lottery commission which receives a share of each machine's revenue. The machines accept cash but don't pay out in cash; instead, they print out a receipt which must be taken to a cashier. Slot machines, as well as blackjack and poker are only permitted at Indian casinos and in Deadwood.

Deadwood was once most famous for being the home of Wild Bill Hickok who was shot to death while playing cards in the No. 10 Saloon. The hand he held at the time was two pairs: black aces and eights, which ever since is usually referred to as a "dead man's hand." Wild Bill is buried in the local cemetery along with another local celebrity: Calamity Jane.

Today, Deadwood is still well known for those colorful characters, but it's also known as the home of slot machines, poker and blackjack ever since voters approved those forms of gambling more than 12 years ago. When the first casinos opened on November 1, 1989 the promoters expected betting of $4 million a year. The estimate was a little low because in the first two years alone the betting totaled more than $500 million!

All of the buildings in the downtown area are required to conform with the city's authentic 1880's architecture and many of the casinos are located in historic structures. As a matter of fact, the No. 10 Saloon is still there and you can actually gamble in the same spot where old Wild Bill bit the dust! One of the casinos - Midnight Star, is owned by movie actor Kevin Costner and his brother, Dan.

South Dakota law limits each casino licensee to a maximum of 30 slot machines in a building and no business is allowed to hold more than three licenses. The law also limits blackjack, poker, let it ride and 3-card poker bets to a maximum of $5, however, you are permitted to play more than one hand at a time.

In addition to the Deadwood casinos, there are also nine Indian casinos in South Dakota. These casinos are also subject to the $5 maximum bet restrictions except for Dakota Sioux which offers a $100 betting limit on blackjack.

Here are statistics from the South Dakota Commission on Gaming for the payback percentages on all of Deadwood's slot machines for the five-month period from January 1 through May 31, 2000:

Denomination	Payback %
5¢ Slots	91.58
10¢ Slots	91.75
25¢ Slots	90.47
50¢ Slots	91.43
$1 Slots	91.64
$5 Slots	94.46

Most casinos are open from 8am until 12am Sunday through Thursday and 8am until 2am on the weekends. Unless otherwise noted, all casinos offer slot machines and video poker. The minimum gambling age is 21 (18 at Indian casinos that don't serve alcohol).

For South Dakota tourism information call (800) 952-3625. For information on visiting Deadwood call the city's Chamber of Commerce at (800) 999-1876.

Deadwood

Map Location: **#1** (in the Black Hills, 41 miles N.W. of Rapid City. Take I-90 W. Get off at the second Sturges exit and take Hwy. 14-A into Deadwood)

B. B. Cody's
681 Main Street
Deadwood, SD 57732
(605) 578-3430

Hours: 8am-12am/3am (Fri-Sat)
Other Games: Blackjack, LIR
Special Features: Video arcade

Nestled in the Black Hills of South Dakota, the entire city of Deadwood has been designated a national historic landmark. Free historic walking tours are offered daily.

Best Western Hickok House
137 Charles Street
(605) 578-1611

Reservation Number: 800-528-1234
Rooms: 38 Price Range: $69-$99
Restaurants: 1
Hours: 6:30am-2am
Special Features: Hot tub and sauna. 20% AAA room discount. Beer and wine served.

Bodega Bar
662 Main Street
(605) 578-1996

Restaurants: 1
Hours: 11am-12am
Other Games: Blackjack

Buffalo Saloon
658 Main Street
(605) 578-9993

Hours: 24 hours daily
Other games: Blackjack (Thu-Sat)

Bullock Express
68 Main Street
(605) 578-3476

Reservation Number: 800-526-8277
Rooms: 38 Price Range: $65-$77
Restaurants: 1
Hours: 24 hours daily
Special Features: 10% room discount for AAA or AARP members.

Bullock Hotel
633 Main Street
(605) 578-1745
Web Site: www.bullockhotel.com

Reservation Number: 800-336-1876
Rooms: 29 Price Range: $75-$95
Suites: 7 Price Range: $135-$155
Restaurants: 1
Hours: 24 hours daily
Special Features: Deadwood's oldest hotel. Victorian-styled rooms. Gift shop. Exercise facility. 3-Diamond AAA rated. 10% room discount to AAA members.

Celebrity Hotel & Casino
629 Main Street
(605) 578-1909

Toll-Free Number: (888) 399-1886
Rooms: 9 Price Range: $49-$89
Special Features: Car and motorcycle museum. Free to hotel guests, otherwise $2.50 for adults and $1.50 for seniors (55 or older) and children (6-12). 10% AAA room discount.

Dakota Territory Saloon
652 Main Street
(605) 578-3566

Deadwood Dick's Saloon/Nickel Dick's
51-55 Sherman Street
(605) 578-3224
Web Site: www.deadwooddicks.com

Rooms: 5 Price Range: $56
Suites: 6 Price Range: $70-$200
Restaurants: 1
Hours: 10am-2am
Other Games: Blackjack
Special Features: Deadwood's only microbrewery. Brew pub and daily tours of brewery. Antiques mall. 30% room discount for stays of over 3 days.

Deadwood Gulch Resort
Highway 85 South/P.O. Box 643
(605) 578-1294
Web Site: www.deadwoodgulch.com

Reservation Number: (800) 695-1876
Rooms: 95 Price Range: $62-$109
Suites: 3 Price Range: $100-$135
Restaurants: 2
Hours: 24 hours daily
Casino Size: 7,000 Square Feet
Other Games: Blackjack
Fun Book: Given to hotel guests
Special Features: 10% room discount to AAA and AARP members. Convenience store and gas station. Family fun park with go-carts, bumper boats, miniature golf, batting cages, kiddie playland and indoor arcade. Outdoor swimming pool and indoor hot tub. Pets allowed with $10 nonrefundable deposit.

Deadwood Gulch Saloon
560 Main Street
(605) 578-1207

Hours: 9am-2am

Deadwood Inn
27 Deadwood Street
(605) 578-7700

Toll Free Number: (877) 815-7974
Rooms: 19 Price Range: $49-$89
Suites: 4 Price Range: $89-$175
Casino Size: 1,000 Square Feet.
Other Games: Poker
Special Features: Includes **Palace Express** Casino. 10% room discount for AAA members and seniors 65 years of age, or older. Free continental breakfast with room. Free parking.

Double Diamond
29 Lee Street
(605) 578-3546

Hours: 8am-10am/12am (Fri-Sat)

Elk's Lodge
696 Main Street #508
(605) 578-1333

Hours: 5pm-10pm

First Gold Hotel & Gaming
270 Main Street
(605) 578-9777
Web Site: www.firstgold.com

Reservation Number: (800) 274-1876
Rooms: 98 Price Range: $39-$74
Suites: 3 Price Range: $84-$129
Restaurants: 2
Buffets: D-$7.77
Hours: 24 hours daily
Casino Size: 7,000 Square Feet
Other Games: Blackjack, TCP
Casino Marketing: (800) 410-3732
Fun Book: Given to hotel and RV guests, or club members may receive one at front desk.
Senior Discount: 10% off room, if 60, or older
Special Features: 79¢ breakfast and $1.99 lunch specials. RV park located next door. Also contains the **Horseshoe** and **Black Jack** casinos.

Four Aces
531 Main Street
(605) 578-2323

Restaurants: 1
Buffets: B-$2.95 L-$5.95 D-$9.95
Hours:8am-12am
Casino Size: 12,000 Square Feet
Other Games: Blackjack, 3-Card Poker

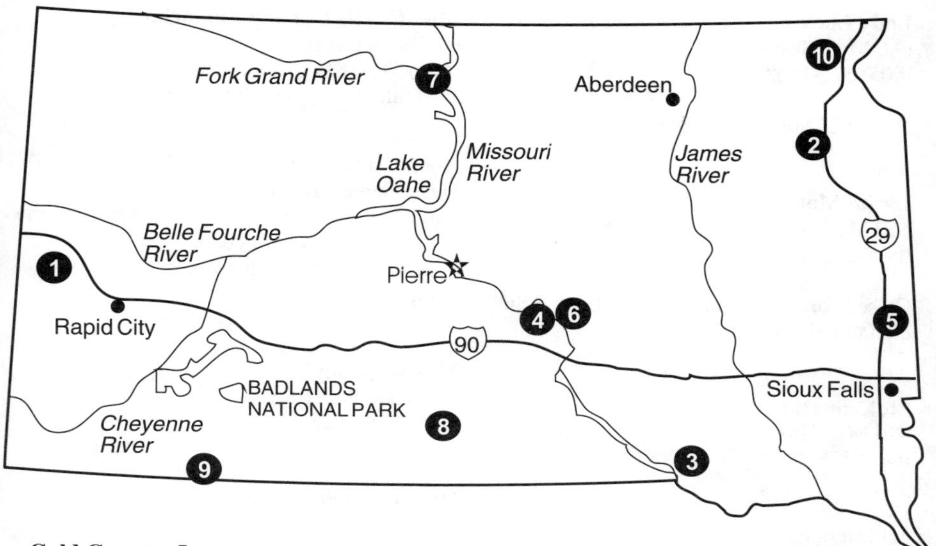

Gold Country Inn
801 Main Street
Deadwood, SD 57732
(605) 578-2393

Reservation Number: (800) 287-1251
Rooms: 53 Price Range: $45-$59
Restaurants: 1

Gold Dust Gaming & Entertainment Complex
688 Main Street
(605) 578-2100

Toll-Free Number: 800-456-0533
Rooms: 56 Price Range: $69-$150
Suites: 22 Price Range: $150-$250
Restaurants: 1
Buffets: B-$4.99 L-$5.99 D-$9.99/$10.99 (Sat)/$11.95 (Fri)
Hours: 24 hours Daily
Casino Size: 22,000 Square Feet
Other Games: Blackjack, Poker
Fun Book: Join slot club to get newsletter with coupons
Senior Discount: $1 off buffets, if 55, or older
Special Features: Largest gaming complex in Deadwood with five casinos including: **Legends, French Quarter and Silver Dollar.** Two lounges. Gold Dust Players Club offers free parties, Comedy Club and instant winner drawings. Hotel offers AARP discount, free continental breakfast, indoor pool, gym, whirlpool, arcade. Hotel is a Holiday Inn Express and Suites.

Goldberg's/Old San Francisco Mint
670 Main Street
(605) 578-1515

Restaurants: 2
Hours: 24 hours daily
Fun Book: Write ahead to request.
Special features: Red beans, sausage and rice offered for 99¢ from 10pm-5am daily.

Hickok's Saloon
685 Main Street
(605) 578-2222

Hours: 9am-2am (Wed/Thu)/24 hrs (Fri-Tue)
Other Games: Blackjack

Historic Franklin Hotel
700 Main Street
(605) 578-2241
Web Site: www.deadwood.net/franklin

Reservation Number: 800-688-1876
Rooms: 66 Price Range: $27-$92
Suites: 15 Price Range: $122-$162
Restaurants: 1
Buffets: B-$5.95 (Sun)
Other Games: Blackjack, Poker
Fun Book: Given to hotel guests and when you join the slot club
Senior Discount: 10% off room, if 65, or older
Special Features: Historic 91-year-old hotel. Three lounges feature entertainment on weekends. Wedding chapel.

Lady Luck
660 Main Street
(605) 578-1162

Hours: 24 hours daily

Lariat Motel
360 Main Street
(605) 578-1500

Closed for remodeling at press time. Scheduled to reopen by early 2001.

McKenna's Gold
470 Main Street
(605) 578-3207

Midnight Star
677 Main Street
(605) 578-1555
Web Site: www.themidnightstar.com

Toll-Free Number: (800) 999-6482
Restaurants: 2
Hours: 8am-2am (Sun-Thu)/24 hours (Fri/Sat)
Other Games: Blackjack, Let It Ride, 3-Card Poker
Fun Book: Call (800) 999-6482 to receive by mail
Special Features: Kevin Costner is part-owner and the property features a museum with authentic costumes and memorabilia from his movies. Sports Bar & Grill. Original Deadwood tour departs from the front entrance.

Mineral Palace Hotel & Gaming Complex
601 Main Street
(605) 578-2036
Web Site: www.mineralpalace.com

Reservation Number: (800) 84-PALACE
Rooms: 63 Price Range: $69-$99
Suites : $79-$195
Restaurants: 1
Hours: 24 hours daily
Other Games: Blackjack
Casino Marketing: (800) 84-PALACE
Special Features: Contains **Cousin Jack's**, **Carrie Nation's** and **Deadwood Livery** casinos. Nonsmoking rooms available. Cappuccino and espresso bar. free parking.

Miss Kitty's Gaming Emporium
647 Main Street
(605) 578-1811
Web Site: www.misskittys.com

Restaurants: 2
Hours: 24 hours daily/ close 12am (sun-Mon)
Other Games: Blackjack, Poker
Fun Book: Look in brochure racks for card to take to Welcome Center
Special Features: Chinese and Mexican restaurants.

Mustang Sally's
634 Main Street
(605) 578-2025

Old Style Saloon #10
657 Main Street
(605) 578-3346
Web Site: www.saloon10.com

Toll-Free Number: (800) 952-9398
Restaurants: 1
Casino Size: 4,000 Square Feet
Other Games: Blackjack, Poker, 3-Card Poker
Special Features: During summer there is a reenactment of the "Shooting of Wild Bill Hickok" four times daily. Wild Bill's chair and other Old West artifacts on display.

Oyster Bay/Fairmont Hotel
628 Main Street
(605) 578-2205

Restaurants: 1
Special Features: Historic restoration of 1895 brothel and spa. Features first-class oyster bar.

Silverado Gaming & Restaurant
709 Main Street
(605) 578-3670
Web Site: www.silveradocasino.com

Toll-Free Number: (800) 584-7005
Restaurants: 1
Buffets: B-$5.95 L-$5.95 D-$10.95/$11.95 (Fri-Sat)
Hours: 24 hours daily
Casino Size: 10,000 Square Feet
Other Games: Blackjack, Let It Ride, 3-Card Poker
Fun Book: Call or write for information

Super 8 Lodge/Lucky 8 Gaming Hall
196 Cliff Street
(605) 578-2535
Web Site: www.deadwoodsuper8.com

Reservation Number: (800) 800-8000
Rooms: 51 Price Range: $40-$130
Suites: 3 Price Range: $75-$130
Restaurants: 1
Hours: 24 hours daily
Fun Book: Given to guests at check-in
Senior Discount: 10% room discount for AARP members
Special Features: Trolley service. Indoor heated pool and spa. Nonsmoking rooms available. Free breakfast bar. Video arcade.

Thunder Cove Inn
Highway 85 South
(605) 578-3045

Toll-Free Number: (800) 209-7361
Rooms: 24 Price Range: $44-$64
Suites: 1 Price Range: $55-$85
Special Features: Free continental breakfast for inn guests. Scheduled shuttle service to downtown Deadwood. All nonsmoking rooms.

Tin Lizzie Gaming
555 Main Street
(605) 578-1715
Web Sit: www.tinlizzie.com

Toll-Free Number: (800) 643-4490
Restaurants: 1
Buffets: B-$1.99
Hours: 24 hours daily
Casino Size: 8,300 Square Feet
Other Games: Blackjack
Fun Book: Can request online, or write to receive by mail
Special Features: Also contains **Casey's** and **Mustang** casinos. Stay and win packages available for lodging at several local hotels.

Twin City Cleaners
795 Main Street
(605) 578-1260

Veteran's Of Foreign War
10 Pine Street
(605) 578-9914

Wild West Winners Casino
608-622 Main Street
(605) 578-1100
Web Site: www.wildwestwinners.com

Toll-Free Number: (800) 873-1876
Restaurants: 1
Other Games: Simulcasting
Fun Book: Call or write for information
Special Features: Also houses **Miss P.J.'s Parlor** and **Wild Bill Bar and Gambling Hall**. Deadwood's only simulcasting facility.

Wooden Nickel
9 Lee Street
(605) 578-1952

Indian Casinos

Dakota Connection
RR 1, Box 177-B
Sisseton, South Dakota 57262
(605) 698-4273
Map Location: **#10** (165 miles N. of Sioux Falls)

Restaurants: 1 Liquor: No
Buffets: D-$6.95 (Fri-Sun)
Hours: 24 Hours Daily
Other Games: Blackjack, Poker

Dakota Sioux Casino
16415 Sioux Conifer Road
Watertown, South Dakota 57201
(605) 882-2051
Web Site: www.dakotasioux.com
Map Location: **#2** (104 miles N. of Sioux Falls)

Toll-Free Number: (800) 658-4717
Restaurants: 1 (open 24 hours) Liquor: Yes
Hours: 24 hours daily
Other Games: Blackjack, Poker, 3-Card Poker

Fort Randall Casino
West Hwy. 46/RR 1, Box 46
Wagner, South Dakota 57380
(605) 487-7871
Map Location: **#3** (100 miles S.W. of Sioux Falls)

Room Reservations: (800) 362-6333
Rooms: 57 Price Range: $49.60
Suites: 2 Price Range: $71.00

Restaurants: 1 Liquor: Yes
Buffets: D-$4.95/$6.95 (Thu)
D-$7.95 (Fri)/$9.95 (Sat)
Hours: 24 hours daily
Other Games: Blackjack, Poker, Bingo
Fun Book: Only given to groups

Golden Buffalo Casino
P.O. Box 204
Lower Brule, South Dakota 57548
(605) 473-5577
Map Location: **#4** (45 miles S.E. of Pierre)

Room Reservations: (605) 473-5506
Rooms: 38 Price Range: $38-$45
Restaurants: 1 Liquor: Yes
Hours: 7am-1am/3am Hours (Fri/Sat)
Other Games: Blackjack, Poker, 3-Card Poker
Fun Book: Only given to groups

Grand River Casino
P.O. Box 639
Mobridge, South Dakota 57601
(605) 845-7104
Map Location: **#7** (240 miles N.E. of Rapid City)

Toll-Free Number: (800) 475-3321
Restaurants: 1 Liquor: Yes
Hours: 8am-3am
Other Games: Blackjack, Poker

Lode Star Casino
P.O. Box 140
Fort Thompson, South Dakota 57339
(605) 245-6000
Map Location: **#6** (150 miles N.W. of Sioux Falls)

Restaurants: 1 Liquor: Yes
Hours: 7am-2am/4am (Fri/Sat)
Other Games: Blackjack, Poker

Prairie Wind Casino
HC 49, Box 10
Pine Ridge, South Dakota 57770
(605) 867-6300
Web Site: www.prairiewindcasino.net
Map Location: **#9** (85 miles S.E. of Rapid City)

Toll-Free Number: (800) 705-9463
Restaurants: 1 Liquor: No
Hours: 24 hours Daily
Other Games: Blackjack, Poker, 3-Card Poker
Special Features: Casino is located 12 miles East of Oelrichs off Hwy. 385 and 8 miles West of Oglala on Hwy. 18.

Rosebud Casino
HC 14, Box 135
Valentine, Nebraska 69201
(605) 378-3800
Web Site: www.rosebudcasino.com
Map Location: **#8** (22 miles S. of Mission)

Toll-Free Number: (800) 786-7673
Rooms: 60 Price Range: $45-$74
Suites: 2 Price Range: $79-$89
Restaurants: 2 Liquor: Yes
Buffets: D-$7.77
Hours: 24 hours daily
Other Games: Blackjack, Poker, Bingo
Senior Discount: If 55, or older, ask for Senior Club Cards
Fun Book: Ask at marketing office
Special Features: Mailing address is in Nebraska but casino is in South Dakota near the Nebraska state line. Hotel is affiliated with Quality Inn and offers free continental breakfast. AAA, AARP and Internet discounts available.

Royal River Casino Bingo & Motel
607 S. Veterans Street
Flandreau, South Dakota 57028
(605) 997-3746
Web Site: www.royalrivercasino.com
Map Location: **#5** (35 miles N. of Sioux Falls on I-29)

Toll-Free Number: (800) 833-8666
Rooms: 54 Price Range: $45-$50
Suites: 6 Price Range: $90-$95
Restaurants: 1 Liquor: Yes
Buffets: B-$4.95/ $7.95(Sun)
L-$5.95/$7.95 (Sun) D-$9.95 (Fri-Sun)
$7.95 (Tue-Thu)/$12.95 (Mon)
Hours: 24 hours daily
Casino Size: 15,000 Square Feet
Other Games: Blackjack, Poker, Bingo
Fun Book: Only given to groups
Special Features: $3 buffet discount if you have a Player's Club Card. RV parking available for $10 per day. AAA and AARP discounts available.

TEXAS

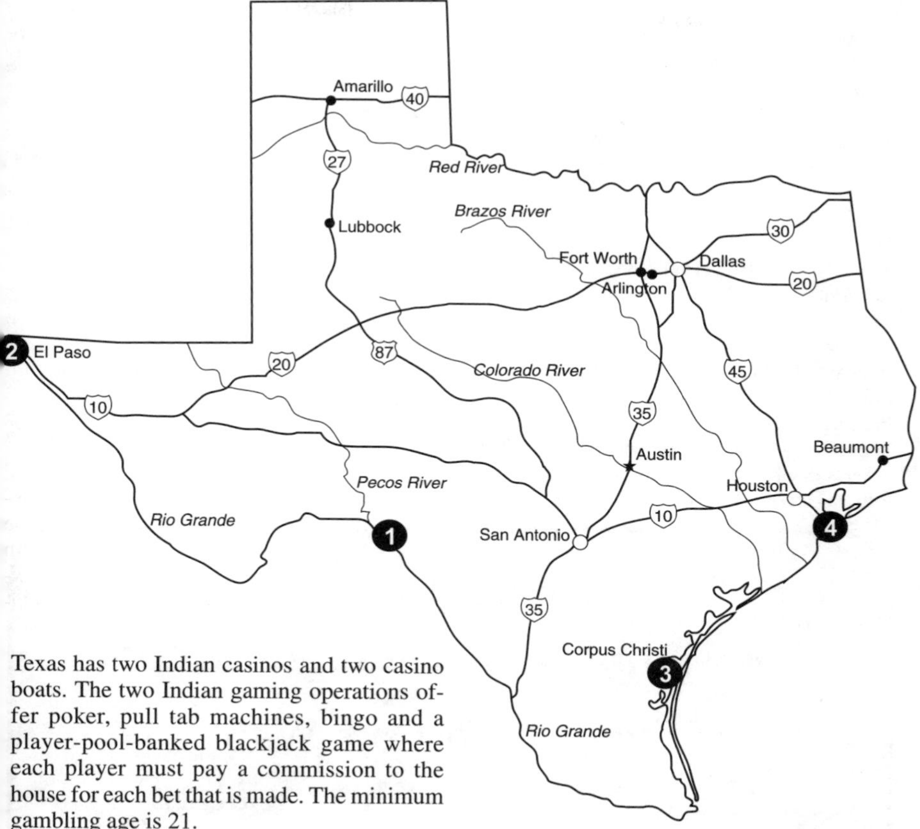

Texas has two Indian casinos and two casino boats. The two Indian gaming operations offer poker, pull tab machines, bingo and a player-pool-banked blackjack game where each player must pay a commission to the house for each bet that is made. The minimum gambling age is 21.

For more information on visiting Texas call (800) 888-8TEX.

Kickapoo Lucky Eagle Casino
Rt 1, Box 7777
Eagle Pass, Texas 78852
(830) 758-1995
Map Location: **#1** (150 miles N.W. of San Antonio)

Toll-Free Number: (888) 255-8259
Restaurants: 1 Liquor: Yes
Hours: 12pm-2am(Mon/Tue)/4am(Wed/Thu)
24 Hours (Fri-Sun)
Casino Size: 16,000 Square Feet
Special Features: Blackjack commission is 50¢ per $25 bet.

Speaking Rock Casino
122 S. Old Pueblo Road
El Paso, Texas 79907
(915) 860-7777
Web Site: www.speakingrockcasino.com
Map Location: **#2**

Toll-Free Number: (800) 77-BINGO
Restaurants: 1 Liquor: Yes
Buffets: B-$4.99 (Fri-Sun)
L-$6.99 D-$8.99(Thur/Sun)
Hours: 24 Hours Daily
Other Games: Keno
Casino Size: 60,000 Square Feet
Special Features: Blackjack commission is flat 50¢ per bet, regardless of amount.

The two casino boats in Texas sail nine miles out into the Gulf of Mexico where casino gambling is permitted and both boats offer: blackjack, craps, roulette, slots and video poker.

Texas Treasure Casino Cruises
1401 W. Wheeler Avenue
Aransas Pass, Texas 78336
(361) 758-4444
Map Location: **#3** (10 miles N.E. of Corpus Christi)

Reservation Number: (800) 472-5215
Gambling Age: 21
Meal Service: Buffet Included
Schedule:
12:00pm - 5:30pm (Daily)
7:00pm - 12:00am/1am (Fri/Sat)
Prices: $19.99/$24.95 (Fri Eve/Saturdays)
Port Charges: None
Parking: Free
Special Features: 600-passenger *Texas Treasurer* sails from dock near ferry in Aransas Pass. Must be 21, or older, to board.

Fantasea Casino Cruises
Texas City, Texas
Web Site: www.fantaseacasino.com
Map Location: **#4** (40 miles S. of Houston)

EXPECTED TO OPEN BY EARLY 2001
Special Features: 250-passenger *Fantasea* formerly sailed from Panama City, Florida. Check web site for more current details.

WASHINGTON

As of August 2000 there were 21 Indian casinos operating in Washington and one new casino was expected to open by early 2001.

Fourteen of the state's casinos are affiliated with tribes that have compacts with the state that allow them to offer table games, as well as a special kind of gaming machine that is similar to a slot machine. These gaming machines all have video screens and aren't allowed to accept cash. Instead, a cashless system is used whereby you have to go to a cashier cage, or a kiosk, and buy a smart card which then deducts losses, or credits wins to your account.

Of the state's remaining eight casinos, four are affiliated with the Spokane Tribe, three are operated by the Colville Confederated Tribes and one is affiliated with the Shoalwater Tribe. All of these Tribes have an ongoing dispute with the state and are operating without compacts. All eight of their casinos offer regular slot machines as well as table games.

Unless otherwise noted, all casinos are open 24 hours and offer: blackjack, craps, roulette and pull tabs. Optional games offered include: baccarat (B), mini-baccarat (MB), poker (P), pai gow poker (PGP), Caribbean stud poker (CSP), big 6 wheel (B6), keno (K) and bingo (BG). The minimum gambling age is 18 (21 if liquor is served).

Although most of the casinos have toll-free numbers be aware that some of those numbers will only work for calls made within Washington.

For more information on visiting Washington call the state's tourism department at (800) 544-1800.

Chewelah Casino
2555 Smith Road
Chewelah, Washington 99109
(509) 935-6167
Map Location: **#13** (50 miles N. of Spokane)

Toll-Free Number: (800) 322-2788
Restaurants: 1 Deli Liquor: No
Hours: 9am-2am Daily
Casino Size: 22,000 Square Feet
Other Games: Slots, Video Poker, BG
Senior Discount: $1 lunch buffet and $25 for $20 buy-in on Wed. from 11:30am-4pm, if 55, or older
Fun Book: Given out on Fridays
Special Features: One block from Double Eagle Casino.

Coulee Dam Casino
515 Birch Street
Coulee Dam, Washington 99155
(509) 633-0766
Map Location: **#11** (190 miles E. of Seattle)

Toll-Free Number: (800) 556-7492
Restaurants: 1 Deli Liquor: No
Hours: 9am-Mid/2am (Fri/Sat)
Other Games: Slots, Video Poker
Casino Marketing: (800) 648-2946
Fun Book: Only given to tour groups
Senior Discount: Ask to join Triple Play Club if 55, or older
Special features: Gift shop. BJ tables open 4pm-12am/2am (Fri/Sat)/2pm-10pm (Sun)

Double Eagle Casino
2539 Smith Road
Chewelah, Washington 99109
(509) 935-4406
Map Location: **#13** (50 miles N. of Spokane)

Restaurants: 1 Deli Liquor: No
Hours: 9am-1am
Other Games: PGP, Slots, Video Poker, No Craps
Special Features: One block from Spokane Indian Bingo & Casino.

Emerald Queen Casino
2102 Alexander Avenue
Tacoma, Washington 98421
(206) 594-7777
Map Location: **#15**

Toll-Free Number: (888) 831-7655
Restaurants: 1 Liquor: Yes
Buffets: B-$12.75 (Sun) D-$16.75 (Mon)/
$12.75 (Sun/Tue)/$13.75 (Wed/Fri)/
$14.75 (Thu)/$17.75 (Sat)
Hours: 10am-6am Daily
Other Games: Gaming Machines, B, MB, P,
PGP, CSP, LIR, K
Special Features: Property has two casinos: one is on a riverboat and the other is in a shoreside facility.

Kalispel Casino
Usk, Washington 99180
(509) 445-1147
Map Location: **#20** (50 miles N. of Spokane)

EXPECTED TO OPEN EARLY 2001
Other Games: Gaming machines

Little Chiefs Casino
P.O. Box 130
Wellpinit, Washington 99040
(509) 258-4544
Map Location: **#2** (25 miles N.W. of Spokane)

Restaurants: 1 Liquor: No
Hours: 9am-2am/10pm (Tue)
Other Games: Only Slots and Video Poker
Special Features: Casino is in city of Ford.

Little Creek Casino
West 91 Highway 108
Shelton, Washington 98584
(360) 427-7711
Web Site: www.little-creek.com
Map Location: **#9** (23 miles N. of Olympia)

Toll-Free Number: (800) 667-7711
Restaurants: 2 Liquor: Yes
Buffets: D-$9.95 (Wed)/$13.95 (Thu)
Hours: 10am-4am/6am (Thu-Sat)
Casino Size: 36,000 Square Feet
Other Games: Gaming Machines, MB, P, PGP,
CSP, LIR, K, BG (Thu-Sun)
Senior Discount: Various 15% discounts available, if 55, or older.

Lucky Eagle Casino
12888 188th Road S.W.
Rochester, Washington 98579
(360) 273-2000
Map Location: **#12** (10 miles S. of Olympia)

Toll-Free Number: (800) 720-1788
Restaurants: 2 Liquor: Yes
Buffets: B-$10.95 (Sun)
Hours: 10am-4am/10am-6am (Fri/Sat)
Casino Size: 48,000 Square Feet
Other Games: Gaming Machines, C, R, MB,
P, CSP, LIR, B6, K, BG
Fun Book: Given to new slot club members
and with coupon obtained through
local hotels and businesses.
Special Features: Live music and dancing Fri/Sat evenings.

Mill Bay Casino
455 E. Wapato Lake Road
Manson, Washington 98831
(509) 687-2102
Map Location: **#5** (200 miles N.E. of Seattle on the N. shore of Lake Chelan)

Toll-Free Number: (800) 648-2946
Restaurants: 1 Liquor: No
Buffets: B-$8.95 (Sun)
Other Games: PGP, Slots, Video Poker
Senior Discount: Ask to join Triple Play Club
if 55, or older
Fun Book: Distributed by local motels and also given to groups

Muckleshoot Casino
2402 Auburn Way South
Auburn, Washington 98002
(206) 804-4944
Web Site: www.casino-fun.com
Map Location: **#6** (20 miles S. of Seattle)

Toll-Free Number (800) 804-4944
Restaurants: 3 Liquor: Yes
Buffets: D-$12.95(Fri-Sun) /$14.95 (Mon/Thu)
Hours: 10am-5:45am Daily
Other Games: Gaming Machines, B, MB, P, PGP, CSP, LIR, K, BG, Simulcasting

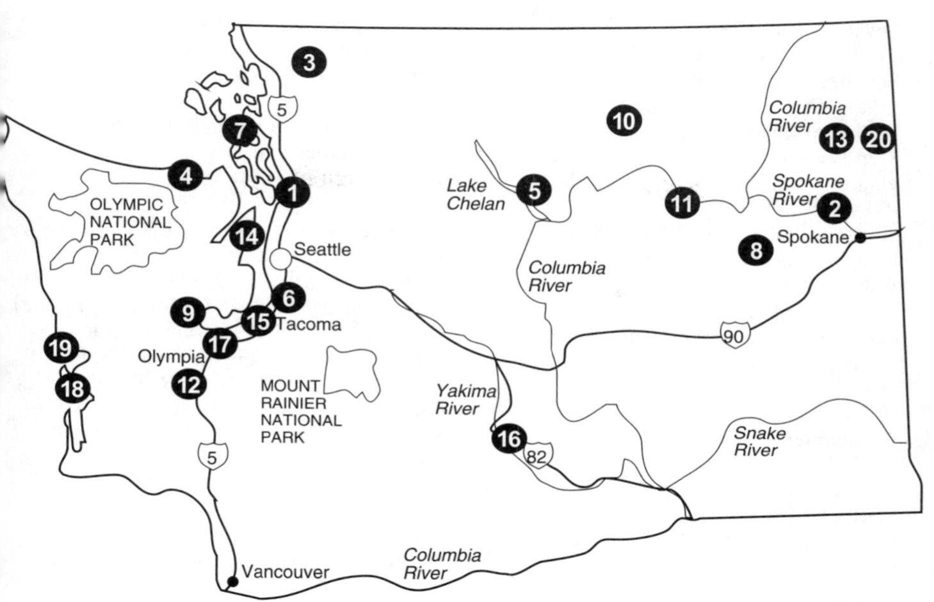

Nooksack River Casino
5048 Mt. Baker Highway
Deming, Washington 98244
(360) 592-5472
Web Site: www.nooksackcasino.com
Map Location: **#3** (14 miles E. of Bellingham)

Toll-Free Number: (800) 233-2573
Restaurants: 1 Liquor: Yes
Buffets: L-$7.95 D-$13.95/$15.95 (Fri/Sat)
Hours: 10am-3am/5am (Fri/Sat)
Casino Size: 21,500 Square Feet
Other Games: Gaming Machines, MB, P, PGP, CSP, LIR
Senior Discount: $2 off buffets, if 55, or older
Special Features: Live entertainment Friday and Saturday.

Okanogan Bingo and Casino
41 Appleway Road
Okanogan, Washington 98840
(509) 422-4646
Map Location: **#10** (165 miles E. of Seattle)

Toll-Free Number: (800) 559-4643
Restaurants: 1 Snack Bar Liquor: No
Hours: 9am-Mid/2am (Fri/Sat)
Other Games: Only Slots, Video Poker and Bingo

Quinault Beach Resort
78 Route 115
Ocean Shores, Washington 98569
(360) 289-9466
Map Location: **#19** (90 miles W. of Tacoma)

Toll-Free Number: (888) 461-2214
Rooms: 159 Price Range: $150-$220
Suite: 9 Price Range: $309-750
Restaurants: 2 Liquor: Yes
Buffets: D-$24.99 (Fri-Sat)
Hours: 11am-2am/10am-4:30am (Fri-Sat)
Other Games: Gaming Machines, B, PGP, LIR, CSP
Senior Discount: Room discount for AARP members
Special Features: All rooms have stove and refrigerator.

Red Wind Casino
12819 Yelm Highway
Olympia, Washington 98513
(360) 412-5000
Map Location: **#17**

Restaurants: 1 Liquor: Yes
Hours: 10am-4am Daily
Other Games: Gaming Machines, PGP, CSP, LIR, K

Seven Cedars Casino
270756 Highway 101
Sequim, Washington 98382
(360) 683-7777
Web Site: www.7cedarscasino.com
Map Location: **#4** (70 miles N.W. of Seattle via ferry)

Toll-Free Number: (800) 4-LUCKY-7
Restaurants: 1 Liquor: Yes
Buffets: D-$14.95 (Fri-Sat)
Hours: 12pm-1am/3am (Fri-Sat)
Other Games: Gaming Machines, PGP, LIR, K, BG, Simulcasting

Shoalwater Casino
4112 Highway 105
Tokeland, Washington 98590
(360) 267-2048
Map Location: **#18** (75 miles S.W. of Olympia)

Toll-Free Number: (800) 801-3401
Restaurants: 1 Liquor: No
Hours: 10am-12am/2am (Fri/Sat)
Other Games: Gaming Machines, P,
No Craps or Roulette
Senior Discount: Tuesday specials if 55, or older

Skagit Valley Casino
590 Dark Lane
Bow, Washington 98232
(360) 724-7777
Map Location: **#7** (75 miles N. of Seattle)

Restaurants: 3 Liquor: Yes
Buffets: B-$4.99 L-$6.99/$4.99 (Thu)
D-$9.99/$12.99 (Fri/Sat)
Hours: 9am-2am/3am (Fri/Sat)
Casino Size: 26,075 Square Feet
Other Games: Gaming Machines, B, MB, PGP, CSP, LIR, BG

Suquamish Clearwater Casino
15347 Suquamish Way N.E./Box 1210
Suquamish, Washington 98392
(360) 598-6889
Web Site: www.clearwatercasino.com
Map Location: **#14** (15 miles W. of Seattle via Bainbridge Ferry)

Toll-Free Number: (800) 375-6073
Restaurants: 2 Liquor: Yes
Buffets: L/D-$5.00/$7.95 (Tue)
$8.95 (Sun/Wed-Thu)/$12.95 (Fri/Sat)
Hours: 10am-2am/11am-4am (Fri/Sat)
Other Games: Gaming Machines, B, MB, P,
PGP, CSP, LIR, K, BG
Fun Book: Call event coordinator at ext-244
Senior Discount: $1 off buffets, if 55, or older
Special Features: Closest casino to Seattle. Free shuttle service.

Swinomish Casino and Bingo
837 Casino Drive
Anacortes, Washington 98221
(360) 293-2691
Web Site: www.swinomishcasino.com
Map Location: **#7** (70 miles N. of Seattle, between I-5 and Anacortes on Hwy. 20)

Restaurants: 2 Liquor: Yes
Buffets: B-$8.95 (Sun) L-$5.95
D-$8.95/$14.95 (Fri/Sat)
Hours: 11am-4am/6am (Fri/Sat)
Casino Size: 73,000 Square Feet
Other Games: Gaming Machines, P, PGP, CSP,
LIR, BG, Red Dog, Simulcasting
Senior Discount: $1 off buffet, if 60, or older
Special Features: Double-deck blackjack offered. 10x odds on craps. RV parking. Gift shop.

Tulalip Casino
6410 33rd Avenue N.E.
Marysville, Washington 98271
(360) 651-1111
Map Location: **#1** (30 miles N. of Seattle)

Toll-Free Number: (888) 272-1111
Restaurants: 2 Liquor: Yes
Buffets: B-$8.95 (Sun)
Hours: 10am-6am Daily
Other Games: Gaming Machines, MB, P, CSP, PGP, LIR, K, BG

Two Rivers Casino
6828-B Highway 25 South
Davenport, Washington 99122
(509) 722-4000
Map Location: **#8** (60 miles W. of Spokane)

Toll-Free Number: (800) 722-4031
Restaurants: 1 Snack Bar Liquor: No
Hours: 9am-1am/24 Hours (Fri/Sat)
Casino Size: 10,000 Square Feet
Other Games: PGP, Slots, Video Poker, Video Keno
Fun Book: Only given to groups
Special Features: Full-service 35-space RV park. 100-slip marina.

Yakama Nation Legends Casino
580 Fort Road
Toppenish, Washington 98948
(509) 865-8800
Map Location: **#16** (20 miles S. of Yakima)

Toll-Free Number: (877) 7-COME-11
Restaurants: 1 Liquor: Yes
Buffets: B-$8.99 L-$5.99
D-$7.99/$14.99 (Fri)/$10.99 (Sat)
Hours: 10am-3am/4am (Fri/Sat)
Casino Size: 51,000 Square Feet
Other Games: Gaming Machines, P, PGP, LIR CSP, K, BG
Fun Book: Given to out-of-state visitors, to Birthday Club members and for special events
Senior Discount: 10% off buffets, if 55, or older and Fun Book on Tuesdays
Special Features: Supervised children's play area. Indoor waterfall. Gift shop. Free shuttle service.

Card Rooms

Card rooms have been legal in Washington since 1974. Initially limited to just five tables per location, the law was changed in 1996 to allow up to 15 tables. Then, one year later, a provision was added to allow house-banked games. Permissible games include: blackjack, Caribbean stud poker, pai gow poker, let it ride and casino war. The games of baccarat, craps, roulette and keno are not allowed.

The maximum bet at each card room is dependant on certain licensing requirements and is capped at either $3, $25 or $100. Additionally, the rooms can be open no more than 20 hours per day. These card rooms are now commonly called "mini-casinos."

Each city and county has the option to ban the card rooms so they are not found in every major city (Seattle has none). Listed below are names, addresses, and most phone numbers, of all Washington card rooms as of August 2000:

Aces Sports Bars
10001 E. Sprague
Spokane, WA 99214
(509) 892-5242

All Star Lanes Restaurant
P.O. Box 3104
Silverdale, WA 98383
(360) 692-5760

Big Al's
12715 4th Ave. W.
Everett, WA 98206
(253) 568-2470

Cafe International
1125 Commerce Avenue
Longview, WA 98632
(360) 501-4328

Cafe International
PO Box 446
Blaine, WA 98230
(360) 332-6035

Chef's Restaurant
1329 N. Hamilton
Spokane, WA 99202
(509) 487-0393

Chip's Casino
1500 N.E. Riddell Rd.
Bremerton, WA 98320
(360) 377-8322

Commercial Inn
101 S. Gum Street
Kennewick, WA 99336
(509) 585-9246

Diamond Lil's
321 Rainier Ave. S.
Renton, WA 98055
(425) 226-2763

Dodge City Saloon
7201 N.E. 18th Street
Vancouver, WA 98687
(360) 253-6603

Double Down Saloon
PO Box 910
La Center, WA 98629
(360) 263-2988

Drift On Inn
16708 Auroroa Ave. N.
Shoreline, WA 98133
(206) 546-8040

El Papagayo's
PO Box 577
Moses Lake, WA 98837
(509) 765-1265

Fiesta Bowl
624 Wellsian Way
Richland, WA 99532
(509) 943-1173

Fordet Grove
4230 Birch Bay Lyden Road
Blaine, WA 98230
(360) 371-7011

Freddie's Club-Auburn
333 15th Street NE
Auburn, WA 98002

Freddie's Club - Everett
7903 Evergreen Way
Everett, WA 98203
(425) 290-7531

Freddies' Club-Renton
111 S. 3rd
Renton, WA 98155
(425) 228-3700

Golden Nugget
14025 Interurban Ave. S.
Tukwila, WA 98188
(206) 246-8545

Goldies Casino
15030 Auroroa Ave. N.
Shoreline, WA 98133
(206) 241-8163

Great Wall
3121 S. 38th St.
Tacoma, WA 98409
(253) 473-2500

Grove Tavern
6504 Evergreen Way
Everett, WA 98203
(425) 355-4656

Hank's Country Inn
PO Box 398
Belfair, WA 98528
(360) 275-4547

Jack Niemann's Steakhouse
4156 Meridian St.
Bellingham, WA 98226
(360) 647-7066

Jimmy G's
2602 S. 80th St.
Lakewood, WA 98499
(253) 582-2464

Kegler's Choice
704 Grant Road
E. Wenatchee, WA 98802
(509) 884-3593

Kenmore Lanes
7638 N.E. Bothell Way
Bethel, WA 98011
(425) 486-8646

Last Frontier
PO Box 187
La Center, WA 98629
(360) 263-1290

Lilac Lanes
1112 E. Magnesium Rd.
Spokane, WA 99208
(509) 467-5228

Luciano's Casino
3327 N. Ruston Way
Tacoma, Wa 98354
(253) 756-5611

New Phoenix
225 W. 4th Street
La Center, WA 98629
(360) 263-1221 or 573-5622

Palace Casino
P.O. Box 910
La Center, WA 98629
(360) 263-2988

Paradise Bowl
12505 Pacific Ave.
Tacoma, WA 98444
(206) 537-6012

Parkers
17001 Aurora Ave. N.
Shoreline, WA 98133
(206) 546-6161

Pete's Flying Aces
14101 Pacific Highway S.
Tukwila, WA 98168
(206) 248-1224

PJ Pockets
1320 S. 324th St. #A-10
Federal Way, WA 98003
(253) 839-9922

Players & Spectators
12828 E. Sprague Avenue
Spokane, WA 99216
(509) 924-5141

Quarterback Pub and Eatery
356 36th Street
Bellingham, WA 98225
(360) 647-8132 or 671-3322

Rascal's Casino
10737 Glen Acres S.
Seattle, WA 98168
(206) 763-7428

Riverbend Casino
2721 N. Market St.
Spokane, WA 99207
(509) 483-4393

Riverside Casino
14060 Interurban Ave. South
Tukwila, WA 98168
(206) 244-5400

Royal Casino
13010 Highway 99 S.
Everett, WA 98204
(425) 743-9200

Ruby's Casino
19611 84 Ave. S.
Kent, WA 98032
(253) 872-6595

Sidney's Restaurant & Sports Bar
512 W. Heron
Aberdeen, WA 98520
(360) 533-6635

Silver Dollar
14027 Interurban Ave. S.
Tukwila, WA 98168
(206) 241-9526

Silver Dollar Casino/SEATAC
23655 S.E. 208th
Maple Valley, WA 98188
(206) 824-2340

Silver Lanes
3023 East 28th Avenue
Spokane, WA 99223
(509) 535-2961

Six Card Charlie's Gambling Hall
14422 Pacific Ave. S.
Spanaway, WA 98444
(253) 536-1533

Skyway Park Bowl
11819 Renton Ave. South
Seattle, WA 98178
(206) 772-4125

Slo Pitch Pub and Eatery
1145 E. Sunset Dr. #130
Bellingham, WA 98226
(360) 733-2255

Sports Center
214 E. Yakima Avenue
Yakima, WA 98901

Stockyards
E. 3827 Boone Avenue
Spokane, WA 99202

Sunset Junction
W. 1801 Sunset Boulevard
Spokane, WA 99204
(509) 455-9131

Wizards
15739 Ambaum Boulevard S.W.
Burien, WA 98166
(206) 444-6100

WEST VIRGINIA

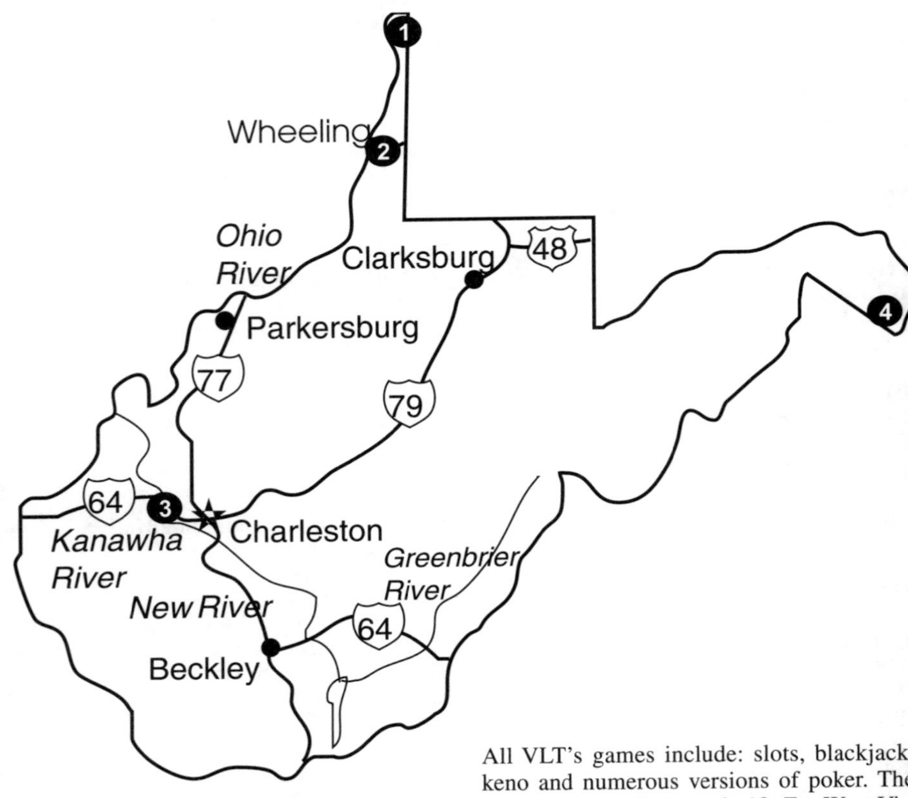

West Virginia has four pari-mutuel facilities that feature video lottery terminals. The VLT's are the same as regular video gaming devices but are called lottery terminals because they are regulated by the state's lottery commission which receives a share of each machine's revenue.

The maximum allowable bet on a machine is $2. Most of the gaming machines pay out coins or tokens but there are also some machines which will only print out a receipt which must be taken to a cashier.

West Virginia law requires that VLT's return a minimum of 80% to a maximum of 95% over time. For the 2000 fiscal year from July 1, 1999 through June 30, 2000 the average return on VLT's was: 91.95% at Tri-State Park, 91.66% at Mountaineer Park, 91.45% at Wheeling Downs and 91.53% at Charles Town Races.

All VLT's games include: slots, blackjack, keno and numerous versions of poker. The minimum gambling age is 18. For West Virginia tourism information call (800) 225-5982.

Charles Town Races
P.O. Box 551
Charles Town, West Virginia 25414
(304) 725-7001
Web Site: www.ctownraces.com
Map Location: **#4**

Toll-Free Number: (800) 795-7001
Restaurants: 2
Buffets: L-$8.95 (Sun) D-$8.95 (Wed-Thu)/ $19.95 (Fri)/$14.95 (Sat)
Hours: 9am-2am/3am (Fri-Sat)
1pm-2am (Sun)
Special Features: Live horse racing Mon/Wed/Fri-Sun. Daily simulcasting of horse and dog racing. 10 minutes from Harpers Ferry.

Mountaineer Racetrack & Gaming Resort
State Route #2
Chester, West Virginia 26034
(304) 387-2400
Web Site: www.mtrgaming.com
Map Location: **#1** (35 miles N. of Wheeling)

Toll-Free Number: (800) 804-0468
Room Reservations: (800) 489-8192
Rooms: 101 Price Range: $65-$99
Restaurants: 4
Hours: 9am-3:30am/3am (Sat)
1pm-3:30am (Sun)
Fun Book: Given to Slot Club members
Special Features: Rooms are at on-site Mountaineer Lodge. Live horse racing Thur-Mon. Daily simulcasting of horse and dog racing. 18-hole golf course.

Tri-State Racetrack & Gaming Center
1 Greyhound Lane
Cross Lanes, West Virginia 25356
(304) 776-1000
Map Location: **#3** (10 miles N.W. of Charleston)

Toll-Free Number: (800) 224-9683
Restaurants: 1
Hours: 11am-3am/1pm-3am (Sun)
Casino Size: 30,000 Square Feet
Special Features: Live dog racing Wed-Mon. Daily simulcasting of horse and dog racing. Advantage Player's Club for slot players.

Wheeling Downs
Race Track & Gaming Center
1 S. Stone Street
Wheeling, West Virginia 26003
(304) 232-5050
Web Site: www.wheelingdowns.com
Map Location: **#2**

Toll-Free Number: (877) WIN-HERE
Restaurants: 1
Buffets: L-$8.95 D-$12.95
Hours: 11am-3am/10am-3am (Sat)
12pm-3am (Sun)
Special Features: Live dog racing Wed-Mon. Daily simulcasting of horse and dog racing.

WISCONSIN

All Wisconsin casinos are located on Indian reservations and blackjack is the only table game permitted. Most of the casinos are small with 8 to 12 blackjack tables and food facilities that are closer to concession stands rather than restaurants. The largest operation is Oneida Bingo & Casino in Green Bay which has more than 2,500 reel slots and video machines.

The Indian tribes are not required to release information on their slot machine percentage paybacks, but according to the terms of the compact between the state and the tribes "for games not affected by player skill, such as slot machines, the machine is required to return a minimum of 80% and a maximum of 100% of the amount wagered."

Unless otherwise noted, all casinos are open 24 hours and the only games offered are: blackjack, slots and video poker. The minimum gambling age is 18 at all casinos (21 if liquor is served). For visitor information call the state's department of tourism at (800) 432-8747.

Bad River Lodge & Casino
Highway 2, P.O. Box 11
Odanah, Wisconsin 54861
(715) 682-6102
Web Site: www.badriver.com
Map Location: **#1** (halfway between Ironwood, MI and Ashland, WI; 45 miles east of Duluth, MN on US 2)

Toll-Free Number: (800) 777-7449
Hotel Reservations: (800) 795-7121
Rooms: 50 Price Range: $32-$90
Restaurants: 2 Liquor: Yes
Hours: 8am-2am (Off Season)/4am (Summer)
Other Games: Video Keno
Casino Marketing: (800) 777-7449
Special Features: AAA and AARP members get 10% room discount.

Grindstone Creek Casino
13767 West County Road B
Hayward, Wisconsin 54843
(715) 634-2430
Map Location: **#2**

Restaurants: 1 snack bar Liquor: No
Hours: 10am-10pm Daily
Other Games: Machines Only
Special Features: Located 2-1/2 miles south of LCO Casino.

Ho Chunk Casino
S3214A Highway 12
Baraboo, Wisconsin 53913
(608) 356-6210
Web Site: www.ho-chunk.com
Map Location: **#4** (40 miles N. of Madison. On Hwy. 12 just S. of Delton)

Toll-Free Number: (800) 7-HO-CHUNK
Rooms: 295 Price Range: $100-$150
Suites: 20 Price Range: $150-$305
Restaurants: 5 (1 open 24 hrs) Liquor: Yes
Buffets: B-$6.95 L-$8.95/$9.95 (Sun)
D-$11.95/$14.95 (Wed)
Casino Size: 86,000 Square Feet
Other Games: Video Keno, Bingo
Casino Marketing: (800) 7-HO-CHUNK ask for extension 2140
Special Features: Valet parking. Gift shop. Discount smoke shop. Shuttle service from all local area motels.

Hole In The Wall Casino & Hotel
P.O. Box 98, Highways 35 & 77
Danbury, Wisconsin 54830
(715) 656-3444
Map Location: **#5** (26 miles E. of Hinckley, MN)

Toll-Free Number: (800) BET-U-WIN
Rooms: 38 Price Range: $50-$55
Restaurants: 1 Liquor: Yes
Hours: 8am-2am/4am (Fri/Sat)
Other Games: Video Keno
Special Features: Save $10 on room rate by showing slot club card (which is available for free inside casino). 35-site RV park. Gift shop.

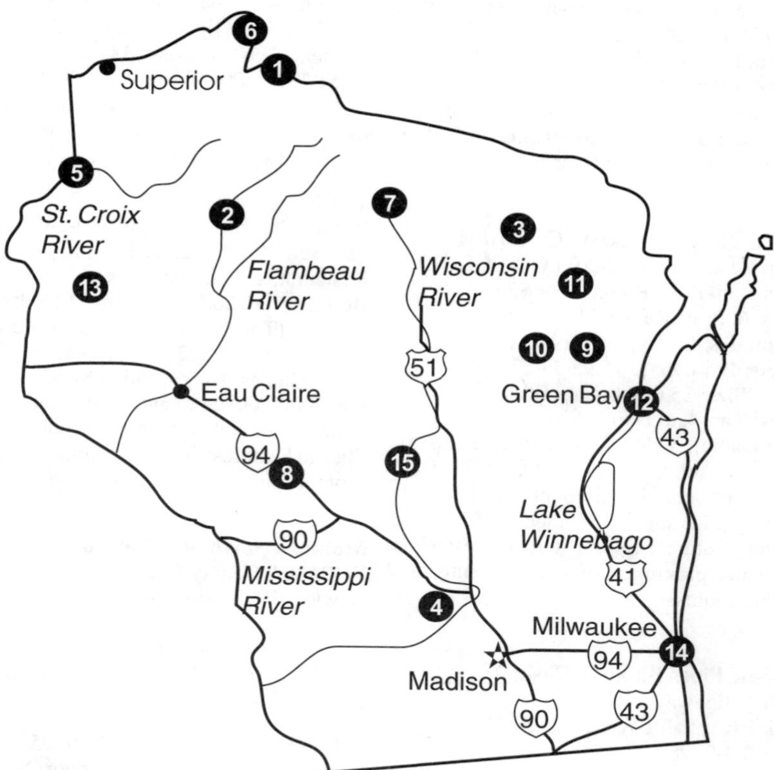

Isle Vista Casino
Hwy 13 North, Box 1167
Bayfield, Wisconsin 54814
(715) 779-3712
Map Location: **#6** (70 miles E. of Duluth, MN on Hwy. 13, 3 miles N. of Bayfield)

Toll-Free Number: (800) 226-8478
Restaurants: 1 Liquor: Yes
Hours: 10am-12am/2am (Wed-Sat)
Other Games: Video Keno,
Bingo (Thu/Sat-Mon)

Lake of the Torches Resort/Casino
510 Old Abe Road
Lac du Flambeau, Wisconsin 54538
(715) 588-7070
Web Site: www.180025torch.com
Map Location: **#7** (160 miles N.W. of Green Bay. Heading N. on Hwy. 57, go left on Hwy. 47, 12 miles to casino)

Toll-Free Number: (800) 25-TORCH
Room Reservations: (888) 599-9200
Rooms: 103 Price Range: $78-$98
Suites: 1 Price Range: $92-$120
Restaurants: 2 Liquor: Yes
Buffets: B-$4.95 (Sat-Sun) L-$6.95
D-$8.95/$10.95 (Thu/Sat/Sun)/$13.95 (Fri)
Other Games: Video Keno, Bingo (Tue-Sun)
Special Features: Torchlight Players Club members get 20% off room rate (sign up for free in casino), plus other discounts. Room rates include complimentary breakfasts and a $20 match play coupon.

LCO Casino, Lodge & Convention Center
13767 W County Road B
Hayward, Wisconsin 54843
(715) 634-5643
Web Site: www.lcocasino.com
Map Location: **#2** (55 miles S.E. of Duluth, MN. 3 miles N.E. of Hayward on county trunk B)

Toll-Free Number: (800) LCO-CASH
Room Reservations: (800) LCO-LODGE
Rooms: 55 Price Range: $49-$69
Suites: 6 Price Range: $85-$105
Restaurants: 2 Liquor: Yes
Buffets: B-$4.95 L-$6.95 D-$7.95
Casino Size: 35,000 Square Feet
Hours: 9am-4am Daily
Other Games: Video Keno, Bingo (Sun-Fri)
Casino Marketing: (800) LCO-CASH ext-173
Senior Discount: 5% discount at Lodge and free prize spin on Sundays if 55, or older
Special Features: Sports lounge. Gift shop. Free valet parking. Convention center and meeting rooms.

Majestic Pines Bingo & Casino
W9010 Highway 54 East
Black River Falls, Wisconsin 54615
(715) 284-9098
Web Site: www.ho-chunk.com
Map Location: **#8** (110 miles M.W. of Madison on Hwy. 54, 4 miles E. of I-94)

Toll-Free Number: (800) 657-4621
Rooms: 60 Price Range: $59-$68
Suites: 6 Price Range: $88
Restaurants: 3 Liquor: Yes
Buffets: L-$6.50 D-$8.95/$11.95 (Wed)
Hours: 8am-2am/ 24 hrs (Fri/Sat/Memorial Day to Labor Day)
Size: 75,000 Square Feet
Other Games: Bingo, Video Keno
Fun Book: Only sold to bus patrons
Senior Discount: Spin prize wheel on Wednesdays, $5 off bingo packs on Sundays, if 55, or older
Special Features: Local motels offer casino coupons. Dinner brunch is $4.95 on Tuesdays with a Power Play card. No Wednesday bingo.

Menominee Casino, Bingo & Hotel
P.O. Box 760, Highways 47 & 55
Keshena, Wisconsin 54135
(715) 799-3600
Web Site: www.menomineecasinoresort.com
Map Location: **#9** (40 miles N.W. of Green Bay on Hwy. 47, 7 miles N. of Shawano)

Toll-Free Number: (800) 343-7778
Rooms: 100 Price Range: $60-$80
Suites: 8 Price Range: $80-$159
Restaurants: 1 Liquor: Yes
Buffets: L-$6.50/$8.75 (Sun) D-$8.95/$10.95 (Thu-Fri)/$11.50 (Sat)/$7.95 (Sun)
Casino Size: 21,402 Square Feet
Other Games: Bingo, Video Keno
Fun Book: Given to guests of local motels
Senior Discount: 10% AARP room discount
Special Features: Gift shop. Smoke shop. 10% room discount for AAA members.

Mohican North Star Casino
W12180A County Road A
Bowler, Wisconsin 54416
(715) 787-3110
Web Site: www.mohican.com
Map Location: **#10** (50 miles N.W. of Green Bay)

Toll-Free Number: (800) 952-0195
Restaurants: 1 Snack Bar Liquor: Yes
Hours: 8am-2am/24 Hours (Thu-Sat)
Other Games: Video Keno, Bingo (Sun-Thu)
Special Features: Smoke shop. Local area motels offer casino packages.

Mole Lake/Regency Casino
Highway 55
Mole Lake, Wisconsin 54520
(715) 478-5290
Web Site: www.molelake.com
Map Location: **#3** (100 miles N.W. of Green Bay on Hwy. 55, 7 miles S. of Crandon)

Toll-Free Number: (800) 236-WINN
Motel Reservations: (800) 457-4312
Rooms: 25 Price Range: $55
Restaurants: 1 Cafeteria Liquor: Yes
Hours: 10am-1am/3am (Fri/Sat)
Other Games: Video Keno, Bingo (Fri-Tue)
Senior Discount: $5 match play on Wednesdays, if 55, or older
Special Features: Two casinos housed in separate buildings. Motel is two blocks from casino. Blackjack opens at 12 p.m. $10 match play coupons given to hotel guests.

Oneida Bingo & Casino
2020/2100 Airport Drive
Green Bay, Wisconsin 54313
(414) 494-4500
Web Site: www.oneidabingoandcasino.net
Map Location: **#12** (across from Austin Straubel Airport, take Interstate 43 to Highway 172)

Toll-Free Number: (800) 238-4263
Reservation Number: (800) 333-3333
Rooms: 301 Price Range: $79-$159
Suites: 29 Price Range: $159-$229
Restaurants: 3 Liquor: No
Buffets: B-$7.95 L-$7.95
Hours: 24 Hours Daily (Slots)
Hours: 10am-4am (Tables)
Other Games: Bingo, Video Keno
Casino Marketing: (800) 238-4263
Fun Book: Only offered to bus groups
Senior Discount: Free early bird bingo pack on Wednesday, if 55, or older
Special Features: Two casinos. One is connected to Radisson Inn where the rooms are located. Liquor is served at hotel lounge. Buffet is located at Radisson Inn. Shuttle bus offered from airport and local hotels/motels. Gift shop. Discount smoke shop. Match Play coupons available at hotel with casino packages.

Potawatomi Bingo Casino
1721 W. Canal Street
Milwaukee, Wisconsin 53233
(414) 645-6888
Web Site: www.paysbig.com
Map Location: **#14**

Toll-Free Number: (800) PAYS-BIG
Restaurants: 1 Snack Bar Liquor: No
Hours: 24 Hours Daily
Games Offered: Bingo (Mon-Fri)
Casino Size: 38,400 Square Feet

Potawatomi Bingo/Northern Lights Casino
P.O. Box 140, Highway 32
Carter, Wisconsin 54566
(715) 473-2021
Map Location: **#11** (85 miles N. of Green Bay on Hwy. 32)

Toll-Free Number: (800) 487-9522
Lodge Reservations: (800) 777-1640
Rooms: 70 Price Range: $65-$85
Suites: 29 Price Range: $70-$105
Restaurants: 2 Liquor: Yes
Casino Size: 12,000 Square Feet
Hours: 9am-2am/4am (Fri/Sat)
Other Games: Bingo (Sun-Thu)
Senior Discount: On Mondays seniors get a lunch discount and match play coupons.
Special Features: Indian Springs Lodge is located across the parking lot from the casino and offers hotel/casino packages. 10% discount on room rate for AAA and AARP Members. Special liquor-free slot area for 18-20 year-old players. 24-hour gas station and convenience store.

Rainbow Casino & Bingo
949 County Road G
Nekoosa, Wisconsin 54457
(715) 886-4560
Web Site: www.ho-chunk.com
Map Location: **#15** (50 miles S. of Wausau)

Toll-Free Number: (800) 782-4560
Restaurants: 2 Liquor: Yes
Buffets: L-$8.95 D-$9.95
Hours: 9am-2am/24 hours (Fri/Sat)
Other Games: Video Keno, Bingo
Senior Discount: On Wed get $10 for $5 coupon from 10am-6pm, prize drawings and 25% off lunch or dinner entrees, if 55, or older
Special Features: Smoke and gift shop. Motel and tour packages.

St. Croix Casino & Hotel
777 US Highway 8
Turtle Lake, Wisconsin 54889
(715) 986-4777
Web Site: www.stcroixcasino.com
Map Location: **#13** (105 miles S. of Duluth, MN on Hwy. 8)

Toll-Free Number: (800) U-GO-U-WIN
Room Reservations: (800) STAY-W-US
Rooms: 158 Price Range: $56-$80
Restaurants: 3 (1 open 24 hours) Liquor: Yes
Buffets: B-$4.20 L-$8.40 D-$11.60/$17 (Thu)
Casino Size: 95,000 Square Feet
Hours: 24 Hours Daily
Other Games: Bingo, Video Keno
Special Features: 20% discount on hotel rates if you have a player's card (which is available for free inside the casino). Free valet parking. Banquet and meeting facilities.

CANADA

Following is a list of some of the major Canadian casinos. Each casino offers the following games: blackjack, craps, roulette, baccarat, let it ride, Caribbean stud poker, pai gow poker and big six wheel. The minimum gambling age in Ontario is 19 and in Quebec it's 18. All prices listed are in Canadian dollars and, unless otherwise noted, all casinos are open 24 hours.

Ontario

Casino Niagara
5705 Falls Avenue
Niagara Falls, Ontario L2E 6T3
(905) 374-3598
Web Site: www.casinoniagara.com

Toll-Free Number: (888) 946-3255
Restaurants: 4
Buffets: B-$5.95 L-$9.95 D-$14.95
Casino Size: 96,000 Square Feet

Casino Rama
Box 176, RR Number 6
Rama, Ontario L0K 1T0
(705) 329-3325

Toll-Free Number: (800) 832-7529
Restaurants: 3
Buffets; B-$7.95 L-$11.95 D-$16.95
Casino Size: 65,000 Square Feet
Other Games: Mini-Baccarat

Casino Windsor
377 Riverside Drive East
Windsor, Ontario N9A 7H7
(519) 258-7878
Web Site: www.casinowindsor.com

Toll-Free Number: (800) 991-7777
Room Reservations: (800) 991-8888
Rooms: 349 Price Range: $165-$225
Suites: 40 Price Range: $250-$1,450
Restaurants: 5 (1 open 24 hours)
Buffets: L-$12.50 D-$15.95/$19.95 (Fri-Sat)
Casino Size: 100,000 Square Feet
Senior Discount: 10% AARP room discount.

Quebec

Casino de Charlevoix
183 Avenue Richelieu
Pointe-au-Pic, Quebec G0T 1M0
(418) 665-5300
Web Site: www.casinos-quebec.com

Toll-Free Number: (800) 665-2274
Restaurants: 3
Casino Hours: 10am-3am Daily
Casino Size: 40,000 Square Feet
Special Features: Restaurants are at nearby Le Manor Richielieu Hotel.

Casino de Hull
1 Boulevard du Casino
Hull, Quebec J8Y 6W3
(819) 772-2100
Web Site: www.casinos-quebec.com

Toll-Free Number: (800) 665-2274
Restaurants: 3
Buffets: D-$17.95
Casino Hours: 11am-3am Daily
Casino Size: 40,000 Square Feet

Casino de Montreal
1 Avenue du Casino
Hull, Quebec J8Y 6W3
(514) 392-2746
Web Site: www.casinos-quebec.com

Toll-Free Number: (800) 665-2274
Restaurants: 4
Buffets: L-$10.95 D-$17.95
Casino Size: 40,000 Square Feet

Casino Index

A

B

C

D

E

F

G

Q

R

S

AMERICAN CASINO GUIDE

Buy One, Get One FREE

Redeem this coupon at the Broadway Buffet to enjoy two buffets for the price of one. See back for full details.

TRUMP PLAZA

CASINO COUPON

AMERICAN CASINO GUIDE

One FREE Cocktail

Redeem this coupon at the Terrace Lounge to receive your FREE Cocktail beverage. Not to exceed $5.00 value. See back for full details.

TRUMP PLAZA

CASINO COUPON

AMERICAN CASINO GUIDE

Board the Ship for a FREE gift!

Present this coupon with $10 in same-day mall receipts at the Customer Service Desk (2nd Deck - Food Court) and receive a FREE Gift!

One gift per person. While supplies last. Expires 12/31/02.

CASINO COUPON

Coupon must be presented at the Broadway Buffet in Trump Plaza.
Must be 21 years of age. May not be used in conjunction with any other offers.
Not valid on Saturdays or Sundays or holidays. Limit one coupon per person.
Offer subject to cancellation without notice.
Valid thru 12/30/01.

TRUMP PLAZA

Coupon must be presented at the Terrace Lounge in Trump Plaza.
Must be 21 years of age. May not be used in conjunction with any other offers.
Not valid on Saturdays or Sundays or holidays. Limit one coupon per person.
Offer subject to cancellation without notice.
Valid thru 12/30/01.

TRUMP PLAZA

Open year'round. Over 100 shops, a food court and four full service restaurants with magnificent views onboard Atlantic City's only shopping mall. Featuring The Gap, Foot Locker, Sam Goody, McDonald's and many more. Located on the boardwalk directly opposite Caesars. Call (609)347-8082.

www.oceanonemall.com

AMERICAN CASINO GUIDE

Ripley's **Believe It or Not!**®

Two-For-One Admission

Present this coupon and get one free admission with the purchase of one adult admission at Ripley's Believe It or Not.® Located on the famous Atlantic City Boardwalk. See back for full details.

CASINO COUPON

AMERICAN CASINO GUIDE

FOXWOODS
RESORT CASINO

$10 Match Play Voucher

Present this voucher and your valid Wampum Card at any Wampum Club Center in exchange for one $10 Match Play coupon. Valid for even money bets on designated games. Must be at least 21. One coupon per person, per day.

CASINO COUPON

AMERICAN CASINO GUIDE

Buy One Buffet Get One FREE !

Present this coupon to the cashier at the Queen's Courtyard Buffet to receive one FREE buffet upon the purchase of another buffet at the regular price. Offer expires 12/30/01.

#99941

CASINO COUPON

On the Boardwalk at
New York Avenue
Atlantic City, NJ 08401
(609) 347-2001

Open year 'round
Call for operating hours

Adults: $8.95
Children (5-12) $6.95
4 and under Free

Not valid with any other offer. Limit: two free tickets per coupon. Expires December 30, 2001.

Route 2
Mashantucket, CT 06339
(860) 312-3000
(800) PLAY-BIG

Can be used only once • Non-negotiable • No cash value • Coupons will be retained by the dealer after each wager • One coupon per person, per day • Must have a valid Wampum Card • Non-transferable • Cannot be sold • Non-replaceable • Considered void if altered in any fashion • Must be at least 21 • Subject to change or cancellation at any time • Other restrictions may apply • Offer expires December 30, 2001.

200 South Front Street
East St. Louis, IL 62201
(618) 874-5000
(800) 777-0777

Purchase one buffet and receive the second buffet FREE! This offer may not be combined with any other offer, is non-transferable, not valid on holidays, and does not apply to the purchase of alcoholic beverages. One coupon per couple, per day. Tax and gratuity are not included. Casino Queen reserves the right to change or revoke this offer without prior notice.

$5 CASH COUPON

This coupon is redeemable for five dollars in cash or tokens at any open cashier's cage in the casino.

Limit one coupon redeemable per customer per visit. Must be 21 years or older to receive or redeem at the cashier's cage.

Expires December 31, 2001

ECAGD5

CASINO COUPON

AMERICAN CASINO GUIDE

Buy One Breakfast Buffet, Get One Free!

Present this coupon and receive one Breakfast Buffet FREE with the purchase of a Breakfast Buffet of equal value. Valid Monday through Saturday from 7 am until 10 am. Located on Clubhouse Level 4.

CASINO COUPON

AMERICAN CASINO GUIDE

Please present this coupon at the **Fire Keeper's Club Booth**

Coupon redeemable Sunday through Thursday

$5 MATCH PLAY

CASINO COUPON

1-888-ROMAN-4-U
www.caesarsindiana.com

Must be 21 years or older to redeem. Photo I.D. is required to redeem. Winners know when to quit.
For help with gambling problems, call 1-800-9-WITH-IT.

- Limit one coupon per purchase.
- Not valid on holidays or with other coupons, discounts, or Senior Tuesday coupons.
- Valid until December 30, 2001.
- Code 642acg00

1 Prairie Meadows Drive
Altoona, IA 50009
(800) 325-9015
(515) 967-1000

BINGO · CASINO

1721 W. Canal Street
Milwaukee, WI 53233
1-800-PAYS-BIG
www.paysbig.com

Valid for one complimentary $5.00 MATCH PLAY
when a second $5.00 MATCH PLAY of equal or greater value is purchased.

- **Showcase for high stakes bingo offering $5 million in cash payouts daily**
- **Daily bingo games**
- **Las Vegas-style slot machines**
- **Live entertainment**
- **Player's Club**

Limit one coupon per customer per visit. Must be 21 years of age.
Valid with slot machines only.
Management reserves the right to cancel or modify this offer.
Expires 12/30/01

AMERICAN CASINO GUIDE

$15 Off!

Drive Happy℠

Alamo

1-800-354-2322
alamo.com

- Just reserve a compact through minivan in the United States or Canada, or a compact through intermediate 4-door car in Latin America or the Caribbean
- Valid on rentals of at least three days
- Valid 9/1/00 through 12/31/01
- Book with your travel agent or Alamo. Be sure to request ID #641394, Rate Code BY, and Coupon Code D0FB at time of reservation..

See terms and conditions on reserve side of this coupon.

D0FB

CASINO COUPON

AMERICAN CASINO GUIDE

One FREE Day!

Drive Happy℠

1-800-354-2322
alamo.com

- Just reserve a compact through fullsize 4-door car in the United States or Canada, a Group B through F in Europe, or a compact through intermediate 4-door car in Latin America or the Caribbean.
- Valid on rentals of at least four days
- Valid 9/1/00 through 12/31/01
- Book with your travel agent or Alamo. Be sure to request ID #641394, Rate Code BY, and Coupon Code F9GB at time of reservation.

See terms and conditions on reserve side of this coupon.

F9GB

CASINO COUPON

AMERICAN CASINO GUIDE

Up to 10% Off Car Rental Rates!

Drive Happy℠

Alamo

1-800-354-2322
alamo.com

Save up to 10% off Alamo's great rates, year-round. Plus, you will receive unlimited mileage and no charge for additional drivers. Alamo makes renting cars a fun part of your trip. For reservations, contact your travel agent or call Alamo. Be sure to request ID #641394 and Rate Code BY.

See terms and conditions on reserve side of this coupon.

CASINO COUPON

Terms and Conditions

- One certificate per Alamo rental and void once redeemed.
- Original certificate must be presented at counter upon arrival.
- Discount applies to basic rate, which does not include taxes (including VLF taxes up to $1.89 per day in California and GST), governmentally-authorized or imposed surcharges, license and concession recoupment fees, airport fees or other optional items.
- Offer is subject to standard rental conditions.
- Blackout dates may apply.
- Not valid with any other discount or promotional rate.
- Subject to availability and good only at participating Alamo locations.
- Offer not valid in San Jose, California.
- Travel Agents GDS:ID-XA641394/RC-BY/SI-C-D0FB

1-800-354-2322
alamo.com

Terms and Conditions

- One certificate per Alamo rental and void once redeemed.
- Original certificate must be presented at counter upon arrival.
- Free day is pro-rated against basic rate of entire rental period, which does not include taxes (including VLF taxes up to $1.89 per day in California, VAT and GST), governmentally-authorized or imposed surcharges, license and concession recoupment fees, airport fees or other optional items.
- Offer is subject to standard rental conditions.
- Blackout dates may apply.
- Not valid with any other discount or promotional rate.
- Subject to availability and good only at participating Alamo locations.
- Offer not valid in San Jose, California.
- Travel Agents GDS:ID-XA641394/RC-BY/SI-C-F9GB

Drive Happy
Alamo
1-800-354-2322
alamo.com

Terms and Conditions

Discount applies to base rate only. Taxes (including VLF taxes up to US$1.89 per day in California and GST/VAT) other governmentally-authorized or imposed surcharges, license and concession recoupment fees, airport fees and optional items are extra.

Renter must meet standard age, driver and credit requirements.24-hour advance reservation required (48-hour for licensee locations).

May not be combined with other discounts.

Availability is limited. Black out dates may apply.

Drive Happy
Alamo
1-800-354-2322
alamo.com

AMERICAN CASINO GUIDE

$100 Off Per Person

This coupon entitles the bearer to a $100 discount, per person, on the regular registration fee for the 13th Annual World Championship Bingo Tournament & Gaming Cruise. Enjoy a spectacular 8-day Caribbean "Voyage of Victory" with more than $63,000 in guaranteed cash payouts.

Call 1-800-326-0373 for a free full-color brochure that includes complete cruise information. Offer expires 10/31/01

CASINO COUPON

AMERICAN CASINO GUIDE

FREE 6-Month IGT Charge Card Membership or 50% off the annual $48 Membership fee!

Use the IGT charge card to save 25% on all of your purchases at thousands of IGT card merchants throughout the U.S. including restaurants, airlines, vacation packages to Las Vegas and the Mississippi Gulf Coast, cruises to Alaska, cleaners, attractions, gambling chip purchases on casino boats in Florida, Freeport (Long Island, N.Y.) and Gloucester (Mass.), plus much more! See page 207 in this book for more details on the IGT card, or the back of this coupon for details on how to apply for your card at these savings.

CASINO COUPON

AMERICAN CASINO GUIDE

$3 off Admission

Experience a great Dining, Dancing and Casino value aboard the Stardancer Casino in Myrtle Beach, South Carolina! See reverse for full terms and conditions of this special offer. For reservations, or information call **1-800-2345-WIN.** Offer Expires 12/30/01.

CASINO COUPON

More Than $63,000 in Bingo prizes!

- Offer valid for 2 adults (18 or older) per coupon. Advance reservations required for this world class event, which has sold-out for the past 12 consecutive years.
- Call 1-800-326-0373 and mention the "American Casino Guide" coupon when making reservations to receive this discount.
- Space subject to availability. Offer valid through 10/31/01. Offer not valid with any other promotion. Program subject to change or cancellation without notice.

The IGT card has been saving its members money for more than 25 years. Just charge your purchase to the IGT card and when your monthly bill arrives you'll get an automatic 25% discount from the full purchase price (except tax and tip).

Residents of Florida, Atlanta, Chicago, Los Angeles/Palm Springs, and the metropolitan New York City area (including Long Island, Westchester, Northern New Jersey and Southern Connecticut) get a FREE 6-month membership. All others pay just $24 for their one year membership fee - a 50% discount off the usual $48 annual fee!

To apply for your card call (800) 4-IGT-USA and mention code "AC5" to receive this special offer. All applications are subject to IGT's standard credit policies. Offer expires 12/31/01.

Name

Address

City, St, Zip

1-Advance reservations required. 2-This coupon is not combinable with any other Stardancer offer 3-Applies to full fare purchase only plus taxes and surcharges. 4-Coupon must be presented at ticket booth on day of sailing. 5-Limit (4) people per coupon. 6-Taxes and surcharges not included in this offer. 7-Certain restrictions apply. Offer subject to change without notice. 8- Coupon expires on date indicated. Service charges will be applicable on extension requests. 9-This coupon is not transferable

AMERICAN CASINO GUIDE

Buy $20, Get $10 Free In Chips Or Tokens!

Must be a new or existing Total Rewards member

This coupon entitles you to receive a bonus of $10 in slot tokens or chips when you buy $20. That's an extra $10 bonus! To get yours, bring this coupon, your Harrah's Total Rewards Card and a valid photo I.D. to the Total Rewards Center at Harrah's Shreveport Casino. **Valid dates: November 1,2000-December 30, 2001**

Guest Name:____________________ **Total Rewards Card #**________________

CASINO COUPON

AMERICAN CASINO GUIDE

Buy One Buffet Get One Free!

President Casino by the Arch

St Louis, Missouri 63102
1-800-772-3647

Celebrate lunch, dinner or Sunday brunch with the President...at the President's Buffet on our top deck.

Purchase one buffet at regular price, present this coupon and receive a second buffet FREE!

Good For Lunch, Dinner Or Sunday Brunch. Expires December 30, 2001.

CASINO COUPON

AMERICAN CASINO GUIDE

2-FOR-1 CRUISE!

Sailing from Downtown Brunswick, GA

Five and six hour fun-filled cruises. Enjoy dining, international casino action, dancing, music, entertainment, bingo and more!

THE EMERALD PRINCESS
SOUTHEAST GEORGIA'S MOST EXCITING ATTRACTION

See reverse side for more information.

CASINO COUPON

Harrah's SHREVEPORT

315 Clyde Fant Parkway
Shreveport, LA 71101
(318) 424-7777
(800) HARRAHS

Offer non-transferable and cannot be combined with any other offer. Must be at least 21 years of age. Limit one coupon per person, per day. Harrah's is not responsible for lost or stolen vouchers and reserves the right to change or cancel this program with prior notification to the Division. Employees of Harrah's Shreveport not eligible. Know When to Stop Before You Start.® Gambling Problem? Call 1-800-522-4700. ©2000 Harrah's Entertainment, Inc. 0190-700-074

American Casino Guide

President Casino by the Arch

Free casino shuttles from all downtown hotels. Free parking on the St. Louis Riverfront and in historic Laclede's Landing with casino validation. Valet parking available at main entrance.

Name: ____________________
Address: ____________________
City: ____________________
State: __________ Zip: __________

Not valid with any other offer. Non-transferable. Subject to change or cancellation without prior notice. Alcoholic beverages are not included. No cash value. Tax and gratuity not included. Must be 21 or older. Not for sale. Not valid on 12/31/00. Good only at President Casino by the Arch, St. Louis, MO.

For cruise schedules and reservations:
(800) 842-0115

Coupon valid Tuesday through Sunday, excluding Wednesday and Thursday. Limit one coupon per person, per cruise. Offer not valid with any other discount or coupon. Not valid on holidays or selected cruises. Coupon expires11/30/01.

Emerald Princess
DOWNTOWN BRUNSWICK

Golden Isles Cruise Lines, Inc.
1 St. Andrews Court, Brunswick, GA 31520

(BRUNSWICK, GEORGIA IS LOCATED MIDWAY BETWEEN SAVANNAH, GA AND JACKSONVILLE, FL.)
SHIP'S REGISTRY: PANAMA

AMERICAN CASINO GUIDE

1/2 Price Buffet

Valid December 1, 2000 through June 30, 2001.

Present this coupon at Laffitte's All-You-Can-Eat Buffet at Treasure Bay Casino Resort in Biloxi, Mississippi to receive your buffet for 1/2 price! Not valid on holidays. Gratuity not included.

CASINO COUPON

AMERICAN CASINO GUIDE

1/2 Price Buffet

Valid December 1, 2000 through June 30, 2001.

Present this coupon at Laffitte's All-You-Can-Eat Buffet at Treasure Bay Casino Resort in Biloxi, Mississippi to receive your buffet for 1/2 price! Not valid on holidays. Gratuity not included.

CASINO COUPON

AMERICAN CASINO GUIDE

BOOMTOWN CASINO
BILOXI

FREE
Casino Fun Book!

Filled with Valuable Gaming, Food & Merchandise offers.
Present this voucher at the Players Club Booth.

Name ______________________________

Address ____________________ **City** ____________________

State ________ **Zip** ____________ **Date of Birth** ____________

CASINO COUPON

1980 Beach Boulevard
Biloxi, MS 39531
(800) PIRATE-9
(228) 385-6000

Subject to change or cancellation. Must be 21 or older with valid photo ID. Limit one per person. Not reponsible for lost or stolen coupons. Not valid with any other offer. Non-negotiable. Non-transferable. Non-refundable. Only valid December 1, 2000 through June 30, 2001.

1980 Beach Boulevard
Biloxi, MS 39531
(800) PIRATE-9
(228) 385-6000

Subject to change or cancellation. Must be 21 or older with valid photo ID. Limit one per person. Not reponsible for lost or stolen coupons. Not valid with any other offer. Non-negotiable. Non-transferable. Non-refundable. Only valid December 1, 2000 through June 30, 2001.

BOOMTOWN CASINO
BILOXI

676 Bayview Ave.
Biloxi, MS 39530
1-800-627-0777
or (228) 435-7000

www.boomtownbiloxi.com

Must be 21 or older with valid photo I.D. Limit one offer per person, per week. Not valid with other offers or tour bus packages. Management reserves all rights. Some restrictions may apply.

Offer expires: 12/30/01
Code: ACG98

AMERICAN CASINO GUIDE

Biloxi, MS
1-800-5-MAGIC-5

10% Room Discount

Save 10% on our prevailing daily room rate with this coupon. See reverse for full details.

CASINO COUPON

AMERICAN CASINO GUIDE

TUNICA
CASINO & HOTEL

Two-For-One Buffet

Present this coupon, along with your Harrah's Total Rewards Card, to the cashier at the Fresh Market Square Buffet at Harrah's Tunica Casino & Hotel to receive one FREE buffet upon the purchase of another buffet of equal or greater value.

Total Rewards# ______________________

CG

CASINO COUPON

AMERICAN CASINO GUIDE

YOUR PLACE TO SHINE™

Buy One Epic Buffet and Get One Free!

Enjoy two buffets for the price of one at Hollywood's Epic Buffet! Dine and play among movie memorabilia in an authentic Hollywood atmosphere...7 days a week! See reverse side for full details.

CASINO COUPON

Biloxi, MS
1-800-5-MAGIC-5

195 E. Beach Boulevard
Biloxi, MS 39530
(228) 467-9257

Call 1-800-5-MAGIC-5 to make your ADVANCE reservations and ask for the American Casino Guide discount. Offer not available for groups or conventions. Must be 21 years or older. Limited availability. Excludes special events & holiday periods. Management reserves the right to change or cancel this offer at any time. Offer expires 12/30/01.

TUNICA
CASINO & HOTEL

1100 Casino Strip Resorts Blvd.
Robinsonville, MS
1-800-HARRAHS

You must have a Harrah's Total Rewards Card when using this coupon. To instantly become a Harrah's Total Rewards Card member simply present a valid ID at the Total Rewards Card Center during your next visit.

This offer is only valid at Harrah's Tunica Casino and Hotel. It is nontransferable and cannot be used in conjunction with any other offer or promotion. Management reserves the right to withdraw this offer without prior notice. Must be 21 years of age or older. Valid through 12/30/01. No photocopies accepted.

Sign up for a Screen Test card at the Marquee Promotions Booth on the casino floor. Then present this coupon at the Promotions Booth to receive your buy-one-get-one-free Epic Buffet coupon.

Hollywood Casino Tunica reserves the right to modify or cancel this promotion at anytime without prior notice. Offer not valid on Friday or Saturday from 6p.m. to midnight. This coupon cannot be combined with any other promotion. Offer expires 12/31/01.

YOUR PLACE TO SHINE™

1150 Casino Strip Resorts Blvd.
Robinsonville, MS 38671
(800) 871-0711
(662) 357-7700

AMERICAN CASINO GUIDE

Buy 1 Buffet Get 1 FREE!

Present this coupon along with your Fitzgeralds Card to the Hostess at the Castle Court Buffet MONDAY thru THURSDAY 7 a.m. to 11 p.m. and receive one FREE buffet when you purchase one. See other side for full terms and conditions.

MKTG

CASINO COUPON

AMERICAN CASINO GUIDE

25% Off at O'Lucky Gift Shoppe

Present this coupon with any purchase of $10 or more and receive 25% off your total purchase price at Fitzgeralds Casino's O'Lucky Gift Shoppe (exclusive of tobacco, food, drug and sale items). See other side for full terms and conditions.

MKTG

CASINO COUPON

AMERICAN CASINO GUIDE

BALLY'S CASINO·TUNICA

Free Cornucopia Buffet

Bring this coupon to the Cornucopia Buffet/Cafe to receive two buffets for the price of one. Must have a Bally's Gold Star card. Valid through 12/30/01, excluding holidays. Limit one coupon per day, per person. See back for full details.

ACG

CASINO COUPON

711 Lucky Lane
Robinsonville, MS 38664
1-800-766-LUCK
For Hotel Reservations
1-888-766-LUCK

Gratuity and alcoholic beverages not included. Limit one coupon per guest per day. Not valid with any other coupon or offer. Management reserves the right to change or discontinue this coupon at any time. Must be 21 years or older with valid I.D. Offer expires 12/30/01.

711 Lucky Lane
Robinsonville, MS 38664
1-800-766-LUCK
For Hotel Reservations
1-888-766-LUCK

Limit one coupon per person per day. Not valid with any other coupon or offer. Management reserves the right to change or discontinue this coupon at any time. Must be 21 years or older with valid I.D. Offer expires 12/30/01.

BALLY'S
CASINO • TUNICA

1450 Bally's Blvd.
Robinsonville, MS 38664
1-(800) 38-BALLY

Offer valid for adults 21 years of age or older and subject to change without notice. May not be used in conjunction with any other promotional offer. Limited to one coupon per person, per day. To receive a FREE Bally's Gold Star card simply present a valid photo ID at the Promotions Booth. Offer expires 12/30/01.

ACG

AMERICAN CASINO GUIDE

Go Greyhound. Lucky Streak

$5 Discount on a Greyhound Casino Ticket

This coupon entitles the bearer to a $5 discount on the purchase of a round-trip Greyhound casino ticket at any Greyhound office in California or Arizona. For more information on Greyhound travel call (800) 231-2222

CASINO COUPON

AMERICAN CASINO GUIDE

Go Greyhound. Lucky Streak

$5 Discount on a Greyhound Casino Ticket

This coupon entitles the bearer to a $5 discount on the purchase of a round-trip Greyhound casino ticket at any Greyhound office in California or Arizona. For more information on Greyhound travel call (800) 231-2222

CASINO COUPON

AMERICAN CASINO GUIDE

Free Casino Fun Money

Please present this coupon at the Casino Cashier Cage to receive a FREE Casino Fun Money sheet loaded with valuable offers. See reverse side for full details.

CASINO COUPON

Go Greyhound®
Lucky Streak®

(800) 231-2222

Convenient Daily Schedules To All Major Casino Gaming Destinations!

¥ Special open ended tickets allow you to return anytime within 5 or 7 days from the day you leave.

¥ Special room rates for Greyhound customers at each casino property.

Offer valid for one adult (21 or older), per coupon, at any Greyhound ticket office in Arizona or California. Offer not valid with any other discount or promotion. Program subject to change or cancellation without notice. Offer valid through 12/30/01.

Go Greyhound®
Lucky Streak®

(800) 231-2222

Convenient Daily Schedules To All Major Casino Gaming Destinations!

¥ Special open ended tickets allow you to return anytime within 5 or 7 days from the day you leave.

¥ Special room rates for Greyhound customers at each casino property.

Offer valid for one adult (21 or older), per coupon, at any Greyhound ticket office in Arizona or California. Offer not valid with any other discount or promotion. Program subject to change or cancellation without notice. Offer valid through 12/30/01.

P.O. Box 3239
Incline Village, NV 89450
(775) 832-1234
(800) 233-1234

Limit one coupon per guest. Must be 21 years of age, or older. No cash value. Not valid with any other offer. Management reserves the right to cancel or modify this offer. Expires 12/30/01.

AMERICAN CASINO GUIDE

Reno Hilton

Buy One Buffet Get One FREE

Buy one breakfast, lunch or dinner at the Grand Canyon Buffet and receive the second for FREE. See back for full details

CASINO COUPON

AMERICAN CASINO GUIDE

Reno Hilton

$10 Room Discount

Save $10 on our prevailing daily room rate with this coupon. See reverse for full details.

CASINO COUPON

AMERICAN CASINO GUIDE

Reno Hilton

FREE Comedy Club Ticket

Buy one ticket to the Comedy Club and get a second ticket for FREE. See back for details.

CASINO COUPON

2500 E. Second St.
Reno, NV 89595
(702) 789-2000
(800) 648-5080

Present this coupon to the cashier at the Grand Canyon Buffet. Not valid in conjunction with any other offer or discounts. Must be 21 years or older.

Management reserves the right to change or cancel this offer at any time. Offer expires 12/24/01.

D-53

Reno Hilton

2500 E. Second St.
Reno, NV 89595
(702) 789-2000
(800) 648-5080

Call 1-800-648-5080 to make your ADVANCE reservations. Ask for reservation code ACG. Coupon must be presented on arrival. Promotional offer not available for groups or conventions. Must be 21 years or older. Limited availability. Excludes special events & holiday periods. Management reserves the right to change or cancel this offer at any time. Offer expires 12/24/01.

Reno Hilton

2500 E. Second St.
Reno, NV 89595
(702) 789-2000
(800) 648-5080

Present this coupon at the Ticket Office. Comedy Club dark on Mondays. Not valid in conjunction with any other offer or discounts. Must be 21 years or older.

Management reserves the right to change or cancel this offer at any time. Offer expires 12/24/01.

CL #6485

AMERICAN CASINO GUIDE

2-FOR-1 Room

Buy one room at our current rack rate and get your second night FREE! Reservation must be Sunday through Thursday. See reverse for full details.

CASINO COUPON

AMERICAN CASINO GUIDE

Flamingo RENO

2-For-1 tickets to Carnival of Wonders

Buy one regular priced adult ticket to "Reno's Best Show," *Carnival of Wonders* and receive the second ticket FREE! See reverse for full details..

CASINO COUPON

AMERICAN CASINO GUIDE

Early Bird Special

Dine early at Reno's only rooftop restaurant, ***Top of the Flamingo***, or ***Benihana Japanese Steakhouse*** and receive 15% off your entire check!

CASINO COUPON

255 N. Sierra St.
Reno, NV 89501
(775) 322-1111
(800) 648-4882

Call 1-800-648-4882 to make your reservations. Offer good on rack rate only. Not available with any other offer, package, group rate or discount. Single or double occupancy. Based on availability.

Advance reservations required and coupon must be presented on arrival. Offer expires 12/28/01. Management reserves all rights.

Code: ACG

255 N. Sierra St.
Reno, NV 89501
(775) 322-1111
(800) 648-4882

Bring this coupon to the Flamingo Showroom Box Office on the second floor to receive one FREE ticket to Carnival of Wonders when you buy one adult ticket at the regular price.

Subject to availability. Not to be used in conjunction with any other offer. Only good for "Carnival of Wonders" show which will be dark during the month of December. Offer expires 11/30/01. Management reserves all rights. Subject to change without notice.

Code: ACG

255 N. Sierra St.
Reno, NV 89501
(775) 322-1111
(800) 648-4882

Enjoy dinner at "Reno's Most Romantic" restaurant, ***Top of the Flamingo**** or ***Benihana Japanese Steakhouse***** between 5 p.m. and 5:30 p.m. to receive 15% off your entire check with this coupon. Management reserves all rights. Offer expires 11/30/01. Reservations recommended.

* Closed Tuesday
** Closed Monday

Code: ACG

AMERICAN CASINO GUIDE

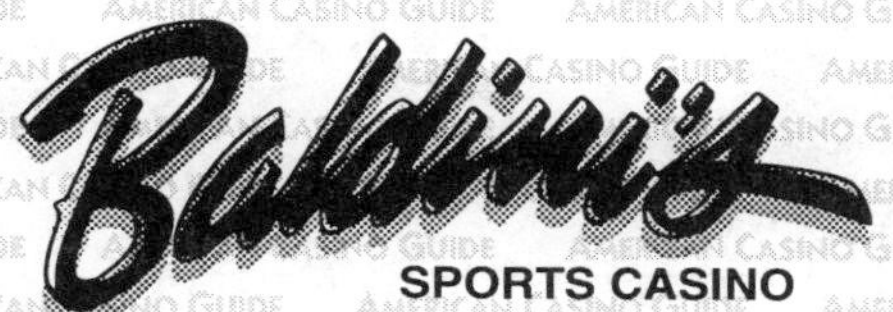

Free Buffet!

Present this coupon to the cashier at Baldini's Buffet to buy one buffet at regular price and receive another FREE!

CASINO COUPON

AMERICAN CASINO GUIDE

Free Coupon Package

Includes: $1 food credit • 50-cent keno discount
Two 2-for-1 drinks • 3 Gift Shop discounts
See back for full details

CASINO COUPON

AMERICAN CASINO GUIDE

Guaranteed Winner!

Present this coupon at the Lucky Forest on the second floor of Fitzgeralds Casino/Hotel in Reno to win up to $1,000 cash or another great prize on the Fantastic Fun Machine.

CASINO COUPON

856 S. Rock Blvd.
Sparks, NV 89431
(702) 358-0116

"Reno's Premier International Buffet"

Must be 21 years of age or older. Not valid on holidays. Not valid with any other offer. Management reserves the right to cancel or alter this coupon at any time without prior notice. Offer expires 12/30/01.

450 N. Arlington Ave.
Reno, NV 89503
1-800-648-5490

Present this coupon at the Courtesy Booth on the 2nd floor in the casino for your Fun Book. Limit one coupon per person. Available to persons 21 years of age or older. This offer subject to change or cancellation without notice. Offer expires 12/30/01.

255 N. Virginia St.
Reno, NV 89504
(775) 785-3300
1-800-648-5022

Must be 21 or older. Limit one play per day. Non-transferable. Management reserves the right to revise or cancel this promotion without prior notice. No cash value. Your valid, non-expired picture ID, showing your current address may be requested. Non-negotiable. Cannot be used in conjunction with any other promotion. Expires 12/30/01.

AMERICAN CASINO GUIDE

Free Fun Book

Present this coupon at the Prospector Club Booth to receive a FREE Comstock Fun Book!

CASINO COUPON

AMERICAN CASINO GUIDE

Two-For-One Admission

$3.5 million of original Elvis Presley memorabilia on display. FREE shows with admission. View Elvis' 1955 Cadillac limousine, army trunk and uniform, Hollywood movie clothing, karate outfits, 1962 boat, love letters and much more. Relive Rock N' Roll history!

CASINO COUPON

AMERICAN CASINO GUIDE

Two-For-One Admission
The "King" in Concert

The Ultimate Tribute show • Save $16.45

An hour-long concert of award-winning impersonator Tim Welch, belting out the "King's" hits of the 50's, 60's and 70's. Endorsed by the Elvis-A-Rama Museum. Enjoy the greatest tribute show to the King of Rock N' Roll.

CASINO COUPON

200 W. Second St.
Reno, NV 89501
(800) COMSTOC
(775) 329-1880

Limit one per guest, per day. Must be 21 years or older. No cash value. Not valid with any other offer. Management reserves the right to cancel or modify this offer. Expires 12/30/01.

Get one FREE admission with the purchase of one admission. Not valid with any other offer. Expires December 30, 2001.

Voted best museum of Las Vegas in 2000. The Elvis-A-Rama Museum has been praised as the "Las Vegas Highlight" by tourists.

View a complete history of the "king's" life and career. Live shows included FREE with admission. Bring back great memories for all that visit. Pay homage to the "entertainer of the century."

Admission: $9.95
Under 12: Free
Open 7 days a week
10a.m. to 7p.m

(Just 1 block off the Strip)
3401 Industrial Boulevard
(702) 309-7200

Call for Free shuttle!

The "King" in Concert
The Ultimate Tribute Show

Located at the Flamingo's O'Shea's Casino (next to the Flamingo Hilton)
3555 Las Vegas Blvd. S. Call (702) 309-7202 for show reservations

Get one FREE admission with the purchase of one admission.
Not valid with any other offer. Expires December 30, 2001.
Enjoy the greatest tribute show to the "King" of Rock N' Roll.

AMERICAN CASINO GUIDE

JERRY'S NUGGET

Up to $20 Off Dinner in the Magnolia Room

Visit the Magnolia Room for ultimate dining in a casually elegant atmosphere. Enjoy steaks, seafood, Greek specialties and much more. Reservations suggested 399-3000 ext.-158. Present this coupon to Food Server with your bill and receive $5 off per person, per dinner entree.

CASINO COUPON

AMERICAN CASINO GUIDE

JERRY'S NUGGET

Up to $12 off Dinner in the Canal Street Cafe

Our 24-hour Canal Street Cafe serves up all your favorites, from award winning prime rib, to Mexican specialties like Carne Asada, to build your own omelettes. Present this coupon to Cashier with your bill and receive $3 off per person, per dinner entree.

CASINO COUPON

AMERICAN CASINO GUIDE

JERRY'S NUGGET

2-for-1 Dessert in the European Bakery

Don't forget to save room for a mouth watering dessert, made fresh in our own bakery - like chocolate strawberry ring, luscious Bavarian or, creamy cheese cake. Purchase one dessert in the European Bakery and receive the second dessert free.

CASINO COUPON

JERRY'S NUGGET

1821Las Vegas Boulevard North
N. Las Vegas, NV 89030
(702) 399-3000 • www.jerrysnugget.com

MAGNOLIA ROOM

Limit one coupon per customer. Present this coupon to Food Server upon paying. The Magnolia Room is open Wed. through Sun. Coupon good for 1 to 4 persons, with $15 or more purchased per person. Tax and gratuity not included. Not valid on holidays. No cash value. Must be 21. Management reserves all rights. Offer expires 12/30/01.

JERRY'S NUGGET

1821Las Vegas Boulevard North
N. Las Vegas, NV 89030
(702) 399-3000 • www.jerrysnugget.com

The CANAL STREET Cafe

Limit one coupon per customer. Present to Cashier upon paying. The Canal Street Cafe is open 24 hours. Offer valid Sun. through Thurs. Not valid on holidays. Cannot be redeemed for cash. Not valid with any other offer or promotion. Coupon good for 1 to 4 persons, with $7 or more purchased per person. No take-out orders. Tax and gratuity not included. Must be 21 to redeem. Management reserves all rights. Offer expires 12/30/01.

1821Las Vegas Boulevard North
N. Las Vegas, NV 89030
(702) 399-3000 • www.jerrysnugget.com

EUROPEAN BAKERY

Present this coupon when ordering and receive a complimentary dessert in the European Bakery when purchasing another dessert of equal or greater value. Not valid for the purchase of whole pies or cakes. Not valid on holidays. Tax and gratuity not included. Must be 21. No cash value. One coupon per person. Cannot be used with any other offer. Management reserves all rights. Offer expires 12/30/01.

AMERICAN CASINO GUIDE

Redeem This Voucher at the Hard Rock Hotel & Casino Back Stage Pass Booth For Your Complimentary Six Pack.

A $50 Value!

Six Pack Offers Include: $5 in free slot play • $59 room rate Complimentary shot glass or deck of playing cards Complimentary Lucky Dog t-shirt • 2x pay on any table game even money bet • Complimentary dessert at the Pink Taco

CASINO COUPON

AMERICAN CASINO GUIDE

RIVIERA Hotel & Casino
The Entertainment Center of Las Vegas
The Alternative for Grown-Ups

Two-For-One Show Tickets

Las Vegas' original comedy showcase. Two shows nightly at 8:00 and 10:00. Extra 11:45 show on Friday and Saturday. See other side for full details.

CASINO COUPON

AMERICAN CASINO GUIDE

RIVIERA Hotel & Casino
The Entertainment Center of Las Vegas
The Alternative for Grown-Ups

Two-For-One Show Tickets

Las Vegas' sexiest topless revue. Two shows nightly (except Monday) at 8:30 and 10:30. Extra midnight show on Saturday. See other side for full details.

CASINO COUPON

A Peter Morton Hotel
4455 Paradise Road
Las Vegas, Nevada 89109
www.hardrockhotel.com
(702) 693-5000
(800) HRD-ROCK

SOME RESTRICTIONS APPLY. Gaming certificates require Casino play. Limit one Six Pack per Back Stage Pass account per calendar month. Must be 21 or older. Photo I.D. required. Management reserves the right to substitute all or poritons of these offers with services, goods or merchandise of equal or simialr value. **OFFERS WILL CHANGE QUARTERLY**. Voucher expires 12/30/01.

ACG

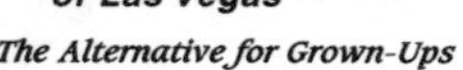

2901 Las Vegas Blvd. S. ¥ Las Vegas, NV ¥ (702) 734-5110

Coupon must be presented to Riviera box office. Must be 21. Not valid Saturdays, or Saturdays and Sundays of a holiday weekend, or with any other offer. One coupon per person. Offer may be cancelled at any time without notice. No cash value. Offer expires 12/30/01.

Crazy Girls

2901 Las Vegas Blvd. S. ¥ Las Vegas, NV ¥ (702) 734-5110

Coupon must be presented to Riviera box office. Must be 21. Not valid Saturdays or Saturdays and Sundays of a holiday weekend or with any other offer. One coupon per person. Offer may be cancelled at any time without notice. No cash value. Offer expires 12/30/01.

AMERICAN CASINO GUIDE

Lady Luck
Casino Hotel • Las Vegas

Buy One Buffet Get One FREE!

Present this coupon to the Lady Luck Buffet cashier to receive one FREE buffet upon the purchase of another buffet at the regular price. Offer expires December 30, 2001.

CASINO COUPON

AMERICAN CASINO GUIDE

Fitzgeralds
Casino - Las Vegas/Downtown

FREE Fremont Street Souvenir Poster

Valued at $5

Present this coupon at the Card Center on the second floor to receive a FREE Souvenir Poster.

CC007/1200

CASINO COUPON

AMERICAN CASINO GUIDE

CONEY ISLAND EMPORIUM
New York-New York Hotel & Casino Las Vegas
"We Create Smiles..."®
www.coneyislandemporium.com

ACG

Buy one bracelet for unlimited interactive action and get one FREE!

Daytona Simulator
Virtual Reality
Laser Patrol
Bumper Cabs

Coney Island Emporium
NY-NY Hotel & Casino
Phone: (702) 736-4100

Limit 1 per person

CASINO COUPON

Lady Luck
Casino Hotel • Las Vegas

206 N. Third Street
Las Vegas, NV 89101
(702) 477-3000
(800) 634-6580

Please present this coupon to the Lady Luck Buffet cashier. Subject to availability. Gratuity not included. Must be 21 or older. Not redeemable for cash. Limit one per customer. Management reserves all rights. Offer expires December 30, 2001.

301 E. Fremont St.
Las Vegas, NV 89101
(702) 388-2400
1-800-274-LUCK
FitzgeraldsLasVegas.com

Must be 21 years of age or older. Non-negotiable. No cash value. May be revoked, confiscated or cancelled at management's discretion. Subject to availability while supplies last. Fitzgeralds Team Members not eligible. Offer expires 12/24/01.

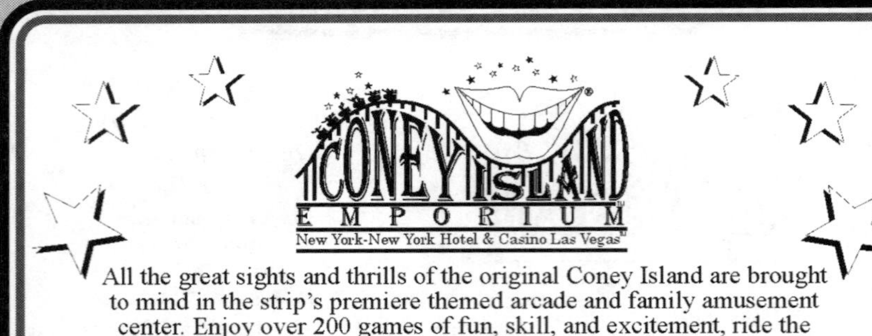

All the great sights and thrills of the original Coney Island are brought to mind in the strip's premiere themed arcade and family amusement center. Enjoy over 200 games of fun, skill, and excitement, ride the Bumper Cabs, win a teddy bear, and don't forget the cotton candy!!

Offer expires 12/30/01.

FREE FUNBOOK!

Present this coupon at either the Market Express across from THE Steakhouse, or Headliners located on the Promenade level. Must be 21 years old.

CIRCUS CIRCUS
LAS VEGAS

One coupon per person per day. Offer may be cancelled/revised by management at any time. No cash value. Expires 12-23-01.

CASINO COUPON

AMERICAN CASINO GUIDE

FASHION OUTLET
LAS VEGAS
Your Best Bet For Outlet Shopping

Two-For-One Shuttle Ride

Present this coupon at the shuttle desk inside the New York New York Hotel and Casino, or the MGM Grand Hotel and Casino, to receive two rides for the price of one on the Fashion Outlet Las Vegas shuttle. Shop for your favorite designer fashions at discount prices. Call 1-888-424-6898 and select option #3 for reservations or information. Regular price is $10 per person.

CASINO COUPON

AMERICAN CASINO GUIDE

$1.00 Off Full Adult Admission

Present this coupon and get $1 off full adult admission at "Race for Atlantis," and challenge the Gods to the ultimate race, located in the Forum Shops at Caesars Palace..

CASINO COUPON

CIRCUS CIRCUS®

2880 Las Vegas Boulevard South
Las Vegas, NV 89109
(702) 734-0410
Reservations (800) 444-2472

FASHION OUTLET
LAS VEGAS

Your Best Bet For Outlet Shopping

Located just 30 minutes south of the Las Vegas Strip on I-15 at the California border in Primm, Nevada

10 a.m. - 9 p.m. (Mon-Sat)
10 a.m - 8 p.m. (Sun)

3 daily shuttles from New York New York Hotel and Casino - 9:15 a.m. • 11:15 a.m. • 2:15 p.m.
3 daily shuttles from MGM Grand Hotel and Casino - 10:15 a.m. • 12:15 p.m. • 3:15 p.m.

Limit: two people (one free ride) per coupon. Subject to change or cancellation without notice. This coupon has no cash value and is not valid with any other specials or discounts. Valid through 12/31/01.

In the Forum Shops at Caesars Palace in Las Vegas, Nevada
(888) 910-RACE
(702) 733-9000

Sun.-Thur. 10am-11pm
Fri.-Sat. 10am-Midnight

Adults: $9.50
Children (under 12): $6.75
Seniors (55+): $8.50

You must be at least 42 inches tall to ride "Race for Atlantis"

Save $1.00 per ticket on up to four tickets. Not valid with any other offer. Expires December 31, 2001.

AMERICAN CASINO GUIDE

Two FREE Buffets! or Buy One Entree, Get One FREE!

This coupon is valid for two FREE buffets at Gold Strike Hotel & Gambling Hall. Or, if you prefer, buy one regular priced entree and two beverages at any of our restaurants and enjoy a second entree of equal or lesser value, FREE! Choose from a variety of entrees, including, our succulent shrimp scampi at The Gold Strike Steak House.

CASINO COUPON

AMERICAN CASINO GUIDE

Two FREE Buffets! or Buy One Entree, Get One FREE!

This coupon is valid for two FREE buffets at Nevada Landing Hotel & Casino. Or, if you prefer, buy one regular priced entree and two beverages at any of our restaurants and enjoy a second entree of equal or lesser value, FREE! Choose from a variety of entrees, including our famous all-you-can-eat sweet & sour pork at Nevada Landing's Jade Room.

CASINO COUPON

AMERICAN CASINO GUIDE

Two-For-One Admission

Present this coupon and get one free admission when a second admission of equal or greater value is purchased.

CASINO COUPON

1 Main Street
Jean, NV 89019
(800) 634-1359 or (702) 477-5000

Conveniently located on I-15 just 25 minutes South of Las Vegas on your way to California

Must be 21 years of age or older. Must present coupon to server before ordering to receive complimentary buffets or buy one, get one free entree. Can NOT be combined with any other offer. If dining alone, one entree will be discounted 50 percent. Management reserves all rights. Duplicate copies of this coupon will NOT be accepted. Coupon good at all Gold Strike restaurants, excluding Burger King. Coupon expires December 24, 2001.

NEVADA LANDING
HOTEL & CASINO

#2 Goodsprings Rd. • Jean, NV 89019
(800) 628-6682 or (702) 387-5000

Conveniently located on I-15 just 25 minutes South of Las Vegas on your way to California

Must be 21 years of age or older. Must present coupon to server before ordering to receive complimentary buffets or buy one, get one free entree. Can NOT be combined with any other offer. If dining alone, one entree will be discounted 50 percent. Management reserves all rights. Duplicate copies of this coupon will NOT be accepted. Coupon good at all Nevada Landing restaurants. Coupon expires December 24, 2001.

GUINNESS
WORLD RECORDS
MUSEUM

2780 Las Vegas Blvd. S.
Las Vegas, NV 89109
(702) 792-0640

Open 7 days a week, including holidays, 9 a.m. to 6 p.m. Located 1/2 block north of the Circus Cicus Hotel on the Las Vegas Strip

This wacky, weird and wonderful museum brings The Guinness Book of Records to life with color videos, hands-on displays and life-sized replicas.

Not valid with any other offer.
Expires December 30, 2001.

AMERICAN CASINO GUIDE

Established 1906

GOLDEN GATE

HOTEL & CASINO • ONE FREMONT STREET • LAS VEGAS

FREE Deck of Cards

Receive a FREE deck of cards from Las Vegas' Most Historic Hotel at One Fremont Street.

See reverse side for full details.

CASINO COUPON

AMERICAN CASINO GUIDE

Voted the "WOW of the Millennium!"

Save $50 Per Person on Pegasus "VIP" Grand Canyon Flight

Fly, Descend, Land... Into The **GRAND CANYON**

Heli USA Airways

See reverse for more information

Save $20 Per Person on Any Night Flight Over Las Vegas

CASINO COUPON

AMERICAN CASINO GUIDE

Buy one adult admission and get one FREE!

Present this coupon at the Liberace Museum and get one free admission with the puchase of each adult admission. See back for full details.

CASINO COUPON

Established 1906

GOLDEN GATE

HOTEL & CASINO • ONE FREMONT STREET • LAS VEGAS

One Fremont Street
Las Vegas, NV 89101
(702) 385-1906
Reservations (800) 426-1906

Present this coupon to our Casino Cage and receive a FREE deck of cards. Limit: one deck of cards per person. Must be 21 years of age or older. Subject to change or cancellation without notice. While supplies last. Offer expires December 30, 2001.

Land at the bottom of the Grand Canyon where you can actually touch the Colorado River!

Heli USA Airways

Toll Free 24 Hour Reservations

800.359.8727

702.736.8787

Save $50 Per Person on Pegasus "VIP" Grand Canyon Flight

275 E. Tropicana Ave.
In The Las Vegas Int'l Airport Executive Terminal
Visit us on the Web at www.HeliUSA.net

Save $20 Per Person on Any Night Flight Over Las Vegas

Not valid with any other offer. Must call direct. Must mention code CASG. Expires 12-31-01.

Liberace®

Liberace Museum
1775 E. Tropicana Ave.
Las Vegas, NV 89119
(702) 798-5595

Mon-Sat: 10a.m. to 5p.m.
Sunday: 1p.m. to 5p.m.

This offer is not redeemable for cash and is not valid with any other offer. Offer expires December 30, 2001.

$5.00 Off THRILL PASS

Unlimited Rides, All Day Long!

Quicken your pulse with unlimited rides on these great attractions!
Regularly priced at $19.95.

Coupon may not be duplicated. Coupon has no cash value. Coupon cannot be combined with any other offer. Management reserves the right to modify or cancel this promotion at any time. Offer expires December 30, 2001.

HOTEL AND CASINO
This Place Is Hot!℠

CASINO COUPON

AMERICAN CASINO GUIDE

$1.00 OFF Sahara Buffet

Offer valid for up to four (4) people. Coupon may not be duplicated. Coupon has no cash value.. Coupon cannot be combined with any other offer. Management reserves the right to modify or cancel this promotion at any time.
Comp #814. Offer expires December 30, 2001.

HOTEL AND CASINO
This Place Is Hot!℠

CASINO COUPON

AMERICAN CASINO GUIDE

FREE Fun Book

Present this coupon at our casino cage to receive a FREE Fun Book - a $100 value!. Offer expires 12/30/01.

CASINO COUPON

NASCAR Cafe
2535 Las Vegas Blvd., South
Las Vegas, NV 89109

702.734.7223

www.nascarcafelasvegas.com

Sahara Hotel and Casino
2535 Las Vegas Blvd., South
Las Vegas, NV 89109

1.702.737.2111

www.saharavegas.com

377 E. Flamingo Rd • Las Vegas, NV 89109
(702) 733-7777 • (800) 634-6617

Must be at least 21 years of age. This offer subject to change or cancellation without prior notice.

AMERICAN CASINO GUIDE

20% Discount on any tour

Book a half-day or full-day tour with Scenic Airlines and receive a 20% discount. Please present this coupon at check-in to receive discount. Coupon valid only by calling Scenic directly at (800) 634-6801 or (702) 638-3300. Good for up to four people. Not valid with any other offer or promotion. Offer expires 12/31/01.

CASINO COUPON

AMERICAN CASINO GUIDE

Up To Six FREE Admissions

Present this coupon at the Imperial Player Booth on the main casino floor across from the Mai Tai Lounge to receive up to six FREE admissions to the AUTO COLLECTIONS & COLLECTIBLES. The collection is located on the fifth floor of the Imperial Palace parking facility and is open daily from 9:30am to 9:30pm. Offer expires 11/30/01.

CASINO COUPON

AMERICAN CASINO GUIDE

Save $5 Off the price of Regular Admission

See legendary superstars from the past and present recreated live in a multi-million-dollar full-stage production. This ever-changing light and sound spectacular also features the fabulous Legend Singers and Dancers and the great sounds of the Legends Orchestra, making this the"MUST SEE" show in Las Vegas. Spectacular stars nightly. Acts may vary.

CASINO COUPON

FLY THE NATIONAL PARKS!

Grand Canyon • Monument Valley • Bryce Canyon

20% Discount

- Half-day or full-day tours
- High wings & giant windows for best view
- Digital quality tour narration en route
- Tour facility located two blocks from "Strip"
- Free flight certificate

Reservations: (800) 634-6801 • (702) 638-3300

www.scenic.com

Center Strip • (702) 731-3311

The Imperial Palace Auto Collections & Collectibles.
Over 300 inspired works of automotive design.
This offer subject to cancellation at any time.

Show times 7:30 & 10:30 nightly except Sundays
Show reservations (702) 794-3261 • Toll-Free (800) 777-7664

Not valid in combination with any other discounts. Must present coupon at the Imperial Palace's Show Reservations Desk (main casino floor) for discount. Tickets for show must be purchased at least one hour prior to show time. Legends In Concert is not responsible for lost or stolen coupons. Good for up to a party of six. Offer expires December 30, 2001.

AMERICAN CASINO GUIDE

Casino Legends Hall of Fame
FREE Admission to the World's Largest Gambling Museum
Over 15,000 Exhibits!

A Gang of Gamblers • A Gallery of Gangsters • A Montage of Movies
The Smithsonian of Showgirls • Vegas Visionaries • Hall of Headliners
Fires & Implosions • See reverse for full details.

CASINO COUPON

AMERICAN CASINO GUIDE

$5 Off
Folies Bergere

Redeem this ticket at the Tropicana Show Ticket Booth to receive $5 off the 7:30 pm show or the 10 pm show. See reverse for full details.

CASINO COUPON

AMERICAN CASINO GUIDE

$5 Off
The Illusionary Magic of Rick Thomas

Redeem this ticket at the Tropicana Show Ticket Booth.
See reverse for full details.

CASINO COUPON

3801 Las Vegas Blvd. S.
Las Vegas, NV 89109
(702) 739-2222
Reservations (800) GO-2-TROP

Casino Legends Hall of Fame

Open Daily
7 a.m. - 9 p.m.
For more information call (702) 739-2222.

Redeem this coupon at the museum. Coupon good for up to four people. Must be 18 unless accompanied by an adult. Offer expires 12/30/2001.

3801 Las Vegas Blvd. S.
Las Vegas, NV 89109
(702) 739-2222
Reservations (800) GO-2-TROP

This coupon is good for a maximum of two people. Special discounted prices are not applicable to booth seating. Subject to availability. Tax included in price. Management reserves the right to cancel or modify this offer without prior notice. Must present coupon at time of purchase.

Offer expires 12/11/2001. For more information call (702) 739-2411

3801 Las Vegas Blvd. S.
Las Vegas, NV 89109
(702) 739-2222
Reservations (800) GO-2-TROP

This coupon is good for a maximum of two people. Special discounted prices are not applicable to booth seating. Subject to availability. Tax included in price. Management reserves the right to cancel or modify this offer without prior notice. Must present coupon at time of purchase.

Offer expires 12/30/2001. For more information call (702) 739-2411

AMERICAN CASINO GUIDE

FREE Show For Two!

Voted Best Afternoon Show

Free Viva Las Vegas Show With Purchase of One Drink for $6.95 per person. Coupon must be presented at the box office ticket counter. See back for full details.

MKPG-ACG

CASINO COUPON

AMERICAN CASINO GUIDE

Two-For-One Show Tickets

Get one FREE "American Superstars" Show with the purchase of one American Superstars Show. Coupon must be presented at the box office ticket counter. See back for full details.

MKPG-ACG

CASINO COUPON

AMERICAN CASINO GUIDE

$5* Off A SeaEscape Cruise

Fabulous Buffets • Live Entertainment

Las Vegas Style Casino Action On A Real CruiseShip

Not valid on Saturday night. Offer expires 12/15/01. See reverse.

CASINO COUPON

2000 Las Vegas Blvd. S. • Las Vegas, NV 89104
(800) 99-TOWER • (702) 380-7777

Valid for up to two people. Gratuity on drink not included. Minors must be accompanied by an adult. Must be 5 years of age or older. Seating begins 60 minutes prior to showtime. Not valid with any other offer. Management reserves all rights. Not for resale. Subject to availability. Valid through December 27, 2001. **Coupon must be presented at the box office ticket counter.**

2000 Las Vegas Blvd. S. • Las Vegas, NV 89104
(800) 99-TOWER • (702) 380-7777

Valid for up to two people. Minors must be accompanied by an adult. Must be 5 years of age or older. Subject to availability. Seating begins 60 minutes prior to showtime. Not valid with any other offer. Management reserves all rights. Not for resale. Valid through December 27, 2001. **Coupon must be presented at the box office ticket counter.**

(954) 453-3333
(877) SEA-ESCAPE
www.seaescape.com

For reservations ask for code "CG"

SeaEscape 2000 Casino Cruises

Departs from Fort Lauderdale

Sail with us 13 times a week on a five, or six-hour cruise and thrill to the action of Slots, Roulette,Craps, Blackjack, Poker, Pai Gow Poker, Caribbean Stud, Let It Ride and Video Gaming.

*No cash value. One coupon valid for up to 4 people per sailing. Restrictions apply. Advance reservations required. $3 federal departure tax additional. Cannot be combined with any other offer. Ship's registry Bahamas.

AMERICAN CASINO GUIDE

FREE Bahamas Trip

The Casino at Bahamia

Grand Bahama Island from Ft. Lauderdale, FL

Offer includes: roundtrip 727 jet air from Ft. Lauderdale, Florida, roundtrip taxi transfers (airport/casino/airport) and $10 food credit in the casino's Garden Cafe. Does not include: $42 U.S. departure/APHIS/Airport facility taxes and fees, $18 Bahamas departure tax, 15% gratuity on all food and beverages (figured before discount), all items not specified. See reverse for full details. Offer expires 12/20/01.

For reservations & information call (800) 432-2294

CASINO COUPON

AMERICAN CASINO GUIDE

FREE Bahamas Trip

The Casino at Bahamia

Grand Bahama Island from Ft. Lauderdale, FL

Offer includes: roundtrip 727 jet air from Ft. Lauderdale, Florida, roundtrip taxi transfers (airport/casino/airport) and $10 food credit in the casino's Garden Cafe. Does not include: $42 U.S. departure/APHIS/Airport facility taxes and fees, $18 Bahamas departure tax, 15% gratuity on all food and beverages (figured before discount), all items not specified. See reverse for full details. Offer expires 12/20/01.

For reservations & information call (800) 432-2294

CASINO COUPON

AMERICAN CASINO GUIDE

STARDANCER Casino

Two-For-One Cruise

Experience a great Dining, Dancing and Casino value aboard the Stardancer Casino in Miami Beach, Florida! See reverse for full terms and conditions of this special offer. For reservations, or information call **1-877-STARR-21.** Offer Expires 12/30/01.

CASINO COUPON

Offer subject to availability and expires December 20, 2001. Must be 18 years of age or older. Limit one person per coupon. **VALID PROOF OF CITIZENSHIP IS REQUIRED. All taxes**, fees, airport facilities charges, etc. must be paid at airport in cash. Credit cards and checks are not accepted at airport.

Reservations are highly recommended. Stand-bys are subject to availability only. **Instruct** reservationist you are requesting the "American Casino Guide" promotion to receive this offer.

Terms & conditions: Taxes and fees are subject to change, valid on LB Limited (formerly Laker Airways (Bahamas) Ltd., no cash value on offer or any of its parts, no checked baggage allowed. Offer may be withdrawn without notice.

Availability: Offer available on day excursions Monday through Friday, night excursions on Thursday, not available on weekends or holidays. Other blackout dates may apply.

All bookings are subject to the General Conditions of Grand Bahama Vacations. All bookings will be confirmed on a space available basis only. **Casino at Bahamia and/or Grand Bahama Vacations** reserves the right to deny reservation and/or boarding to any person deemed unsuitable or previously denied travel for any reason.Grand Bahama Vacations acts only as a marketing agent for Casino Bahamia in the U.S.

Offer subject to availability and expires December 20, 2001. Must be 18 years of age or older. Limit one person per coupon. **VALID PROOF OF CITIZENSHIP IS REQUIRED. All taxes**, fees, airport facilities charges, etc. must be paid at airport in cash. Credit cards and checks are not accepted at airport.

Reservations are highly recommended. Stand-bys are subject to availability only. **Instruct** reservationist you are requesting the "American Casino Guide" promotion to receive this offer.

Terms & conditions: Taxes and fees are subject to change, valid on LB Limited (formerly Laker Airways (Bahamas) Ltd., no cash value on offer or any of its parts, no checked baggage allowed. Offer may be withdrawn without notice.

Availability: Offer available on day excursions Monday through Friday, night excursions on Thursday, not available on weekends or holidays. Other blackout dates may apply.

All bookings are subject to the General Conditions of Grand Bahama Vacations. All bookings will be confirmed on a space available basis only. **Casino at Bahamia and/or Grand Bahama Vacations** reserves the right to deny reservation and/or boarding to any person deemed unsuitable or previously denied travel for any reason.Grand Bahama Vacations acts only as a marketing agent for Casino Bahamia in the U.S.

Name

Address

City, St, Zip

1-Advance reservations required. 2-This coupon is not combinable with any other Stardancer offer 3-Applies to full fare purchase only plus taxes and surcharges. 4-Coupon must be presented at ticket booth on day of sailing. 5-Limit (4) people per coupon. 6-Taxes and surcharges not included in this offer. 7-Certain restrictions apply. Offer subject to change without notice. 8- Coupon expires on date indicated. Service charges will be applicable on extension requests. 9-This coupon is not transferable

Free Cruise For Two

aboard
"Florida's Best Value Casino Ships"

Use this coupon for a FREE cruise aboard SunCruz Casino in Hollywood • Key Largo • Palm Beach • Port Canaveral Daytona Beach • Crystal River • Port Richey • Clearwater John's Pass, T.I. • N. Myrtle Beach, S.C.

Ships' registry U.S.

CASINO COUPON

AMERICAN CASINO GUIDE

$20 FREE with $20 Purchase

Get $20 FREE with any purchase of $20 or more at the Diamond Club Internet casino. Certain conditions apply. Just go to: http://www.diamondclubcasino.com/guide Software by Boss Media. Offer expires 12/31/01.

CASINO COUPON

AMERICAN CASINO GUIDE

$10 FREE

$10 FREE. Plus purchase $50 and get between $40 and $500 in our Mystery Bonus Offer! Visit http://www.gamingclub.com/more Conditions apply. Software by Microgaming. Offer expires 12/31/01.

CASINO COUPON

1-800-474-DICE

No other ships pay out more!

**Hollywood • Key Largo • Palm Beach
Port Canaveral • Daytona Beach • Crystal River
Port Richey • Clearwater • John's Pass, T.I.
N. Myrtle Beach, South Carolina**

Just like Las Vegas only offshore!

Offer valid for two persons on SunCruz CASINO at any of the above locations. Coupon cannot be combined with any other offers. Reservations are required. Government tax per person is additional. For reservations or information call 1-800-474-DICE. Offer expires 12/30/01.

Buy $20/Get $20 at http://www.diamondclubcasino.com/guide

Certain restrictions apply to this offer. Visit the web site for full details. Internet gaming may be prohibited in some jurisdictions. Check with your local authorities if you are not sure of the legality in your jurisdiction.

Get $10 for FREE at

http://www.gamingclub.com/more

Plus purchase $50 and get between $40 and $500 in our Mystery Bonus Offer!

Certain restrictions apply to this offer. Visit the web site for full details. Internet gaming may be prohibited in some jurisdictions. Check with your local authorities if you are not sure of the legality in your jurisdiction.

AMERICAN CASINO GUIDE

$50 FREE

Tried online gaming? Here's $50 for free to give it a try at http://www.orbitalcasino.com/free Certain conditions apply. Software by Microgaming. Offer expires 12/31/01.

CASINO COUPON

AMERICAN CASINO GUIDE

$50 FREE

Board the greatest Li'l Ol' Riverboat Casino and claim your free $50. Step onto the River Belle at www.riverbelle.com/offer Terms and conditions apply. Software by Microgaming. Offer expires 12/31/01.

CASINO COUPON

AMERICAN CASINO GUIDE

$25 FREE

Come and enjoy the free excitement of the oldest online casino! Visit www.luckynugget.com/coupon to receive $25 for FREE! Certain conditions apply. Software by Microgaming. Offer expires 12/31/01.

CASINO COUPON

Get $50 for FREE at http://www.orbitalcasino.com/free

Certain restrictions apply to this offer. Visit the web site for full details. Internet gaming may be prohibited in some jurisdictions. Check with your local authorities if you are not sure of the legality in your jurisdiction.

Get $50 for FREE at
www.riverbelle.com/offer

Certain restrictions apply to this offer. Visit the web site for full details. Internet gaming may be prohibited in some jurisdictions. Check with your local authorities if you are not sure of the legality in your jurisdiction.

Get $25 for FREE at
www.luckynugget.com/coupon

Certain restrictions apply to this offer. Visit the web site for full details. Internet gaming may be prohibited in some jurisdictions. Check with your local authorities if you are not sure of the legality in your jurisdiction.